TRINITY ⚠ HYMNAL

REVISED EDITION

GREAT COMMISSION PUBLICATIONS

Orthodox Presbyterian Church • Presbyterian Church in America

Copyright © 1990, Great Commission Publications, Inc.
3640 Windsor Park Drive
Suwanee, GA 30024

Fourteenth printing, 2006

The publisher gratefully acknowledges permission to reprint texts, tunes and arrangements granted by the publishers, organizations and individuals listed with the appropriate hymns and on pages 881-882. Every effort has been made to secure current copyright permission information on the hymns used. If any right has been infringed, the publisher promises to make the correction in subsequent printings as the additional information is received.

Scripture quotations from the HOLY BIBLE, NEW INTERNATIONAL VERSION
Copyright © 1973, 1978, 1984, International Bible Society
Used by permission of Zondervan Publishing House

ISBN 0-934688-60-5 (pew edition)
ISBN 0-934688-61-3 (accompanist edition)
ISBN 0-934688-62-1 (leather-bound edition)

Design: John Tolsma
Computer software: Finale, FreeHand, Word and PageMaker
Type: Petrucci (music), Times and Helvetica (text)
Printer: Edwards Brothers, Inc., Ann Arbor, Michigan

TABLE
OF
CONTENTS

HYMNS

PSALTER READINGS
pages 785–841

CREEDS

INDEXES

PREFACE

Since the dawn of creation—when "the morning stars sang together, and all the sons of God shouted for joy"—and throughout history, singing has characterized God's people in worship. Mandated and exemplified in the Bible, singing is integral to corporate worship and is itself an act of worship. Psalms and hymns are a fundamental means by which believers respond to divine grace, communicate their praise, affirm their faith and proclaim spiritual truth.

It is essential for Christian hymnody to flow from the Word of God and to reflect the church's belief system. To that end, *Trinity Hymnal* has been prepared to nourish and equip those in the Presbyterian/Reformed community for worship that is pleasing in the Lord's sight. The hymnal is rooted in the rich tradition of the Reformation—with a zeal for the gospel, a high regard for doctrinal purity, and a focus on worship as defined in Scripture.

Trinity Hymnal is presented with the prayer that it may supply a recognized need for a truly ecumenical hymnal, theocentric in orientation, biblical in content and containing suitable hymns for every proper occasion of public and private worship of God. It has been compiled with the full consciousness that "the acceptable way of worshiping the true God is instituted by God himself, and so limited by his own revealed will, that he may not be worshiped according to the imaginations and devices of men...or any...way not prescribed in the Holy Scripture" (Westminster Confession of Faith XXI:I).

This paragraph from the Preface of the first edition of *Trinity Hymnal* summarizes the principles and objectives that guided those who worked on the original volume. Particular attention was given to "the function of worship in bringing glory to the triune God." Hymns were "chosen to meet the various needs of the people of God, from the simplest informal services in the home among the smallest children to the most solemn occasions in the life of the church."

Those same criteria governed the committee and staff who worked on the revision. The mandate was to produce a hymnal that includes a broad style of hymnody representing the eras of church history, while retaining the Reformed character and integrity of the original edition. The committee's expressed desire was "to make a good hymnal even better!"

Trinity Hymnal was first published in 1961 by the Orthodox Presbyterian Church (OPC). The General Assembly established a special committee in 1949, and for more than a decade these men tirelessly labored to put the hymnal together. In 1975 Great Commission Publications was incorporated as a joint publishing agency of the OPC and the recently formed Presbyterian Church in America (PCA). One of the responsibilities of the joint venture was to continue publication of the hymnal.

While plans to revise *Trinity Hymnal* had been in the making for several years, the project was formally launched in 1984 when a hymnal committee was named. The group consists of individuals (listed below) appointed from across the two constituent denominations. The revision process began with several phases of research among PCA and OPC churches and an assessment of the data received. Based on its findings, the committee determined changes to be made in the hymnal, but with scriptural and theological criteria controlling those decisions. Four theological advisors—two each from the OPC and the PCA—assisted the committee. Hundreds of hours were spent reviewing hymns to be removed and new ones to be added, and the list was amended dozens of times before a final manuscript was approved.

In 1986 the PCA General Assembly endorsed the *Trinity Hymnal* revision as fulfilling previous overtures to produce a denominational hymnal. The 1987 OPC Assembly approved the project and released it for publication.

With 742 hymns, the revised edition of *Trinity Hymnal* is comparable in size to the original volume. The major change consists of 156 new selections, which include both classical and contemporary hymns. In assembling the collection of ongoing and new hymns, the committee sought to preserve the completeness of each section in the hymnal and the priority of Psalms and Psalm-based hymns. The hymnal continues to have a strong biblical focus—with each hymn preceded by a Scripture reference—and a topical structure drawn from the Westminster Confession of Faith. Where possible, archaic word forms are updated.

Several hymn texts are paired with new tunes or have an alternate tune added. Some keys are lowered to make the tunes easier to sing.

The Psalter readings are rendered in the New International Version of the Bible. Breaks in the readings are designed to reflect more closely the poetry and thought patterns of the Psalms rather than merely to follow the numerical verse divisions.

The section on creeds provides doctrinal statements for ready reference and use in worship. The Westminster Confession of Faith and Shorter Catechism are retained—their presence uniquely identifying the hymnal with churches that hold to the Westminster Standards.

The Apostles' Creed and the Nicene Creed are also included.

The objective in *Trinity Hymnal* is to furnish a collection of "psalms, hymns and spiritual songs" that are faithfully based on God's Word, clearly teach the doctrines of grace, and facilitate the biblical worship of God among his people. The prayer of all who had a part in the revision project is that the church will be edified, and our triune God will be praised and glorified through the use of *Trinity Hymnal*.

> Sing to the Lord, praise his name;
> proclaim his salvation day after day.
> Declare his glory among the nations,
> his marvelous deeds among all peoples.
>
> — Psalm 96:2, 3

Trinity Hymnal Revision Committee

> Jean Clowney
> Ronald DeMaster
> Peyton H. Gardner, *Chairman*
> Paul D. Kooistra
> Calvin R. Malcor
> Ronald A. Matthews
> Donald M. Poundstone
> Lawrence C. Roff, *Editor*
> Dennis Stager
> Ford S. Williams
> William K. Wymond

Acknowledgments

We acknowledge with deep appreciation the myriad of people who were involved in the revision of *Trinity Hymnal*. The editor and the hymn committee members, with their unique cluster of gifts and high commitment to the task at hand, were the driving force behind the project. Countless hours of preparation, travel and meetings were contributed—a debt we seek to pay with our heartfelt gratitude and the publication of the fruit of their labors.

In addition, the theological advisors—John M. Frame and Jack J. Peterson of the OPC, and Joseph A. Pipa and Robert G. Rayburn of the PCA—provided invaluable service in reviewing hymns and advising the committee.

Once the manuscript was completed, a sizeable temporary staff was assembled to handle production. Particular thanks go to production editor James W. Scott, lyric and music computer-entry personnel Marsha L. Gilbert and Susan E. Schmurr, plus many others who assisted with indexes, copyrights and proofreading.

Finally, we appreciate the host of saints across the church who offered ideas, answered surveys and reacted to committee reports. That input had a significant impact on the project, serving to refine the revision and bring it more in tune with the church's needs.

— *The Publisher*

INTRODUCTION

To the Pastor

God has called you to be a worship leader. You are a preacher, administrator, educator and counselor. But all of those tasks merge into one when you stand before your flock to lead them into God's presence. Worship is the highest calling, and guiding a congregation through worship is one of your greatest privileges. What happens in corporate worship is a foretaste of and preparation for eternity as we join with all the saints surrounding the Lamb's throne to sing his glory!

You will find *Trinity Hymnal* to be a helpful guide in equipping God's people for worship. You would do well to become familiar with the contents of this volume so you can make good use of the rich texts and tunes available. Note the topical arrangement of hymns and how it follows the order of doctrines in the Westminster Confession of Faith. Acquaint yourself with the seven indexes. The index of Scripture references and the detailed index of topics will be of particular help to you.

Get to know the hymns themselves—spending time learning new ones as well as reviewing those whose familiarity may keep you from looking closely at the truths they proclaim. Research the background of the hymns, getting to know the godly people, events and themes that flow through the selections. And use the hymnal in private worship, singing in the study in preparation for singing from the pulpit.

Your preparation will have its fruit in the worship service. When it comes time to sing, you might tell the worshipers about the hymn's origin, theme and appropriateness for the service. The way you sing (your attitude, posture, facial expression) will guide the congregation. Seek to enable worshipers to catch the excitement of singing "the wonders of God's grace."

To the Accompanist

God has called you to be a worship supporter. As you play the organ, piano or other instrument, you are assisting in the worship of God. You have the tools to bring hymns to life on the lips and in the hearts of the people. Your manner of playing interprets the truths of the hymn texts so that thoughts, as well as feelings, are more completely engaged.

To do your job well, you will want to know far enough in advance which hymns have been selected, in order to make careful preparation for the worship service. Prayerful analysis of each hymn (both tune and text) will enable you to play each stanza with sensitivity to its unique content. Thorough practice will insure that mistakes do not distract from the singing. Note the tune names used in *Trinity Hymnal*, and build a library of music so you can present the hymns in a manner that will encourage thoughtful participation. For organists, planning of registration will use the sounds of the organ to reflect the truths of each hymn.

Remember, you are not there simply as a musician—but to help facilitate the performance of every worshiper before God. Therefore, hymn introductions, accompaniments, harmonizations and interludes should be designed to turn the congregational hymn into a congregational anthem.

To the Congregation

God has called us to be worshipers. To glorify God in this way is our chief end, both in this life and in the life to come. Too easily the pews become seats where spectators sit to enjoy a performance by others. The Bible knows nothing of such a passive dimension in worshiping God. Worship involves the entire congregation in performing for the enjoyment of a divine audience. The pastor and other leaders are there to guide us. Worship is ours to do, and to do as well as we can! One key place where all of us become active is in the singing of hymns.

You know how helpful it is to have your own Bible, with key passages underlined and notes written in the margins. It is helpful as well to have your own hymnal, with personal notations—and even to take it with you to worship services.

In preparing for worship, think of *Trinity Hymnal* as part of your script. It helps you to know what you are to say and do in several aspects of the service. Meditate on each hymn to be sung. Note the topic at the top of the page (indicating the overall theme) and the Scripture. Below the hymn appear the names of the author of the words (to the left) and the composer of the music (to the right). Even if these are not familiar names—such as Luther or Wesley or Bach—the dates will help you to place the hymn in its historical setting. You are voicing some of the same heartfelt praise that was offered by God's people who preceded you.

All of God's people are worshipers—what a privilege!

—The Editor

10

SYMBOLS, NOTATIONS AND ABBREVIATIONS

Accompanists' introduction brackets (⌐ ¬) appear above the staff, normally in two sets. When an organist or pianist wishes to provide a short introduction to a hymn, these brackets indicate what to play.

Bullets (•) in the left margin help the worshiper find the correct line when there are five stanzas between staves.

Italicized stanza numbers recommend the two or three stanzas to use if the entire hymn will not be sung.

Guitar chording is provided on 182 of the hymns. Capo chords (in parentheses) are simpler to play than regular chords.

Many hymn texts have been altered since they were first written or translated, for either theological or stylistic purposes. Alterations introduced by another publisher are indicated by "alt." in the source information about the text, below the hymn. Alterations made for *Trinity Hymnal* are indicated by "alt. 1961" (for the first edition) or "alt. 1990" (for the revised edition). Some tunes have been altered and similar notations appear in the source information.

Where possible, archaic language of an entire hymn text has been unobtrusively modernized; for example, "you are" replaces "thou art." In these cases, "mod." appears in the information about the hymn text.

Three types of Psalms are included in *Trinity Hymnal* and are identified as follows:
Metrical Psalm — "Psalm (number)"
Psalm version — "From Psalm (number)"
Psalm paraphrase — "Based on Psalm (number)"

Abbreviations used in the source information:

al.	with alleluias	irreg.	irregular
alt.	altered	L.M.	long meter
anon.	anonymous	mod.	modernized language
arr.	arranged	ref.	with refrain
attr.	attributed	rep.	repeat(s)
b.	born	rev.	revised
ca.	circa	S.M.	short meter
cent.	century	st.	stanza(s)
C.M.	common meter	tr.	translated
D.	doubled	trans.	translation

HOW TO ADD AMENS

You may want to add an amen at the end of a hymn (especially when it is a prayer). If you are unsure of the notes to play, use the model that has the same key signature as the hymn. This pattern will always be appropriate, although for some hymns lower-pitched chords would be better. Accompanists are encouraged to learn a variety of amens and how to adapt them.

A Minor

E Minor

C Major

F Major

D Minor

G Major

B flat Major

G Minor

D Major

E flat Major

C Minor

A Major

A flat Major

F Minor

E Major

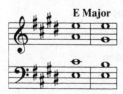

D flat Major

B flat Minor

12

GUITAR CHORD CHART

The chord diagrams on this page will aid the average guitarist in playing music from this hymnal. In chording 182 of these hymns, the publisher assumed that usually a keyboard would not be played along with the guitar. If they are played together, occasional chord adjustments would be needed for the guitar.

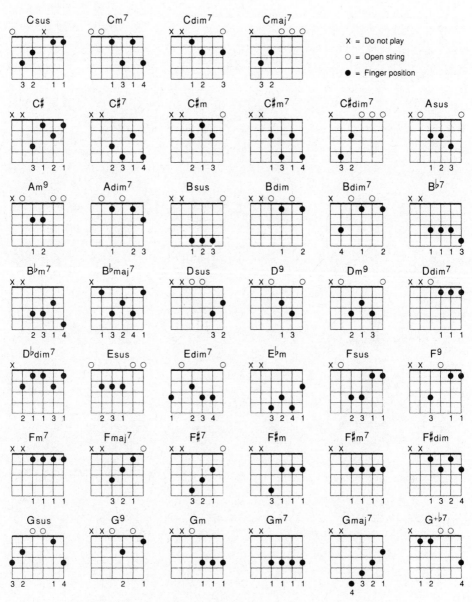

HYMNS

All People That on Earth Do Dwell

1

Shout for joy to the LORD, all the earth. Ps. 100:1

1. All peo - ple that on earth do dwell, sing
2. The Lord ye know is God in - deed; with -
3. O en - ter then his gates with praise, ap -
4. For why? The Lord our God is good, his

to the Lord with cheer - ful voice; him serve with fear, his
out our aid he did us make; we are his folk, he
proach with joy his courts un - to; praise, laud, and bless his
mer - cy is for - ev - er sure; his truth at all times

praise forth - tell, come ye be - fore him and re - joice.
doth us feed, and for his sheep he doth us take.
name al - ways, for it is seem - ly so to do.
firm - ly stood, and shall from age to age en - dure.

Psalm 100
William Kethe, 1561

OLD HUNDREDTH L.M.
Louis Bourgeois's *Genevan Psalter*, 1551

2

O Worship the King

All you have made will praise you, O LORD; your saints will extol you. Ps. 145:10

1. O wor-ship the King all-glo-rious a-bove, O grate-ful-ly sing his pow'r and his love; our shield and De-fend-er, the An-cient of Days, pa-vil-ioned in splen-dor and gird-ed with praise.

2. O tell of his might, O sing of his grace, whose robe is the light, whose can-o-py space. His char-iots of wrath the deep thun-der-clouds form, and dark is his path on the wings of the storm.

3. The earth with its store of won-ders un-told, Al-might-y, your pow'r has found-ed of old; has 'stab-lished it fast by a change-less de-cree, and round it has cast, like a man-tle, the sea.

4. Your boun-ti-ful care what tongue can re-cite? It breathes in the air; it shines in the light; it streams from the hills; it de-scends to the plain; and sweet-ly dis-tils in the dew and the rain.

5. Frail children of dust, and feeble as frail,
in you do we trust, nor find you to fail;
your mercies how tender, how firm to the end,
our Maker, Defender, Redeemer, and Friend!

6. O measureless Might! Ineffable Love!
While angels delight to hymn you above,
the humbler creation, though feeble their lays,
with true adoration shall lisp to your praise.

Based on Psalm 104
Robert Grant, 1833
Mod.

LYONS 10.10.11.11.
Johann Michael Haydn, 1737–1806
Arr. in William Gardiner's *Sacred Melodies*. 1815

Give to Our God Immortal Praise

3

Give thanks to the LORD, for he is good. His love endures forever. Ps. 136:1

1. Give to our God im - mor - tal praise; mer - cy and
2. Give to the Lord of lords re - nown; the King of
3. He built the earth, he spread the sky, and fixed the
4. He fills the sun with morn - ing light; he bids the

truth are all his ways: won - ders of grace to God be -
kings with glo - ry crown: his mer - cies ev - er shall en -
star - ry lights on high: won - ders of grace to God be -
moon di - rect the night: his mer - cies ev - er shall en -

long; re - peat his mer - cies in your song.
dure, when lords and kings are known no more.
long; re - peat his mer - cies in your song.
dure, when suns and moons shall shine no more.

5. He sent his Son with pow'r to save
from guilt and darkness and the grave:
wonders of grace to God belong;
repeat his mercies in your song.

6. Through this vain world he guides our feet,
and leads us to his heav'nly seat:
his mercies ever shall endure,
when this vain world shall be no more.

Based on Psalm 136
Isaac Watts, 1719

WARRINGTON L.M.
Ralph Harrison, 1784

4 All Praise to God, Who Reigns Above

Let them give thanks to the LORD for his unfailing love and his wonderful deeds for men. Ps. 107:15

1. All praise to God, who reigns a - bove, the God of all cre-
2. What God's al - might - y pow'r hath made his gra- cious mer - cy
3. I cried to him in time of need: Lord God, O hear my
4. The Lord for - sak - eth not his flock, his cho - sen gen - er-

a - tion, the God of won - ders, pow'r, and love, the God of our sal-
keep - eth; by morn - ing dawn or eve-ning shade his watch-ful eye ne'er
call - ing! For death he gave me life in-deed and kept my feet from
a - tion; he is their ref - uge and their rock, their peace and their sal-

va - tion! With heal - ing balm my soul he fills, the God who
sleep - eth; with - in the king - dom of his might, lo, all is
fall - ing. For this my thanks shall end - less be; O thank him,
va - tion. As with a moth - er's ten - der hand he leads his

ev - ery sor - row stills. To God all praise and glo - ry!
just and all is right. To God all praise and glo - ry!
thank our God with me. To God all praise and glo - ry!
own, his cho - sen band. To God all praise and glo - ry!

5. Ye who confess Christ's holy name, to God give praise and glory!
Ye who the Father's pow'r proclaim, to God give praise and glory!
All idols underfoot be trod, the Lord is God! The Lord is God!
To God all praise and glory!

6. Then come before his presence now and banish fear and sadness;
to your Redeemer pay your vow and sing with joy and gladness:
Though great distress my soul befell, the Lord, my God, did all things well.
To God all praise and glory!

Johann J. Schütz, 1675
Tr. by Frances E. Cox, 1864

MIT FREUDEN ZART 8.7.8.7.8.8.7.
Bohemian Brethren's *Gesangbuch*, 1566

God, My King, Thy Might Confessing 5

I will exalt you, my God the King; I will praise your name for ever and ever. Ps. 145:1

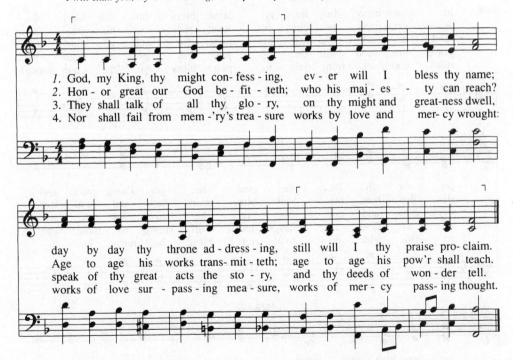

1. God, my King, thy might con-fess-ing, ev-er will I bless thy name;
2. Hon-or great our God be-fit-teth; who his maj-es - ty can reach?
3. They shall talk of all thy glo-ry, on thy might and great-ness dwell,
4. Nor shall fail from mem-'ry's trea-sure works by love and mer-cy wrought:

day by day thy throne ad-dress-ing, still will I thy praise pro-claim.
Age to age his works trans-mit-teth; age to age his pow'r shall teach.
speak of thy great acts the sto-ry, and thy deeds of won-der tell.
works of love sur - pass-ing mea-sure, works of mer-cy pass-ing thought.

5. Full of kindness and compassion,
slow to anger, vast in love,
God is good to all creation;
all his works his goodness prove.

6. All thy works, O Lord, shall bless thee;
thee shall all thy saints adore.
King supreme shall they confess thee,
and proclaim thy sovereign pow'r.

From Psalm 145
Richard Mant, 1824; alt. 1990

STUTTGART 8.7.8.7.
Psalmodia Sacra, Gotha, 1715; arr.

6   O Come, My Soul, Bless Thou the Lord

Praise the LORD, O my soul; all my inmost being, praise his holy name. Ps. 103:1

1. O come, my soul, bless thou the Lord thy Mak - er, and all with -
2. Good is the Lord and full of kind com - pas - sion, most slow to
3. His love is like a fa - ther's to his chil - dren, ten - der and
4. We fade and die like flow'rs that grow in beau - ty, like ten - der
5. High in the heav'ns his throne is fixed for - ev - er, his king - dom

in me bless his ho - ly name; bless thou the Lord, for -
an - ger, plen - te - ous in love; rich is his grace to
• kind to all who fear his name; for well he knows our
grass that soon will dis - ap - pear; but ev - er - more the
rules o'er all from pole to pole; bless ye the Lord through

get not all his mer - cies, his par - d'ning grace and
all that hum - bly seek him, bound - less and end - less
• weak - ness and our frail - ty, he knows that we are
love of God is change - less, still shown to those who
all his wide do - min - ion, bless his most ho - ly

REFRAIN

sav - ing love pro - claim.
as the heav'ns a - bove.
• dust, he knows our frame. Bless him for - ev - er, won - drous in
look to him in fear.
name, O thou my soul.

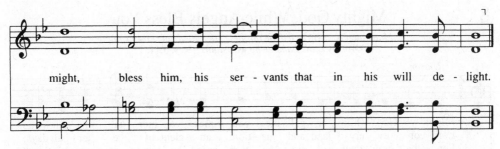

might, bless him, his ser - vants that in his will de - light.

From Psalm 103
The Psalter, 1912; alt. 1961

TIDINGS 11.10.11.10.ref.
James Walch, 1875

From All That Dwell below the Skies 7

Praise the LORD, all you nations; extol him, all you peoples. Ps. 117:1

1. From all that dwell be - low the skies let the Cre -
2. In ev - ery land be - gin the song; to ev - ery
3. E - ter - nal are your mer - cies, Lord; e - ter - nal

a - tor's praise a - rise; let the Re - deem - er's name be
land the strains be - long. In cheer - ful sound all voic - es
truth at - tends your word. Your praise shall sound from shore to

sung through ev - ery land, by ev - ery tongue.
raise and fill the world with joy - ful praise.
shore till suns shall rise and set no more.

Based on Psalm 117
Isaac Watts, 1719; mod.

DUKE STREET L.M.
John Hatton, 1793

8
Mighty God, While Angels Bless You

Many angels ... encircled the throne.... In a loud voice they sang:
"Worthy is the Lamb, who was slain." Rev. 5:11, 12

1. Might-y God, while an-gels bless you, may a mor-tal sing your name?
2. Lord of ev-ery land and na-tion, an-cient of e-ter-nal days,
3. For the gran-deur of your na-ture, grand be-yond a ser-aph's thought,
4. But your rich, your free re-demp-tion, dark through bright-ness all a-long,

Lord of men as well as an-gels, you are ev-ery crea-ture's theme.
sound-ed through the wide cre-a-tion be your just and law-ful praise.
for cre-at-ed works of pow-er, works with skill and kind-ness wrought.
thought is poor, and poor ex-pres-sion, who dare sing that won-drous song?

Harmony

Al - le-lu - ia! Al - le-lu - ia! Al - le-lu - ia! A - men.

5. Brightness of the Father's glory,
   shall your praise unuttered lie?
   Fly, my tongue, such guilty silence,
   sing the Lord who came to die.
   (Alleluias)

6. From the highest throne in glory,
   to the cross of deepest woe,
   all to ransom guilty captives,
   flow my praise, forever flow.
   (Alleluias)

Robert Robinson, 1774
Alt. 1990, mod.

ALLELUIA (LOWE) 8.7.8.7.al.
Albert Lowe, 1868

All You That Fear Jehovah's Name

You who fear the LORD, praise him! Ps. 22:23

1. All you that fear Jehovah's name, his glory tell, his praise proclaim; you children of his chosen race, stand... in awe before his face, stand... in awe before his face.

2. The suff'ring One he has not spurned, who unto him for help has turned; from him he has not hid his face, but answered his request in grace, but answered his request in grace.

3. O Lord, your goodness makes me raise amid your people songs of praise; before all them that fear you, now I worship you and pay my vow, I worship you and pay my vow.

4. For all the meek you will provide; they shall be fed and satisfied; all they that seek the Lord shall live and never-ending praises give, and never-ending praises give.

5. The Lord's unfailing righteousness all generations shall confess; from age to age shall men be taught what wondrous works the Lord has wrought, what wondrous works the Lord has wrought.

Psalm 22:23–26, 31
The Psalter, 1912; alt. 1990, mod.

PARK STREET L.M.rep.
Frederick M. A. Venua. ca. 1810; arr.

10 Hallelujah! Hallelujah!

Praise the LORD. Praise God in his sanctuary. Ps. 150:1

1. Hal - le - lu - jah! Hal - le - lu - jah! In his tem - ple God be praised;
2. Hal - le - lu - jah! Praise Je - ho - vah for his might - y acts of fame;
3. Hal - le - lu - jah! Praise Je - ho - vah with the trum - pet's joy - ful sound;
4. Hal - le - lu - jah! Hal - le - lu - jah! All that breathe, Je - ho - vah praise;

in the high and heav'n - ly plac - es be the sound - ing an - them raised.
ex - cel - lent his might and great - ness, fit - ting prais - es then pro - claim.
praise with harp and praise with or - gan, let his glo - rious praise a - bound.
let the voic - es God has giv - en joy - ful an - thems to him raise.

Hal - le - lu - jah! Hal - le - lu - jah! Hal - le - lu - jah! A - men.

From Psalm 150
The Psalter, 1912

ALLELUIA (LOWE) 8.7.8.7.al.
Albert Lowe, 1868

Now Blessed Be the Lord Our God

Praise be to the LORD God, the God of Israel, who alone does marvelous deeds.
Ps. 72:18

1. Now bless - ed be the Lord our God, the God of Is - ra - el, for he a - lone does won - drous works in glo - ry that ex - cel.
2. And bless - ed be his glo - rious name to all e - ter - ni - ty; the whole earth let his glo - ry fill. A - men, so let it be.
3. His wide do - min - ion shall ex - tend from sea to ut - most sea, and un - to earth's re - mot - est bounds his peace - ful rule shall be.
4. Yea, all the kings shall bow to him, his rule all na - tions hail; he will re - gard the poor man's cry when oth - er help - ers fail.

Psalm 72:8, 11, 12, 18, 19
Scottish Psalter, 1650
Mod.

McKEE C.M.
Spiritual
Arr. by Harry T. Burleigh, 1939

12 Exalt the Lord, His Praise Proclaim

Praise the LORD. Praise the name of the LORD; praise him, you servants of the LORD. Ps. 135:1

1. Ex - alt the Lord, his praise pro - claim; all ye his ser - vants,
2. I know the Lord is high in state, a - bove all gods our
3. Ex - alt the Lord, his praise pro - claim; all ye his ser - vants,

praise his name, who in the Lord's house ev - er stand and hum - bly
Lord is great; the Lord per - forms what he de - crees, in heav'n and
praise his name, who in the Lord's house ev - er stand and hum - bly

serve at his com - mand. The Lord is good, his praise pro - claim; since
earth, in depths and seas. He makes the va - pors to as - cend in
serve at his com - mand. For - ev - er praise and bless his name, and

it is pleas - ant, praise his name; his peo - ple for his
clouds from earth's re - mot - est end; the light - nings flash at
in the church his praise pro - claim; in Zi - on is his

own   he takes and   his   pe - cu - liar trea - sure makes.
his   com - mand; he   holds   the   tem - pest in his hand.
dwell - ing place; praise ye the   Lord,   show forth his grace.

Psalm 135:1–7, 21   CREATION L.M.D.
The Psalter, 1912   From Franz Joseph Haydn, The Creation, 1798; arr.

O Come, Let Us Sing to the Lord   13

Come, let us sing for joy to the LORD; let us shout aloud to the Rock of our salvation.
Ps. 95:1

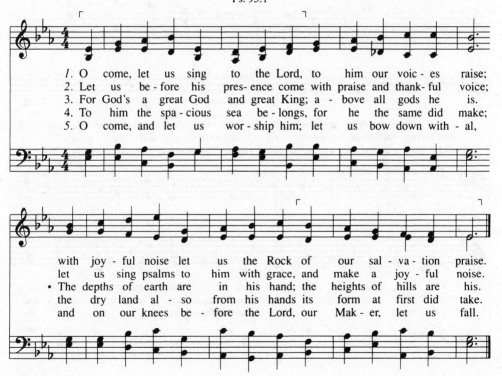

1. O   come, let   us   sing   to   the Lord, to   him our voic - es   raise;
2. Let   us   be - fore his   pres- ence come with praise and thank- ful   voice;
3. For God's   a great God   and great King; a - bove all gods he   is.
4. To   him the spa - cious   sea be - longs, for   he the same did   make;
5. O   come, and let   us   wor - ship him; let   us bow down with - al,

with   joy - ful noise let   us   the Rock of   our sal - va - tion praise!
let   us sing psalms to   him with grace, and make   a   joy - ful noise.
• The depths of earth are   in   his hand; the heights of hills are   his.
the   dry land al - so   from his hands its   form   at first did   take.
and   on   our knees be - fore the Lord, our Mak - er, let   us   fall.

Psalm 95:1–6   CAITHNESS C.M.
Scottish Psalter, 1650   Edinburgh Psalter, 1635

14 New Songs of Celebration Render

Shout for joy to the LORD, all the earth, burst into jubilant song with music. Ps. 98:4

1. New songs of cel - e - bra - tion ren - der to him who has great
2. Joy - ful - ly, heart - i - ly re - sound - ing, let ev - 'ry in - stru -
3. Riv - ers and seas and tor - rents roar - ing, hon - or the Lord with

won - ders done; love sits en - throned in age - less splen - dor;
ment and voice peal out the praise of grace a - bound - ing,
wild ac - claim; moun - tains and stones, look up a - dor - ing,

come and a - dore the might - y One. He has made known his great sal -
call - ing the whole world to re - joice. Trum- pets and or - gans, set in
and find a voice to praise his name. Righ- teous, com - mand - ing, ev - er

va - tion, which all his friends with joy con - fess. He has re -
mo - tion such sounds as make the heav - ens ring; all things that
glo - rious, prais - es be his that nev - er cease: just is our

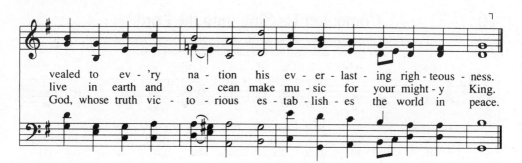

vealed to ev - 'ry na - tion his ev - er - last - ing righ - teous - ness.
live in earth and o - cean make mu - sic for your might - y King.
God, whose truth vic - to - rious es - tab - lish - es the world in peace.

From Psalm 98
Erik Routley, 1972

RENDEZ A DIEU 9.8.9.8.D.
Strasbourg Psalter, 1545
Arr. in Louis Bourgeois's *Genevan Psalter*, 1551; alt. 1990

Stand Up and Bless the Lord   15

Stand up and praise the LORD your God, who is from everlasting to everlasting.
Neh. 9:5

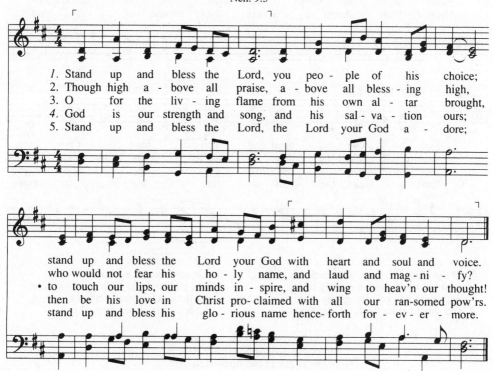

1. Stand up and bless the Lord, you peo - ple of his choice;
2. Though high a - bove all praise, a - bove all bless - ing high,
3. O for the liv - ing flame from his own al - tar brought,
4. God is our strength and song, and his sal - va - tion ours;
5. Stand up and bless the Lord, the Lord your God a - dore;

stand up and bless the Lord your God with heart and soul and voice.
who would not fear his ho - ly name, and laud and mag - ni - fy?
• to touch our lips, our minds in - spire, and wing to heav'n our thought!
then be his love in Christ pro - claimed with all our ran - somed pow'rs.
stand up and bless his glo - rious name hence- forth for - ev - er - more.

James Montgomery, 1824, 1825
Mod.

CARLISLE S.M.
Charles Lockhart. 1769

16   Come, Let Us Sing unto the Lord

*Sing to the LORD a new song, for he has done marvelous things; his right hand
and his holy arm have worked salvation for him. Ps. 98:1*

1. Come, let us sing un - to the Lord new songs of
2. The great sal - va - tion of our God is seen through
3. He called to mind his truth and grace in prom - ise
4. All lands, to God lift up your voice; sing praise to

praise with sweet ac - cord; for won - ders great by
all the earth a - broad; be - fore the hea - then's
made to Is - rael's race; and un - to earth's re -
him, with shouts re - joice; with voice of joy and

him are done, his hand and arm have vic - t'ry won.
won - d'ring sight he has re - vealed his truth and right.
mot - est bound glad tid - ings of sal - va - tion sound.
loud ac - claim let all u - nite and praise his name.

5. Praise God with harp, with harp sing praise,
with voice of psalms his glory raise;
with trumpets, cornets, gladly sing
and shout before the Lord, the King.

6. Let earth be glad, let billows roar
and all that dwell from shore to shore;
let floods clap hands with one accord,
let hills rejoice before the Lord.

7. For lo, he comes; at his command
all nations shall in judgment stand;
in justice robed and throned in light,
the Lord shall judge, dispensing right.

Psalm 98
Associate Reformed Presbyterian *Psalter*, 1931; mod.

DUKE STREET L.M.
John Hatton, 1793

Praise the Lord: Ye Heavens Adore Him

17

All you have made will praise you, O Lord; your saints will extol you. Ps. 145:10

1. Praise the Lord: ye heav'ns a - dore him; praise him, an - gels, in the height;
2. Praise the Lord, for he is glo - rious; nev- er shall his prom-ise fail:
3. Wor - ship, hon - or, glo - ry, bless - ing, Lord, we of - fer un - to thee;

sun and moon, re - joice be - fore him; praise him all ye stars and light.
God hath made his saints vic - to - rious; sin and death shall not pre - vail.
young and old, thy praise ex - press - ing, in glad hom - age bend the knee.

Praise the Lord, for he hath spo - ken; worlds his might - y voice o - beyed:
Praise the God of our sal - va - tion; hosts on high, his pow'r pro - claim:
All the saints in heav'n a - dore thee; we would bow be - fore thy throne:

laws which nev - er shall be bro - ken for their guid - ance hath he made.
heav'n and earth and all cre - a - tion, laud and mag - ni - fy his name.
as thine an - gels serve be - fore thee, so on earth thy will be done.

Based on Psalm 145
St. 1–2, anon., ca. 1801
St. 3. Edward Osler. 1836

FABEN 8.7.8.7.D.
John H. Willcox, 1849

18 You Holy Angels Bright

Praise him, all his angels, praise him, all his heavenly hosts. Ps. 148:2

1. You ho - ly an - gels bright, who wait at God's right hand, or
2. You bless - ed souls at rest, who ran this earth - ly race, and
3. All na - tions of the earth, ex - tol the world's great King; with
4. Sing forth Je - ho - vah's praise, you saints, that on him call! Him

through the realms of light fly at your Lord's com - mand, as - sist our
now, from sin re - leased, be - hold the Sav - ior's face; God's prais - es
mel - o - dy and mirth his glo - rious prais - es sing; for he still
mag - ni - fy al - ways, his ho - ly church - es all! In him re -

song, for else the theme too high does seem for mor - tal tongue.
sound, as in his sight with sweet de - light you do a - bound.
reigns, and will bring low the proud - est foe that him dis - dains.
joice, and there pro - claim his ho - ly name with sound - ing voice.

5. My soul, bear now your part,
   triumph in God above;
   with a well-tun-ed heart
   sing now the songs of love;
   you are his own, whose precious blood
   shed for your good his love made known.

6. Away, distrustful care!
   I have your promise, Lord;
   to banish all despair,
   I have your oath and word;
   and therefore I shall see your face
   and there your grace shall magnify.

7. With your triumphant flock
then I shall numbered be;
built on th'eternal Rock,
his glory we shall see.
The heav'ns so high with praise shall ring
and all shall sing in harmony.

Based on Psalm 148
Richard Baxter, 1672; alt.; alt. 1990, mod.

DARWALL 6.6.6.6.8.8.
John Darwall, 1770

Thee We Adore, Eternal Lord!   19

I heard every creature … singing: "To him who sits on the throne and to the Lamb
be praise and honor and glory and power, for ever and ever!" Rev. 5:13

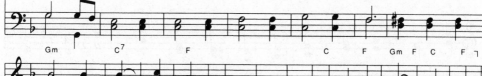

1. Thee we a - dore, e - ter - nal Lord! We praise thy name with
2. To thee a - loud all an - gels cry, the heav'ns and all the
3. A - pos - tles join the glo - rious throng, and proph - ets swell th'im -
4. From day to day, O Lord, do we ex - alt and high - ly

one ac - cord. Thy saints, who here thy good - ness see, through all the
pow'rs on high: thee, ho - ly, ho - ly, ho - ly King, Lord God of
mor - tal song; thy mar - tyrs' no - ble ar - my raise e - ter - nal
hon - or thee! Thy name we wor - ship and a - dore, world with - out

world do wor - ship thee, through all the world do wor - ship thee.
Hosts, they ev - er sing, Lord God of Hosts, they ev - er sing.
an - thems to thy praise, e - ter - nal an - thems to thy praise.
end, for - ev - er - more, world with - out end, for - ev - er - more.

Moravian Collection, 1724

PARK STREET L.M.rep.
Frederick M. A. Venua, ca. 1810: arr.

20 Let All the World in Every Corner Sing

Sing to the LORD a new song; sing to the LORD, all the earth. Ps. 96:1

Unison

1. Let all the world in ev - ery cor - ner sing: My God and King!
2. Let all the world in ev - ery cor - ner sing: My God and King!

The heav'ns are not too high, his praise may up - ward fly; the
The church with psalms must shout, no door can keep them out; but,

earth is not too low, his prais - es there may grow. Let
more than all, the heart must bear the long - est part. Let

all the world in ev - ery cor - ner sing: My God and King!
all the world in ev - ery cor - ner sing: My God and King!

George Herbert, 1633
Alt. 1990

ALL THE WORLD 14.12.12.14.
Robert G. McCutchan, 1934

Sing Praise to the Lord!

21

Praise the LORD. Praise God in his sanctuary; praise him in his mighty heavens.
Ps. 150:1

1. Sing praise to the Lord! Praise him in the height;
   re - joice in his word, you an - gels of light.
   You heav - ens, a - dore him by whom you were made,
   and wor - ship be - fore him in bright - ness ar - rayed.

2. Sing praise to the Lord! Praise him on the earth
   in tune - ful ac - cord, you saints of new birth.
   Praise him who has brought you his grace from a - bove;
   praise him who has taught you to sing of his love.

3. Sing praise to the Lord! All things that give sound,
   each ju - bi - lant chord, re - ech - o a - round.
   Loud or - gans, his glo - ry tell forth in deep tone,
   and trum - pets, the sto - ry of what he has done.

4. Sing praise to the Lord! Thanks - giv - ing and song
   to him be out - poured all a - ges a - long!
   For love in cre - a - tion, for heav - en re - stored,
   for grace of sal - va - tion, sing praise to the Lord!

Based on Psalm 150
Henry W. Baker, 1875; alt.

LAUDATE DOMINUM 10.10.11.11.
C. Hubert H. Parry, 1894

22 O That I Had a Thousand Voices

The LORD has done great things for us, and we are filled with joy. Ps. 126:3

1. O that I had a thou-sand voic-es to praise my
2. O all ye pow'rs that he im-plant-ed, a-rise, and
3. All crea-tures that have breath and mo-tion, that throng the
4. O Fa-ther, deign thou, I be-seech thee, to lis-ten

God with thou-sand tongues! My heart, which in the Lord re-
si-lence keep no more; put forth the strength that he hath
earth, the sea, and sky, now join me in my heart's de-
to my earth-ly lays; a no-bler strain in heav'n shall

joic-es, would then pro-claim in grate-ful songs to all, wher-
grant-ed, your no-blest work is to a-dore. O soul and
vo-tion, help me to raise his prais-es high. My ut-most
reach thee, when I with an-gels hymn thy praise and learn a-

ev-er I might be, what great things God hath done for me.
bod-y, be ye meet with heart-felt praise your Lord to greet!
pow'rs can ne'er a-right de-clare the won-ders of his might.
mid their choirs to sing loud hal-le-lu-jahs to my King.

Johann Mentzer, 1704, cento
Trans. composite

O DASS ICH TAUSEND 9.8.9.8.8.8.
Johann B. König, 1738

God of Gods, We Sound His Praises

23

The LORD is the great God, the great King above all gods. Ps. 95:3

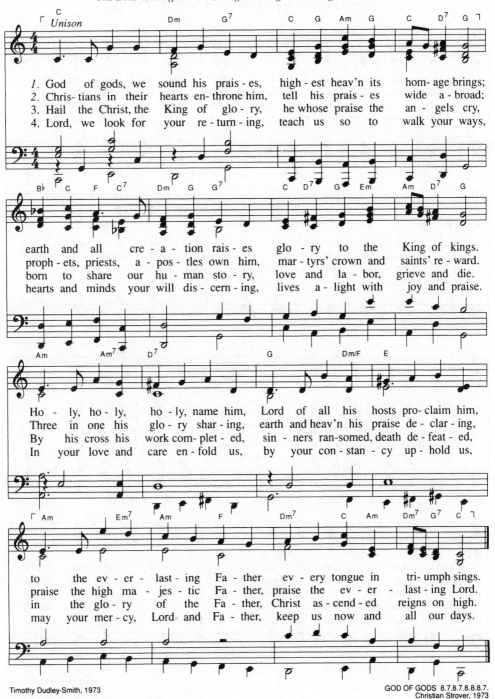

1. God of gods, we sound his prais - es, high - est heav'n its hom- age brings;
2. Chris- tians in their hearts en- throne him, tell his prais - es wide a - broad;
3. Hail the Christ, the King of glo - ry, he whose praise the an - gels cry,
4. Lord, we look for your re - turn - ing, teach us so to walk your ways,

earth and all cre - a - tion rais - es glo - ry to the King of kings.
proph - ets, priests, a - pos - tles own him, mar - tyrs' crown and saints' re - ward.
born to share our hu - man sto - ry, love and la - bor, grieve and die.
hearts and minds your will dis - cern - ing, lives a - light with joy and praise.

Ho - ly, ho - ly, ho - ly, name him, Lord of all his hosts pro- claim him,
Three in one his glo - ry shar - ing, earth and heav'n his praise de - clar - ing,
By his cross his work com- plet - ed, sin - ners ran-somed, death de - feat - ed,
In your love and care en - fold us, by your con - stan - cy up - hold us,

to the ev - er - last - ing Fa - ther ev - ery tongue in tri- umph sings.
praise the high ma - jes - tic Fa - ther, praise the ev - er - last - ing Lord.
in the glo - ry of the Fa - ther, Christ as - cend - ed reigns on high.
may your mer - cy, Lord and Fa - ther, keep us now and all our days.

Timothy Dudley-Smith, 1973

GOD OF GODS 8.7.8.7.8.8.8.7.
Christian Strover, 1973

24   Vast the Immensity, Mirror of Majesty

Before the mountains were born or you brought forth the earth and the world,
from everlasting to everlasting you are God. Ps. 90:2

1. Vast the im - men - si - ty, mir - ror of maj - es - ty,
2. Sounds your cre - a - tive word, form - ing both star and bird,
3. Who can your wis - dom scan? Who com - pre - hend your plan?
4. Tri - une your maj - es - ty, tri - une your love to me,

gal - ax - ies spread in a cur - tain of light;
shap - ing the cos - mos to win your de - light;
How can the mind of man your truth em - brace?
fixed from e - ter - ni - ty in heav'n a - bove.

Lord, your e - ter - ni - ty ris - es in mys - ter - y
or - der from cha - os springs, form that your wis - dom brings,
Here does your Word dis- close more than your pow - er shows,
Fa - ther, what mys - ter - y, in your in - fi - ni - ty

there where no eye can see, in - fi - nite height!
guid - ing cre - at - ed things, in - fi - nite might!
love that to Cal - v'ry goes, in - fi - nite grace!
you gave your Son for me, in - fi - nite love!

Edmund P. Clowney, 1985

MAJESTAS 6.6.10.6.6.10.
Michael Baughen, 1973
Arr. by Noël Tredinnick, b. 1949

O Light That Knew No Dawn

God is light; in him there is no darkness at all. 1 John 1:5

1. O Light that knew no dawn, that shines to end - less day,
2. Thy grace, O Fa - ther, give, that I may serve in fear;
3. That, cleansed from stain of sin, I may meet hom - age give,
4. In sup - pli - ca - tion meek to thee I bend the knee,
5. Thy grace, O Fa - ther, give, I hum - bly thee im - plore;

all things in earth and heav'n are lus - tred by thy ray; no eye can
a - bove all boons, I pray, grant me thy voice to hear; from sin thy
and, pure in heart, be - hold thy beau - ty while I live; clean hands in
O Christ, when thou shalt come, in love re - mem - ber me, and in thy
and let thy mer - cy bless thy ser - vant more and more. All grace and

to thy throne as - cend, nor mind thy bright - ness com - pre - hend.
child in mer - cy free, and let me dwell in light with thee:
ho - ly wor - ship raise, and thee, O Christ my Sav - ior, praise.
king - dom, by thy grace, grant me a hum - ble ser - vant's place.
glo - ry be to thee, from age to age e - ter - nal - ly.

Gregory of Nazianzus, 325–390
Tr. by John Brownlie, 1859–1925

WAVERTON 6.6.6.6.8.8.
Robert Jackson. 1876

26   Tell Out, My Soul, the Greatness of the Lord

My soul glorifies the Lord and my spirit rejoices in God my Savior. Luke 1:46, 47

1. Tell out, my soul, the great-ness of the Lord: un-num-bered bless-ings give my spir-it voice; ten-der to me the prom-ise of his word; in God my Sav-ior shall my heart re-joice.
2. Tell out, my soul, the great-ness of his name: make known his might, the deeds his arm has done; his mer-cy sure, from age to age the same; his ho-ly name, the Lord, the Might-y One.
3. Tell out, my soul, the great-ness of his might: pow'rs and do-min-ions lay their glo-ry by; proud hearts and stub-born wills are put to flight, the hun-gry fed, the hum-ble lift-ed high.
4. Tell out, my soul, the glo-ries of his word: firm is his prom-ise, and his mer-cy sure. Tell out, my soul, the great-ness of the Lord to chil-dren's chil-dren and for-ev-er-more.

Timothy Dudley-Smith, 1965

WOODLANDS 10.10.10.10.
Walter Greatorex, 1919

Text © 1962. Renewal 1990. Hope Publishing Co. All rights reserved. Used by permission. Tune by permission of Oxford University Press.

Great God, How Infinite Art Thou!

27

You, O Lord, reign forever; your throne endures from generation to generation.
Lam. 5:19

1. Great God, how in - fi - nite art thou! How
2. Thy throne e - ter - nal a - ges stood, ere
3. E - ter - ni - ty, with all its years, stands
4. Our lives through var - ious scenes are drawn, and
5. Great God, how in - fi - nite art thou! How

poor and weak are we! Let the whole race of
seas or stars were made: thou art the ev - er -
• pres - ent in thy view; to thee there's noth - ing
vexed with tri - fling cares; while thine e - ter - nal
poor and weak are we! Let the whole race of

crea - tures bow, and pay their praise to thee.
liv - ing God, were all the na - tions dead.
• old ap - pears; to thee there's noth - ing new.
thought moves on thine un - dis - turbed af - fairs.
crea - tures bow, and pay their praise to thee.

Based on Psalm 102:17–27
Isaac Watts, 1707; alt.
Alt. 1961

WINDSOR C.M.
Christopher Tye, 1533
Arr. in William Daman's *Booke of Musicke*. 1591

28 O God, the Rock of Ages

Lord, you have been our dwelling place throughout all generations. Ps. 90:1

Unison

1. O God, the Rock of Ages, who ev-er-more hast been,
2. Our years are like the shad-ows on sun-ny hills that lie,
3. O thou who canst not slum-ber, whose light grows nev-er pale,
4. Lord, crown our faith's en-deav-or with beau-ty and with grace,

what time the tem-pest ra-ges, our dwell-ing place se-rene:
or grass-es in the mead-ows that blos-som but to die;
teach us a-right to num-ber our years be-fore they fail;
till, clothed in light for-ev-er, we see thee face to face:

be-fore thy first cre-a-tions, O Lord, the same as now,
a sleep, a dream, a sto-ry by strang-ers quick-ly told,
on us thy mer-cy light-en, on us thy good-ness rest,
a joy no lan-guage mea-sures; a foun-tain brim-ming o'er;

to end-less gen-er-a-tions the Ev-er-last-ing Thou!
an un-re-main-ing glo-ry of things that soon are old.
and let thy Spir-it bright-en the hearts thy-self hast blessed.
an end-less flow of plea-sures; an o-cean with-out shore.

Based on Psalm 90
Edward H. Bickersteth, 1860

WEDLOCK 7.6.7.6.D.
J. T. White's *The Sacred Harp*, 1844
Arr. by Austin C. Lovelace, 1964; alt. 1990

Tune arr. © 1964, Abingdon Press. Reprinted from *The Book of Hymns* by permission.

The Lord Has Heard and Answered Prayer

29

He will respond to the prayer of the destitute; he will not despise their plea.
Ps. 102:17

1. The Lord has heard and an-swered prayer and saved his
2. The Lord, ex-alt-ed on his throne, looked down from
3. All men in Zi-on shall de-clare his gra-cious
4. The earth and heav'ns shall pass a-way, like ves-ture
5. You, O Je-ho-vah, shall en-dure, your throne for-

peo-ple in dis-tress; this to the com-ing
heav'n with pity-ing eye to still the low-ly
name with one ac-cord, when kings and na-tions
worn and laid a-side, but change-less you shall
ev-er is the same; and to all gen-er-

age de-clare, that they his ho-ly name may bless.
cap-tive's moan and save his peo-ple doomed to die.
gath-er there to serve and wor-ship God the Lord.
live al-way, your years for-ev-er shall a-bide.
a-tions sure shall be your great me-mo-rial name.

Psalm 102:17–27
The Psalter, 1912; alt. 1990, mod.
Tune © 1973 from the *Oxford Book of Carols* by permission of Oxford University Press.

THE HOLY SON L.M.
Peter Hurford, b. 1930

30 Our God, Our Help in Ages Past

Lord, you have been our dwelling place throughout all generations. Ps. 90:1

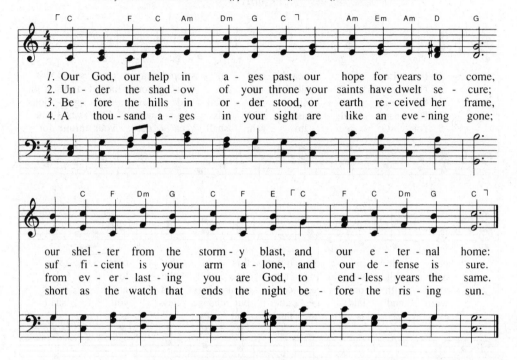

1. Our God, our help in a - ges past, our hope for years to come,
2. Un - der the shad - ow of your throne your saints have dwelt se - cure;
3. Be - fore the hills in or - der stood, or earth re - ceived her frame,
4. A thou - sand a - ges in your sight are like an eve - ning gone;

our shel - ter from the storm - y blast, and our e - ter - nal home:
suf - fi - cient is your arm a - lone, and our de - fense is sure.
from ev - er - last - ing you are God, to end - less years the same.
short as the watch that ends the night be - fore the ris - ing sun.

5. The busy tribes of flesh and blood,
   with all their lives and cares,
   are carried downward by your flood,
   and lost in foll'wing years.

6. Time, like an ever-rolling stream,
   bears all its sons away;
   they fly forgotten, as a dream
   dies at the op'ning day.

7. Our God, our help in ages past,
   our hope for years to come:
   O be our guard while troubles last,
   and our eternal home.

From Psalm 90
Isaac Watts, 1719
Alt. 1990, mod.

ST. ANNE C.M.
Attr. to William Croft, 1678–1727
Tate and Brady's *Supplement to the New Version*, 1708

Have You Not Known, Have You Not Heard

Do you not know? Have you not heard? The LORD is the everlasting God, the Creator of the ends of the earth. He will not grow tired or weary. Is. 40:28

1. Have you not known, have you not heard that firm re-
mains on high the ev - er - last - ing throne of him who formed the earth and sky?

2. Are you a - fraid his pow'r shall fail when comes your e - vil day? And can an all - cre - at - ing arm grow wea - ry or de - cay?

3. Su - preme in wis - dom as in pow'r the Rock of A - ges stands, though him you can - not see, nor trace the work - ing of his hands.

4. He gives the con - quest to the weak, sup - ports the faint - ing heart; and cour - age in the e - vil hour his heav'n - ly aids im - part.

5. Mere human pow'r shall fast decay,
and youthful vigor cease;
but they who wait upon the Lord
in strength shall still increase.

6. They with unwearied feet shall tread
the path of life divine;
with growing ardor onward move,
with growing brightness shine.

7. On eagles' wings they mount, they soar—
their wings are faith and love—
till, past the cloudy regions here,
they rise to heav'n above.

Isaac Watts, 1707
Alt. in *Scottish Paraphrases*, 1781; mod.

HERMON C.M.
Lowell Mason, 1832

32   Great Is Thy Faithfulness

Because of the LORD's great love we are not consumed, for his compassions never fail.
They are new every morning; great is your faithfulness. Lam. 3:22, 23

1. Great is thy faith - ful - ness, O God my Fa - ther; there is no
2. Sum - mer and win - ter and spring-time and har - vest, sun, moon, and
3. Par - don for sin and a peace that en - dur - eth, thine own dear

shad - ow of turn - ing with thee; thou chang- est not, thy com -
stars in their cours - es a - bove, join with all na - ture in
pres - ence to cheer and to guide, strength for to - day and bright

pas- sions, they fail not; as thou hast been thou for - ev - er wilt be.
man - i - fold wit - ness to thy great faith - ful - ness, mer - cy, and love.
hope for to - mor- row, bless- ings all mine, with ten thou- sand be - side!

REFRAIN

Great is thy faith - ful - ness! Great is thy faith - ful - ness! Morn- ing by

morn - ing new mer - cies I see: all I have need - ed thy hand hath pro -

vid - ed— Great is thy faith - ful - ness, Lord, un - to me!

Thomas O. Chisholm, 1923

FAITHFULNESS 11.10.11.10.ref.
William M. Runyan, 1923

Let Us with a Gladsome Mind 33

Give thanks to the LORD, for he is good. His love endures forever. Ps. 136:1

1. Let us with a glad - some mind praise the Lord, for he is kind:
2. Let us sound his name a - broad, for of gods he is the God:
3. He with all - com - mand- ing might filled the new-made world with light:
4. All things liv - ing he does feed; his full hand sup - plies their need:

REFRAIN

for his mer - cies shall en - dure, ev - er faith - ful, ev - er sure.

5. He his chosen race did bless in the wasteful wilderness:
   (Refrain)

6. He has with a piteous eye looked upon our misery:
   (Refrain)

7. Let us then with gladsome mind praise the Lord for he is kind:
   (Refrain)

From Psalm 136
John Milton, 1624; alt.
Alt. 1990. mod.

INNOCENTS 7.7.7.7.
French melody, 13th cent.
Arr. in *The Parish Choir*, 1850

34 The God of Abraham Praise

Without faith it is impossible to please God, because anyone who comes to him must believe that he exists and that he rewards those who earnestly seek him. Heb. 11:6

1. The God of A-braham praise, who reigns en-throned a-bove,
2. The God of A-braham praise, at whose su-preme com-mand
3. He by him-self hath sworn, I on his oath de-pend;
4. The good-ly land I see, with peace and plen-ty blest,

An-cient of ev-er-last-ing days and God of love.
from earth I rise, and seek the joys at his right hand.
I shall, on ea-gles' wings up-borne, to heav'n as-cend.
a land of sa-cred lib-er-ty and end-less rest.

Je-ho-vah! Great I AM! by earth and heav'n con-fessed;
I all on earth for-sake, its wis-dom, fame, and pow'r,
I shall be-hold his face, I shall his pow'r a-dore,
There milk and hon-ey flow, and oil and wine a-bound,

I bow and bless the sa-cred name, for-ev-er blest.
and him my on-ly por-tion make, my shield and tow'r.
and sing the won-ders of his grace for-ev-er-more.
and trees of life for-ev-er grow, with mer-cy crowned.

5. There dwells the Lord our King, the Lord our Righteousness,
   triumphant o'er the world and sin, the Prince of Peace.
   On Zion's sacred height his kingdom he maintains,
   and glorious with his saints in light forever reigns.

6. The whole triumphant host gives thanks to God on high;
   "Hail, Father, Son, and Holy Ghost! " they ever cry.
   Hail, Abraham's God and mine! I join the heav'nly lays;
   all might and majesty are thine, and endless praise.

Thomas Olivers, 1770

LEONI 6.6.8.4.D.
Jewish melody
Arr. by Meyer Lyon, 1770

My God, How Wonderful Thou Art   35

*Who is like the LORD our God, the One who sits enthroned on high, who stoops
down to look on the heavens and the earth?* Ps. 113:5, 6

1. My God, how won-der-ful thou art, thy maj-es-ty how bright!
2. Won-drous are thine e-ter-nal years, O ev-er-last-ing Lord,
3. O how I fear thee, liv-ing God, with deep-est, ten-d'rest fears,
4. Yet I may love thee too, O Lord, al-might-y as thou art;

How beau-ti-ful thy mer-cy seat, in depths of burn-ing light!
by ho-ly an-gels day and night un-ceas-ing-ly a-dored!
and wor-ship thee with trem-bling hope, and pen-i-ten-tial tears.
for thou hast stooped to ask of me the love of my poor heart.

5. No earthly father loves like thee,
   no mother half so mild
   bears and forbears, as thou hast done
   with me, thy sinful child.

6. How wonderful, how beautiful,
   the sight of thee will be,
   thine endless wisdom, boundless pow'r,
   and awesome purity!

From Psalm 113
Frederick W. Faber, 1848; alt. 1961, 1990

ST. ETHELDREDA C.M.
Thomas Turton, 1780–1864

36 Lord, Thou Hast Searched Me

O LORD, you have searched me and you know me. Ps. 139:1

1. Lord, thou hast searched me, and dost know wher - e'er I
2. My words from thee I can - not hide; I feel thy
3. Where can I go a - part from thee, or whith - er
4. If I the wings of morn - ing take, and far a -
5. If deep - est dark - ness cov - er me, the dark - ness

rest, wher - e'er I go; thou know - est all that
pow'r on ev - ery side; O won - drous knowl - edge,
• from thy pres - ence flee? In heav'n?— it is thy
way my dwell - ing make, the hand that lead - eth
hid - eth not from thee; to thee both night and

I have planned, and all my ways are in thy hand.
awe - some might, un - fath - omed depth, un - mea - sured height!
• dwell - ing fair; in death's a - bode?— lo, thou art there.
me is thine, and my sup - port thy pow'r di - vine.
day are bright, the dark - ness shin - eth as the light.

Psalm 139:1–12
The Psalter, 1912
Alt. 1990

Tune arr. by permission of Oxford University Press.

PUER NOBIS NASCITUR L.M.
Melody adapted by Michael Praetorius, 1609
Arr. by George R. Woodward, 1910

All That I Am I Owe to Thee

*I praise you because I am fearfully and wonderfully made; your works are
wonderful, I know that full well. Ps. 139:14*

1. All that I am I owe to thee; thy wis-dom, Lord, has fash-ioned me. I give my Mak-er thank-ful praise, whose won-drous works my soul a-maze.

2. Ere in-to be-ing I was brought, thine eye did see, and in thy thought my life in all its per-fect plan was or-dered ere my days be-gan.

3. Thy thoughts, O God, how man-i-fold, more pre-cious un-to me than gold! I muse on their in-fin-i-ty, a-wak-ing I am still with thee.

4. The wick-ed thou wilt sure-ly slay; from me let sin-ners turn a-way. They speak a-gainst the name di-vine; I count God's en-e-mies as mine.

5. Search me, O God, my heart dis-cern; try me, my in-most thought to learn; and lead me, if in sin I stray, to choose the ev-er-last-ing way.

Psalm 139:14–24
The Psalter, 1912

FEDERAL STREET L.M.
Henry K. Oliver, 1832

38 ## Immortal, Invisible, God Only Wise

Now to the King eternal, immortal, invisible, the only God, be honor and glory
for ever and ever. Amen. 1 Tim. 1:17

1. Im - mor - tal, in - vis - i - ble, God on - ly wise,
2. Un - rest - ing, un - hast - ing and si - lent as light,
3. Great Fa - ther of glo - ry, pure Fa - ther of light,

in light in - ac - ces - si - ble hid from our eyes,
nor want - ing, nor wast - ing, thou rul - est in might;
thine an - gels a - dore thee, all veil - ing their sight;

most bless - ed, most glo - rious, the An - cient of Days,
thy jus - tice like moun - tains high soar - ing a - bove
all praise we would ren - der; O help us to see

al - might - y, vic - to - rious, thy great name we praise.
thy clouds which are foun - tains of good - ness and love.
'tis on - ly the splen - dor of light hid - eth thee!

Walter Chalmers Smith, 1867

JOANNA (or ST. DENIO) 11.11.11.11.
Traditional Welsh hymn melody

O God, Most Holy Are Your Ways

Your ways, O God, are holy. What god is so great as our God? Ps. 77:13

1. O God, most ho - ly are your ways, and who like you de -
2. O God, from you the wa - ters fled, the depths were moved with
3. Your way was in the sea, O God, through might - y wa - ters,

serves my praise? You on - ly do such won - drous things, the
might - y dread, the swell - ing clouds their tor - rents poured, and
deep and broad. None un - der - stood but God a - lone, to

whole wide world your glo - ry sings; your out - stretched arm your
o'er the earth the tem - pest roared; 'mid light - ning's flash and
man your foot - steps were un - known; but safe your peo - ple

peo - ple saved, though sore dis - tressed and long en - slaved.
thun - der's sound great trem - bling shook the sol - id ground.
you did keep, al - might - y Shep - herd of your sheep.

Psalm 77:13–20
The Psalter, 1912; alt. 1990, mod.

VATER UNSER 8.8.8.8.8.8.
V. Schumann's *Geistliche Lieder*, 1539

40 God Is Our Refuge and Our Strength

God is our refuge and strength, an ever-present help in trouble. Ps. 46:1

1. God is our ref-uge and our strength, our ev - er - pres - ent aid,
2. A riv - er flows whose streams make glad the cit - y of our God,
3. The na - tions raged, the king-doms moved, but when his voice was heard,
4. O come, be - hold what won-drous works Je - ho - vah's hand has wrought;
5. "Be still and know that I am God, o'er all ex - alt - ed high;

and there-fore though the earth re - move, we will not be a - fraid;
the ho - ly place where - in the Lord Most High has his a - bode.
• the trou - bled earth was stilled to peace be - fore his might - y word.
come, see what des - o - la - tion great he on the earth has brought."
the sub - ject na - tions of the earth my name shall mag - ni - fy."

though hills a - midst the sea be cast, though foam - ing wa - ters roar,
Since God is in the midst of her, un - moved her walls shall stand,
• The Lord of Hosts is on our side, our safe - ty to se - cure;
To ut - most ends of all the earth he caus - es war to cease;
The Lord of Hosts is on our side, our safe - ty to se - cure;

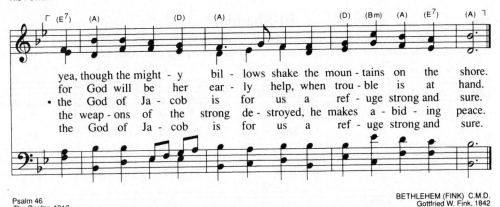

yea, though the might - y bil - lows shake the moun - tains on the shore.
for God will be her ear - ly help, when trou - ble is at hand.
• the God of Ja - cob is for us a ref - uge strong and sure.
the weap - ons of the strong de - stroyed, he makes a - bid - ing peace.
the God of Ja - cob is for us a ref - uge strong and sure.

Psalm 46
The Psalter, 1912

BETHLEHEM (FINK) C.M.D.
Gottfried W. Fink, 1842

The Praises of Thy Wonders, Lord 41

*The heavens praise your wonders, O Lord, your faithfulness, too, in the assembly
of the holy ones.* Ps. 89:5

1. The prais - es of thy won - ders, Lord, the heav - ens shall ex - press;
2. Thou hast an arm that's full of pow'r; thy hand is great in might;
3. Jus - tice and judg - ment of thy throne are made the dwell - ing place;
4. O great - ly blessed the peo - ple are the joy - ful sound that know;

and in the con - gre - ga - tion of saints thy faith - ful - ness.
and thy right hand ex - ceed - ing - ly ex - alt - ed is in height.
mer - cy, ac - com - pa - nied with truth, shall go be - fore thy face.
in bright - ness of thy face, O Lord, they ev - er on shall go.

5. Because the glory of their strength
doth only stand in thee;
and in thy favor shall our horn
and pow'r exalted be.

6. For God is our defense; and he
to us doth safety bring:
the Holy One of Israel
is our almighty King.

Psalm 89:5, 13–18
The Book of Psalms, 1886

BISHOPTHORPE C.M.
Jeremiah Clarke, ca. 1670–1707
Arr. in *Select Portions of the Psalms of David*, 1786

42

El-Shaddai*

The LORD appeared to [Abram] and said, "I am God Almighty; walk before me and be blameless. I will confirm my covenant between me and you." Gen. 17:1, 2

1. El - Shad - dai,* El - Shad - dai, El - El - yon* na A - do-
2. Through your love and through the ram you saved the son of A - bra-
3. Through the years you made it clear that the time of Christ was
4. El - Shad - dai, El - Shad - dai, El - El - yon na A - do-

nai,* age to age you're still the same, by the pow - er of the
ham; through the pow - er of your hand you turned the sea in - to dry
near, though the peo - ple could - n't see what Mes - si - ah ought to
nai, age to age you're still the same, by the pow - er of the

name. El - Shad - dai, El - Shad - dai, Er - kam - ka* na A - do-
land. To the out - cast on her knees you were the God who real - ly
be. Though your Word con - tained the plan, they just could not un - der-
name. El - Shad - dai, El - Shad - dai, Er - kam - ka na A - do-

nai, we will praise and lift you high, El - Shad - dai.
sees, and by your might you set your chil - dren free.
stand, your most awe- some work was done in your Son.
nai, I will praise you till I die, El - Shad - dai.

Michael Card, 1981
Alt. 1990

* El-Shaddai: *God Almighty*   na Adonai: *O Lord*
El-Elyon: *God Most High*   Erkamka: *we will love you*

EL-SHADDAI Irreg.
John Thompson, 1981
Arr. by Lawrence C. Roff, 1988

You Righteous, in the Lord Rejoice

Sing joyfully to the LORD, you righteous; it is fitting for the upright to praise him.
Ps. 33:1

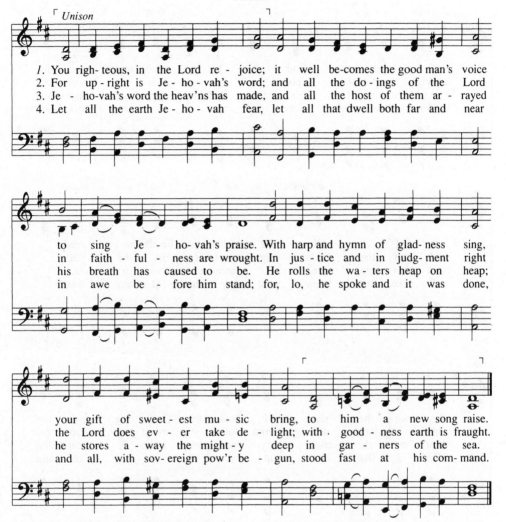

1. You righ-teous, in the Lord re - joice; it well be-comes the good man's voice
2. For up - right is Je - ho - vah's word; and all the do - ings of the Lord
3. Je - ho-vah's word the heav'ns has made, and all the host of them ar - rayed
4. Let all the earth Je - ho - vah fear, let all that dwell both far and near

to sing Je - ho-vah's praise. With harp and hymn of glad-ness sing,
in faith - ful - ness are wrought. In jus - tice and in judg-ment right
his breath has caused to be. He rolls the wa - ters heap on heap;
in awe be - fore him stand; for, lo, he spoke and it was done,

your gift of sweet - est mu - sic bring, to him a new song raise.
the Lord does ev - er take de - light; with good - ness earth is fraught.
he stores a - way the might - y deep in gar - ners of the sea.
and all, with sov-ereign pow'r be - gun, stood fast at his com-mand.

5. He makes the nations' counsels vain,
the plans the peoples would maintain
are thwarted by his hand.
Jehovah's counsel stands secure,
his purposes of heart endure,
forevermore they stand.

6. O truly is the nation blessed
whose God, before the world confessed,
Jehovah is alone;
and blessed the people are whom he
has made his heritage to be,
and chosen for his own.

Psalm 33:1–12
Compiled from several sources
Mod.
Tune arr. © 1964, Abingdon Press. Reprinted from *The Book of Hymns* by permission.

OLD 113TH 8.8.6.D.
Matthäus Greiter's *Strassburger Kirchenamt*, 1525
Arr. by V. Earle Copes, 1964; alt. 1990

44

How Great Thou Art

Great is the LORD, and most worthy of praise. Ps. 48:1

1. O Lord my God, when I in awe-some won-der
2. When thro' the woods and for-est glades I wan-der
3. And when I think that God, his Son not spar-ing,
4. When Christ shall come with shout of ac-cla-ma-tion

con-sid-er all the worlds thy hands have made,
and hear the birds sing sweet-ly in the trees,
sent him to die, I scarce can take it in,
and take me home, what joy shall fill my heart!

I see the stars, I hear the roll-ing thun-der,
when I look down from loft-y moun-tain gran-deur,
that on the cross, my bur-den glad-ly bear-ing,
Then I shall bow in hum-ble ad-o-ra-tion,

thy pow'r thro' out the u-ni-verse dis-played.
and hear the brook and feel the gen-tle breeze;
he bled and died to take a-way my sin.
and there pro-claim, my God, how great thou art.

Stuart K. Hine, 1949; alt.

O STORE GUD 11.10.11.10.ref.
Swedish folk melody
Arr. by Stuart K. Hine, 1949

The author's original words for "worlds" and "rolling" in st. 1 are "works" and "mighty."

45 Now unto Jehovah, Ye Sons of the Mighty

Ascribe to the LORD, O mighty ones, ascribe to the LORD glory and strength. Ps. 29:1

1. Now un-to Je-ho-vah, ye sons of the might-y, all glo-ry and strength and do-min-ion ac-cord; as-cribe to him glo-ry, and ren-der him hon-or. In beau-ty of ho-li-ness wor-ship the Lord, in beau-ty of ho-li-ness wor-ship the Lord.

2. The voice of Je-ho-vah comes down on the wa-ters; in thun-der the God of the glo-ry draws nigh. Lo, o-ver the waves of the wide-flow-ing wa-ters Je-ho-vah as King is en-thron-ed on high! Je-ho-vah as King is en-thron-ed on high!

3. The voice of Je-ho-vah is might-y, is might-y; the voice of Je-ho-vah in maj-es-ty speaks: the voice of Je-ho-vah the ce-dars is break-ing; Je-ho-vah the ce-dars of Leb-a-non breaks, Je-ho-vah the ce-dars of Leb-a-non breaks.

4. Each one in His tem-ple His glo-ry pro-claim-eth. He sat on the flood; he is King on his throne. Je-ho-vah all strength to his peo-ple im-part-eth; Je-ho-vah with peace ev-er bless-eth his own, Je-ho-vah with peace ev-er bless-eth his own.

Psalm 29:1–5, 9–11
St. 1, *The Psalter*, 1912
St. 2–4, *Book of Psalms*, 1871; alt.
Tune © 1990, RAM Music Publications. Used by permission.

WILLOW GROVE 12.11.12.11.
Ronald Alan Matthews, 1985

Round the Lord in Glory Seated

And they were calling to one another: "Holy, holy, holy is the Lord Almighty;
the whole earth is full of his glory." Is. 6:3

1. Round the Lord in glo - ry seat - ed, cher - u - bim and ser - a - phim
2. Heav'n is still with glo - ry ring - ing, earth takes up the an - gels' cry,
3. With his ser - aph train be - fore him, with his ho - ly church be - low,
4. Thus your glo - rious name con - fess- ing, we a - dopt your an - gels' cry,

filled his tem - ple, and re - peat - ed each to each th'al - ter - nate hymn:
"Ho - ly, ho - ly, ho - ly," sing - ing, "Lord of Hosts, the Lord Most High."
thus u - nite we to a - dore him, bid we thus our an - them flow:
"Ho - ly, ho - ly, ho - ly," bless - ing you, the Lord of Hosts Most High.

REFRAIN

"Lord, your glo - ry fills the heav - en, earth is with its ful - ness stored;

un - to you be glo - ry giv - en, ho - ly, ho - ly, ho - ly Lord!"

Compiled from Richard Mant, 1837
Alt. 1990. mod.

SANCTUS 8.7.8.7.D.
John Richards (Isalaw), 1843–1908

47 God the Lord Is King

The LORD reigns, let the nations tremble; he sits enthroned between the cherubim, let the earth shake. Ps. 99:1

1. God the Lord is King: be - fore him earth with all your
2. God the Lord is King of glo - ry; Zi - on, tell the
3. Laws di - vine to them were spo - ken from the pil - lar
4. But their Fa - ther, God, for - gave them when they sought his

na - tions, wait! Where the cher - u - bim a - dore him
world his fame; an - cient Is - ra - el, the sto - ry
of the cloud; sa - cred pre - cepts quick - ly bro - ken;
face once more: ev - er read - y was to save them,

sits our God in roy - al state. He is ho - ly;
of his faith - ful - ness pro - claim. He is ho - ly;
fierce - ly then his ven - geance flowed. He is ho - ly;
ten - der - ly did he re - store. He is ho - ly;

he is ho - ly; bless - ed on - ly Po - ten - tate!
he is ho - ly; ho - ly is his awe - some name.
he is ho - ly; to the dust their hearts were bowed.
he is ho - ly; we too will his grace im - plore.

From Psalm 99
George Rawson, 1807–1889; alt. 1990, mod.

EDEN CHURCH 8.7.8.7.8.7.
Dale Wood, b. 1934

O Lord Most High, with All My Heart

I will praise you, O LORD, with all my heart; I will tell of all your wonders. Ps. 9:1

1. O Lord Most High, with all my heart your won-drous
2. The Lord, the ev-er-last-ing King, is seat-ed
3. Je-ho-vah will a ref-uge prove, a ref-uge
4. All they, O Lord, that know your name their con-fi-
5. Sing prais-es to the Lord Most High, to him who

works I will pro-claim; I will be glad and
on his judg-ment throne; the righ-teous Judge of
strong for all op-pressed, a safe re-treat, where
dence in you will place, for you have ne'er for-
does in Zi-on dwell; de-clare his might-y

give you thanks and sing the prais-es of your name.
all the world will make his per-fect jus-tice known.
wea-ry souls in trou-bled times may sure-ly rest.
sak-en them who ear-nest-ly have sought your face.
deeds a-broad, his deeds a-mong the na-tions tell.

Psalm 9:1, 2, 7–11
The Psalter, 1912; alt. 1990, mod.

ROCKINGHAM OLD L.M.
Arr. by Edward Miller, 1790

49   O Lord, Thou Judge of All the Earth

O Lord, the God who avenges, O God who avenges, shine forth. Ps. 94:1

1. O Lord, thou Judge of all the earth, to whom all
2. How long, O Lord, in boast - ful pride shall wick - ed
3. Be wise, ye fools and brut - ish men; shall not he
4. The Lord will judge in righ - teous - ness, from him all

ven - geance doth be - long, a - rise and show thy glo - ry
men tri - um - phant stand? How long shall they af - flict thy
see, who formed the eye? Shall not he hear, who formed the
truth and knowl - edge flow; the fool - ish thoughts of wick - ed

forth, re - quite the proud, con - demn the wrong.
saints and scorn thy wrath, thy dread - ful hand?
ear, and judge, who reign - eth God Most High?
men, how vain they are the Lord doth know.

5. That man is blest whom thou, O Lord,
with chast'ning hand dost teach thy will,
for in the day when sinners fall,
that man in peace abideth still.

6. Unless the Lord had been my help,
my life had quickly passed away;
but when my foot had almost slipped,
O Lord, thy mercy was my stay.

Psalm 94:1–5, 8–13, 17, 18
The Psalter, 1912; alt. 1961

THE KING'S MAJESTY L.M.
George Graham, 1941

O Lord, Be Thou My Helper True

50

Help, LORD, for the godly are no more; the faithful have vanished from among men.
Ps. 12:1

1. O Lord, be thou my help - er true, for
2. The lips that speak, the truth to hide, the
3. Be - cause the poor are sore op - pressed, be -
4. Je - ho - vah's prom - is - es are sure, his

just and god - ly men are few; the faith - ful who can
tongues of ar - ro - gance and pride, that boast - ful words em -
cause the need - y are dis - tressed, and bit - ter are their
words are true, his words are pure as sil - ver from the

find? From truth and wis - dom men de - part, with
ploy, false - speak - ing tongues that boast their might, that
cries, the Lord will be their help - er strong; to
flame. Though base men walk on ev - 'ry side, his

flat - t'ring lips and dou - ble heart they speak their e - vil mind.
own no law, that know no right, Je - ho - vah will de - stroy.
save them from con - tempt and wrong Je - ho - vah will a - rise.
saints are safe, what - e'er be - tide, pro - tec - ted by his name.

Psalm 12
The Psalter, 1912

COLWYN BAY 8.8.6.D.
Thomas Joseph Linekar, b. 1858

51

O Jehovah, Hear My Words

*Give ear to my words, O LORD, consider my sighing. Listen to my cry for help,
my King and my God, for to you I pray. Ps. 5:1, 2*

1. O Je - ho - vah, hear my words, to my thoughts at - ten - tive be;
2. Thou, Je - ho - vah, art a God who de - light - est not in sin;
3. In the ful - ness of thy grace to thy house I will re - pair;
4. False and faith- less are my foes, in their mouth no truth is found;
5. O let all that trust thy care ev - er glad and joy - ful be;

hear my cry, my King, my God, I will make my prayer to thee.
e - vil shall not dwell with thee, nor the proud thy fa - vor win.
bow - ing toward thy ho - ly place, in thy fear to wor - ship there.
dead - ly are the words they speak, all their thoughts with sin a - bound.
let them joy who love thy name, safe - ly guard - ed, Lord, by thee.

With the morn - ing light, O Lord, thou shalt hear my voice a - rise,
E - vil - do - ers thou dost hate, ly - ing tongues thou wilt de - feat;
Lead me in thy righ - teous-ness, let my foes as - sail in vain;
Bring, O God, their plans to naught, hold them guilt - y in thy sight,
For a bless - ing from thy store to the righ - teous thou wilt yield;

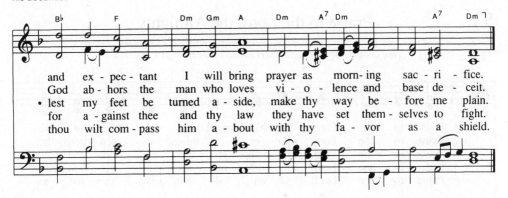

and ex - pec - tant I will bring prayer as morn-ing sac - ri - fice.
God ab - hors the man who loves vi - o - lence and base de - ceit.
• lest my feet be turned a - side, make thy way be - fore me plain.
for a - gainst thee and thy law they have set them - selves to fight.
thou wilt com - pass him a - bout with thy fa - vor as a shield.

Psalm 5
The Psalter, 1912

ABERYSTWYTH 7.7.7.7.D.
Joseph Parry, 1879

O Praise the Lord! O Thank the Lord! 52

Praise the LORD. Give thanks to the LORD, for he is good; his love endures forever.
Ps. 106:1

1. O praise the Lord! O thank the Lord! For boun - ti - ful is he;
2. Who can ex - press Je - ho-vah's praise or tell his deeds of might?
3. Re - gard me with the fa - vor, Lord, which thou dost bear to thine.
4. That I may see thy peo - ple's good and in their joy re - joice,

be - cause his lov - ing - kind - ness lasts to all e - ter - ni - ty.
O blessed are they who jus - tice keep and ev - er do the right.
O vis - it thou my soul in love; make thy sal - va - tion mine:
and may with thine in - her - i - tance ex - ult with cheer - ful voice.

Psalm 106:1–5
The Book of Psalms for Singing, 1973

EXETER C.M.
Henry L. Mason, 1923

53   Praise to the Lord, the Almighty

Praise the LORD, O my soul; all my inmost being, praise his holy name. Praise the LORD, O my soul, and forget not all his benefits. Ps. 103:1, 2

1. Praise to the Lord, the Al - might - y, the King of cre -
2. Praise to the Lord, who o'er all things so won - drous - ly
3. Praise to the Lord, who doth pros - per thy work and de -
4. Praise to the Lord, who with mar - vel - ous wis - dom hath
5. Praise to the Lord! O let all that is in me a -

a - tion! O my soul, praise him, for he is thy
reign - eth, shel - ters thee un - der his wings, yea, so
fend thee! Sure - ly his good - ness and mer - cy here
made thee, decked thee with health, and with lov - ing hand
dore him! All that hath life and breath, come now with

health and sal - va - tion! All ye who hear, now to his
gent - ly sus - tain - eth! Hast thou not seen how thy de -
dai - ly at - tend thee; pon - der a - new what the Al -
guid - ed and stayed thee. How oft in grief hath not he
prais - es be - fore him! Let the a - men sound from his

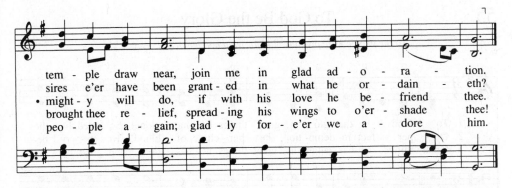

tem - ple draw near, join me in glad ad - o - ra - tion.
sires e'er have been grant - ed in what he or - dain - eth?
• might - y will do, if with his love he be - friend thee.
brought thee re - lief, spread - ing his wings to o'er - shade thee!
peo - ple a - gain; glad - ly for - e'er we a - dore him.

Based on Psalm 103
Joachim Neander, 1680
Tr. by Catherine Winkworth, 1863; alt. 1990

LOBE DEN HERREN 14.14.4.7.8.
Stralsund Gesangbuch, 1665
Arr. in *Praxis Pietatis Melica*,1668

Hallelujah! Raise, O Raise

54

Praise the LORD. Praise, O servants of the LORD, praise the name of the LORD.
Ps. 113:1

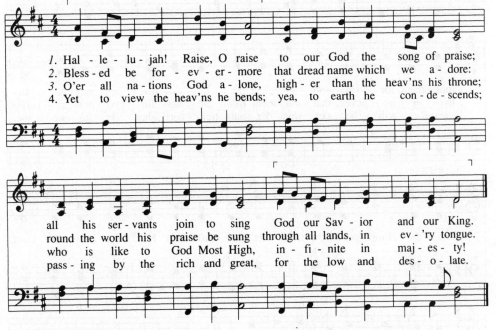

1. Hal - le - lu - jah! Raise, O raise to our God the song of praise;
2. Bless - ed be for - ev - er - more that dread name which we a - dore:
3. O'er all na - tions God a - lone, high - er than the heav'ns his throne;
4. Yet to view the heav'ns he bends; yea, to earth he con - de - scends;

all his ser - vants join to sing God our Sav - ior and our King.
round the world his praise be sung through all lands, in ev - 'ry tongue.
who is like to God Most High, in - fi - nite in maj - es - ty!
pass - ing by the rich and great, for the low and des - o - late.

5. He can raise the poor to stand
with the princes of the land;
wealth upon the needy show'r:
set him with the high in pow'r.

6. He the broken spirit cheers:
turns to joy the mourner's tears;
such the wonders of his ways;
praise his name, forever praise!

Psalm 113
Josiah Conder, 1789–1855; alt. 1961

ALCESTER 7.7.7.7.
Arr. by Samuel S. Wesley, 1810–1876

55

To God Be the Glory

All the people were praising God for what had happened. Acts 4:21

1. To God be the glo - ry, great things he has done! So loved he the
2. O per - fect re - demp - tion, the pur - chase of blood! To ev - 'ry be -
3. Great things he has taught us, great things he has done, and great our re -

world that he gave us his Son, who yield - ed his life an a -
liev - er the prom - ise of God; the vil - est of - fend - er who
joic - ing through Je - sus the Son; but pur - er and high - er and

tone - ment for sin, and o - pened the life - gate that we may go in.
tru - ly be - lieves, that mo - ment from Je - sus for - give - ness re - ceives.
great - er will be our won - der, our trans - port, when Je - sus we see.

REFRAIN

Praise the Lord, praise the Lord, let the earth hear his voice! Praise the Lord,

praise the Lord, let the peo - ple re - joice! O come to the Fa - ther thro'

Je - sus the Son, and give him the glo - ry, great things he has done!

Fanny J. Crosby, 1875; alt.
Mod.

TO GOD BE THE GLORY 11.11.11.11.
William H. Doane, 1875

When All Your Mercies, O My God
56

Surely goodness and love will follow me all the days of my life, and I will dwell
in the house of the LORD forever. Ps. 23:6

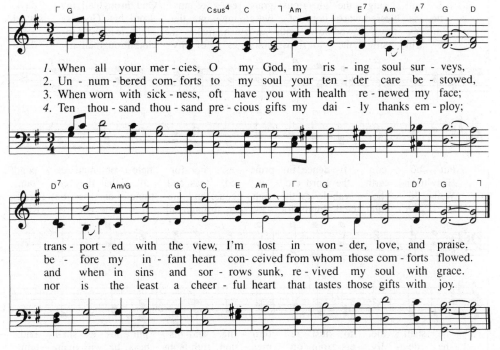

1. When all your mer - cies, O my God, my ris - ing soul sur - veys,
2. Un - num - bered com - forts to my soul your ten - der care be - stowed,
3. When worn with sick - ness, oft have you with health re - newed my face;
4. Ten thou - sand thou - sand pre - cious gifts my dai - ly thanks em - ploy;

trans - port - ed with the view, I'm lost in won - der, love, and praise.
be - fore my in - fant heart con - ceived from whom those com - forts flowed.
and when in sins and sor - rows sunk, re - vived my soul with grace.
nor is the least a cheer - ful heart that tastes those gifts with joy.

5. Through ev'ry period of my life
   your goodness I'll pursue;
   and after death, in distant worlds,
   the glorious theme renew.

6. Through all eternity to you
   a joyful song I'll raise;
   for oh, eternity's too short
   to utter all your praise.

Joseph Addison, 1712; mod.

MANOAH C.M.
Arr. in Henry W. Greatorex's *Collection*, 1851

57 Hallelujah, Praise Jehovah, O My Soul

Praise the LORD. Praise the LORD, O my soul. I will praise the LORD all my life; I will sing praise to my God as long as I live. Ps. 146:1, 2

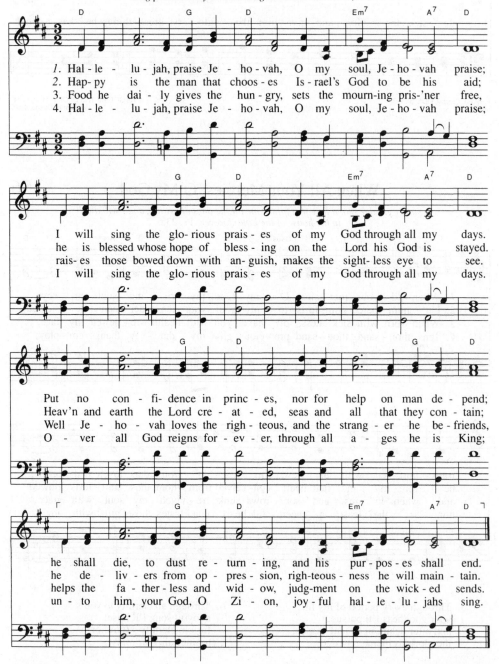

1. Hal - le - lu - jah, praise Je - ho - vah, O my soul, Je - ho - vah praise;
2. Hap - py is the man that choos - es Is - rael's God to be his aid;
3. Food he dai - ly gives the hun - gry, sets the mourn-ing pris-'ner free,
4. Hal - le - lu - jah, praise Je - ho - vah, O my soul, Je - ho - vah praise;

I will sing the glo - rious prais - es of my God through all my days.
he is blessed whose hope of bless - ing on the Lord his God is stayed.
rais - es those bowed down with an - guish, makes the sight- less eye to see.
I will sing the glo - rious prais - es of my God through all my days.

Put no con - fi - dence in princ - es, nor for help on man de - pend;
Heav'n and earth the Lord cre - at - ed, seas and all that they con - tain;
Well Je - ho - vah loves the righ - teous, and the strang - er he be - friends,
O - ver all God reigns for - ev - er, through all a - ges he is King;

he shall die, to dust re - turn - ing, and his pur - pos - es shall end.
he de - liv - ers from op - pres - sion, right-teous - ness he will main - tain.
helps the fa - ther - less and wid - ow, judg-ment on the wick - ed sends.
un - to him, your God, O Zi - on, joy - ful hal - le - lu - jahs sing.

Psalm 146
The Psalter, 1912
Mod.

RIPLEY 8.7.8.7.D.
Gregorian chant
Arr. by Lowell Mason, 1839

O Splendor of God's Glory Bright

In him was life, and that life was the light of men. John 1:4

1. O Splen-dor of God's glo-ry bright, from light e-ter-nal bring-ing light, O Light of light, light's liv-ing Spring, true Day, all days il-lu-min-ing:

2. Come, ver-y Sun of heav-en's love, in last-ing ra-diance from a-bove, and pour the Ho-ly Spir-it's ray on all we think or do to-day.

3. And now to you our pray'rs as-cend, O Fa-ther, glo-rious with-out end; we plead with Sov-ereign Grace for pow'r to con-quer in temp-ta-tion's hour.

4. Con-firm our will to do the right, and keep our hearts from en-vy's blight; let faith her ea-ger fires re-new, and hate the false, and love the true.

5. O joyful be the passing day
with thoughts as pure as morning's ray,
with faith like noontide shining bright,
our souls unshadowed by the night.

6. Dawn's glory gilds the earth and skies,
let him, our perfect Morn, arise,
the Word in God the Father one,
the Father imaged in the Son.

Ambrose of Milan, 340–397
Trans. compiled by Louis F. Benson, 1910; alt. 1990, mod.

WINCHESTER NEW L.M.
Musikalisches Handbuch, Hamburg, 1690; alt. 1990

59 Forever Settled in the Heavens

Your word, LORD, is eternal; it stands firm in the heavens. Ps. 119:89

1. For - ev - er set - tled in the heav'ns, thy word, O
2. Thy word and works un - moved re - main, thine ev - 'ry
3. I should have per - ished in my woe had not I
4. The wick - ed would de - stroy my soul, but in thy

Lord, shall firm - ly stand; thy faith - ful - ness shall nev - er
pur - pose to ful - fil; all things are thine and thee o -
loved thy law di - vine; that law I nev - er can for -
truth is ref - uge sure; ex - ceed- ing broad is thy com -

fail; the earth a - bides at thy com - mand.
bey, and all as ser - vants wait thy will.
get; O save me, Lord, for I am thine.
mand, and in per - fec - tion shall en - dure.

Psalm 119:89–97
The Psalter, 1912; alt. 1961

DUKE STREET L.M.
John Hatton. 1793

Thy Mercy and Thy Truth, O Lord

Your love, LORD, reaches to the heavens, your faithfulness to the skies. Ps. 36:5

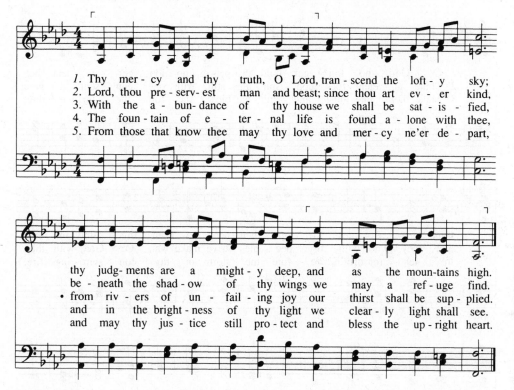

1. Thy mer - cy and thy truth, O Lord, tran - scend the loft - y sky;
2. Lord, thou pre - serv - est man and beast; since thou art ev - er kind,
3. With the a - bun - dance of thy house we shall be sat - is - fied,
4. The foun - tain of e - ter - nal life is found a - lone with thee,
5. From those that know thee may thy love and mer - cy ne'er de - part,

thy judg - ments are a might - y deep, and as the moun - tains high.
be - neath the shad - ow of thy wings we may a ref - uge find.
• from riv - ers of un - fail - ing joy our thirst shall be sup - plied.
and in the bright - ness of thy light we clear - ly light shall see.
and may thy jus - tice still pro - tect and bless the up - right heart.

Psalm 36:5–10
The Psalter, 1912

WALSALL C.M.
English melody
Arr. in Anchor's *A Choice Collection*, ca. 1721: alt. 1990

61   O God, No Longer Hold Thy Peace

O God, do not keep silent; be not quiet, O God, be not still. Ps. 83:1

1. O God, no lon - ger hold thy peace, no lon - ger si - lent be;
2. Thine an - cient foes, con - spir - ing still, with one con - sent a - gree,
3. Make them like dust and stub - ble blown be - fore the whirl-wind dire,

thine en - e - mies lift up their head to fight thy saints and thee.
and they who with thy peo - ple strive make war, O God, with thee.
in ter - ror driv'n be - fore the storm of thy con - sum - ing fire.

A - gainst thine own, whom thou dost love, their craft thy foes em - ploy;
O God, who in our fa - thers' time didst smite our foes and thine,
Con - found them in their sin till they to thee for par - don fly,

they think to cut thy peo - ple off, thy church they would de - stroy.
so smite thine en - e - mies to - day who in their pride com - bine.
till in dis - may they, trem - bling, own that thou art God Most High.

From Psalm 83
The Psalter, 1912

ST. MATTHEW C.M.D.
William Croft. 1708

Sing to the Lord, Sing His Praise

Sing to the LORD a new song; sing to the LORD, all the earth. Ps. 96:1

1. Sing to the Lord, sing his praise, all you peo- ples, new be your song as new hon - ors you pay; sing of his maj - es - ty, bless him for - ev - er, show his sal - va - tion from day to day.

2. Tell of his won-drous works, tell of his glo- ry, till through the na - tions his name is re - vered; praise and ex - alt him, for he is al - might- y; God o - ver all let the Lord be feared.

3. Vain are the hea - then gods, i - dols and help-less; God made the heav'ns, and his glo - ry they tell; hon - or and maj - es - ty shine out be - fore him, beau - ty and strength in his tem - ple dwell.

4. Give un - to God Most High glo - ry and hon- or, come with your of - f'rings and hum - bly draw near; in ho - ly beau - ty now wor - ship Je - ho - vah, trem - ble be - fore him with god - ly fear.

5. Make all the nations know God reigns forever;
   earth is established as he did decree;
   righteous and just is the King of the nations,
   judging the people with equity.

6. Let heav'n and earth be glad; waves of the ocean,
   forest and field, exultation express;
   for God is coming, the Judge of the nations,
   coming to judge in his righteousness.

From Psalm 96
The Psalter, 1912; mod.

WESLEY 11.10.11.10.
Lowell Mason, 1830

63 Jehovah Reigns; Let Earth Be Glad

The LORD reigns, let the earth be glad; let the distant shores rejoice. Ps. 97:1

1. Je - ho - vah reigns; let earth be glad, and all the isles their joy make known; with clouds and dark - ness he is clad, on truth and jus - tice rests his throne.

2. Con - sum - ing fire de - stroys his foes, a - round the world his light - nings blaze; the trem - bling earth his pres - ence knows, the moun - tains melt be - fore his gaze.

3. The heav'ns his righ - teous - ness pro - claim, through earth his glo - ry shines a - broad; from i - dol wor - ship turn with shame and bow be - fore the liv - ing God.

4. Your church re - joic - es to be - hold your judg - ments in the earth, O Lord; your glo - ry to the world un - fold, su - preme o'er all you are a - dored.

5. All you that truly love the Lord,
   hate sin, for he is just and pure;
   to saints his help he will accord
   and keep them in his love secure.

6. For good men light and joy are sown
   to bless them in the harvesttime;
   O saints, your joy in God make known
   and ever praise his name sublime.

From Psalm 97
The Psalter, 1912; alt. 1990, mod.

BRYNTEG L.M.
John Ambrose Lloyd, 1815–1874; alt. 1990

God, the Lord, a King Remaineth

The LORD reigns, He is robed in majesty; the LORD is robed in majesty and is armed with strength. Ps. 93:1

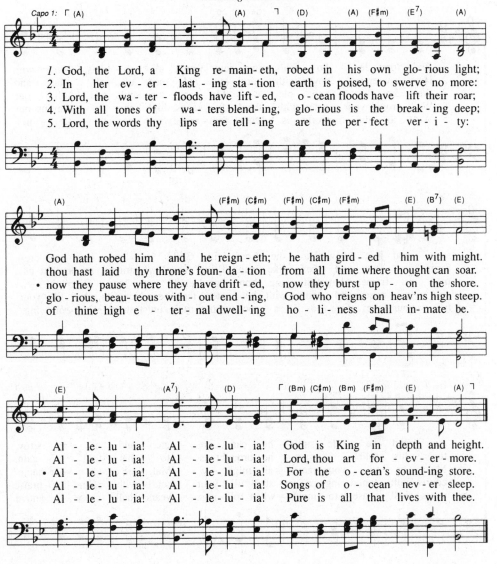

1. God, the Lord, a King re- main- eth, robed in his own glo- rious light;
2. In her ev - er - last - ing sta - tion earth is poised, to swerve no more:
3. Lord, the wa - ter - floods have lift - ed, o - cean floods have lift their roar;
4. With all tones of wa - ters blend- ing, glo- rious is the break - ing deep;
5. Lord, the words thy lips are tell - ing are the per - fect ver - i - ty:

God hath robed him and he reign - eth; he hath gird - ed him with might.
thou hast laid thy throne's foun- da - tion from all time where thought can soar.
now they pause where they have drift - ed, now they burst up - on the shore.
glo - rious, beau- teous with - out end - ing, God who reigns on heav'ns high steep.
of thine high e - ter - nal dwell- ing ho - li - ness shall in- mate be.

Al - le - lu - ia! Al - le-lu - ia! God is King in depth and height.
Al - le - lu - ia! Al - le-lu - ia! Lord, thou art for - ev - er - more.
Al - le - lu - ia! Al - le-lu - ia! For the o - cean's sound-ing store.
Al - le - lu - ia! Al - le-lu - ia! Songs of o - cean nev - er sleep.
Al - le - lu - ia! Al - le-lu - ia! Pure is all that lives with thee.

From Psalm 93
John Keble, 1839

REGENT SQUARE 8.7.8.7.8.7.
Henry Smart, 1867

65 Before Jehovah's Awesome Throne

Shout for joy to the LORD, all the earth. Worship the LORD with gladness; come
before him with joyful songs. Ps. 100:1, 2

1. Be - fore Je - ho - vah's awe - some throne, all na - tions, bow with sa - cred joy; know that the Lord is God a - lone, he can cre - ate, and he de - stroy— he can cre - ate, and he de - stroy.
2. His sov - ereign pow'r, with - out our aid, made us of dust and formed us men; and when like wan - d'ring sheep we strayed, he brought us to his fold a - gain— he brought us to his fold a - gain.
3. We are his peo - ple, we his care, our souls and all our mor - tal frame; what last - ing hon - ors shall we rear, al - might - y Mak - er, to your name?— al - might - y Mak - er, to your name?
4. We'll crowd your gates with thank - ful songs, high as the heav'ns our voic - es raise; and earth, with her ten thou - sand tongues, shall fill your courts with sound - ing praise— shall fill your courts with sound - ing praise.
5. Wide as the world is your com - mand, vast as e - ter - ni - ty your love; firm as a rock your truth must stand, when roll - ing years shall cease to move— when roll - ing years shall cease to move.

From Psalm 100
Isaac Watts, 1705, 1719
St. 1 alt. by John Wesley; alt. 1961, 1990, mod.

PARK STREET L.M.rep.
Frederick M. A. Venua, ca. 1810; arr.

God Is Known among His People

66

In Judah God is known; his name is great in Israel. Ps. 76:1

1. God is known a-mong his peo-ple, ev-ery mouth his prais-es fill;
2. Ex - cel - lent and glo - rious are you, with your tro-phies from the fray;
3. When from heav'n your sen- tence sound-ed, all the earth in fear was still,
4. Vow and pay un - to Je - ho - vah, him your God for - ev - er own;

from of old he has es - tab-lished his a - bode on Zi - on's hill;
you have slain the might- y war- riors, wrapped in sleep of death are they;
while to save the meek and low - ly God in judg- ment wrought his will;
all men, bring your gifts be - fore him, wor - ship him, and him a - lone;

there he broke the sword and ar - row, bade the noise of war be still.
when your an - ger once is ris - en, who can stand in that dread day?
e'en the wrath of man shall praise you, your de - signs it shall ful - fil.
might-y kings o - bey and fear him, princ- es bow be - fore his throne.

From Psalm 76
The Psalter. 1912; alt. 1990, mod.

LAUDA ANIMA 8.7.8.7.8.7.
John Goss, 1869

67 Not unto Us, O Lord of Heaven

Not to us, LORD, not to us but to your name be the glory, because of your love and faithfulness. Ps. 115:1

1. Not un-to us, O Lord of heav'n, but un-to you be glo-ry giv'n; in love and truth you do ful-fil the coun-sels of your sov-ereign will; though na-tions fail your pow'r to own, yet you do reign, and you a-lone.

2. Let Is-rael trust in God a-lone, the Lord whose grace and pow'r are known; to him your full al-le-giance yield, and he will be your help and shield. All those who fear him God will bless; his saints have proved his faith-ful-ness.

3. All you that fear him and a-dore, the Lord in-crease you more and more; both great and small who him con-fess, you and your chil-dren he will bless. Yes, we will ev-er bless his name; praise you the Lord, his praise pro-claim.

From Psalm 115:1–3, 9–14, 18
The Psalter, 1912; mod.

GAIRNEY BRIDGE 8.8.8.8.8.8.
Ernest R. Kroeger, 1862–1934

The Earth, with All That Dwell Therein

The earth is the LORD'S, and everything in it, the world, and all who live in it. Ps. 24:1

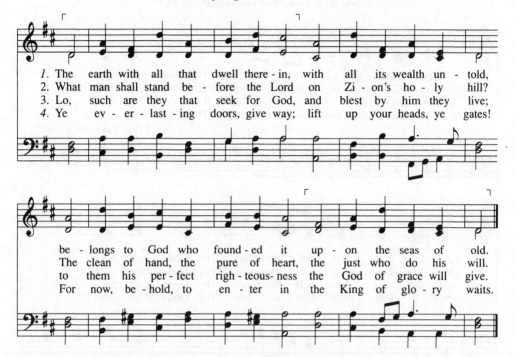

1. The earth with all that dwell there - in, with all its wealth un - told,
2. What man shall stand be - fore the Lord on Zi - on's ho - ly hill?
3. Lo, such are they that seek for God, and blest by him they live;
4. Ye ev - er - last - ing doors, give way; lift up your heads, ye gates!

be - longs to God who found - ed it up - on the seas of old.
The clean of hand, the pure of heart, the just who do his will.
to them his per - fect righ - teous - ness the God of grace will give.
For now, be - hold, to en - ter in the King of glo - ry waits.

5. Who is this glorious King that comes
   to claim his sovereign right?
   It is the Lord omnipotent,
   all-conqu'ring in his might.

6. Ye everlasting doors, give way;
   lift up your heads, ye gates!
   For now, behold, to enter in
   the King of glory waits.

7. Who is this glorious King that comes
   to claim his rightful throne?
   The Lord of Hosts, he is the King
   of glory, God alone.

From Psalm 24
The Psalter, 1912

LONDON NEW C.M.
Scottish Psalter, 1635
Arr. by John Playford, 1671; alt. 1990

69

Thy God Reigneth!

How beautiful on the mountains are the feet of those who bring good news ...
who say to Zion, "Your God reigns!" Is. 52:7

1. Trem-bling soul, be - set by fears, "Thy God reign-eth!"
2. Sin - ful soul, thy debt is paid, "Thy God reign-eth!"
3. Seek-ing soul, to Je - sus turn; "Thy God reign-eth!"
4. Join, ye saints, the truth pro-claim, "Thy God reign-eth!"

"Thy God reign-eth!"

Look a - bove and dry thy tears: "Thy God reign - eth!"
On the Lord thy sins were laid, "Thy God reign - eth!"
None that seek him will he spurn; "Thy God reign - eth!"
Shout it forth with glad ac - claim, "Thy God reign - eth!"

"Thy God reign - eth!"

Though thy foes with pow'r as - sail, naught a - gainst thee shall pre-vail;
On the cross of Cal - va - ry, Je - sus shed his blood for thee,
Wan - d'ring sheep the Shep - herd seeks, and when found he ev - er keeps,
Zi - on, wake! the morn is nigh, see it break from yon - der sky;

trust in him— he'll nev - er fail: "Thy God reign-eth, thy God reign- eth!"
from all sin to set thee free: "Thy God reign-eth, thy God reign- eth!"
for "he slum - bers not nor sleeps": "Thy God reign-eth, thy God reign- eth!"
loud and clear the watch-men cry: "Thy God reign-eth, thy God reign- eth!"

5. Church of Christ, awake, awake! "Thy God reigneth!"
Forward, then, fresh courage take: "Thy God reigneth!"
Soon, descending from his throne,
he shall claim thee for his own;
sin shall then be overthrown:
"Thy God reigneth, thy God reigneth!"

Fred S. Shepherd, 1840–1907

THY GOD REIGNETH 7.4.7.4.7.7.7.
James McGranahan, 1840–1907

With Glory Clad, with Strength Arrayed 70

The LORD reigns, he is robed in majesty; the LORD is robed in majesty and is armed with strength. Ps. 93:1

1. With glo - ry clad, with strength ar - rayed, the Lord, that
o'er all na - ture reigns, the world's foun - da - tions
strong - ly laid, and the vast fab - ric still sus - tains.

2. How sure - ly 'stab - lished is your throne, which shall no
change or per - iod see! For you, O Lord, and
you a - lone, are God from all e - ter - ni - ty.

3. The floods, O Lord, lift up their voice, and toss the
trou - bled waves on high; but God a - bove can
still their noise, and make the an - gry sea com - ply.

4. Your prom - ise, Lord, is ev - er sure, and they that
in your house would dwell, that hap - py sta - tion
to se - cure, must still in ho - li - ness ex - cel.

From Psalm 93
Tate and Brady's *New Version*, 1696, 1698
Mod.

MENDON L.M.
German melody
Arr. by Samuel Dyer, 1828

71

Stand Up, O God, Be Present Now

May God arise, may his enemies be scattered; may his foes flee before him. Ps. 68:1

1. Stand up, O God, be pres - ent now, and all who hate you,
2. Stand up, O God, be pres - ent now, as once on Si - nai
3. Stand up, O God, be pres - ent now, and we, your peo - ple,

let them run like driv - en smoke, like melt - ing wax, bound
you were heard by those who left the pris - on's chain, who
will re - joice, for you have saved us from the pit, for

for de - struc - tion, doomed to die. But let the righ - teous
crossed the sea and faced the sand. They ate the man - na,
you have brought us back from death. So, to your ho - ly

sing and dance, yes, sing and dance and shout for joy, for
drank from springs pro - vid - ed by your gra - cious love. They
place, we come with choirs and mu - sic, young and old. Re -

he who rides up - on the clouds is com - ing, as he
watched as might - y ar - mies fled, and so they gained the
buke the god - less, cast them down till hum - bled, they for

came of old. His jus - tice vin - di - cates the op - pressed, he
prom - ised land. Now, march - ing on to Zi - on's mount, we
mer - cy call; then men shall lis - ten for your voice as

REFRAIN

frees the pris - 'ner, brings him home. Stand up, O God, be
see the heav'n - ly hosts de - scend.
rid - ing through the heav'ns you come.

pres - ent now, and we will sing and shout for joy.

From Psalm 68
Michael Saward, b. 1932
Text and tune © 1973. Hope Publishing Co. All rights reserved. Used by permission.

STAND UP 8.8.8.8.8.8.8.D.
David G. Wilson, b. 1940

72 Amid the Fears That Oppress Our Day

The LORD Almighty has sworn, "Surely, as I have planned, so it will be, and as I have purposed, so it will stand." Is. 14:24

Unison or harmony

1. A - mid the fears that op - press our day, a - cross the clouds that ob -
2. Though wars may rise, and though king-doms fall, though ills may threat - en, and
3. Though fierce the fight 'gainst the hosts of wrong, his Word is sure, and his
4. When Christ shall come to re - ceive his own, when his the king - dom, the

scure our way, one gold - en truth sheds its shin - ing ray— our
fears en - thrall, our God still lives, and he hears our call— our
arm is strong; the day is his: raise his tri - umph song— our
pow'r, the throne, e - ter - nal King he shall reign a - lone— our

REFRAIN

God is sov- ereign still.
God is sov- ereign still.
God is sov- ereign still. His ho - ly pur - pose un-chang-ing stands, the
God is sov- ereign still.

stars still turn at their Lord's com-mands; he holds the world in his

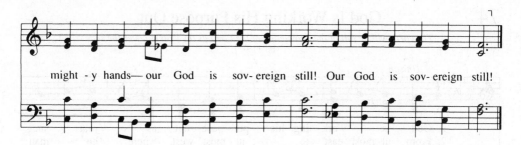

might-y hands—our God is sov-ereign still! Our God is sov-ereign still!

Margaret Clarkson, 1966

LANGHORNE 9.9.9.6.ref.
Ronald Alan Matthews, 1989

Rejoice, All People, Homage Give 73

Clap your hands, all you nations; shout to God with cries of joy. Ps. 47:1

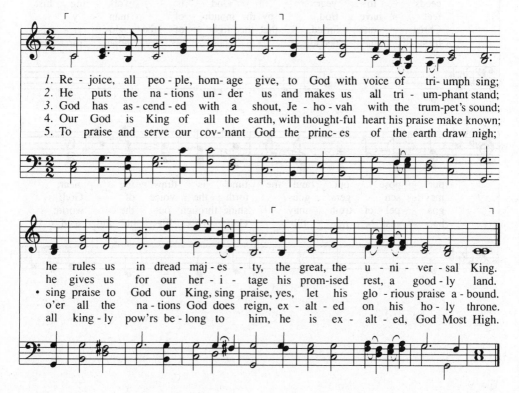

1. Re - joice, all peo - ple, hom - age give, to God with voice of tri - umph sing;
2. He puts the na - tions un - der us and makes us all tri - um-phant stand;
3. God has as - cend - ed with a shout, Je - ho - vah with the trum-pet's sound;
4. Our God is King of all the earth, with thought-ful heart his praise make known;
5. To praise and serve our cov-'nant God the princ- es of the earth draw nigh;

he rules us in dread maj - es - ty, the great, the u - ni - ver - sal King.
he gives us for our her - i - tage his prom-ised rest, a good - ly land.
• sing praise to God our King, sing praise, yes, let his glo - rious praise a - bound.
o'er all the na - tions God does reign, ex - alt - ed on his ho - ly throne.
all king - ly pow'rs be - long to him, he is ex - alt - ed, God Most High.

From Psalm 47
The Psalter, 1912; alt. 1990, mod.

TRURO L.M.
Psalmodia Evangelica, 1789

74   God Is Working His Purpose Out

The earth will be full of the knowledge of the LORD as the waters cover the sea.
Is. 11:9

1. God is work - ing his pur - pose out as year suc -
2. From ut- most east to ut - most west, where hu - man
3. March we forth in the strength of God, with the ban - ner of
4. All we can do is noth - ing worth un - less God

ceeds to year: God is work - ing his
feet have trod, by the mouth of man - y
Christ un - furled, that the light of the glo - ri - ous
bless - es the deed; vain - ly we hope for the

pur - pose out, and the time is draw - ing near;
mes - sen - gers goes forth the voice of God:
gos - pel of truth may shine through - out the world;
har - vest - tide till God gives life to the seed;

near - er and near - er draws the time, the time that shall
"Give ear to me, ye con - ti - nents, ye isles, give
fight we the fight with sor - row and sin to set their
yet near - er and near - er draws the time, the time that shall

sure - ly be, when the earth shall be filled with the glo - ry of
ear to me," that the earth may be filled with the glo - ry of
cap - tives free, that the earth may be filled with the glo - ry of
sure - ly be, when the earth shall be filled with the glo - ry of

st. 1—3   st. 4

God as the wa - ters cov - er the sea.
God as the wa - ters cov - er the sea.
God as the wa - ters cov - er the sea.
God as the wa - ters cov - er the sea.

Arthur Campbell Ainger, 1894

PURPOSE Irreg.
Martin Shaw, 1915

Tune from *Enlarged Songs of Praise* by permission of Oxford University Press.

75   O Father, You Are Sovereign

The LORD Almighty has purposed, and who can thwart him? His hand is stretched out, and who can turn it back? Is. 14:27

1. O Fa - ther, you are sov - ereign in all the worlds you made;
2. O Fa - ther, you are sov - ereign in all af - fairs of man;
3. O Fa - ther, you are sov - ereign, the Lord of hu - man pain,
4. O Fa - ther, you are sov - ereign! We see you dim - ly now,

your might - y word was spo - ken and light and life o - beyed.
no pow'rs of death or dark - ness can thwart your per - fect plan.
trans - mut - ing earth - ly sor - rows to gold of heav'n - ly gain.
but soon be - fore your tri - umph earth's ev - ery knee shall bow.

Your voice com - mands the sea - sons and bounds the o - cean's shore,
All chance and change tran - scend - ing, su - preme in time and space,
All e - vil o - ver - rul - ing, as none but Con - qu'ror could,
With this glad hope be - fore us our faith springs up a - new:

sets stars with - in their cours - es and stills the tem - pest's roar.
you hold your trust - ing chil - dren se - cure in your em - brace.
your love pur - sues its pur - pose—our souls' e - ter - nal good.
our sov - ereign Lord and Sav - ior, we trust and wor - ship you!

Margaret Clarkson, 1982

ST. THEODULPH 7.6.7.6.D.
Melchior Teschner, ca. 1615

Praise, My Soul, the King of Heaven

76

Praise the LORD, all his works everywhere in his dominion. Praise the LORD,
O my soul. Ps. 103:22

1. Praise, my soul, the King of heav-en, to his feet your trib-ute bring;
2. Praise him for his grace and fa-vor to our fa-thers in dis-tress;
3. Fa-ther-like, he tends and spares us; well our fee-ble frame he knows;
4. Frail as sum-mer's flow'r we flour-ish, blows the wind and it is gone;
5. An-gels, help us to a-dore him; you be-hold him face to face;

ran-somed, healed, re-stored, for-giv-en, who, like me, his praise should sing?
praise him, still the same for-ev-er, slow to chide and swift to bless;
in his hands he gent-ly bears us, res-cues us from all our foes;
but while mor-tals rise and per-ish, God en-dures un-chang-ing on.
sun and moon, bow down be-fore him, dwell-ers all in time and space,

Praise him, praise him, praise him, praise him, praise the ev-er-last-ing King.
praise him, praise him, praise him, praise him, glo-rious in his faith-ful-ness.
praise him, praise him, praise him, praise him, wide-ly as his mer-cy goes.
Praise him, praise him, praise him, praise him, praise the High E-ter-nal One.
praise him, praise him, praise him, praise him, praise with us the God of grace.

From Psalm 103
Henry F. Lyte, 1834; mod.

LAUDA ANIMA 8.7.8.7.8.7.
John Goss, 1869

77 Praise, My Soul, the King of Heaven

Praise the LORD, all his works everywhere in his dominion. Praise the LORD,
O my soul. Ps. 103:22

1. Praise, my soul, the King of heav-en, to his feet your
2. Praise him for his grace and fa-vor to our fa-thers
3. Fa-ther-like, he tends and spares us; well our fee-ble
4. Frail as sum-mer's flow'r we flour-ish, blows the wind and
5. An-gels, help us to a-dore him; you be-hold him

trib-ute bring; ran-somed, healed, re-stored, for - giv-en,
in dis-tress; praise him, still the same for - ev-er,
• frame he knows; in his hands he gent-ly bears us,
it is gone; but while mor-tals rise and per-ish,
face to face; sun and moon, bow down be - fore him,

who, like me, his praise should sing? Al - le - lu - ia!
slow to chide and swift to bless. Al - le - lu - ia!
• res - cues us from all our foes. Al - le - lu - ia!
God en - dures un - chang-ing on. Al - le - lu - ia!
dwell - ers all in time and space. Al - le - lu - ia!

Al - le - lu - ia! Praise the ev - er - last - ing King.
Al - le - lu - ia! Glo - rious in his faith - ful - ness.
· Al - le - lu - ia! Wide - ly as his mer - cy goes.
Al - le - lu - ia! Praise the High E - ter - nal One.
Al - le - lu - ia! Praise with us the God of grace.

From Psalm 103
Henry F. Lyte, 1834; mod.

ANDREWS 8.7.8.7.8.7.
Mark Andrews, 1930

O Bless the Lord, My Soul
78

Praise the LORD, O my soul; all my inmost being, praise his holy name. Ps. 103:1

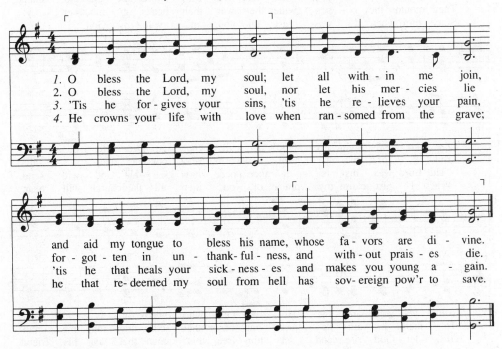

1. O bless the Lord, my soul; let all with - in me join,
2. O bless the Lord, my soul, nor let his mer - cies lie
3. 'Tis he for - gives your sins, 'tis he re - lieves your pain,
4. He crowns your life with love when ran - somed from the grave;

and aid my tongue to bless his name, whose fa - vors are di - vine.
for - got - ten in un - thank - ful - ness, and with - out prais - es die.
'tis he that heals your sick - ness - es and makes you young a - gain.
he that re - deemed my soul from hell has sov - ereign pow'r to save.

5. He fills the poor with good;
   he gives the suff'rers rest:
   the Lord has judgments for the proud
   and justice for th'oppressed.

6. His wondrous works and ways
   he made by Moses known,
   but sent the world his truth and grace
   by his beloved Son.

From Psalm 103
Isaac Watts. 1719: mod.

ST. MICHAEL S.M.
Genevan Psalter, 1543

79 My God, My God, O Why Have You Forsaken Me?

My God, my God, why have you forsaken me? Why are you so far from saving me,
so far from the words of my groaning? Ps. 22:1

1. My God, my God, O why have you for-sak-en me? O why
2. Our fa-thers put their trust in you; from you their res-cue came.
3. All those who look at me will laugh and cast re-proach at me.
4. You took me from my moth-er's womb to safe-ty at the breast.

are you so far from giv-ing help and from my groan-ing cry?
They begged you and you set them free; they were not put to shame.
Their mouths they o-pen wide; they wag their heads in mock-er-y:
Since birth when I was cast on you, in you, my God, I rest.

By day and night, my God, I call; your an-swer still de-lays.
But as for me, I am a worm and not a man at all.
"The Lord was his re-li-ance once; now see what God will send.
When I pro-claim my praise of you, then all the church will hear,

And yet you are the Ho-ly One who dwells in Is-rael's praise.
To men I am de-spised and base; their scorn-ings on me fall.
Yes, let God rise and set him free, this man that was his friend."
and I will pay my vows in full where men hold him in fear.

Psalm 22:1–10, 25
The Book of Psalms for Singing, 1973

KINGSFOLD C.M.D.
Traditional English melody
Arr. by Ralph Vaughan Williams, 1906

Tune from the *English Hymnal* by permission of Oxford University Press.

Lord, with Glowing Heart I'd Praise Thee

80

*To the praise of his glorious grace, which he has freely given us in the
One he loves. Eph. 1:6*

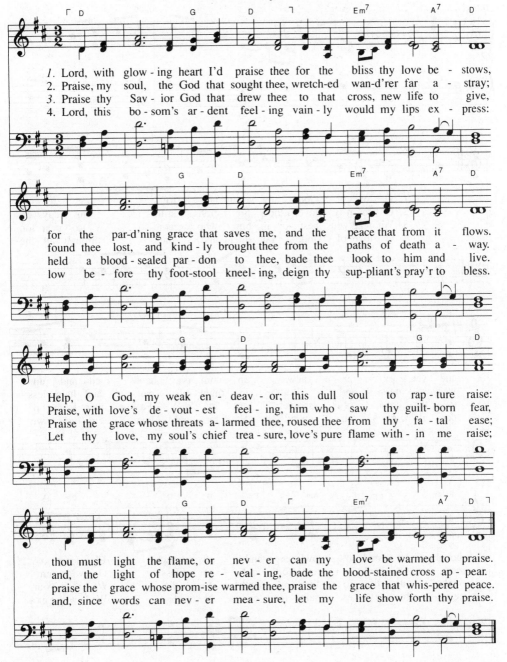

1. Lord, with glow-ing heart I'd praise thee for the bliss thy love be - stows,
2. Praise, my soul, the God that sought thee, wretch-ed wan-d'rer far a - stray;
3. Praise thy Sav - ior God that drew thee to that cross, new life to give,
4. Lord, this bo - som's ar - dent feel - ing vain - ly would my lips ex - press:

for the par-d'ning grace that saves me, and the peace that from it flows.
found thee lost, and kind - ly brought thee from the paths of death a - way.
held a blood - sealed par - don to thee, bade thee look to him and live.
low be - fore thy foot-stool kneel- ing, deign thy sup-pliant's pray'r to bless.

Help, O God, my weak en - deav - or; this dull soul to rap - ture raise:
Praise, with love's de - vout - est feel - ing, him who saw thy guilt- born fear,
Praise the grace whose threats a- larmed thee, roused thee from thy fa - tal ease;
Let thy love, my soul's chief trea - sure, love's pure flame with - in me raise;

thou must light the flame, or nev - er can my love be warmed to praise.
and, the light of hope re - veal - ing, bade the blood-stained cross ap - pear.
praise the grace whose prom-ise warmed thee, praise the grace that whis-pered peace.
and, since words can nev - er mea - sure, let my life show forth thy praise.

Francis Scott Key, 1817

RIPLEY 8.7.8.7.D.
Gregorian chant
Arr. by Lowell Mason, 1839

81   O Love of God, How Strong and True

I pray that you ... may have power ... to grasp how wide and long and high and deep is
the love of Christ, and to know this love that surpasses knowledge. Eph. 3:17–19

1. O love of God, how strong and true,   e - ter - nal
2. O heav'n-ly love, how pre - cious still,   in days of
3. We read you best in him who came   to bear for
4. O love of God, our shield and stay   through all the

and yet ev - er new, un - com - pre - hend - ed and un -
wea - ri - ness and ill, in nights of pain and help - less -
us the cross of shame; sent by the Fa - ther from on
per - ils of our way! E - ter - nal love, in you we

bought, be - yond all knowl - edge and all thought! O love of
ness, to heal, to com - fort, and to bless! O wide - em -
high, our life to live, our death to die. We read your
rest, for - ev - er safe, for - ev - er blest. We will ex -

God, how deep and great, far deep-er than man's deep-est
brac - ing, won - drous love! We read you in the sky a -
pow'r to bless and save, e'en in the dark - ness of the
alt you, God and King, and we will ev - er praise your

hate; self - fed, self - kin - dled like the light, change-less, e -
bove, we read you in the earth be - low, in seas that
grave; still more in res - ur - rec - tion light we read the
name; we will ex - tol you ev - 'ry day, and ev - er -

Interlude

ter - nal, in - fi - nite.
swell, and streams that flow.
ful - ness of your might.
more your praise pro - claim.

Final ending

Horatius Bonar, 1858
Mod.

JERUSALEM (PARRY) L.M.D.
C. Hubert H. Parry, 1916
Arr. by Janet Wyatt, 1977

82   **Great God of Wonders!**

Who is a God like you, who pardons sin and forgives the transgression? Mic. 7:18

1. Great God of won - ders! All thy ways are match - less, god - like,
2. In won - der lost, with trem - bling joy we take the par - don
3. O may this strange, this match - less grace, this god - like mir - a -

and di - vine; but the fair glo - ries of thy grace more god - like
of our God; par - don for crimes of deep - est dye, a par - don
cle of love, fill the whole earth with grate - ful praise, and all th'an -

and un - ri - valed shine, more god- like and un - ri - valed shine.
bought with Je - sus' blood, a par - don bought with Je - sus' blood.
gel - ic choirs a - bove, and all th'an - gel - ic choirs a - bove.

REFRAIN

Who is a par - d'ning God like thee? Or who has grace so

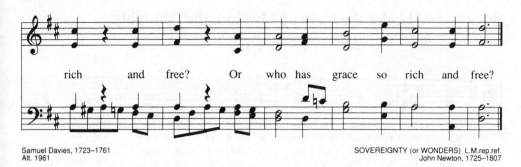

rich and free? Or who has grace so rich and free?

Samuel Davies, 1723–1761
Alt. 1961

SOVEREIGNTY (or WONDERS) L.M.rep.ref.
John Newton, 1725–1807

O Praise the Lord, for He Is Good   83

Give thanks to the LORD, for he is good; his love endures forever. Ps. 107:1

1. O praise the Lord, for he is good, his mer - cies still en - dure;
2. He gath - ered them from out the lands, from north, south, east and west.
3. Their wea - ry soul with - in them faints when thirst and hun - ger press;
4. He made the way be - fore them straight, him - self be - came their guide,

thus say the ran - somed of the Lord, from all their foes se - cure.
They strayed in de - sert's path - less way, no cit - y found for rest.
in trou - ble then they cried to God, he saved them from dis - tress.
that they might to a cit - y go where - in they might a - bide.

5. O that men would Jehovah praise
for all his kindness shown,
and for his works so wonderful
which he to men makes known!

6. Because the longing soul by him
with food is satisfied,
the hungry soul that looks to him
with goodness is supplied.

Psalm 107:1–9
Book of Psalms, 1940

RICHMOND C.M.
Thomas Haweis, 1794
Arr. by Samuel Webbe, Jr., 1770–1843

84 Under the Care of My God, the Almighty

He will cover you with his feathers, and under his wings you will find refuge.
Ps. 91:4

1. Un - der the care of my God, the Al - might - y, safe in the
2. Be not a - fraid for the ter - ror of mid - night, nor for the
3. Seek the Most High for thy sure hab - i - ta - tion, un - to Je -
4. Love thou the Lord, sure - ly he will de - liv - er; he will ex -

se - cret place of the Most High! He is my ref - uge, the
ar - row that hast - eth to slay; fear not the pes - ti - lence
ho - vah for ref - uge now fly; there shall no e - vil be -
alt thee and an - swer thy prayer; he will be with thee to

Lord is my for - tress, him I am trust - ing when trou - ble is nigh.
walk - ing in dark - ness, nor the de - stroy - er that wast - eth by day.
fall thee nor harm thee, un - to thy dwell - ing no plague shall come nigh.
hon - or and give thee life with - out end, his sal - va - tion to share.

REFRAIN
Un - der his wings, un - der his wings, safe in the ref - uge hide thee;

trust - ing his truth and faith - ful - ness, no e - vil can be - tide thee.

From Psalm 91
Bible Songs Hymnal, 1927

UNDER HIS WINGS 11.10.11.10.
Ira D. Sankey, 1840–1908

The Lord's My Shepherd, I'll Not Want 85

The LORD is my shepherd, I shall not be in want. Ps. 23:1

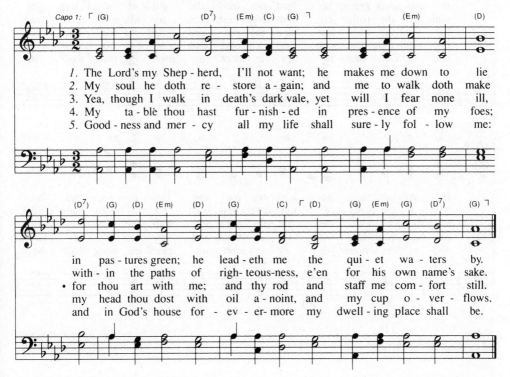

1. The Lord's my Shep - herd, I'll not want; he makes me down to lie
2. My soul he doth re - store a - gain; and me to walk doth make
3. Yea, though I walk in death's dark vale, yet will I fear none ill,
4. My ta - ble thou hast fur - nish - ed in pres - ence of my foes;
5. Good - ness and mer - cy all my life shall sure - ly fol - low me:

in pas - tures green; he lead - eth me the qui - et wa - ters by.
with - in the paths of righ - teous - ness, e'en for his own name's sake.
for thou art with me; and thy rod and staff me com - fort still.
my head thou dost with oil a - noint, and my cup o - ver - flows.
and in God's house for - ev - er - more my dwell - ing place shall be.

Psalm 23
Francis Rous, William Mure, and others
Scottish Psalter, 1650

EVAN C.M.
William H. Havergal, 1846

86 The Lord's My Shepherd, I'll Not Want

The LORD is my shepherd, I shall not be in want. Ps. 23:1

1. The Lord's my Shep - herd, I'll not want; he makes me down to lie
2. My soul he doth re - store a - gain; and me to walk doth make
3. Yea, though I walk in death's dark vale, yet will I fear none ill,
4. My ta - ble thou hast fur - nish - ed in pres - ence of my foes;
5. Good - ness and mer - cy all my life shall sure - ly fol - low me:

in pas - tures green; he lead - eth me the qui - et wa - ters by.
with - in the paths of righ- teous- ness, e'en for his own name's sake;
for thou art with me; and thy rod and staff me com - fort still;
my head thou dost with oil a - noint, and my cup o - ver - flows.
and in God's house for - ev - er - more my dwell - ing place shall be;

He lead - eth me, he lead - eth me the qui - et wa - ters by.
with - in the paths of righ- teous- ness, e'en for his own name's sake.
for thou art with me, and thy rod and staff me com - fort still.
My head thou dost with oil a - noint, and my cup o - ver - flows.
and in God's house for - ev - er - more my dwell- ing place shall be.

Psalm 23
Francis Rous, William Mure, and others
Scottish Psalter, 1650
Tune by permission of Oxford University Press.

BROTHER JAMES' AIR 8.6.8.6.8.6.
J. L. Macbeth Bain, ca. 1840–1925
Arr. by Gordon Jacob, 1934; alt.

The Lord's My Shepherd, I'll Not Want

The LORD is my shepherd, I shall not be in want. Ps. 23:1

1. The Lord's my Shep - herd, I'll not want; he
2. My soul he doth re - store a - gain; and
3. Yea, though I walk in death's dark vale, yet
4. My ta - ble thou hast fur - nish - ed in
5. Good - ness and mer - cy all my life shall

makes me down to lie in pas - tures green; he
me to walk doth make with - in the paths of
will I fear none ill, for thou art with me;
pres - ence of my foes; my head thou dost with
sure - ly fol - low me: and in God's house for -

lead - eth me the qui - et wa - ters by.
righ - teous - ness, e'en for his own name's sake.
and thy rod and staff me com - fort still.
oil a - noint, and my cup o - ver - flows.
ev - er - more my dwell - ing place shall be.

Psalm 23
Francis Rous, William Mure, and others
Scottish Psalter, 1650

CRIMOND C.M.
Jessie Seymour Irvine, 1871
Arr. by T. C. L. Pritchard, 1929; alt.

Tune from the *Scottish Psalter* by permission of Oxford University Press.

88   With Grateful Heart My Thanks I Bring

I will praise you, O Lord, with all my heart; before the "gods" I will sing your praise.
Ps. 138:1

1. With grate - ful heart my thanks I bring, be - fore the great thy
2. I cried to thee and thou didst save, thy word of grace new
3. O Lord, en - throned in glo - ry bright, thou reign - est in the
4. Thou wilt stretch forth thy might - y arm to save me when my

praise I sing; I wor - ship in thy ho - ly place and
cour - age gave; the kings of earth shall thank thee, Lord, for
heav'n - ly height; the proud in vain thy fa - vor seek, but
foes a - larm; the work thou hast for me be - gun shall

praise thee for thy truth and grace; for truth and grace to -
they have heard thy won - drous word; yea, they shall come with
thou hast mer - cy for the meek; through trou - ble though my
by thy grace be ful - ly done; for - ev - er mer - cy

geth - er shine in thy most ho - ly word di - vine.
songs of praise, for great and glo - rious are thy ways.
path - way be, thou wilt re - vive and strength - en me.
dwells with thee; O Lord, my Mak - er, think on me.

From Psalm 138
The Psalter, 1912

ST. PETERSBURG 8.8.8.8.8.8.
Dmitri Bortniansky, 1825

God Is Our Strength and Refuge

God is our refuge and strength, an ever-present help in trouble. Ps. 46:1

1. God is our strength and ref-uge, our pres-ent help in trou-ble;
2. There is a flow-ing riv-er, with-in God's ho-ly cit-y;
3. Come, see the works of our Mak-er, learn of his deeds all pow'r-ful;

and we there-fore will not fear, though the earth should change!
God is in the midst of her— she shall not be moved!
wars will cease a-cross the world when he shat-ters the spear!

Though moun-tains shake and trem-ble, though swirl-ing floods are rag-ing,
God's help is swift-ly giv-en, thrones van-ish at his pres-ence—
Be still and know your Cre-a-tor, up-lift him in the na-tions—

God the Lord of Hosts is with us ev-er-more!
God the Lord of Hosts is with us ev-er-more!
God the Lord of Hosts is with us ev-er-more!

From Psalm 46
Richard Bewes, 1982

DAM BUSTERS MARCH 7.7.7.5.7.7.11.
Eric Coates, 1886–1958
Arr. by John Barnard, b. 1948

90 The Man Who Once Has Found Abode

*He who dwells in the shelter of the Most High will rest in the shadow
of the Almighty.* Ps. 91:1

1. The man who once has found a - bode, with - in the
2. I there - fore of the Lord will say, he is my
3. For he shall with his watch - ful care pre - serve thee
4. His out - spread pin - ions shall thee hide, be - neath his

se - cret place of God shall with Al - might - y
ref - uge and my stay; my cit - a - del of
from the fowl - er's snare; yea, he shall be thy
wings shalt thou con - fide. His faith - ful - ness shall

God a - bide, and in his shad - ow safe - ly hide.
strength is he— my God in whom my trust shall be.
sure de - fense a - gainst the dead - ly pes - ti - lence.
ev - er be a shield and buck - ler un - to thee.

5. No nightly terrors shall alarm,
   no deadly shaft by day shall harm;
   nor pestilence that walks by night,
   nor plagues that waste in noonday light:

6. Because his angels he commands
   to bear thee safely in their hands,
   to guard thy ways, lest left alone,
   thou dash thy foot against a stone.

7. "Because he set his love on Me,
   from danger I will set him free.
   Because to him My name is known,
   on high I'll set him as Mine own."

Psalm 91:1–6, 11, 12, 14
Reformed Presbyterian *Book of Psalms*, 1940

UXBRIDGE L.M.
Lowell Mason, 1830

Bow Down Thine Ear, O Lord, and Hear

91

Hear, O LORD, and answer me, for I am poor and needy. Guard my life, for I am devoted to you. Ps. 86:1, 2

1. Bow down thine ear, O Lord, and hear, for I am
poor and great my need; preserve my soul, for
thee I fear; O God, thy trusting servant heed.

2. O Lord, be merciful to me, for all the
day to thee I cry; rejoice thy servant,
for to thee I lift my soul, O Lord Most High.

3. For thou, O Lord, art good and kind, and ready
to forgive thou art; abundant mercy
they shall find who call on thee with all their heart.

4. O Lord, incline thine ear to me, my voice of
supplication heed; in trouble I will
cry to thee, for thou wilt answer when I plead.

5. There is no God but thee alone,
nor works like thine, O Lord Most High;
all nations shall surround thy throne
and their Creator glorify.

6. In all thy deeds how great thou art!
Thou one true God, thy way make clear;
teach me with undivided heart
to trust thy truth, thy name to fear.

Psalm 86:1–11
The Psalter, 1912

LLEF L.M.
Griffith Hugh Jones, 1849–1919

92   A Mighty Fortress Is Our God

God is our refuge and strength, an ever-present help in trouble. Ps. 46:1

1. A might-y for-tress is our God, a bul-wark nev-er
2. Did we in our own strength con-fide, our striv-ing would be
3. And though this world, with dev-ils filled, should threat-en to un-
4. That Word a-bove all earth-ly pow'rs, no thanks to them, a-

fail - ing; our help-er he a - mid the flood of
los - ing; were not the right man on our side, the
do us, we will not fear, for God hath willed his
bid - eth; the Spir - it and the gifts are ours through

mor - tal ills pre - vail - ing. For still our an - cient foe
man of God's own choos - ing. Dost ask who that may be?
truth to tri - umph through us. The prince of dark - ness grim,
him who with us sid - eth. Let goods and kin - dred go,

doth seek to work us woe; his craft and pow'r are great;
Christ Je - sus, it is he, Lord Sa - ba - oth his name,
we trem - ble not for him; his rage we can en - dure,
this mor - tal life al - so; the bod - y they may kill:

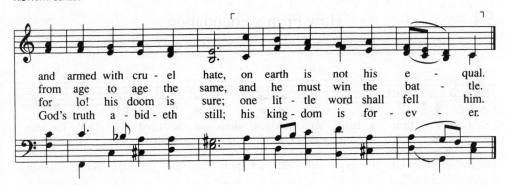

and armed with cru - el hate, on earth is not his e - qual.
from age to age the same, and he must win the bat - tle.
for lo! his doom is sure; one lit - tle word shall fell him.
God's truth a - bid - eth still; his king - dom is for - ev - er.

Based on Psalm 46
Martin Luther, 1529
Tr. by Frederick H. Hedge, 1853

EIN' FESTE BURG 8.7.8.7.6.6.6.6.7.
Martin Luther, 1529

The Tender Love a Father Has   93

As a father has compassion on his children, so the LORD has compassion on those who fear him. Ps. 103:13

1. The ten - der love a fa - ther has for all his chil - dren dear,
2. The Lord re - mem - bers we are dust, and all our frail - ty knows;
3. The flow'r is with - ered by the wind that smites with blight-ing breath;
4. Un - chang-ing is the love of God, from age to age the same,
5. Those who his gra - cious cov -'nant keep the Lord will ev - er bless;

such love the Lord be - stows on them who wor - ship him in fear.
man's days are like the ten - der grass, and as the flow'r he grows.
so man is quick - ly swept a - way be - fore the blast of death.
dis - played to all who do his will and rev - er - ence his name.
their chil- dren's chil- dren shall re - joice to see his righ-teous - ness.

From Psalm 103:13–18
The Psalter. 1912

CAITHNESS C.M.
Scottish Psalter, 1635

94 How Firm a Foundation

*Do not fear, for I am with you; do not be dismayed, for I am your God. I will strengthen
you and help you; I will uphold you with my righteous right hand. Is. 41:10*

1. How firm a foun - da - tion, you saints of the Lord, is laid for your
2. "Fear not, I am with you, O be not dis-mayed; for I am your
3. "When through the deep wa - ters I call you to go, the riv - ers of
4. "When through fi - ery tri - als your path - way shall lie, my grace, all - suf -

faith in his ex - cel - lent Word! What more can he say than to
God, and will still give you aid; I'll strength - en you, help you, and
sor - row shall not o - ver - flow; for I will be with you, your
fi - cient, shall be your sup - ply; the flame shall not hurt you; I

you he has said, to you who for ref - uge to Je - sus have fled?
cause you to stand, up - held by my righ-teous, om - nip - o - tent hand.
trou - bles to bless, and sanc - ti - fy to you your deep - est dis - tress.
on - ly de - sign your dross to con - sume and your gold to re - fine.

5. "E'en down to old age all my people shall prove
   my sovereign, eternal, unchangeable love;
   and when hoary hairs shall their temples adorn,
   like lambs they shall still in my bosom be borne.

6. "The soul that on Jesus has leaned for repose,
   I will not, I will not desert to his foes;
   that soul, though all hell should endeavor to shake,
   I'll never, no never, no never forsake."

Rippon's *Selection of Hymns*, 1787; alt.
Mod.

FOUNDATION 11.11.11.11.
Traditional American melody
J. Funk's *A Compilation of Genuine Church Music*, 1832

Though Troubles Assail Us

95

My God will meet all your needs according to his glorious riches in Christ Jesus.
Phil. 4:19

1. Though trou - bles as - sail us and dan - gers af - fright,
though friends should all fail us and foes all u - nite,
yet one thing se - cures us, what - ev - er be - tide,
the prom - ise as - sures us, "The Lord will pro - vide."

2. The birds, with - out gar - ner or store - house, are fed;
from them let us learn to trust God for our bread.
His saints what is fit - ting shall ne'er be de - nied,
so long as 'tis writ - ten, "The Lord will pro - vide."

3. When Sa - tan as - sails us to stop up our path,
and cour - age all fails us, we tri - umph by faith.
He can - not take from us, though oft he has tried,
this heart - cheer - ing prom - ise, "The Lord will pro - vide."

4. No strength of our own and no good - ness we claim;
yet, since we have known of the Sav - ior's great name,
in this our strong tow - er for safe - ty we hide:
the Lord is our pow - er, "The Lord will pro - vide."

John Newton, 1779
The New Christian Hymnal, 1929

JOANNA (or ST. DENIO) 11.11.11.11.
Traditional Welsh melody

96 Unto the Hills

I lift up my eyes to the hills—where does my help come from? My help comes from the LORD, the Maker of heaven and earth. Ps. 121:1, 2

1. Un - to the hills a - round do I lift up my long-ing eyes:
2. He will not suf - fer that thy foot be moved: safe shalt thou be.
3. Je - ho - vah is him - self thy keep - er true, thy change-less shade;
4. From ev - 'ry e - vil shall he keep thy soul, from ev - 'ry sin:

O whence for me shall my sal - va - tion come, from whence a - rise?
No care - less slum - ber shall his eye - lids close, who keep - eth thee.
Je - ho - vah thy de - fense on thy right hand him - self hath made.
Je - ho - vah shall pre - serve thy go - ing out, thy com - ing in.

From God the Lord doth come my cer - tain aid,
Be - hold our God, the Lord, he slum - b'reth ne'er,
And thee no sun by day shall ev - er smite;
A - bove thee watch - ing, he whom we a - dore

from God the Lord, who heav'n and earth hath made.
who keep - eth Is - rael in his ho - ly care.
no moon shall harm thee in the si - lent night.
shall keep thee hence - forth, yea, for ev - er - more.

Psalm 121
John, duke of Argyll, 1877, 1909

LUX BEATA 10.4.10.4.10.10.
Albert L. Peace. 1885

We Praise You, O God, Our Redeemer, Creator

97

Our Redeemer—the LORD Almighty is his name—is the Holy One of Israel. Is. 47:4

1. We praise you, O God, our Re - deem - er, Cre - a - tor;
in grate - ful de - vo - tion our tri - bute we bring.
We lay it be - fore you, we kneel and a - dore you;
we bless your ho - ly name, glad prais - es we sing.

2. We wor - ship you, God of our fa - thers, we bless you;
through life's storm and tem - pest our Guide you have been.
When per - ils o'er - take us, es - cape you will make us,
and with your help, O Lord, our bat - tles we win.

3. With voic - es u - nit - ed our prais - es we of - fer,
to you, great Je - ho - vah, glad an - thems we raise.
Your strong arm will guide us, our God is be - side us;
to you, our great Re - deem - er, for - ev - er be praise.

Julia Cady Cory, 1902
Mod.

KREMSER 12.11.12.11.
Adrianus Valerius's *Nederlandtsch Gedenckclank*, 1626
Arr. by Edward Kremser, 1877

98
Now Thank We All Our God

Now, our God, we give you thanks, and praise your glorious name. 1 Chron. 29:13

1. Now thank we all our God with heart and hands and voic - es,
2. O may this boun - teous God through all our life be near us,
3. All praise and thanks to God the Fa - ther now be giv - en,

who won - drous things hath done, in whom his world re - joic - es;
with ev - er - joy - ful hearts and bless - ed peace to cheer us;
the Son, and him who reigns with them in high - est heav - en—

who from our moth - ers' arms, hath blessed us on our way
and keep us in his grace, and guide us when per - plexed,
the one e - ter - nal God, whom earth and heav'n a - dore;

with count - less gifts of love, and still is ours to - day.
and free us from all ills in this world and the next.
for thus it was, is now, and shall be ev - er - more.

Martin Rinkart, 1636
Tr. by Catherine Winkworth, 1858

NUN DANKET 6.7.6.7.6.6.6.6.
Johann Crüger, 1647

My Song Forever Shall Record

99

I will sing of the LORD's great love forever; with my mouth I will make your faithfulness known through all generations. Ps. 89:1

1. My song for - ev - er shall re - cord the
2. I sing of mer - cies that en - dure, for -
3. Be - hold God's truth and grace dis - played, for
4. "For him my mer - cy shall en - dure, my

ten - der mer - cies of the Lord; your faith - ful - ness will
ev - er build - ed firm and sure, of faith - ful - ness that
he has faith - ful cov - 'nant made, and he has sworn that
cov - 'nant made with him is sure; his throne and race I

I pro - claim, and ev - ery age shall know your name.
nev - er dies, es - tab - lished change - less in the skies.
Da - vid's son shall ev - er sit up - on his throne:
will main - tain for - ev - er, while the heav'ns re - main."

5. Almighty God, your lofty throne
has justice for its cornerstone,
and shining bright before your face
are truth and love and boundless grace.

6. With blessing is the nation crowned
whose people know the joyful sound;
they in the light, O Lord, shall live,
the light your face and favor give.

7. Your name with gladness they confess,
exalted in your righteousness;
their fame and might to you belong,
for in your favor they are strong.

8. All glory unto God we yield,
Jehovah is our help and shield;
all praise and honor we will bring
to Israel's Holy One, our King.

Psalm 89:1–4, 14–18, 28, 29
The Psalter, 1912; mod.

WINCHESTER NEW L.M.
Musikalisches Handbuch, Hamburg, 1690; alt. 1990

100 Holy, Holy, Holy!

Day and night they never stop saying: "Holy, holy, holy is the Lord God Almighty, who was, and is, and is to come." Rev. 4:8

1. Ho - ly, ho - ly, ho - ly! Lord God Al - might - y!
2. Ho - ly, ho - ly, ho - ly! All the saints a - dore thee,
3. Ho - ly, ho - ly, ho - ly! Though the dark - ness hide thee,
4. Ho - ly, ho - ly, ho - ly! Lord God Al - might - y!

Ear - ly in the morn - ing our song shall rise to thee.
cast - ing down their gold - en crowns a - round the glass - y sea;
though the eye of sin - ful man thy glo - ry may not see,
All thy works shall praise thy name in earth and sky and sea.

Ho - ly, ho - ly, ho - ly! Mer - ci - ful and might - y!
cher - u - bim and ser - a - phim fall - ing down be - fore thee,
on - ly thou art ho - ly; there is none be - side thee
Ho - ly, ho - ly, ho - ly! Mer - ci - ful and might - y!

God in three Per - sons, bless - ed Trin - i - ty!
who wert, and art, and ev - er - more shalt be.
per - fect in pow'r, in love, and pur - i - ty.
God in three Per - sons, bless - ed Trin - i - ty!

Reginald Heber, 1783–1826

NICAEA 11.12.12.10.
John B. Dykes, 1861

Come, Thou Almighty King

101

May the grace of the Lord Jesus Christ, and the love of God, and the fellowship
of the Holy Spirit be with you all. 2 Cor. 13:14

1. Come, thou Al - might - y King, help us thy name to sing,
   help us to praise. Fa - ther, all glo - ri - ous, o'er all vic -
   to - ri - ous, come and reign o - ver us, An - cient of Days.

2. Come, thou In - car - nate Word, gird on thy might - y sword,
   our prayer at - tend. Come, and thy peo - ple bless, and give thy
   Word suc - cess; Spir - it of ho - li - ness, on us de - scend.

3. Come, Ho - ly Com - fort - er, thy sa - cred wit - ness bear
   in this glad hour. Thou who al - might - y art, now rule in
   ev - ery heart, and ne'er from us de - part, Spir - it of pow'r.

4. To the great One in Three e - ter - nal prais - es be,
   hence ev - er - more. His sov - ereign maj - es - ty may we in
   glo - ry see, and to e - ter - ni - ty love and a - dore.

Anon., ca. 1757

TRINITY 6.6.4.6.6.6.4.
Felice de Giardini, 1769

102

All Glory Be to Thee, Most High

Save us, O God our Savior; gather us and deliver us ... that we may give thanks
to your holy name, that we may glory in your praise. 1 Chron. 16:35

1. All glo-ry be to thee, Most High, to thee all ad-o-ra-tion;
2. We praise, we wor-ship thee, we trust, and give thee thanks for-ev-er,
3. O Je-sus Christ, our God and Lord, Son of the heav'n-ly Fa-ther,
4. O Ho-ly Spir-it, pre-cious gift, thou Com-fort-er un-fail-ing,

in grace and truth thou draw-est nigh to of-fer us sal-va-tion;
O Fa-ther, for thy rule is just and wise, and chang-es nev-er;
O thou who hast our peace re-stored, the stray-ing sheep dost ga-ther;
from Sa-tan's snares our souls up-lift, and let thy pow'r, a-vail-ing,

thou show-est thy good-will to men, and peace shall reign on
thy hand al-might-y o'er us reigns, thou do-est what thy
thou Lamb of God, to thee on high out of the depths we
a-vert our woes and calm our dread. For us the Sav-ior's

earth a-gain; we praise thy name for-ev-er.
will or-dains; 'tis well for us thou rul-est.
sin-ners cry: have mer-cy on us, Je-sus!
blood was shed; we trust in thee to save us.

Gloria in Excelsis, 4th cent.
German trans. by Nicolaus Decius, 1522
Anon. English trans.

ALLEIN GOTT IN DER HÖH' 8.7.8.7.8.8.8.7.
V. Schumann's *Geistliche Lieder*, 1539
Arr. by Felix Mendelssohn-Bartholdy, 1809–1847; alt. 1990

Holy God, We Praise Your Name

Holy, holy, holy is the LORD Almighty; the whole earth is full of his glory. Is. 6:3

1. Ho - ly God, we praise your name; Lord of all, we bow be - fore you;
2. Hark, the loud ce - les - tial hymn an - gel choirs a - bove are rais - ing;
3. Lo! the ap - os - tol - ic train join your sa - cred name to hal - low;
4. Ho - ly Fa - ther, Ho - ly Son, Ho - ly Spir - it, Three we name you;

all on earth your scep - ter claim, all in heav'n a - bove a - dore you.
cher - u - bim and ser - a - phim in un - ceas - ing cho - rus prais - ing,
proph - ets swell the glad re - frain, and the white-robed mar - tyrs fol - low;
while in es - sence on - ly One, un - di - vid - ed God we claim you,

In - fi - nite your vast do - main, ev - er - last - ing is your reign.
fill the heav'ns with sweet ac - cord: "Ho - ly, ho - ly, ho - ly Lord."
and from morn to set of sun, through the church the song goes on.
and a - dor - ing bend the knee, while we sing this mys - ter - y.

Based on *Te Deum*, ca. 4th cent.
Attr. to Ignace Franz, ca. 1774
Tr. by Clarence A. Walworth, 1853; alt. 1990, mod.

GROSSER GOTT, WIR LOBEN DICH 7.8.7.8.7.7.
Katholisches Gesangbuch, Vienna, ca. 1774

104   **We Lift Up as Our Shield God's Name**

*Go and make disciples of all nations, baptizing them in the name of the Father and
of the Son and of the Holy Spirit.* Matt. 28:19

1. We lift up as our shield God's name, the strong name of the
2. Im - man - u - el, in - car - nate Lord, from Mar - y's womb was
3. By faith we claim his grace to - day: the pow'r of God to

Trin - i - ty, by in - vo - ca - tion of the same: the
giv - en breath, was bap - tized at the Jor - dan's ford, and
hold and lead, his eye to watch, his might to stay, his

Three in One and One in Three, our Rock and Tow - er, God of
gave his life to con - quer death. He rose tri - um - phant from the
ear to hear - ken to our need; the wis - dom of our God to

Light, E - ter - nal Fa - ther, Spir - it, Word; we claim the name of
tomb, was lift - ed to the Fa - ther's throne to come on God's dread
teach, his hand to guide, his shield to ward, the word of God to

grace and might: sal - va - tion is of Christ the Lord.
day of doom and bring sal - va - tion for his own.
give us speech, his heav'n - ly host to be our guard.

Based on Patrick, 5th cent.
Edmund P. Clowney, 1986, 1989

ST. PATRICK'S BREASTPLATE L.M.D.
Traditional Irish melody
Arr. by Donald Hustad, 1984; alt. 1990

Text © 1990, Edmund P. Clowney.

O God, We Praise Thee

105

Holy, holy, holy is the Lᴏʀᴅ Almighty; the whole earth is full of his glory. Is. 6:3

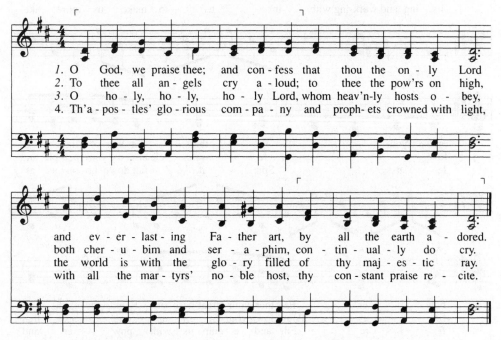

1. O God, we praise thee; and con - fess that thou the on - ly Lord
2. To thee all an - gels cry a - loud; to thee the pow'rs on high,
3. O ho - ly, ho - ly, ho - ly Lord, whom heav'n - ly hosts o - bey,
4. Th'a - pos - tles' glo - rious com - pa - ny and proph - ets crowned with light,

and ev - er - last - ing Fa - ther art, by all the earth a - dored.
both cher - u - bim and ser - a - phim, con - tin - ual - ly do cry.
the world is with the glo - ry filled of thy maj - es - tic ray.
with all the mar - tyrs' no - ble host, thy con - stant praise re - cite.

5. The holy church throughout the world,
O Lord, confesses thee,
that thou Eternal Father art,
of boundless majesty;

6. Thine honored, true, and only Son;
and Holy Ghost, the Spring
of never-ceasing joy: O Christ,
of glory thou art King.

Te Deum, ca. 4th cent.
Tr. in Tate and Brady's *Supplement to the New Version,* 1708

DUNDEE C.M.
Scottish Psalter, 1615

106   Father, Father of All Things

*How can I repay the LORD for all his goodness to me? I will lift up the cup of salvation
and call on the name of the LORD.* Ps. 116:12, 13

1. Fa - ther,   Fa - ther of all things, we   bless   you.
2. Je - sus,   on - ly Son of the   liv - ing God,
3. Spir - it,   sent by the Son to dwell   in   us,

Fa - ther, we love and a - dore   you. O Fa- ther, your chil - dren
Je - sus, you will- ing - ly   suf - fered that thro' you we might know his
liv - ing and work-ing with - in   us to make us more like

praise you.   Fa - ther,   Fa- ther of light and
love.   Je - sus,   cleanse us, your peo-ple, and
Je - sus;   Spir - it,   fall down up- on us as

pow - er,   Fa - ther, your great-ness sur - rounds the earth and
fill us.   Pour down your Spir - it up - on us that
fi - re.   Fill and e - quip us with pow - er and

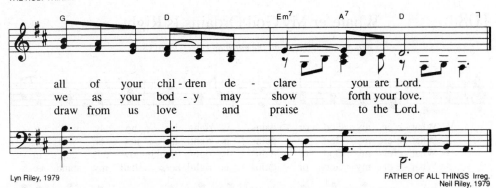

all of your chil - dren de - clare you are Lord.
we as your bod - y may show forth your love.
draw from us love and praise to the Lord.

Lyn Riley, 1979

FATHER OF ALL THINGS Irreg.
Neil Riley, 1979

Praise Ye the Father!

107

*I will ... praise your name for your love and your faithfulness, for you have exalted
above all things your name and your word.* Ps. 138:2

1. Praise ye the Fa - ther! For his lov - ing - kind - ness, ten - der - ly
2. Praise ye the Sa - vior! Great is his com - pas - sion, gra - cious - ly
3. Praise ye the Spir - it! Com - fort - er of Is - rael, sent of the

cares he for his err - ing chil - dren; praise him, ye an - gels,
cares he for his cho - sen peo - ple; young men and maid - ens,
Fa - ther and the Son to bless us; praise ye the Fa - ther,

praise him in the heav - ens, praise ye Je - ho - vah!
ye old men and chil - dren, praise ye the Sav - ior!
Son, and Ho - ly Spir - it, praise ye the tri - une God!

Elizabeth R. Charles, ca. 1859

FLEMMING 11.11.11.6.
Friedrich F. Flemming, 1811

108 Whate'er My God Ordains Is Right

Will not the Judge of all the earth do right? Gen. 18:25

1. What-e'er my God or-dains is right: his ho-ly will a-bid-eth; I will be still what-e'er he doth, and fol-low where he guid-eth. He is my God; though dark my road, he holds me that I shall not fall: where-fore to him I leave it all.

2. What-e'er my God or-dains is right: he nev-er will de-ceive me; he leads me by the prop-er path; I know he will not leave me. I take, con-tent, what he hath sent; his hand can turn my griefs a-way, and pa-tient-ly I wait his day.

3. What-e'er my God or-dains is right: though now this cup, in drink-ing, may bit-ter seem to my faint heart, I take it, all un-shrink-ing. My God is true; each morn a-new sweet com-fort yet shall fill my heart, and pain and sor-row shall de-part.

4. What-e'er my God or-dains is right: here shall my stand be tak-en; though sor-row, need, or death be mine, yet am I not for-sak-en. My Fa-ther's care is round me there; he holds me that I shall not fall: and so to him I leave it all.

Samuel Rodigast, 1675
Tr. by Catherine Winkworth, 1863
Alt. 1961

WAS GOTT TUT 8.7.8.7.4.4.8.8.
Attr. to Severus Gastorius
Weimar Gesangbuch, 1681

Lord, My Weak Thought in Vain Would Climb   109

Oh, the depth of the riches of the wisdom and knowledge of God! How unsearchable his judgments, and his paths beyond tracing out! Rom. 11:33

1. Lord,   my   weak   thought   in   vain   would   climb   to
2. But   weak - er   yet   that   thought   must   prove   to
3. When   my   dim   rea - son   would   de - mand   why
4. When   doubts   dis - turb   my   trou - bled   breast,   and
5. Be   this   my   joy,   that   ev - er - more   thou

search   the   star - ry   vault   pro - found;   in   vain would wing   her
search   thy   great   e - ter - nal   plan,   thy   sov - ereign coun - sels,
• that,   or   this,   thou   dost   or - dain,   by   some   vast   deep   I
all   is   dark   as   night   to   me,   here,   as   on   sol - id
rul - est   all   things   at   thy   will;   thy   sov - ereign   wis - dom

flight   sub - lime   to   find   cre - a - tion's   ut - most   bound.
born   of   love   long   a - ges   ere   the   world   be - gan.
• seem   to   stand,   whose   se - crets   I   must   ask   in   vain.
rock,   I   rest—   that   so   it   seem - eth   good   to   thee.
I   a - dore,   and   calm - ly,   sweet - ly,   trust   thee   still.

Ray Palmer, 1858

CANONBURY   L.M.
Robert Schumann. 1839: arr.

110 Hallelujah, Praise Jehovah

Praise the LORD. Praise the LORD from the heavens, praise him in the heights above.
Ps. 148:1

1. Hal - le - lu - jah, praise Je - ho - vah, from the heav - ens praise his name;
2. Let them prais - es give Je - ho - vah, they were made at his com - mand;
3. All you fruit - ful trees and ce - dars, all you hills and moun - tains high,

praise Je - ho - vah in the high - est, all his an - gels, praise pro - claim.
them for - ev - er he es - tab - lished, his de - cree shall ev - er stand.
creep- ing things and beasts and cat - tle, birds that in the heav - ens fly,

All his hosts, to - geth - er praise him, sun and moon and stars on high;
From the earth, O praise Je - ho - vah, all you seas, you mon - sters all,
kings of earth, and all you peo - ple, princ - es great, earth's judg - es all;

praise him, O you heav'ns of heav - ens, and you floods a - bove the sky.
fire and hail and snow and va - pors, storm- y winds that hear his call.
praise his name, young men and maid - ens, a - ged men, and chil - dren small.

CREATION

REFRAIN

Let them prais - es give Je - ho - vah, for his
Let them prais - es

name a - lone is high, and his glo - ry is ex -
and his glo - ry

alt - ed, and his glo - ry is ex - alt - ed, and his
and his glo - ry

glo - ry is ex - alt - ed far a - bove the earth and sky.
and his glo - ry

Psalm 148:1–13
Bible Songs Hymnal, 1927; mod.

PRAISE JEHOVAH 8.7.8.7.D.ref.
William J. Kirkpatrick, 1838–1921

111 This Is My Father's World

Sovereign Lord ... you made the heaven and the earth and the sea, and everything in them. Acts 4:24

1. This is my Fa - ther's world, and to my lis - t'ning ears,
2. This is my Fa - ther's world, the birds their car - ols raise,
3. This is my Fa - ther's world, O let me ne'er for - get

all na - ture sings, and round me rings the mu - sic of the spheres.
the morn - ing light, the lil - y white, de - clare their Mak - er's praise.
that though the wrong seems oft so strong, God is the Rul - er yet.

This is my Fa - ther's world: I rest me in the thought of
This is my Fa - ther's world: he shines in all that's fair; in the
This is my Fa - ther's world: the bat - tle is not done; Je -

rocks and trees, of skies and seas; his hand the won - ders wrought.
rus - tling grass I hear him pass, he speaks to me ev - ery - where.
sus who died shall be sat - is - fied, and earth and heav'n be one.

Maltbie D. Babcock, 1901

TERRA BEATA S.M.D.
Franklin L. Sheppard, 1915
Arr. by Edward Shippen Barnes, 1926

Praise Ye, Praise Ye the Lord

Praise the LORD. Praise the LORD from the heavens, praise him in the heights above.
Ps. 148:1

1. Praise ye, praise ye the Lord in yon-der heav'n-ly height;
2. Praise him, ye high-est heav'ns, praise him, ye clouds that roll,
3. Ye crea-tures in the sea and crea-tures on the earth,
4. Ye hills and moun-tains, praise, each tree and beast and bird;
5. By all let God be praised, for he a-lone is great;

ye an-gels, all his hosts, in joy-ful praise u - nite; O
cre - a - ted by his pow'r and un - der his con - trol, ye
• your might-y Mak-er praise and tell his match-less worth; praise
ye kings and realms of earth, now let your praise be heard; by
a - bove the earth and heav'n he reigns in glo-rious state; praise

sun and moon, de - clare his might, show forth his praise, ye stars of light.
heav'ns that stand e - ter - nal - ly, es - tab-lished by his firm de - cree.
• him, ye storm - y winds that blow, ye fire and hail, ye rain and snow.
high and low, by young and old, be all his praise and glo - ry told.
him, ye saints, who know his grace and ev - er dwell be - fore his face.

From Psalm 148
The Psalter, 1912
Tune © 1951, Leonard C. Blanton. Used by permission.

COLUMBIA 6.6.6.6.8.8.
Leonard Cooper Blanton, 1951; alt.

113 The Heavens Declare Thy Glory

The heavens declare the glory of God; the skies proclaim the work of his hands.
Ps. 19:1

1. The heav'ns de-clare thy glo - ry, the fir - ma - ment thy pow'r;
2. The sun with roy - al splen - dor goes forth to chant thy praise,
3. All heav'n on high re - joic - es to do its Mak - er's will;

day un - to day the sto - ry re - peats from hour to hour;
and moon-beams soft and ten - der their gen - tler an - them raise;
the stars with sol - emn voic - es re - sound thy prais - es still;

night un - to night re - ply - ing, pro - claims in ev - 'ry land,
o'er ev - ery tribe and na - tion the mu - sic strange is poured,
so let my whole be - hav - ior, thoughts, words, and ac - tions be,

O Lord, with voice un - dy - ing, the won - ders of thy hand.
the song of all cre - a - tion, to thee, cre - a - tion's Lord.
O Lord, my Strength, my Sav - ior, one cease - less song to thee.

From Psalm 19:1–6, 14
Thomas R. Birks, 1874

FAITHFUL 7.6.7.6.D.
Johann Sebastian Bach, 1685–1750

Lord, Our Lord, Thy Glorious Name

114

O Lord, our Lord, how majestic is your name in all the earth! You have set your glory above the heavens. Ps. 8:1

1. Lord, our Lord, thy glo - rious name all thy won - drous works pro-claim;
2. Moon and stars in shin - ing height night - ly tell their Mak - er's might;
3. With do - min- ion crowned he stands o'er the crea - tures of thy hands;

in the heav'ns with ra - diant signs ev - er - more thy glo - ry shines.
when thy won-drous heav'ns I scan, then I know how weak is man.
all to him sub - jec - tion yield in the sea and air and field.

In - fant lips thou dost or - dain wrath and ven- geance to re- strain;
What is man that he should be loved and vis - it - ed by thee,
Lord, our Lord, thy glo- rious name all thy won - drous works pro- claim;

weak - est means ful - fil thy will, might- y en - e - mies to still.
raised to an ex - alt - ed height, crowned with hon - or in thy sight?
thine the name of match- less worth, ex - cel - lent in all the earth.

Psalm 8:1–6, 9
The Psalter. 1912

THANKSGIVING (GILBERT) 7.7.7.7.D.
Walter Bond Gilbert, 1829–1910

115 All Creatures of Our God and King

All you have made will praise you, O LORD; your saints will extol you. Ps. 145:10

1. All crea - tures of our God and King, lift up your voice and
2. Thou rush - ing wind that art so strong, ye clouds that sail in
3. Thou flow - ing wa - ter, pure and clear, make mu - sic for thy
4. And all ye men of ten - der heart, for - giv - ing oth - ers,
5. Let all things their Cre - a - tor bless, and wor - ship him in

with us sing al - le - lu - ia, al - le - lu - ia! Thou burn- ing
heav'n a - long, O praise him, al - le - lu - ia! Thou ris - ing
Lord to hear, al - le - lu - ia, al - le - lu - ia! Thou fire so
take your part, O sing ye, al - le - lu - ia! Ye who long
hum - ble - ness, O praise him, al - le - lu - ia! Praise, praise the

sun with gold - en beam, thou sil - ver moon with soft - er gleam,
morn in praise re - joice, ye lights of eve - ning, find a voice,
mas - ter - ful and bright, that giv - est man both warmth and light,
pain and sor - row bear, praise God and on him cast your care,
Fa - ther, praise the Son, and praise the Spir - it, three in one,

O praise him, O praise him, al - le - lu - ia,

al - le - lu - ia, al - le - lu - ia!

Francis of Assisi, ca. 1225
Tr. by William H. Draper, 1926
Text © 1926, G. Schirmer. All rights reserved. Used by permission. Tune by permission of Oxford University Press.

LASST UNS ERFREUEN L.M.al.
Geistliche Kirchengesänge, Cologne, 1623

For the Beauty of the Earth   116

Every good and perfect gift is from above, coming down from the Father of the
heavenly lights, who does not change like shifting shadows. Jas. 1:17

1. For the beau-ty of the earth, for the glo-ry of the skies,
2. For the beau-ty of each hour of the day and of the night,
3. For the joy of ear and eye, for the heart and mind's de-light,
4. For the joy of hu-man love, broth-er, sis-ter, par-ent, child,
5. For each per-fect gift of thine to our race so free-ly giv'n,

for the love which from our birth o-ver and a-round us lies,
hill and vale, and tree and flow'r, sun and moon and stars of light,
• for the mys-tic har-mo-ny link-ing sense to sound and sight,
friends on earth and friends a-bove, for all gen-tle thoughts and mild,
grac-es hu-man and di-vine, flow'rs of earth and buds of heav'n,

REFRAIN

Lord of all, to thee we raise this our hymn of grate-ful praise.

Folliott S. Pierpoint, 1864

DIX 7.7.7.7.7.7.
Conrad Kocher, 1838
Arr. by William H. Monk, 1861

117 The Spacious Firmament on High

The heavens declare the glory of God; the skies proclaim the work of his hands.
Ps. 19:1

1. The spa-cious fir-ma-ment on high, with all the blue e-the-real sky, and span-gled heav'ns, a shin-ing frame, their great O-rig-i-nal pro-claim. Th'un-wea-ried sun, from day to day, does his Cre-a-tor's pow'r dis-play, and pub-lish-es to

2. Soon as the eve-ning shades pre-vail, the moon takes up the won-drous tale, and night-ly to the lis-t'ning earth re-peats the sto-ry of her birth; whilst all the stars that round her burn, and all the plan-ets in their turn, con-firm the tid-ings

3. What though in sol-emn si-lence all move round this dark ter-res-trial ball? What though no re-al voice nor sound a-midst their ra-diant orbs be found? In rea-son's ear they all re-joice, and ut-ter forth a glo-rious voice; for-ev-er sing-ing

ev	-	'ry	land	the	work	of	an		al	- might	- y	hand.
as		they	roll,	and	spread	the	truth		from	pole	to	pole.
as		they	shine,	"The	hand	that	made		us	is	di	- vine."

Joseph Addison, 1712

CREATION L.M.D.
From Franz Joseph Haydn, *The Creation*, 1798; arr.

Come, Sound His Praise Abroad   118

Come, let us sing for joy to the LORD; let us shout aloud to the Rock of our salvation.
Ps. 95:1

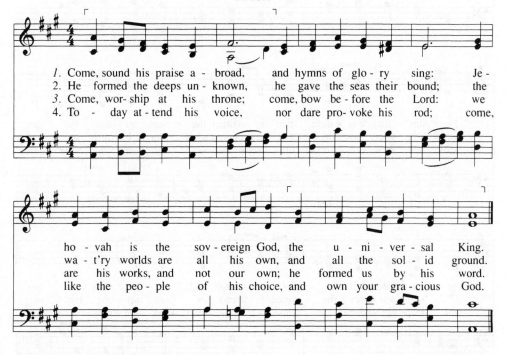

1.	Come,	sound	his	praise a -	broad,	and	hymns	of	glo - ry	sing:	Je -
2.	He	formed	the	deeps un -	known,	he	gave	the	seas their	bound;	the
3.	Come,	wor- ship	at	his	throne;	come,	bow	be - fore the		Lord:	we
4.	To -	day	at - tend	his	voice,	nor	dare	pro - voke his		rod;	come,

ho - vah	is	the	sov - ereign God,	the	u - ni - ver - sal	King.
wa - t'ry	worlds are	all	his own,	and	all the sol - id	ground.
are	his	works, and	not	our own;	he	formed us by his	word.
like	the	peo - ple	of	his choice,	and	own your gra - cious	God.

Based on Psalm 95
Isaac Watts, 1719
Tune © 1990, RAM Music Publications. Used by permission.

KREWSON S.M.
Ronald Alan Matthews, 1985

119 I Sing the Almighty Power of God

Come, let us bow down in worship, let us kneel before the LORD our Maker. Ps. 95:6

1. I sing th'al-might-y pow'r of God that made the moun-tains rise,
2. I sing the good-ness of the Lord that filled the earth with food;
3. There's not a plant or flow'r be-low but makes your glo-ries known;

that spread the flow-ing seas a-broad and built the loft-y skies.
he formed the crea-tures with his word, and then pro-nounced them good.
and clouds a-rise and tem-pests blow by or-der from your throne;

I sing the wis-dom that or-dained the sun to rule the day;
Lord, how your won-ders are dis-played wher-e'er I turn my eye,
while all that bor-rows life from you is ev-er in your care,

the moon shines full at his com-mand and all the stars o-bey.
if I sur-vey the ground I tread or gaze up-on the sky!
and ev-ery-where that man can be, you, God, are pres-ent there.

Isaac Watts, 1715
Mod.

FOREST GREEN C.M.D.
Traditional English melody
Arr. by Ralph Vaughan Williams, 1906

All Things Bright and Beautiful

120

You made the heavens ... and all their starry host, the earth and all that is on it,
the seas and all that is in them. You give life to everything. Neh. 9:6

Unison

(Ref.) All things bright and beau - ti - ful, all crea - tures great and small,

all things wise and won - der - ful, the Lord God made them all. *Fine*

1. Each lit - tle flow'r that o - pens, each lit - tle bird that sings,
2. The pur - ple - head - ed moun- tain, the riv - er run - ning by,
3. The cold wind in the win - ter, the pleas- ant sum - mer sun,
4. The tall trees in the green- wood, the mead- ows where we play,
5. He gave us eyes to see them, and lips that we might tell

D.C.

he made their glow - ing col - ors, he made their ti - ny wings.
the sun - set, and the morn - ing that bright - ens up the sky.
• the ripe fruits in the gar - den, he made them, ev - 'ry one.
the flow - ers by the wa - ter we gath - er ev - 'ry day.
how great is God Al - might - y, who has made all things well.

Cecil F. Alexander, 1848
Alt. 1961

ROYAL OAK 7.6.7.6.D.
English melody, 17th cent.

121 Praise Him, Praise Him, Praise Him

Praise the LORD. Praise the LORD from the heavens, praise him in the heights above.
Ps. 148:1

Unison or harmony

1. Praise him, praise him, praise him, pow'rs and dom - i - na - tions!
2. Praise him, praise him, praise him, o - cean depths and wa - ters!
3. Praise him, praise him, praise him, saints of God who fear him!

Praise his name in glo - rious light, you crea - tures of the day!
El - e - ments of earth and heav'n your sev - 'ral prais - es blend!
To the high- est name of all, con - cert - ed an - thems raise,

Moon and stars, ring prais - es through the con - stel - la - tions:
Birds and beasts and cat - tle, Ad - am's sons and daugh - ters,
all you seed of Is - rael, ho - ly peo - ple near him,

Lord God, whose word shall nev - er pass a - way!
wor - ship the King whose reign shall nev - er end!
whom he ex - alts to pow'r and crowns with praise!

From Psalm 148
Michael Perry, 1982

ST. HELENS 12.13.13.10.
Kenneth W. Coates, b. 1917; alt. 1990

God, All Nature Sings Thy Glory

How many are your works, O LORD! In wisdom you made them all; the earth is full of your creatures. Ps. 104:24

1. God, all na-ture sings thy glo-ry, and thy works pro-claim thy might;
2. Clear-er still we see thy hand in man whom thou hast made for thee;
3. But our sins have spoiled thine im-age; na-ture, con-science on-ly serve
4. God of glo-ry, pow-er, mer-cy, all cre-a-tion prais-es thee;

or-dered vast-ness in the heav-ens, or-dered course of day and night;
rul-er of cre-a-tion's glo-ry, im-age of thy maj-es-ty.
as un-ceas-ing, grim re-mind-ers of the wrath which we de-serve.
we, thy crea-tures, would a-dore thee now and through e-ter-ni-ty.

beau-ty in the chang-ing sea-sons, beau-ty in the storm-ing sea;
Mu-sic, art, the fruit-ful gar-den, all the la-bor of his days,
Yet thy grace and sav-ing mer-cy in thy Word of truth re-vealed
Saved to mag-ni-fy thy good-ness, grant us strength to do thy will;

all the chang-ing moods of na-ture praise the change-less Trin-i-ty.
are the call-ing of his Mak-er to the har-vest feast of praise.
claim the praise of all who know thee, in the blood of Je-sus sealed.
with our acts as with our voic-es thy com-mand-ments to ful-fill.

David Clowney, 1960

ODE TO JOY 8.7.8.7.D.
Ludwig van Beethoven, 1824; arr.

123 God of Everlasting Glory

May the glory of the LORD endure forever; may the LORD rejoice in his works.
Ps. 104:31

1. God of ev - er - last - ing glo - ry, fill - ing earth and sky,
2. As we push man's fron - tiers for - ward in - to out - er space,
3. In the o - pen book of na - ture faith re - mains un - moved—
4. Through the course of hu - man his - t'ry has your pur - pose run,

ev - ery - where your won - ders o - pen to our search - ing eye:
reach - ing for the stars and plan - ets, still your hand we trace;
pat - terns of the Mas - ter Build - er by each fact are proved;
and in sub - stance have we seen you in your glo - rious Son:

in our tel - e - scop - ic prob - ing— light- years from our world,
in the lab - 'ra - to - ry's si - lence, where your se - crets hide,
so with rev - 'rent hearts we pon - der all the grand de - sign
he it was who came to save us and our hopes to raise—

in the a - tom's theo - ried struc - ture sci - ence has un - furled.
there the mar - vels of cre - a - tion are for us sup - plied.
of the u - ni - verse a - round us, wrought by hands di - vine.
God of ev - er - last - ing glo - ry, your great name we praise!

John W. Peterson, 1965; mod.

BRETON ROAD 8.5.8.5.D.
John W. Peterson, 1965

Praise the Lord Our God

Praise the LORD. Praise the LORD from the heavens, praise him in the heights above.
Ps. 148:1

1. Praise the Lord our God, praise the Lord! Praise him
2. Praise him, sun and moon and the stars! Praise him,
3. Praise him, wind and storm, moun - tains steep! Praise him,
4. Kings of earth must praise, rul - ers all! All young

from the heights, praise the Lord! Praise him, an - gel throngs,
sky and clouds and the rain! Let them praise his name,
fruit - ful trees, ce - dars tall! Beasts and cat - tle herds,
men and girls, praise the Lord! Old men, chil - dren small,

praise the Lord; praise God, all his host!
works of God! All crea - tures— praise the Lord!
birds that fly! All crea - tures— praise the Lord!
praise the Lord! All peo - ple— praise the Lord!

From Psalm 148
Richard T. Bewes, 1973

KUM BA YA 8.8.8.6.
Traditional African melody
Arr. by David G. Wilson, b. 1940; alt. 1990

125

Let All Things Now Living

Sing to the LORD, all the earth; proclaim his salvation day after day. 1 Chron. 16:23

CREATION

His ban - ners are o'er us, his light goes be - fore us,
We too should be voic - ing our love and re - joic - ing,

a pil - lar of fire shin - ing forth in the night,
with glad ad - o - ra - tion a song let us raise,

'til shad - ows have van - ished and dark - ness is ban - ished,
'til all things now liv - ing u - nite in thanks - giv - ing

as for - ward we trav - el from light in - to light.
to God in the high - est, ho - san - na and praise!

Katherine K. Davis, 1939
Alt. 1990, mod.

ASH GROVE 12.11.12.11.D.
Traditional Welsh melody
Arr. by Katherine K. Davis, 1939

126

My Soul, Bless the Lord!

*Praise the LORD, O my soul. O LORD my God, you are very great; you are clothed
with splendor and majesty. Ps. 104:1*

1. My soul, bless the Lord! The Lord is most great,
with glo - ry ar - rayed, ma - jes - tic his state;
the light is his gar - ment, the skies are his shade,
and o - ver the wa - ters his courts he has laid.

2. He rides on the clouds, the wings of the storm,
the light - ning and wind his mis - sion per - form;
the earth he has found - ed her sta - tion to keep,
and wrapped as a ves - ture a - bout her the deep.

3. He wa - ters the hills with rain from the skies,
and plen - ti - ful grass and herbs he sup - plies,
sup - ply - ing the cat - tle, and bless - ing man's toil
with bread in a - bun - dance, with wine and with oil.

4. The trees which the Lord has plant - ed are fed,
and o - ver the earth their branch - es are spread;
they keep in their shel - ter the birds of the air,
the life of each crea - ture the Lord makes his care.

5. Your Spirit, O Lord, makes life to abound,
   the earth is renewed, and fruitful the ground;
   to God ascribe glory and wisdom and might,
   let God in his creatures forever delight.

6. Rejoicing in God, my thought shall be sweet,
   while sinners depart in ruin complete;
   my soul, bless Jehovah, his name be adored;
   come, praise him, you people, and worship the Lord.

From Psalm 104
The Psalter, 1912; mod.

HOUGHTON 10.10.11.11.
Henry J. Gauntlett, 1861

With Songs and Honors Sounding Loud 127

*Sing to the LORD with thanksgiving.... He covers the sky with clouds; he supplies
the earth with rain and makes grass grow on the hills. Ps. 147:7, 8*

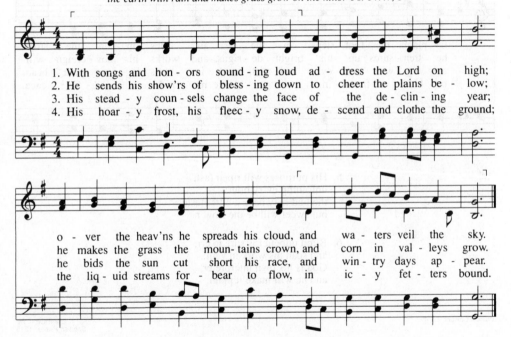

1. With songs and hon - ors sound - ing loud ad - dress the Lord on high;
2. He sends his show'rs of bless - ing down to cheer the plains be - low;
3. His stead - y coun - sels change the face of the de - clin - ing year;
4. His hoar - y frost, his fleec - y snow, de - scend and clothe the ground;

o - ver the heav'ns he spreads his cloud, and wa - ters veil the sky.
he makes the grass the moun - tains crown, and corn in val - leys grow.
he bids the sun cut short his race, and win - try days ap - pear.
the liq - uid streams for - bear to flow, in ic - y fet - ters bound.

5. He sends his word and melts the snow,
   the fields no longer mourn;
   he calls the warmer gales to blow,
   and bids the spring return.

6. The changing wind, the flying cloud,
   obey his mighty word;
   with songs and honors sounding loud
   praise ye the sovereign Lord.

From Psalm 147:7, 8, 15–18
Isaac Watts, 1719

ST. MAGNUS C.M.
Attr. to Jeremiah Clarke, 1701

128 God Moves in a Mysterious Way

I will turn the darkness into light before them and make the rough places smooth.
Is. 42:16

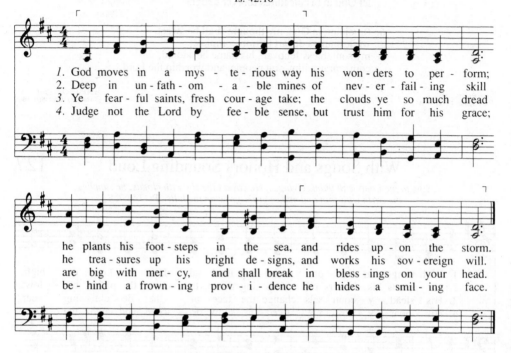

1. God moves in a mys - te - rious way his won - ders to per - form;
2. Deep in un - fath - om - a - ble mines of nev - er - fail - ing skill
3. Ye fear - ful saints, fresh cour - age take; the clouds ye so much dread
4. Judge not the Lord by fee - ble sense, but trust him for his grace;

he plants his foot - steps in the sea, and rides up - on the storm.
he trea - sures up his bright de - signs, and works his sov - ereign will.
are big with mer - cy, and shall break in bless - ings on your head.
be - hind a frown - ing prov - i - dence he hides a smil - ing face.

5. His purposes will ripen fast,
   unfolding ev'ry hour;
   the bud may have a bitter taste,
   but sweet will be the flow'r.

6. Blind unbelief is sure to err,
   and scan his work in vain;
   God is his own interpreter,
   and he will make it plain.

William Cowper, 1774

DUNDEE C.M.
Scottish Psalter, 1615

I Belong to Jesus

You are not your own; you were bought at a price. 1 Cor. 6:19, 20

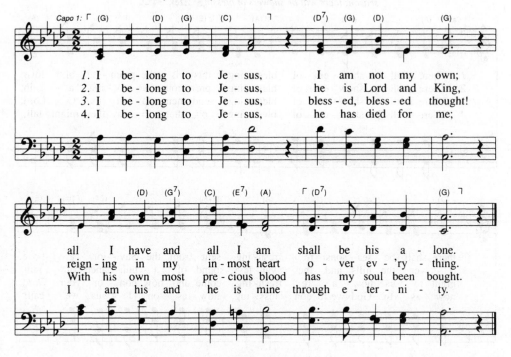

1. I be-long to Je - sus,
   I am not my own;
   all I have and all I am shall be his a - lone.

2. I be-long to Je - sus,
   he is Lord and King,
   reign-ing in my in - most heart o - ver ev - 'ry - thing.

3. I be-long to Je - sus,
   bless - ed, bless - ed thought!
   With his own most pre - cious blood has my soul been bought.

4. I be-long to Je - sus,
   he has died for me;
   I am his and he is mine through e - ter - ni - ty.

5. I belong to Jesus,
   he will keep my soul
   when the deathly waters dark
   round about me roll.

6. I belong to Jesus,
   and ere long I'll stand
   with my precious Savior there
   in the glory land.

M. Fraser

DEDICATION 6.5.7.5.
M. A. Sea

130 Showers of Blessing

I will bless them and the places surrounding my hill. I will send down showers in
season; there will be showers of blessing. Ezek. 34:26

Daniel W. Whittle, 1883
Mod.

SHOWERS OF BLESSING 8.7.8.7.ref.
James McGranahan, 1883

Children of the Heavenly Father

As a father has compassion on his children, so the LORD has compassion on those who fear him. Ps. 103:13

1. Chil - dren of the heav'n - ly Fa - ther safe - ly in his bo - som gath - er; nest - ling bird nor star in heav - en such a ref - uge e'er was giv - en.

2. God his own doth tend and nour - ish, in his ho - ly courts they flour - ish; from all e - vil things he spares them, in his might - y arms he bears them.

3. Nei - ther life nor death shall ev - er from the Lord his chil - dren sev - er; un - to them his grace he show - eth, and their sor - rows all he know - eth.

4. Praise the Lord in joy - ful num - bers, your Pro - tec - tor nev - er slum - bers; at the will of your De - fend - er ev - 'ry foe - man must sur - ren - der.

5. Though he giveth or he taketh,
   God his children ne'er forsaketh;
   his the loving purpose solely
   to preserve them pure and holy.

6. More secure is no one ever
   than the loved ones of the Savior;
   not yon star on high abiding
   nor the bird in home-nest hiding.

Carolina V. Sandell Berg, ca. 1855
Tr. by Ernst W. Olson, 1925

TRYGGARE KAN INGEN VARA L.M.
Traditional Swedish melody
Arr. by Marc Hedlin, 1976

132

O Rejoice in the Lord

We know that in all things God works for the good of those who love him, who have been called according to his purpose. Rom. 8:28

1. God nev-er moves with-out pur-pose or plan when try-ing his
2. I could not see through the shad-ows a-head; so I looked at the
3. Now I can see test-ing comes from a-bove; God strength-ens his

ser-vant and mold-ing a man. Give thanks to the Lord, though the
cross of my Sav-ior in-stead. I bowed to the will of the
chil-dren and purg-es in love. My Fa-ther knows best, and I

test-ing seems long; in dark-ness he gives us a song.
Mas-ter that day; then peace came and tears fled a-way.
trust in his care; through purg-ing more fruit I will bear.

REFRAIN

O re-joice in the Lord. He makes no mis-take. He knows the

end of each path that I take. For when I am tried and

PROVIDENCE

pu - ri - fied, I shall come forth as gold.

Ron Hamilton, 1978
Alt. 1990, mod.

Text © 1978, Ron Hamilton, Musical Ministries in Praises, administered by Majesty Music. Tune © 1990, RAM Music Publications. Used by permission.

WILMINGTON 10.11.11.8.ref.
Ronald Alan Matthews, 1986

God, Who Made the Earth

133

Cast all your anxiety on him because he cares for you. 1 Pet. 5:7

1. God, who made the earth, the air, the sky, the sea,
2. God, who made the grass, the flow'r, the fruit, the tree,
3. God, who made the sun, the moon, the stars, is he
4. God, who made all things, on earth, in air, in sea,

who gave the light its birth, car - eth for me.
the day and night to pass, car - eth for me.
who, when life's clouds come on, car - eth for me.
who chang - ing sea - sons brings, car - eth for me.

5. God, who sent his Son
   to die on Calvary,
   he, if I lean on him,
   will care for me.

6. When in heav'n's bright land
   I all his loved ones see,
   I'll sing with that blest band,
   "God cared for me."

Sarah Betts Rhodes, 1870

SOMMERLIED 5.6.6.4.
Hermann von Müller, b. 1859

134 God Will Take Care of You

Cast all your anxiety on him because he cares for you. 1 Pet. 5:7

1. Be not dis - mayed what - e'er be - tide, God will take care of you;
2. Through days of toil when heart doth fail, God will take care of you;
3. All you may need he will pro - vide, God will take care of you;
4. No mat - ter what may be the test, God will take care of you;

be - neath his wings of love a - bide, God will take care of you.
when dan - gers fierce your path as - sail, God will take care of you.
trust him and you will be sat - is - fied, God will take care of you.
lean, wea - ry one, up - on his breast, God will take care of you.

REFRAIN

God will take care of you, through ev - 'ry day, o'er all the way;

he will take care of you, God will take care of you.
take care of you.

Civilla D. Martin, 1905

GOD CARES C.M.ref.
W. Stillman Martin, 1905

God Sees the Little Sparrow Fall

135

Are not five sparrows sold for two pennies? Yet not one of them is forgotten by
God.... Don't be afraid; you are worth more than many sparrows. Luke 12:6, 7

1. God sees the lit - tle spar - row fall, it meets his ten - der view;
2. He paints the lil - y of the field, per - fumes each lil - y bell;
3. God made the lit - tle birds and flow'rs, and all things large and small;

if God so loves the lit - tle birds, I know he loves me too.
if he so loves the lit - tle flow'rs, I know he loves me well.
he'll not for - get his lit - tle ones, I know he loves them all.

REFRAIN

He loves me too, he loves me too, I know he loves me too;

be - cause he loves the lit - tle things, I know he loves me too.

Maria Straub, 1838–1898

PROVIDENCE C.M.ref.
S. W. Straub. 1842–1899

136 Thy Word Have I Hid in My Heart

I have hidden your word in my heart that I might not sin against you. Ps. 119:11

1. Thy Word is a lamp to my feet, a light to my path al - way, to guide and to save me from sin, and show me the heav'n - ly way.
2. For - ev - er, O Lord, is thy Word es - tab - lished and fixed on high; thy faith - ful - ness un - to all men a - bid - eth for - ev - er nigh.
3. At morn - ing, at noon, and at night I ev - er will give thee praise; for thou art my por - tion, O Lord, and shall be through all my days!
4. Through him whom thy Word hath fore - told, the Sav - ior and Morn - ing Star, sal - va - tion and peace have been brought to those who have strayed a - far.

REFRAIN

Thy Word have I hid in my heart that I might not in my heart

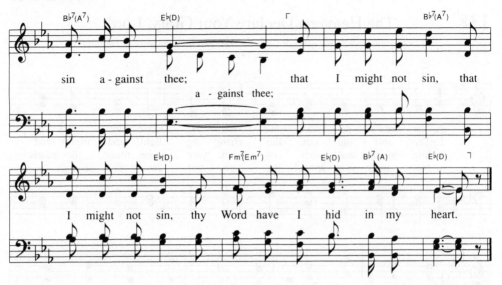

sin a - gainst thee; that I might not sin, that
a - gainst thee;

I might not sin, thy Word have I hid in my heart.

From Psalm 119
E. O. Sellers, 1908

THY WORD 8.7.8.7.ref.
E. O. Sellers, 1908

Holy Bible, Book Divine 137

All Scripture is God-breathed. 2 Tim. 3:16

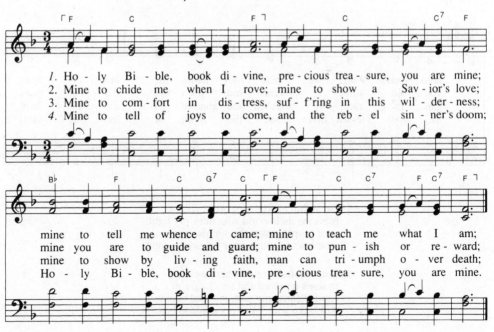

1. Ho - ly Bi - ble, book di - vine, pre - cious trea - sure, you are mine;
2. Mine to chide me when I rove; mine to show a Sav - ior's love;
3. Mine to com - fort in dis - tress, suf - f'ring in this wil - der - ness;
4. Mine to tell of joys to come, and the reb - el sin - ner's doom;

mine to tell me whence I came; mine to teach me what I am;
mine you are to guide and guard; mine to pun - ish or re - ward;
mine to show by liv - ing faith, man can tri - umph o - ver death;
Ho - ly Bi - ble, book di - vine, pre - cious trea - sure, you are mine.

John Burton, 1803
Alt. 1990, mod.

ALETTA 7.7.7.7.
William B. Bradbury, 1860

138 The Heavens Declare Your Glory, Lord

The heavens declare the glory of God; the skies proclaim the work of his hands.
Ps. 19:1

1. The heav'ns de - clare your glo - ry, Lord; in ev - 'ry star your wis - dom shines; but when our eyes be - hold your Word, we read your name in fair - er lines.

2. The roll - ing sun, the chang - ing light, and nights and days, your pow'r con - fess; but the blest vol - ume you did write re - veals your jus - tice and your grace.

3. Sun, moon, and stars con - vey your praise round the whole earth, and nev - er stand; so when your truth be - gan its race, it touched and glanced on ev - 'ry land.

4. Nor shall your spread - ing gos - pel rest till through the world your truth has run; till Christ has all the na - tions blessed that see the light, or feel the sun.

5. Great Sun of Righteousness, arise;
   bless the dark world with heav'nly light:
   your gospel makes the simple wise;
   your laws are pure, your judgments right.

6. Your noblest wonders here we view
   in souls renewed and sins forgiv'n:
   Lord, cleanse my sins, my soul renew,
   and make your Word my guide to heav'n.

From Psalm 19
Isaac Watts, 1719; alt. 1990, mod.

UXBRIDGE L.M.
Lowell Mason, 1830

Your Word Is like a Garden, Lord

139

Open my eyes that I may see wonderful things in your law. Ps. 119:18

1. Your Word is like a gar - den, Lord, with flow - ers bright and fair;
2. Your Word is like a star - ry host: a thou - sand rays of light
3. O may I love your pre - cious Word, may I ex - plore the mine,

and ev - ery - one who seeks may pluck a love - ly clus - ter there.
are seen to guide the trav - el - er, and make his path - way bright.
may I its fra - grant flow - ers glean, may light up - on me shine.

Your Word is like a deep, deep mine; and jew - els rich and rare
Your Word is like an ar - mor - y, where sol - diers may re - pair,
O may I find my ar - mor there, your Word my trust - y sword;

are hid - den in its might - y depths for ev - ery search - er there.
and find, for life's long bat - tle day, all need - ful weap - ons there.
I'll learn to fight with ev - ery foe the bat - tle of the Lord.

Based on Psalm 119
Edwin Hodder, 1863; mod.

SERAPH C.M.D.
Gottfried W. Fink. 1842

140   O Word of God Incarnate

The unfolding of your words gives light; it gives understanding to the simple.
Ps. 119:130

1. O Word of God in - car - nate, O Wis - dom from on high,
2. The church from her dear Mas - ter re - ceived the gift di - vine,
3. It float - eth like a ban - ner be - fore God's host un - furled;
4. O make thy church, dear Sav - ior, a lamp of pur - est gold,

O Truth un-changed, un - chang - ing, O Light of our dark sky;
and still that light she lift - eth o'er all the earth to shine.
it shin - eth like a bea - con a - bove the dark - ling world.
to bear be - fore the na - tions thy true light, as of old.

we praise thee for the ra - diance that from the hal - lowed page,
It is the gold - en cas - ket, where gems of truth are stored;
It is the chart and com - pass that o'er life's surg - ing sea,
O teach thy wan - d'ring pil - grims by this their path to trace,

a lan - tern to our foot - steps, shines on from age to age.
it is the heav'n - drawn pic - ture of Christ, the liv - ing Word.
'mid mists and rocks and quick - sands, still guides, O Christ, to thee.
till, clouds and dark - ness end - ed, they see thee face to face.

William Walsham How, 1867

MUNICH 7.6.7.6.D.
Meiningen Gesangbuch, 1693

God, in the Gospel of His Son

141

The task of testifying to the gospel of God's grace. Acts 20:24

1. God, in the gos - pel of his Son, makes his e - ter - nal coun - sels known; where love in all its glo - ry shines, and truth is drawn in fair - est lines.

2. Here sin - ners of a hum - ble frame may taste his grace, and learn his name; may read, in char - ac - ters of blood, the wis - dom, pow'r, and grace of God.

3. The pris - 'ner here may break his chains; the wea - ry rest from all his pains; the cap - tive feel his bond - age cease; the mourn - er find the way of peace.

4. Here faith re - veals to mor - tal eyes a bright - er world be - yond the skies; here shines the light which guides our way from earth to realms of end - less day.

5. O grant us grace, al - might - y Lord, to read and mark your ho - ly Word; its truths with meek - ness to re - ceive, and by its ho - ly pre - cepts live.

Benjamin Beddome, 1787
Alt. by Thomas Cotterill, 1819; mod.

GERMANY L.M.
William Gardiner's *Sacred Melodies*, 1815

142 Lord, Thy Word Abideth

The law of the LORD is perfect, reviving the soul. The statutes of the LORD are
trustworthy, making wise the simple. Ps. 19:7

1. Lord, thy Word a - bid - eth, and our foot-steps guid - eth;
2. When the storms are o'er us, and dark clouds be - fore us,
3. Word of mer - cy, giv - ing suc - cor to the liv - ing;

who its truth be - liev - eth light and joy re - ceiv - eth.
then its light di - rect - eth, and our way pro - tect - eth.
Word of life, sup - ply - ing com - fort to the dy - ing!

When our foes are near us, then thy Word doth cheer us;
Who can tell the plea - sure, who re - count the trea - sure,
O that we, dis - cern - ing its most ho - ly learn - ing,

word of con - so - la - tion, mes - sage of sal - va - tion,
by thy Word im - part - ed to the sim - ple - heart - ed?
Lord, may love and fear thee, ev - er - more be near thee.

Based on Psalm 27
Henry W. Baker, 1861

GRIEG 6.6.6.6.
Edvard Grieg, 1843–1907
Arr. by Lawrence C. Roff, 1990

How Precious Is the Book Divine

143

Your word is a lamp to my feet and a light for my path. Ps. 119:105

1. How pre - cious is the book di - vine, by in - spi -
ra - tion giv - en; bright as a lamp its doc - trines
shine, to guide our souls to heav'n.

2. It sweet - ly cheers our droop - ing hearts, in this dark
vale of tears; life, light, and joy it still im -
parts, and quells our ris - ing fears.

3. This lamp, through all the te - dious night of life, shall
guide our way, till we be - hold the clear - er
light of an e - ter - nal day.

John Fawcett, 1782

BELMONT C.M.
William Gardiner. 1812: arr.

144   Father of Mercies, in Your Word

Great is his love toward us, and the faithfulness of the LORD endures forever.
Ps. 117:2

1. Fa - ther of mer - cies, in your Word
what end - less glo - ry shines; for - ev - er be your
name a - dored for these ce - les - tial lines.

2. Here may the wretch - ed sons of want
ex - haust - less rich - es find; rich - es a - bove what
earth can grant and last - ing as the mind.

3. Here the Re - deem - er's wel - come voice
• spreads heav'n - ly peace a - round; and life and ev - er -
• last - ing joys at - tend the bliss - ful sound.

4. O may these heav'n - ly pa - ges be
my ev - er - dear de - light; and still new beau - ties
may I see, and still in - creas - ing light.

5. Di - vine In - struc - tor, gra - cious Lord,
O be for - ev - er near; teach me to love your
sa - cred Word, and view my Sav - ior there.

Anne Steele, 1760
Alt. 1990, mod.

BEATITUDO C.M.
John B. Dykes, 1875

The Spirit Breathes upon the Word

145

But the Counselor, the Holy Spirit ... will teach you all things and will remind you of everything I have said to you. John 14:26

1. The Spir - it breathes up - on the Word, and brings the truth to
2. A glo - ry gilds the sa - cred page, ma - jes - tic, like the
3. The Hand that gave it still sup - plies the gra - cious light and
4. Let ev - er - last - ing thanks be thine for such a bright dis -
5. My soul re - joic - es to pur - sue the steps of him I

sight; pre - cepts and prom - is - es af - ford a
sun: it gives a light to ev - ery age; it
heat: his truths up - on the na - tions rise; they
play as makes a world of dark - ness shine with
love, till glo - ry breaks up - on my view in

sanc - ti - fy - ing light, a sanc - ti - fy - ing light.
gives, but bor - rows none, it gives, but bor - rows none.
rise, but nev - er set, they rise, but nev - er set.
beams of heav'n - ly day, with beams of heav'n - ly day.
bright - er worlds a - bove, in bright - er worlds a - bove.

William Cowper, 1779

ORTONVILLE C.M.rep.
Thomas Hastings, 1837

146   Break Thou the Bread of Life

From now on give us this bread. John 6:34

Mary A. Lathbury, 1877
Alt. 1961

BREAD OF LIFE 6.4.6.4.D.
William F. Sherwin, 1877

O God of Light, Your Word, a Lamp Unfailing 147

Your word is a lamp to my feet and a light for my path. Ps. 119:105

Unison

1. O God of light, your Word, a lamp un - fail - ing,
2. From days of old, through swift - ly roll - ing a - ges,
3. Un - dimmed by time, the Word is still re - veal - ing
4. To all the world the mes - sage you are send - ing,

shines through the dark - ness of our earth - ly way,
you have re - vealed your will to mor - tal men,
to sin - ful men your jus - tice and your grace;
to ev - ery land, to ev - ery race and clan;

o'er fear and doubt, o'er black de - spair pre - vail - ing,
speak - ing to saints, to proph - ets, kings, and sa - ges,
and quest - ing hearts that long for peace and heal - ing
and myr - iad tongues, in one great an - them blend - ing,

guid - ing our steps to your e - ter - nal day.
who wrote the mes - sage with im - mor - tal pen.
see your com - pas - sion in the Sav - ior's face.
ac - claim with joy your won - drous gift to man.

Sarah E. Taylor, 1952
Mod.

CHARTERHOUSE 11.10.11.10.
David Evans, 1927

148 How Shall the Young Direct Their Way?

How can a young man keep his way pure? By living according to your word. Ps. 119:9

1. How shall the young di - rect their way? What light shall be their
2. O bless - ed Lord, teach me your law, your righ - teous judg- ments

per - fect guide? Your Word, O Lord, will safe - ly lead, if in its
I de - clare; your tes - ti - mo - nies make me glad, for they are

wis - dom they con - fide. Sin - cere - ly I have sought you, Lord,
wealth be - yond com - pare. Up - on your pre - cepts and your ways

O let me not from you de - part; to know your will and
my heart will med - i - tate with awe; your Word shall be my

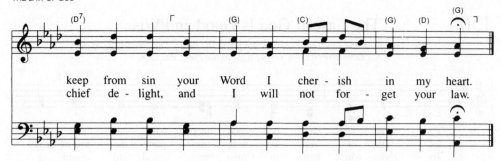

keep from sin your Word I cher - ish in my heart.
chief de - light, and I will not for - get your law.

Psalm 119:9–16
The Psalter, 1912; mod.

DUANE STREET L.M.D.
George Coles, 1835

Teach Me, O Lord, Your Way of Truth 149

Teach me, O LORD, to follow your decrees; then I will keep them to the end. Ps. 119:33

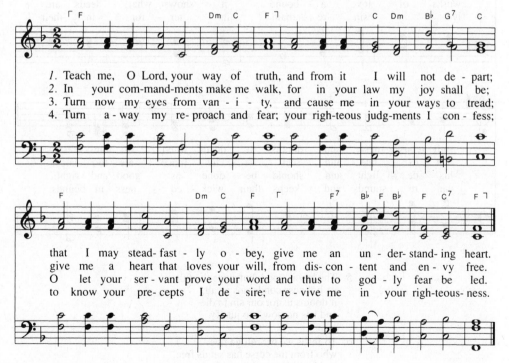

1. Teach me, O Lord, your way of truth, and from it I will not de - part;
2. In your com-mand-ments make me walk, for in your law my joy shall be;
3. Turn now my eyes from van - i - ty, and cause me in your ways to tread;
4. Turn a - way my re- proach and fear; your righ-teous judg-ments I con - fess;

that I may stead- fast - ly o - bey, give me an un - der- stand- ing heart.
give me a heart that loves your will, from dis- con - tent and en - vy free.
O let your ser - vant prove your word and thus to god - ly fear be led.
to know your pre - cepts I de - sire; re - vive me in your righ-teous- ness.

From Psalm 119:33–40
The Psalter, 1912; alt. 1990, mod.

BISHOP L.M.
Joseph P. Holbrook, 1874

150 The Law of God Is Good and Wise

The precepts of the LORD are right, giving joy to the heart. The commands of the LORD are radiant, giving light to the eyes. Ps. 19:8

1. The law of God is good and wise and sets his
   will be - fore our eyes, shows us the way of
   righ - teous - ness, and dooms to death when we trans- gress.

2. Its light of ho - li - ness im - parts the knowl - edge
   of our sin - ful hearts, that we may see our
   lost es - tate and seek de - liv - 'rance ere too late.

3. To those who help in Christ have found and would in
   works of love a - bound it shows what deeds are
   his de - light and should be done as good and right.

4. When men the of - fered help dis - dain and wil - ful -
   ly in sin re - main, its ter - ror in their
   ear re - sounds and keeps their wick - ed - ness in bounds.

5. The law is good; but since the fall
   its holiness condemns us all;
   it dooms us for our sin to die
   and has no pow'r to justify.

6. To Jesus we for refuge flee,
   who from the curse has set us free,
   and humbly worship at his throne,
   saved by his grace through faith alone.

Matthias Loy, 1863

ERHALT UNS, HERR L.M.
Geistliche Lieder, Wittenberg, 1543

Jehovah's Perfect Law

151

Blessed is the man who does not walk in the counsel of the wicked. Ps. 1:1

1. Je - ho - vah's per - fect law re - stores the soul a - gain; his
2. The Lord's com-mands are pure, they light and joy re - store; Je -
3. They are to be de - sired a - bove the fin - est gold; than
4. His er - rors who can know? Cleanse me from hid-den stain; keep
5. When-e'er you search my life, may all my thoughts with - in and

tes - ti - mo - ny sure gives wis - dom un - to men; the
ho - vah's fear is clean, en - dur - ing ev - er - more; his
hon - ey from the comb more sweet-ness far they hold; with
me from wil - ful sins, nor let them o'er me reign; and
all the words I speak your full ap - prov - al win. O

pre - cepts of the Lord are right, and fill the heart with great de - light.
stat - utes, let the world con - fess, are whol - ly truth and righ- teous-ness.
warn - ings they your ser - vant guard, in keep-ing them is great re - ward.
then I up - right shall ap - pear and be from great trans - gres-sions clear.
Lord, you are a Rock to me, and my Re-deem - er you shall be.

From Psalm 19:7–14
The Psalter, 1912; alt. 1990, mod.
Tune © 1990, RAM Music Publications. Used by permission.

HUTCHBY 6.6.6.6.8.8.
Ronald Alan Matthews, 1985

152   The Law of the Lord Is Perfect

The law of the LORD is perfect, reviving the soul. Ps. 19:7

1. The law of the Lord is per-fect, con-vert-ing the soul. The tes-ti-mo-ny of the Lord is sure, mak-ing wise the sim-ple.
2. The stat-utes of the Lord are right, re-joic-ing the heart. The com-mand-ments of the Lord are pure, en-light-'ning the eyes.
3. The fear of the Lord is clean, en-dur-ing for-ev-er. The judg-ments of the Lord are true, and righ-teous al-to-geth-er.

REFRAIN

More to be de - sired are they than gold, yea, than much fine gold. Sweet - er al - so than hon - ey and the hon - ey - comb.

Psalm 19:7–11
Anon.

THE LAW OF THE LORD Irreg.
Anon.; alt. 1990

153 Most Perfect Is the Law of God

Oh, how I love your law! I meditate on it all day long. Ps. 119:97

1. Most per - fect is the law of God, re - stor - ing those that stray;
2. The pre - cepts of the Lord are right; with joy they fill the heart;
3. The fear of God is un - de - filed and ev - er shall en - dure;
4. They warn from ways of wick - ed - ness dis - pleas - ing to the Lord,

his tes - ti - mo - ny is most sure, pro - claim - ing wis - dom's way.
the Lord's com - mand - ments all are pure, and clear - est light im - part.
the stat - utes of the Lord are truth and righ - teous - ness most pure.
and in the keep - ing of his Word there is a great re - ward.

REFRAIN

O how love I thy law! O how love I thy law!

It is my med - i - ta - tion all the day.

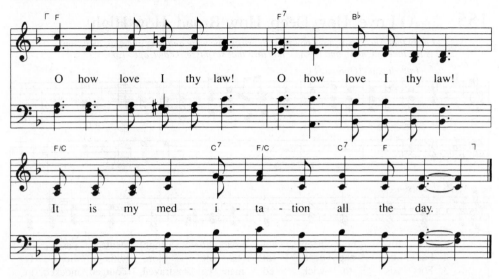

O how love I thy law! O how love I thy law!
It is my med - i - ta - tion all the day.

From Psalm 19:7–11; 119:97
The Psalter, 1912

KINSMAN C.M.ref.
James McGranahan, 1840–1907; alt. 1990

Thou Art the Way

154

I am the way and the truth and the life. No one comes to the Father except through me. John 14:6

1. Thou art the Way: to thee a - lone from sin and death we flee;
2. Thou art the Truth: thy Word a - lone true wis - dom can im - part;
3. Thou art the Life: the rend - ing tomb pro- claims thy con- quering arm,
4. Thou art the Way, the Truth, the Life: grant us that Way to know,

and he who would the Fa - ther seek must seek him, Lord, by thee.
thou on - ly canst in - form the mind, and pu - ri - fy the heart.
and those who put their trust in thee nor death nor hell shall harm.
that Truth to keep, that Life to win, whose joys e - ter - nal flow.

George W. Doane, 1824

ARLINGTON C.M.
Thomas A. Arne, 1762
Arr. by Ralph Harrison, 1784

155 O Love, How Deep, How Broad, How High!

I pray that you ... may have power ... to grasp how wide and long and high and deep
is the love of Christ, and to know this love that surpasses knowledge. Eph. 3:17–19

Introduction (Optional)

Unison

1. O love, how deep, how broad, how high! How pass-ing
2. For us bap-tized, for us he bore his ho-ly
3. For us to wick-ed men be-trayed, scourged, mocked, in
4. For us he rose from death a-gain, for us he
5. All hon-or, laud, and glo-ry be, O Je-sus,

thought and fan-ta-sy, that God, the Son of
fast, and hun-gered sore; for us temp-ta-tions
• crown of thorns ar-rayed; for us he bore the
went on high to reign; for us he sent his
vir-gin-born, to thee; whom with the Fa-ther

God, should take our mor-tal form for mor-tals' sake!
sharp he knew, for us the tempt-er o-ver-threw.
• cross-'s death, for us at length gave up his breath.
Spir-it here to guide, to strength-en, and to cheer.
we a-dore, and Ho-ly Ghost, for-ev-er-more.

Latin hymn, 15th cent.
Tr. by Benjamin Webb, 1854, 1871

DEO GRACIAS (or AGINCOURT HYMN) L.M.
Anon., 1415

O Lord, How Shall I Meet You

156

Here's the bridegroom! Come out to meet him! Matt. 25:6

1. O Lord, how shall I meet you, how wel-come you a - right?
2. Love caused your in - car - na - tion, love brought you down to me;
3. Re - joice, then, you sad - heart - ed, who sit in deep-est gloom,
4. Sin's debt, that fear - ful bur - den, let not your souls dis - tress;

Your peo - ple long to greet you, my hope, my heart's de - light!
your thirst for my sal - va - tion pro - cured my lib - er - ty.
who mourn o'er joys de - part - ed and trem - ble at your doom.
your guilt the Lord will par - don and cov - er by his grace.

O kin - dle, Lord Most Ho - ly, your lamp with - in my breast
O love be - yond all tell - ing, that led you to em - brace,
De - spair not, he is near you, yea, stand - ing at the door,
He comes, for men pro - cur - ing the peace of sin for - giv'n,

to do in spir - it low - ly all that may please you best.
in love all love ex - cel - ling, our lost and fall - en race!
who best can help and cheer you and bids you weep no more.
for all God's sons se - cur - ing their her - i - tage in heav'n.

Paul Gerhardt, 1653, cento
Trans. composite; mod.

ST. THEODULPH 7.6.7.6.D.
Melchior Teschner, ca. 1615

157 None Other Lamb, None Other Name

Whom have I in heaven but you? And earth has nothing I desire besides you.
Ps. 73:25

1. None oth - er Lamb, none oth - er name, none oth - er
hope in heav'n or earth or sea, none oth - er
hid - ing place from guilt and shame, none be - side thee!

2. My faith burns low, my hope burns low; on - ly my
heart's de - sire cries out in me by the deep
thun - der of its want and woe, cries out to thee.

3. Lord, thou art Life, though I be dead; love's fire thou
art, how - ev - er cold I be: nor heav'n have
I, nor place to lay my head, nor home, but thee.

Christina G. Rossetti, 1830–1894

ROSSETTI 8.10.10.4.
William Jeater, 1907

None Other Lamb, None Other Name 158

Whom have I in heaven but you? And earth has nothing I desire besides you.
Ps. 73:25

1. None oth - er Lamb, none oth - er name, none oth - er
2. My faith burns low, my hope burns low; on - ly my
3. Lord, thou art Life, though I be dead; love's fire thou

hope in heav'n or earth or sea, none oth - er hid - ing
heart's de - sire cries out in me by the deep thun - der
art, how - ev - er cold I be: nor heav'n have I, nor

place from guilt and shame, none be - side thee!
of its want and woe, cries out to thee.
place to lay my head, nor home, but thee.

Christina G. Rossetti, 1830–1894

ELLASGARTH 8.10.10.4.
Peggy S. Palmer, 1900–1987

Tune © 1950, The United Reformed Church. Used by permission.

159 O Savior, Precious Savior

Though you have not seen him, you love him; and even though you do not see him now,
you believe in him and are filled with an inexpressible and glorious joy. 1 Pet. 1:8

1. O Sav - ior, pre - cious Sav - ior, whom yet un - seen we love,
2. O bring - er of sal - va - tion, who won - drous - ly have wrought,
3. In you all ful - ness dwell - ing, all grace and pow'r out - pours:
4. O grant the con - sum - ma - tion of this our song a - bove

O Name of might and fa - vor, all oth - er names a - bove;
your - self the rev - e - la - tion of love be - yond our thought;
the glo - ry all - ex - cel - ling, O Son of God, is yours;
in end - less ad - o - ra - tion and ev - er - last - ing love;

we wor - ship you, we bless you, to you a - lone we sing;
we wor - ship you, we bless you, to you a - lone we sing;
we wor - ship you, we bless you, to you a - lone we sing;
then shall we praise and bless you where per - fect prais - es ring,

we praise you, and con - fess you our ho - ly Lord and King.
we praise you, and con - fess you our gra - cious Lord and King.
we praise you, and con - fess you our glo - rious Lord and King.
and ev - er - more con - fess you our Sav - ior and our King.

Frances R. Havergal, 1870
Alt. 1990, mod.

MEIRIONYDD 7.6.7.6.D.
Welsh hymn melody
William Lloyd, 1840; alt. 1990

Shepherd of Tender Youth

He tends his flock like a shepherd: He gathers the lambs in his arms and carries them
close to his heart; he gently leads those that have young. Is. 40:11

1. Shep - herd of   ten - der youth, guid - ing   in   love   and truth
2. You   are   our   ho - ly Lord, the all - sub - du - ing Word,
3. You   are   the   great High Priest, you have pre - pared the feast
4. For - ev - er   be   our Guide, our Shep - herd and   our pride,
5. So   now and   till   we die, sound we your prais - es high,

through wind - ing ways: Christ, our tri - um - phant King,   we come your
heal - er of   strife: you   did your - self a - base, that from sin's
of   heav'n - ly love: while in   our   mor - tal pain, none calls on
our   staff and   song: Je - sus, O Christ of God,   by your pe -
and   joy - ful   sing: in - fants, and the glad throng who to your

name   to sing; here we our   chil - dren bring to shout your praise.
deep   dis - grace you might now save our race, and give us   life.
you   in   vain: help you do   not   dis - dain, help from a - bove.
ren - nial Word, lead us where you have trod; make our faith strong.
church be - long, u - nite to swell the song to Christ our King.

Attr. to Clement of Alexandria, ca. 200
Tr. by Henry M. Dexter, 1846; alt. 1990, mod.

KECK 6.6.4.6.6.6.4.
Ronald Alan Matthews, 1985

161 O Christ, Our Hope, Our Heart's Desire

The rising sun will come to us from heaven. Luke 1:78

1. O Christ, our hope, our heart's de - sire, re - demp-tion's on - ly spring!
2. How vast the mer - cy and the love which laid our sins on thee,
3. But now the bands of death are burst, the ran - som has been paid;
4. O Christ, be thou our last - ing joy, our ev - er - great re - ward!

Cre - a - tor of the world art thou, its Sav - ior and its King.
and led thee to a cru - el death, to set thy peo - ple free.
and thou art on thy Fa - ther's throne, in glo - rious robes ar - rayed.
Our on - ly glo - ry may it be to glo - ry in the Lord.

Latin hymn, 7th or 8th cent.
John Chandler, 1837

BRADFORD C.M.
George Frederick Handel, 1741; arr.

162 Of the Father's Love Begotten

In the beginning was the Word.... The Word was made flesh ... and we beheld his glory,
the glory as of the only begotten of the Father. John 1:1, 14 KJV

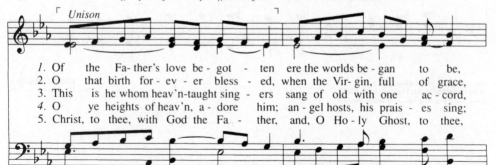

Unison

1. Of the Fa - ther's love be - got - ten ere the worlds be - gan to be,
2. O that birth for - ev - er bless - ed, when the Vir - gin, full of grace,
3. This is he whom heav'n-taught sing - ers sang of old with one ac - cord,
4. O ye heights of heav'n, a - dore him; an - gel hosts, his prais - es sing,
5. Christ, to thee, with God the Fa - ther, and, O Ho - ly Ghost, to thee,

he   is   Al - pha and O - me - ga,   he the Source, the End - ing he,
by   the Ho - ly Ghost con - ceiv - ing,   bore the Sav - ior of   our race;
• whom the Scrip-tures of the proph - ets prom - ised in their faith - ful word;
all   do - min - ions, bow be - fore   him   and ex - tol our God and King;
hymn, and chant, and high thanks- giv - ing,   and un - wea- ried prais - es be,

of   the things that are, that   have   been, and that   fu - ture
and   the babe, the world's Re - deem   -   er,   first   re - vealed his
• now   he shines, the long - ex - pect   -   ed;   let   cre - a - tion
let   no tongue on earth be si   -   lent, ev - 'ry voice in
hon - or,   glo - ry, and do - min   -   ion,   and   e - ter - nal

years   shall   see,   ev - er - more and ev - er - more!
sa - cred   face,   ev - er - more and ev - er - more!
• praise   its   Lord,   ev - er - more and ev - er - more!
con - cert   ring,   ev - er - more and ev - er - more!
vic - to - ry,   ev - er - more and ev - er - more!

Aurelius Clemens Prudentius, 348–413
Tr. by John Mason Neale, 1854;
  Henry W. Baker, 1859

DIVINUM MYSTERIUM 8.7.8.7.8.7.7.
Plainsong, 12th cent.
Arr. by Charles Winfred Douglas, 1916

163

At the Name of Jesus

That at the name of Jesus every knee should bow ... and every tongue confess
that Jesus Christ is Lord, to the glory of God the Father. Phil. 2:10, 11

1. At the name of Je - sus ev - 'ry knee shall bow,
2. At his voice cre - a - tion sprang at once to sight,
3. Hum - bled for a sea - son to re - ceive a name
4. In your hearts en - throne him; there let him sub - due
5. Broth - ers, this Lord Je - sus shall re - turn a - gain,

ev - 'ry tongue con - fess him King of glo - ry now.
all the an - gel fac - es, all the hosts of light,
from the lips of sin - ners un - to whom he came,
all that is not ho - ly, all that is not true:
with his Fa - ther's glo - ry, with his an - gel train;

'Tis the Fa - ther's plea - sure we should call him Lord,
thrones and dom - i - na - tions, stars up - on their way,
faith - ful - ly he bore it spot - less to the last,
crown him as your Cap - tain in temp - ta - tion's hour:
for all wreaths of em - pire meet up - on his brow,

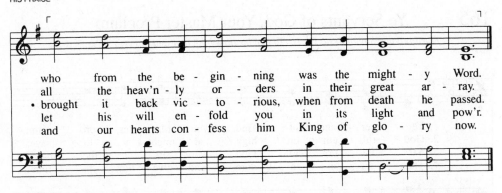

who from the be - gin - ning was the might - y Word.
all the heav'n - ly or - ders in their great ar - ray.
• brought it back vic - to - rious, when from death he passed.
let his will en - fold you in its light and pow'r.
and our hearts con - fess him King of glo - ry now.

Caroline M. Noel, 1870; alt.

KING'S WESTON 6.5.6.5.D.
Ralph Vaughan Williams, 1925

Tune from *Enlarged Songs of Praise* by permission of Oxford University Press.

O for a Thousand Tongues to Sing   164

He jumped to his feet and began to walk. Then he went with them into the temple courts, walking and jumping, and praising God. Acts 3:8

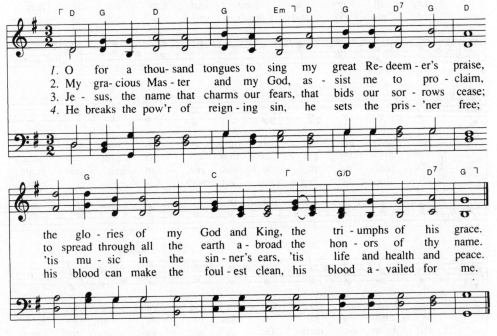

1. O for a thou- sand tongues to sing my great Re- deem - er's praise,
2. My gra- cious Mas - ter and my God, as - sist me to pro - claim,
3. Je - sus, the name that charms our fears, that bids our sor - rows cease;
4. He breaks the pow'r of reign - ing sin, he sets the pris - 'ner free;

the glo - ries of my God and King, the tri - umphs of his grace.
to spread through all the earth a - broad the hon - ors of thy name.
'tis mu - sic in the sin - ner's ears, 'tis life and health and peace.
his blood can make the foul - est clean, his blood a - vailed for me.

5. He speaks and, list'ning to his voice,
new life the dead receive;
the mournful, broken hearts rejoice;
the humble poor believe.

6. Hear him, ye deaf; his praise, ye dumb,
your loosen'd tongues employ;
ye blind, behold your Savior come;
and leap, ye lame, for joy.

Charles Wesley, 1739; alt.
Alt. 1961

AZMON C.M.
Carl G. Gläser, 1784–1829
Arr. by Lowell Mason, 1839

165   Ye Servants of God, Your Master Proclaim

Our Lord and Savior Jesus Christ. To him be glory both now and forever! 2 Pet. 3:18

1. Ye ser - vants of God, your Mas - ter pro - claim,
2. God rul - eth on high, al - might - y to save;
3. Sal - va - tion to God, who sits on the throne!
4. Then let us a - dore, and give him his right,

and pub - lish a - broad his won - der - ful name;
and still he is nigh— his pres - ence we have.
Let all cry a - loud and hon - or the Son.
all glo - ry and pow'r, and wis - dom and might,

the name, all vic - to - rious, of Je - sus ex - tol;
The great con - gre - ga - tion his tri - umph shall sing,
The prais - es of Je - sus the an - gels pro - claim,
all hon - or and bless - ing, with an - gels a - bove,

his king - dom is glo - rious and rules o - ver all.
as - crib - ing sal - va - tion to Je - sus, our King.
fall down on their fac - es and wor - ship the Lamb.
and thanks nev - er ceas - ing for in - fi - nite love.

Charles Wesley, 1744; alt.

LYONS 10.10.11.11.
Johann Michael Haydn, 1737–1806
Arr. in William Gardiner's *Sacred Melodies*, 1815

Wondrous King, All-Glorious

166

Christ, who is God over all, forever praised! Rom. 9:5

1. Won-drous King, all - glo - rious, sov-'reign Lord vic - to - rious, oh, re-ceive our praise with fa - vor! From thee welled God's kind - ness tho' we in our blind - ness strayed from thee, our bless-ed Sav - ior. Strength-en thou, help us now; let our tongues be sing - ing, thee our prais-es bring - ing.

2. Heav-ens, spread the sto - ry of our Mak-er's glo - ry, all the pomp of earth ob - scur - ing. Sun, thy rays be send - ing, thy bright beams ex - pend - ing, light to all the earth as - sur - ing. Moon and star, praise a - far him who glo - rious made you; the vast heav-ens aid you.

3. O my soul, re - joic - ing, sing, thy prais-es voic - ing, sing, with hymns of faith a - dore him! All who here have be - ing, shout, your voic - es free - ing, bow down in the dust be - fore him. He is God Sab - a - oth; praise a - lone the Sav - ior, here and there for - ev - er.

4. Hal - le - lu - jahs ren - der to the Lord most ten - der, ye who know and love the Sav - ior. Hal - le - lu - jahs sing ye, ye re-deemed, oh, bring ye hearts that yield him glad be - hav - ior. Blest are ye end - less - ly; sin - less there for - ev - er, ye shall laud him ev - er.

Joachim Neander, 1680
Tr. by William J. Schaefer, 1938
Text from *The Lutheran Hymnal* © 1941. Concordia Publishing House. Used by permission from CPH.

WUNDERBARER KÖNIG 6.6.8.6.6.8.3.3.6.6.
Joachim Neander, 1680; alt. 1990

167 When Morning Gilds the Skies

I will extol the Lord at all times; his praise will always be on my lips. Ps. 34:1

1. When morn-ing gilds the skies, my heart a-wak-ing cries:
2. When sleep her balm de - nies, my si - lent spir - it sighs:
3. Does sad-ness fill my mind? A so-lace here I find:
4. In heav'n's e - ter - nal bliss the love-liest strain is this:

May Je - sus Christ be praised. A - like at work and prayer
May Je - sus Christ be praised. When e - vil thoughts mo - lest,
May Je - sus Christ be praised. Or fades my earth - ly bliss?
May Je - sus Christ be praised. The pow'rs of dark - ness fear,

to Je - sus I re - pair: May Je - sus Christ be praised.
with this I shield my breast: May Je - sus Christ be praised.
My com - fort still is this: May Je - sus Christ be praised.
when this sweet chant they hear: May Je - sus Christ be praised.

5. Let earth's wide circle round
in joyful notes resound:
May Jesus Christ be praised.
Let air and sea and sky,
from depth to height, reply:
May Jesus Christ be praised.

6. Be this, while life is mine,
my canticle divine:
May Jesus Christ be praised.
Be this th'eternal song,
through all the ages on:
May Jesus Christ be praised.

German, ca. 1800
Tr. by Edward Caswall, 1853, 1858

LAUDES DOMINI 6.6.6.D.
Joseph Barnby, 1868

I Greet Thee, Who My Sure Redeemer Art 168

Who gave himself for our sins to rescue us from the present evil age. Gal. 1:4

1. I greet thee, who my sure Re-deem-er art, my on-ly
2. Thou art the King of mer-cy and of grace, reign-ing om-
3. Thou art the Life, by which a-lone we live, and all our
4. Thou hast the true and per-fect gen-tle-ness, no harsh-ness
5. Our hope is in no oth-er save in thee; our faith is

trust and Sav-ior of my heart, who pain didst un-der-
nip-o-tent in ev-'ry place: so come, O King, and
sub-stance and our strength re-ceive; O com-fort us in
hast thou and no bit-ter-ness: make us to taste the
built up-on thy prom-ise free; O grant to us such

go for my poor sake; I pray thee from our hearts all cares to take.
our whole be-ing sway; shine on us with the light of thy pure day.
death's ap-proach-ing hour, strong-heart-ed then to face it by thy pow'r.
sweet grace found in thee and ev-er stay in thy sweet u-ni-ty.
strong-er hope and sure that we can bold-ly con-quer and en-dure.

Strasbourg Psalter, 1545
Tr. by Elizabeth L. Smith, 1868; alt. 1961

TOULON 10.10.10.10.
Genevan Psalter, 1551

169 My Heart Does Overflow

My heart is stirred by a noble theme as I recite my verses for the king. Ps. 45:1

1. My heart does o-ver-flow, a good-ly theme is mine;
2. Now gird you with your sword, O strong and might-y One,
3. Your strength shall o-ver-come all those that hate the King,
4. Since you were sin-less found, the Lord, by you con-fessed,

my ea-ger tongue with joy-ful song does praise the King di-vine.
in splen-did maj-es-ty ar-rayed, more glo-rious than the sun.
and un-der your do-min-ion strong the na-tions you shall bring.
a-anoint-ed you with per-fect joy— you are su-preme-ly blessed.

Su-preme-ly fair you are, your lips with grace o'er-flow;
Tri-um-phant-ly ride forth for meek-ness, truth, and right;
Your roy-al throne, O God, for-ev-er-more shall stand;
Your gar-ments breathe of myrrh and spic-es sweet and rare;

his rich-est bless-ings ev-er-more does God on you be-stow.
your arm shall gain the vic-to-ry in won-drous deeds of might.
e-ter-nal truth and jus-tice wield the scep-ter in your hand.
glad strains of heav'n-ly mu-sic ring through-out your pal-ace fair.

5. Amid your glorious train kings' daughters waiting stand,
   and fairest gems bedeck your bride, the queen at your right hand.
   O royal bride, give heed, and to my words attend;
   for Christ, the King, forsake the world and ev'ry former friend.

From Psalm 45:1–10
The Psalter, 1912
Alt. 1990, mod.

LEOMINSTER S.M.D.
George William Martin, 1862
Arr. by Arthur S. Sullivan, 1874

Fairest Lord Jesus

170

*You are the most excellent of men and your lips have been anointed with grace, since
God has blessed you forever.* Ps. 45:2

1. Fair - est Lord Je - sus, Rul - er of all na - ture,
2. Fair are the mead - ows, fair are the wood - lands,
3. Fair is the sun - shine, fair is the moon - light,
4. Beau - ti - ful Sav - ior! Lord of the na - tions!

Son of God and Son of Man! Thee will I cher - ish,
robed in the bloom- ing garb of spring: Je - sus is fair - er,
and all the twink- ling, star - ry host: Je - sus shines bright- er,
Son of God and Son of Man! Glo - ry and hon - or,

thee will I hon - or, thou, my soul's glo - ry, joy, and crown.
Je - sus is pur - er, who makes the woe - ful heart to sing.
Je - sus shines pur - er than all the an - gels heav'n can boast.
praise, ad - o - ra - tion, now and for - ev - er - more be thine.

Münster Gesangbuch, 1677
Tr. 1850, 1873

CRUSADER'S HYMN 5.6.8.5.5.8.
Silesian folk song
Schlesische Volkslieder, Leipzig, 1842

171

Fairest Lord Jesus

You are the most excellent of men and your lips have been anointed with grace, since
God has blessed you forever. Ps. 45:2

1. Fair - est Lord Je - sus, Rul - er of all na - ture,
2. Fair are the mead - ows, fair are the wood - lands,
3. Fair is the sun - shine, fair is the moon - light,
4. Beau - ti - ful Sav - ior! Lord of the na - tions!

Son of God and Son of Man! Thee will I cher - ish,
robed in the bloom - ing garb of spring: Je - sus is fair - er,
and all the twink - ling, star - ry host: Je - sus shines bright- er,
Son of God and Son of Man! Glo - ry and hon - or,

thee will I hon - or, thou, my soul's glo - ry, joy, and crown.
Je - sus is pur - er, who makes the woe - ful heart to sing.
Je - sus shines pur - er than all the an - gels heav'n can boast.
praise, ad - o - ra - tion, now and for - ev - er - more be thine.

Münster Gesangbuch, 1677
Tr. 1850, 1873

SCHÖNSTER HERR JESU 5.6.8.5.5.8.
Münster Gesangbuch, 1677

Let Us Love and Sing and Wonder

To him who loves us and has freed us from our sins by his blood ... to him be glory
and power for ever and ever! Rev. 1:5, 6

1. Let us love and sing and won-der, let us praise the Sav-ior's name!
2. Let us love the Lord who bought us, pit - ied us when en - e - mies,
3. Let us sing, though fierce temp-ta - tion threat-en hard to bear us down!
4. Let us won - der; grace and jus - tice join and point to mer - cy's store;
5. Let us praise, and join the cho- rus of the saints en-throned on high;

He has hushed the law's loud thun - der, he has quenched Mount Si - nai's flame:
called us by his grace, and taught us, gave us ears and gave us eyes:
• For the Lord, our strong sal - va - tion, holds in view the con-qu'ror's crown:
when through grace in Christ our trust is, jus - tice smiles and asks no more:
here they trust - ed him be - fore us, now their prais- es fill the sky:

he has washed us with his blood, he has brought us nigh to God.
he has washed us with his blood, he pre - sents our souls to God.
• he who washed us with his blood soon will bring us home to God.
he who washed us with his blood has se - cured our way to God.
"You have washed us with your blood; you are wor - thy, Lamb of God!"

John Newton, 1774
Mod.

ALL SAINTS OLD 8.7.8.7.7.7.
Darmstadt Gesangbuch, 1698

173 Praise Him! Praise Him!

They sang a new song: "You are worthy ... because you were slain, and with your blood you purchased men for God." Rev. 5:9

1. Praise him! praise him! Je - sus, our bless - ed Re - deem - er!
2. Praise him! praise him! Je - sus, our bless - ed Re - deem - er!
3. Praise him! praise him! Je - sus, our bless - ed Re - deem - er!

Sing, O earth, his won - der - ful love pro - claim!
For our sins he suf - fered and bled and died;
Heav'n - ly por - tals loud with ho - san - nas ring!

Hail him! hail him! high - est arch - an - gels in glo - ry;
he our Rock, our hope of e - ter - nal sal - va - tion,
Je - sus, Sav - ior, reign - eth for - ev - er and ev - er;

strength and hon - or give to his ho - ly name!
hail him! hail him! Je - sus the Cru - ci - fied.
crown him! crown him! Proph - et and Priest and King!

Like a shep - herd, Je - sus will guard his chil - dren,
Sound his prais - es! Je - sus who bore our sor - rows,
Christ is com - ing! o - ver the world vic - to - rious,

in his arms he car - ries them all day long:
love un - bound - ed, won - der - ful, deep, and strong:
pow'r and glo - ry un - to the Lord be - long:

REFRAIN

Praise him! praise him! tell of his ex - cel - lent great - ness;

praise him! praise him! ev - er in joy - ful song!

Fanny J. Crosby, 1869

JOYFUL SONG Irreg.
Chester G. Allen. 1869

174   O Christ, Our King, Creator, Lord

This is what the LORD says—your Redeemer, who formed you in the womb: I am
the LORD, who has made all things. Is. 44:24

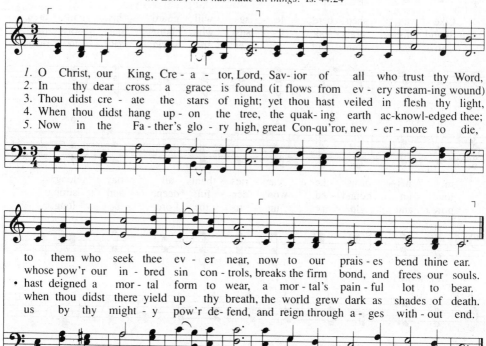

1. O Christ, our King, Cre - a - tor, Lord, Sav - ior of all who trust thy Word,
2. In thy dear cross a grace is found (it flows from ev - ery stream-ing wound)
3. Thou didst cre - ate the stars of night; yet thou hast veiled in flesh thy light,
4. When thou didst hang up - on the tree, the quak - ing earth ac-knowl-edged thee;
5. Now in the Fa - ther's glo - ry high, great Con-qu'ror, nev - er - more to die,

to them who seek thee ev - er near, now to our prais - es bend thine ear.
whose pow'r our in - bred sin con - trols, breaks the firm bond, and frees our souls.
hast deigned a mor - tal form to wear, a mor - tal's pain - ful lot to bear.
when thou didst there yield up thy breath, the world grew dark as shades of death.
us by thy might - y pow'r de - fend, and reign through a - ges with - out end.

Gregory the Great, ca. 540–604
Tr. by Ray Palmer, 1858

OMBERSLEY L.M.
William Henry Gladstone, 1840–1891

175   A Wonderful Savior Is Jesus My Lord

I have ... covered you with the shadow of my hand—I ... who say to Zion,
"You are my people." Is. 51:16

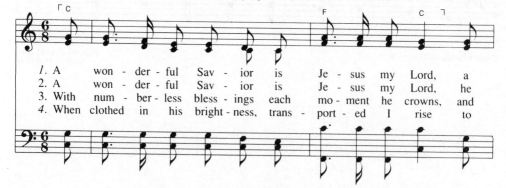

1. A won - der - ful Sav - ior is Je - sus my Lord, a
2. A won - der - ful Sav - ior is Je - sus my Lord, he
3. With num - ber - less bless - ings each mo - ment he crowns, and
4. When clothed in his bright - ness, trans - port - ed I rise to

won - der - ful Sav - ior to me; he hid - eth my soul in the
tak - eth my bur - den a - way; he hold - eth me up, and I
filled with a full - ness di - vine, I sing in my rap - ture, O
meet him in clouds of the sky, his per - fect sal - va - tion, his

cleft of the rock, where riv - ers of plea - sure I see.
shall not be moved, he giv - eth me strength as my day.
glo - ry to God for such a Re - deem - er as mine!
won - der - ful love, I'll shout with the mil - lions on high.

REFRAIN

He hid - eth my soul in the cleft of the rock that shad - ows a dry, thirst - y

land; he hid - eth my life in the depths of his love, and cov - ers me

there with his hand, and cov - ers me there with his hand.

Fanny J. Crosby, 1890

KIRKPATRICK 11.8.11.8.ref.
William J. Kirkpatrick, 1890

176 Hail, Thou Once Despised Jesus!

Worthy is the Lamb, who was slain, to receive power and wealth and wisdom and strength and honor and glory and praise! Rev. 5:12

1. Hail, thou once de - spis - ed Je - sus! Hail, thou Gal - i - le - an King!
2. Pas - chal Lamb, by God ap - point - ed, all our sins on thee were laid;
3. Je - sus, hail! en - throned in glo - ry, there for - ev - er to a - bide;
4. Wor - ship, hon - or, pow'r and bless-ing thou art wor - thy to re - ceive;

Thou didst suf - fer to re - lease us; thou didst free sal - va - tion bring.
by al - might - y love a - noint - ed, thou hast full a - tone-ment made.
all the heav'n - ly hosts a - dore thee, seat - ed at thy Fa - ther's side.
loud - est prais - es, with - out ceas - ing, meet it is for us to give.

Hail, thou ag - o - niz - ing Sav - ior, bear - er of our sin and shame!
All thy peo - ple are for - giv - en through the vir - tue of thy blood;
There for sin - ners thou art plead - ing; there thou dost our place pre - pare;
Help, ye bright an - gel - ic spir - its, bring your sweet- est, no - blest lays;

By thy mer - its we find fa - vor; life is giv - en through thy name.
o - pened is the gate of heav - en; peace is made 'twixt man and God.
ev - er for us in - ter - ced - ing; till in glo - ry we ap - pear.
help to sing our Sav - ior's mer - its, help to chant Em - man - uel's praise!

John Bakewell, 1757
Alt. by Martin Madan, 1760;
Augustus Toplady, 1776

IN BABILONE 8.7.8.7.D.
Traditional Netherlands melody, 1710
Arr. by Julius Röntgen, ca. 1906

O Could I Speak the Matchless Worth

177

I looked and heard the voice of many angels.... In a loud voice they sang,
"Worthy is the Lamb." Rev. 5:11, 12

1. O could I speak the match - less worth,
2. I'd sing the pre - cious blood he spilt,
3. I'd sing the char - ac - ters he bears,
4. Well, the de - light - ful day will come

O could I sound the glo - ries forth which in my Sav - ior shine,
my ran - som from the dread - ful guilt of sin, and wrath di - vine:
and all the forms of love he wears, ex - alt - ed on his throne:
when my dear Lord will bring me home, and I shall see his face;

I'd soar, and touch the heav'n - ly strings, and vie with Ga - briel
I'd sing his glo - rious righ - teous - ness, in which all - per - fect,
in loft - iest songs of sweet - est praise, I would to ev - er -
then with my Sav - ior, Broth - er, Friend, a blest e - ter - ni -

while he sings in notes al - most di - vine, in notes al - most di - vine.
heav'n - ly dress my soul shall ev - er shine, my soul shall ev - er shine.
last - ing days make all his glo - ries known, make all his glo - ries known.
ty I'll spend, tri - um - phant in his grace, tri - um - phant in his grace.

Samuel Medley, 1789

ARIEL 8.8.6.8.8.6.6.
Wolfgang Amadeus Mozart, 1756–1791
Arr. by Lowell Mason, 1836

178   There Is No Name So Sweet on Earth

God exalted him to the highest place and gave him the name that is above every name.
Phil. 2:9

1. There is no name so sweet on earth, no name so sweet in heav-en,
2. And when he hung up-on the tree, they wrote this name a-bove him;
3. So now, up-on his Fa-ther's throne, al-might-y to re-lease us
4. To Je-sus ev-'ry knee shall bow, and ev-'ry tongue con-fess him,
5. O Je-sus, by that match-less name, your grace shall fail us nev-er;

the name be-fore his won-drous birth to Christ the Sav-ior giv-en.
that all might see the rea-son we for-ev-er-more must love him.
from sin and pains, he glad-ly reigns, the Prince and Sav-ior Je-sus.
and we u-nite with saints in light, our on-ly Lord to bless him.
to-day as yes-ter-day the same, you are the same for-ev-er.

REFRAIN

We love to sing a-round our King, and hail him bless-ed Je-sus;

for there's no word ear ev-er heard so dear, so sweet as "Je-sus."

Anon., ca. 1858
Mod.

THE SWEETEST NAME 8.7.8.7.D.
William B. Bradbury, 1861

Hallelujah! Thine the Glory

179

Sing praises to God, sing praises. Ps. 47:6

1. We praise thee, O God! for the days of our youth,
2. We praise thee, O God! for the Son of thy love,
3. We praise thee, O God! for thy Spir - it of light,
4. All glo - ry and praise to the Lamb that was slain,

for the bright lamp that shin - eth— the Word of thy truth.
for Je - sus who died and is now gone a - bove.
who has shown us our Sav - ior and scat - tered our night.
who has borne all our sins and has cleansed ev - 'ry stain!

REFRAIN

Ha - le - lu - jah! thine the glo - ry, hal - le - lu - jah! we sing;

ha - le - lu - jah! thine the glo - ry, our praise now we bring.

William P. Mackay, 1863, 1867
St. 1 added and refrain alt.
by Henry J. Kuiper, 1929

THINE THE GLORY 5.6.7.5.ref.
John J. Husband, 1760–1825

180   I Will Sing the Wondrous Story

The song of the Lamb: "Great and marvelous are your deeds, Lord God Almighty."
Rev. 15:3

1. I will sing the won-drous sto-ry of the Christ who died for me, how he left the realms of glo-ry for the cross on Cal-va-ry.

2. I was lost: but Je-sus found me, found the sheep that went a-stray, raised me up and gent-ly led me back in-to the nar-row way.

3. Faint was I, and fears pos-sessed me, bruised was I from man-y a fall; hope was gone, and shame dis-tressed me: but his love has par-doned all.

4. Days of dark-ness still may meet me, sor-row's paths I oft may tread; but his pres-ence still is with me, by his guid-ing hand I'm led.

5. He will keep me till the riv-er rolls its wa-ters at my feet: then he'll bear me safe-ly o-ver, made by grace for glo-ry meet.

Francis H. Rowley, 1886

WONDROUS STORY 8.7.8.7.ref.
Peter P. Bilhorn, 1886

181   We Come, O Christ, to You

I am the way and the truth and the life. John 14:6

1. We come, O Christ, to you, true Son of God and man, by whom all things con-sist, in whom all life be-gan: in you a-lone we live and move, and have our be-ing in your love.

2. You are the Way to God, your blood our ran-som paid; in you we face our Judge and Mak-er un-a-fraid. Be-fore the throne ab-solved we stand, your love has met your law's de-mand.

3. You are the liv-ing Truth! All wis-dom dwells in you, the Source of ev-ery skill, the one e-ter-nal TRUE! O great I AM! In you we rest, sure an-swer to our ev-ery quest.

4. You on-ly are true Life, to know you is to live the more a-bun-dant life that earth can nev-er give: O ris-en Lord! We live in you: in us each day your life re-new!

5. We wor-ship you, Lord Christ, our Sav-ior and our King, to you our youth and strength a-dor-ing-ly we bring: so fill our hearts, that all may view your life in us, and turn to you.

E. Margaret Clarkson, 1957, 1985

DARWALL 6.6.6.6.8.8.
John Darwall, 1770

My Song Is Love Unknown

182

The Son of God, who loved me and gave himself for me. Gal. 2:20

1. My song is love un-known, my Sav-ior's love to me, love
2. He came from his blest throne, sal-va-tion to be-stow; but
3. Some-times they strew his way, and his sweet prais-es sing; re-
4. Why, what hath my Lord done? What makes this rage and spite? He
5. They rise, and needs will have my dear Lord made a-way; a

to the love-less shown, that they might love-ly be. O
men cared not, and none the longed-for Christ would know. But
sound-ing all the day ho-san-nas to their King. Then
made the lame to run, he gave the blind their sight. Sweet
mur-der-er they save, the Prince of Life they slay. Yet

who am I, that for my sake my Lord should take frail flesh and die?
oh, my Friend, my Friend in-deed, who at my need his life did spend!
"Cru-ci-fy!" is all their breath, and for his death they thirst and cry.
in-ju-ries! Yet all his deeds their ha-tred feeds; they 'gainst him rise.
will-ing he to suf-f'ring goes, that he his foes from thence might free.

6. In life, no house, no home
my Lord on earth might have;
in death, no friendly tomb
but what a stranger gave.
What may I say? Heav'n was his home,
but mine the tomb wherein he lay.

7. Here might I stay and sing,
no story so divine;
never was love, dear King,
never was grief like thine.
This is my Friend, in whose sweet praise
I all my days could gladly spend.

Samuel Crossman, ca. 1624–1683
Alt. 1990

ST. JOHN (CALKIN) 6.6.6.6.4.4.4.4.
John Baptiste Calkin, 1827–1905

183 Awake, My Soul, in Joyful Lays

How priceless is your unfailing love! Ps. 36:7

1. A - wake, my soul, in joy - ful lays, and sing your great Re -
2. He saw me ru - ined in the fall, yet loved me not - with -
3. Through might - y hosts of cru - el foes, where earth and hell my
4. So when I pass death's gloom - y vale, and life and mor - tal
5. Then shall I mount, and soar a - way to the bright world of

deem - er's praise. He just - ly claims a song from me,
stand - ing all, and saved me from my lost es - tate,
way op - pose, he safe - ly leads my soul a - long,
pow'rs shall fail, O may my last ex - pir - ing breath
end - less day; there shall I sing, with sweet sur - prise,

his lov - ing - kind - ness is so free. Lov - ing - kind - ness,
his lov - ing - kind - ness is so great. Lov - ing - kind - ness,
his lov - ing - kind - ness is so strong. Lov - ing - kind - ness,
his lov - ing - kind - ness sing in death. Lov - ing - kind - ness,
his lov - ing - kind - ness in the skies. Lov - ing - kind - ness,

lov - ing - kind - ness, his   lov - ing - kind - ness is   so   free.
lov - ing - kind - ness, his   lov - ing - kind - ness is   so   great.
• lov - ing - kind - ness, his   lov - ing - kind - ness is   so   strong.
lov - ing - kind - ness, his   lov - ing - kind - ness sing in   death.
lov - ing - kind - ness, his   lov - ing - kind - ness in   the   skies.

Samuel Medley, 1782
Mod.

LOVING-KINDNESS L.M.ref.
Joshua Leavitt's *The Christian Lyre*, 1831

The King of Love My Shepherd Is   184

The LORD is my shepherd, I shall not be in want. Ps. 23:1

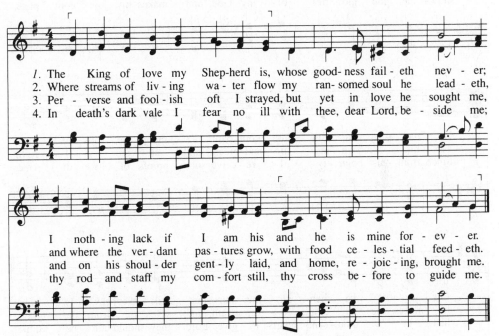

1. The   King of love my   Shep-herd is, whose good-ness fail - eth   nev - er;
2. Where streams of liv - ing   wa - ter flow my   ran- somed soul he   lead - eth,
3. Per - verse and fool - ish   oft I strayed, but   yet in love he   sought me,
4. In   death's dark vale I   fear no ill with   thee, dear Lord, be - side   me;

I   noth - ing lack if   I   am his and   he   is mine for - ev - er.
and where the ver - dant   pas - tures grow, with food   ce - les - tial   feed - eth.
and   on   his shoul - der   gent - ly laid, and home, re - joic - ing, brought me.
thy   rod   and staff my   com - fort still, thy   cross be - fore to   guide me.

5. Thou spread'st a table in my sight;
   thine unction grace bestoweth;
   and O what transport of delight
   from thy pure chalice floweth.

6. And so through all the length of days
   thy goodness faileth never:
   Good Shepherd, may I sing thy praise
   within thy house forever.

From Psalm 23
Henry W. Baker, 1868

DOMINUS REGIT ME 8.7.8.7.
John B. Dykes, 1868

185 Majestic Sweetness Sits Enthroned

We see Jesus ... now crowned with glory and honor because he suffered death.
Heb. 2:9

1. Ma - jes - tic sweet - ness sits en - throned up - on the Sav - ior's brow;
2. He saw me plunged in deep dis - tress, he flew to my re - lief;
3. To heav'n, the place of his a - bode, he brings my wea - ry feet;

his head with ra - diant glo - ries crowned, his lips with grace o'er - flow.
for me he bore the shame - ful cross, and car - ried all my grief.
shows me the glo - ries of my God, and makes my joys com - plete.

No mor - tal can with him com - pare, a - mong the sons of men;
To him I owe my life and breath, and all the joys I have;
Since from his boun - ty I re - ceive such proofs of love di - vine,

fair - er is he than all the fair that fill the heav'n - ly train.
he makes me tri - umph o - ver death, and saves me from the grave.
had I a thou - sand hearts to give, Lord, they should all be thine.

Samuel Stennett, 1787; alt.

HETHERTON C.M.D.
John K. Robb. 1949

One There Is, above All Others

186

There is a friend who sticks closer than a brother. Prov. 18:24

1. One there is, a - bove all oth - ers, well de- serves the name of Friend;
2. Which of all our friends, to save us, could or would have shed his blood?
3. When he lived on earth a - bas - ed, "Friend of sin - ners" was his name;
4. Could we bear from one an - oth - er what he dai - ly bears from us?
5. O for grace our hearts to soft - en! Teach us, Lord, at length to love;

his is love be - yond a broth - er's, cost - ly, free, and knows no end.
But our Je - sus died to have us rec - on - ciled in him to God.
Now a - bove all glo - ry rais - ed, he re - joic - es in the same;
Yet this glo - rious Friend and Broth - er loves us though we treat him thus:
we, a - las! for - get too of - ten what a Friend we have a - bove:

They who once his kind- ness prove find it ev - er - last - ing love.
This was bound- less love in - deed; Je - sus is a Friend in need.
still he calls them breth- ren, friends, and to all their wants at - tends.
though for good we ren - der ill, he ac - counts us breth- ren still.
but when home our souls are brought, we will love you as we ought.

John Newton, 1779
Mod.

GODESBERG 8.7.8.7.7.7.
Heinrich Albert, 1643

187 There Were Ninety and Nine

*There will be more rejoicing in heaven over one sinner who repents than over
ninety-nine righteous persons who do not need to repent. Luke 15:7*

1. There were nine - ty and nine that safe - ly lay in the
2. "Lord, thou hast here thy nine - ty and nine; are
3. But none of the ran - somed ev - er knew how
4. "Lord, whence are those blood - drops all the way that
5. But all thro' the moun - tains, thun - der - riv'n, and

shel - ter of the fold, but one was out on the
they not e - nough for thee?" But the Shep - herd made an - swer:
deep were the wa - ters crossed; nor how dark was the night that the
mark out the moun - tain's track? "They were shed for the one who had
up from the rock - y steep, there a - rose a glad cry to the

hills a - way, far off from the gates of gold—
"This of mine has wan - dered a - way from me,
Lord passed thro' ere he found his sheep that was lost.
gone a - stray ere the Shep - herd could bring him back."
gate of heav'n, "Re - joice! I have found my sheep!"

HIS LOVE AND GRACE

a - way on the moun - tains wild and bare,
and al - though the road be rough and steep,
Out in the des - ert he heard its cry—
"Lord, whence are thy hands so rent and torn?"
And the an - gels ech - oed a - round the throne,

a - way from the ten - der Shep - herd's care,
I go to the des - ert to find my sheep,
sick and help - less, and read - y to die;
"They're pierced to - night by man - y a thorn;
"Re - joice, for the Lord brings back his own!

a - way from the ten - der Shep - herd's care.
I go to the des - ert to find my sheep."
sick and help - less, and read - y to die.
they're pierced to - night by man - y a thorn."
Re - joice, for the Lord brings back his own!"

Elizabeth C. Clephane, 1868
Alt. 1990

THE NINETY AND NINE Irreg.
Ira D. Sankey, 1874

188 Jesus, I Am Resting, Resting

Let us fix our eyes on Jesus, the author and perfecter of our faith. Heb. 12:2

1. Je - sus, I am rest - ing, rest - ing in the joy of what thou art;
2. O how great thy lov - ing - kind - ness, vast - er, broad - er than the sea!
3. Sim - ply trust - ing thee, Lord Je - sus, I be - hold thee as thou art,
4. Ev - er lift thy face up - on me as I work and wait for thee;

I am find - ing out the great - ness of thy lov - ing heart.
O how mar - vel - ous thy good - ness lav - ished all on me!
and thy love, so pure, so change - less, sat - is - fies my heart;
rest - ing 'neath thy smile, Lord Je - sus, earth's dark shad - ows flee.

Thou hast bid me gaze up - on thee, as thy beau - ty fills my soul,
Yes, I rest in thee, Be - lov - ed, know what wealth of grace is thine,
sat - is - fies its deep - est long - ings, meets, sup - plies its ev - 'ry need,
Bright - ness of my Fa - ther's glo - ry, sun - shine of my Fa - ther's face,

for   by   thy   trans - form - ing   pow - er,   thou   hast   made   me   whole.
know   thy   cer - tain - ty   of   prom - ise   and   have   made   it   mine.
com - pass - eth   me   round   with   bless - ings: thine   is   love   in - deed.
keep   me   ev - er   trust - ing,   rest - ing,   fill   me   with   thy   grace.

REFRAIN

Je - sus,   I   am   rest - ing, rest - ing   in   the   joy   of   what   thou   art;

I   am   find - ing   out   the   great - ness   of   thy   lov - ing   heart.

Jean Sophia Pigott, 1876; alt.

TRANQUILLITY 8.7.8.5.D.ref.
James Mountain. 1876

189 Jesus Loves Me, This I Know

I live by faith in the Son of God, who loved me and gave himself for me. Gal. 2:20

1. Je - sus loves me, this I know, for the Bi - ble tells me so;
2. Je - sus loves me, he who died, heav - en's gates to o - pen wide;
3. Je - sus loves me, loves me still, though I'm ver - y weak and ill;
4. Je - sus loves me, he will stay close be - side me all the way:

lit - tle ones to him be - long, they are weak but he is strong.
he will wash a - way my sin, let his lit - tle child come in.
from his shin - ing throne on high comes to watch me where I lie.
if I love him, when I die he will take me home on high.

REFRAIN

Yes, Je - sus loves me! Yes, Je - sus loves me!

Yes, Je - sus loves me! The Bi - ble tells me so.

Anna B. Warner, 1859

JESUS LOVES ME 7.7.7.7.ref.
William B. Bradbury, 1861

I Think When I Read That Sweet Story of Old 190

*Let the little children come to me, and do not hinder them, for the kingdom of God
belongs to such as these.* Mark 10:14

1. I think when I read that sweet sto - ry of old,
   when Je - sus was here a - mong men,
   how he called lit - tle chil - dren as lambs to his fold,
   I should like to have been with them then.

2. I wish that his hands had been placed on my head,
   that his arm had been thrown a - round me,
   and that I might have seen his kind look when he said,
   "Let the lit - tle ones come un - to me."

3. Yet still to his foot - stool in prayer I may go,
   and ask for a share in his love;
   and if I now ear - nest - ly seek him be - low,
   I shall see him and hear him a - bove;

4. In that beau - ti - ful place he has gone to pre - pare
   for all who are washed and for - giv'n;
   and man - y dear chil - dren are gath - er - ing there,
   for of such is the king - dom of heav'n.

Jemima T. Luke, 1841

SWEET STORY 11.8.12.9.
Greek melody
Arr. by William B. Bradbury, 1859

191 I Am So Glad That Our Father in Heaven

I live by faith in the Son of God, who loved me and gave himself for me. Gal. 2:20

1. I am so glad that our Fa-ther in heav'n tells of his
2. Though I for-get him and wan-der a-way, still he does
3. O if there's on-ly one song I can sing, when in his

love in the book he has giv'n: won-der-ful things in the
love me wher-ev-er I stray; back to his dear lov-ing
beau-ty I see the great King, this shall my song in e-

Bi-ble I see; this is the dear-est, that Je-sus loves me.
arms do I flee, when I re-mem-ber that Je-sus loves me.
ter-ni-ty be: "O what a won-der that Je-sus loves me."

REFRAIN

I am so glad that Je-sus loves me, Je-sus loves me, Je-sus loves me;

I am so glad that Je-sus loves me, Je-sus loves e-ven me.

Philip P. Bliss, 1838–1876
Mod.

GLADNESS 10.10.10.10.ref.
Philip P. Bliss, 1838–1876

I Am Jesus' Little Lamb

192

He tends his flock like a shepherd: He gathers the lambs in his arms and carries them
close to his heart. Is. 40:11

1. I am Jesus' lit-tle lamb, ev-er glad at heart I am;
2. Day by day, at home, a-way, Je-sus is my staff and stay.
3. Who so hap-py as I am, e-ven now the Shep-herd's lamb?

for my Shep-herd gent-ly guides me, knows my need, and well pro-vides me,
When I hun-ger, Je-sus feeds me, in-to pleas-ant pas-tures leads me;
And when my short life is end-ed, by his an-gel host at-tend-ed,

loves me ev-'ry day the same, e-ven calls me by my name.
when I thirst, he bids me go where the qui-et wa-ters flow.
he shall fold me to his breast, there with-in his arms to rest.

Henrietta L. von Hayn, 1778

WEIL ICH JESU SCHÄFLEIN BIN 7.7.8.8.7.7.
Brüder Choral-Buch, 1784

193 Let All Mortal Flesh Keep Silence

The LORD is in his holy temple; let all the earth be silent before him. Hab. 2:20

1. Let all mor - tal flesh keep si - lence, and with fear and
2. King of kings, yet born of Mar - y, as of old on
3. Rank on rank the host of heav - en spreads its van - guard
4. At his feet the six - winged ser - aph; cher - u - bim, with

trem - bling stand; pon - der noth - ing earth - ly - mind - ed,
earth he stood, Lord of lords, in hu - man ves - ture,
on the way, as the Light of light de - scend - eth
sleep - less eye, veil their fac - es to the pres - ence,

for with bless - ing in his hand, Christ our God to
in the bod - y and the blood, he will give to
from the realms of end - less day, that the pow'rs of
as with cease - less voice they cry, "Al - le - lu - ia,

earth de - scend - eth, our full hom - age to de - mand.
all the faith - ful his own self for heav'n - ly food.
hell may van - ish as the dark - ness clears a - way.
al - le - lu - ia, al - le - lu - ia, Lord Most High!"

Liturgy of St. James, 5th cent.
Adapted by Gerard Moultrie, 1864

PICARDY 8.7.8.7.8.7.
French melody, 17th cent.
Arr. by Ralph Vaughan Williams, 1906

O Come, O Come, Emmanuel

"The Redeemer will come to Zion, to those in Jacob who repent of their sins,"
declares the LORD. Is. 59:20

1. O come, O come, Em - man - u - el, and ran - som cap - tive
2. O come, O come, thou Lord of might, who to thy tribes, on
3. O come, thou Rod of Jes - se, free thine own from Sa - tan's
4. O come, thou Day- spring from on high, and cheer us by thy
5. O come, thou Key of Da - vid, come and o - pen wide our

Is - ra - el, that mourns in lone - ly ex - ile here,
Si - nai's height, in an - cient times didst give the law
• tyr - an - ny; from depths of hell thy peo - ple save,
draw - ing nigh; dis - perse the gloom - y clouds of night,
heav'n - ly home; make safe the way that leads on high,

un - til the Son of God ap - pear.
in cloud and maj - es - ty and awe.
• and give them vic - t'ry o'er the grave. Re - joice! Re - joice! Em -
and death's dark shad - ows put to flight.
and close the path to mis - er - y.

man - u - el shall come to thee, O Is - ra - el.

Latin antiphons, 12th cent.
Latin hymn, 1710
Tr. by John Mason Neale, 1851; alt. 1961

VENI EMMANUEL L.M.ref.
Plainsong, 13th cent.
Arr. by Thomas Helmore, 1856

195

Joy to the World! The Lord Is Come

Shout for joy to the LORD, all the earth. Ps. 98:4

1. Joy to the world! The Lord is come: let earth re-ceive her King; let ev-ery heart pre-pare him room, and heav'n and na-ture sing, and heav'n and na-ture sing, and heav'n, and heav'n and na-ture sing.

2. Joy to the earth! The Sav-ior reigns: let men their songs em-ploy; while fields and floods, rocks, hills, and plains re-peat the sound-ing joy, re-peat the sound-ing joy, re-peat, re-peat the sound-ing joy.

3. No more let sins and sor-rows grow, nor thorns in-fest the ground; he comes to make his bless-ings flow far as the curse is found, far as the curse is found, far as, far as the curse is found.

4. He rules the world with truth and grace, and makes the na-tions prove the glo-ries of his righ-teous-ness and won-ders of his love, and heav'n and na-ture sing, and won-ders, won-ders of his love.

Based on Psalm 98
Isaac Watts, 1719

ANTIOCH C.M.rep.
George Frederick Handel, 1742
Arr. by Lowell Mason, 1836

Come, Thou Long-Expected Jesus

196

Waiting for the consolation of Israel. Luke 2:25

1. Come, thou long-ex-pect-ed Je-sus, born to set thy peo-ple free;
2. Joy to those who long to see thee, Day-spring from on high, ap-pear;
3. Come to earth to taste our sad-ness, he whose glo-ries knew no end;
4. Born thy peo-ple to de-liv-er, born a child and yet a king,

from our fears and sins re-lease us; let us find our rest in thee.
come, thou prom-ised Rod of Jes-se, of thy birth we long to hear!
by his life he brings us glad-ness, our Re-deem-er, Shep-herd, Friend.
born to reign in us for-ev-er, now thy gra-cious king-dom bring.

Is-rael's strength and con-so-la-tion, hope of all the earth thou art,
O'er the hills the an-gels sing-ing news, glad tid-ings of a birth:
Leav-ing rich-es with-out num-ber, born with-in a cat-tle stall;
By thine own e-ter-nal Spir-it rule in all our hearts a-lone;

dear De-sire of ev-'ry na-tion, joy of ev-'ry long-ing heart.
"Go to him, your prais-es bring-ing; Christ the Lord has come to earth."
this the ev-er-last-ing won-der, Christ was born the Lord of all.
by thine all-suf-fi-cient mer-it, raise us to thy glo-rious throne.

St. 1, 4, Charles Wesley, 1744
St. 2–3, Mark E. Hunt, 1978
Text of stanzas 2 & 3 © 1978, InterVarsity Christian Fellowship. Used by permission.

HYFRYDOL 8.7.8.7.D.
Rowland Hugh Pritchard, 1855

197
Comfort, Comfort Ye My People

Comfort, comfort my people, says your God. Speak tenderly to Jerusalem. Is. 40:1, 2

1. Com - fort, com - fort ye my peo - ple, speak ye peace, thus saith our God;
2. Yea, her sins our God will par - don, blot- ting out each dark mis- deed;
3. For the her - ald's voice is cry - ing in the des - ert far and near,
4. Make ye straight what long was crook- ed, make the rough- er plac - es plain;

com - fort those who sit in dark - ness, mourn-ing 'neath their sor- row's load.
all that well de - served his an - ger he no more will see or heed.
bid - ding all men to re - pen - tance, since the king - dom now is here.
let your hearts be true and hum - ble, as be - fits his ho - ly reign.

Speak ye to Je - ru - sa - lem of the peace that waits for them; tell her
She hath suf- fered man - y a day, now her griefs have passed a - way; God will
O that warn - ing cry o - bey! Now pre- pare for God a way; let the
For the glo - ry of the Lord now o'er earth is shed a - broad; and all

that her sins I cov - er, and her war - fare now is o - ver.
change her pin - ing sad - ness in - to ev - er - spring - ing glad - ness.
val - leys rise to meet him, and the hills bow down to greet him.
flesh shall see the to - ken, that his word is nev - er bro - ken.

Johannes Olearius, 1671
Tr. by Catherine Winkworth, 1863

THIRSTING 8.7.8.7.7.7.8.8.
Louis Bourgeois, 1551
Arr. by Henry A. Bruinsma; alt. 1990

Lift Up Your Heads, Ye Mighty Gates!

Lift up your heads, O you gates; be lifted up, you ancient doors, that the King of glory may come in. Ps. 24:7

1. Lift up your heads, ye might-y gates! Be-hold, the King of glo-ry waits; the King of kings is draw-ing near, the Sav-ior of the world is here.

2. A help-er just he comes to thee, his char-iot is hu-mil-i-ty, his king-ly crown is ho-li-ness, his scep-ter, pi-ty in dis-tress.

3. O blest the land, the cit-y blest, where Christ the Rul-er is con-fessed! O hap-py hearts and hap-py homes to whom this King in tri-umph comes!

4. Fling wide the por-tals of your heart; make it a tem-ple, set a-part from earth-ly use for heav'n's em-ploy, a-dorned with prayer and love and joy.

5. Redeemer, come! I open wide
my heart to thee; here, Lord, abide!
Let me thy inner presence feel;
thy grace and love in me reveal.

6. So come, my Sovereign, enter in!
Let new and nobler life begin!
Thy Holy Spirit, guide us on,
until the glorious crown be won.

Based on Psalm 24
Georg Weissel, 1642
Tr. by Catherine Winkworth, 1855; alt.

TRURO L.M.
Psalmodia Evangelica, 1789

199

See, amid the Winter's Snow

*Your attitude should be the same as that of Christ Jesus: ... being found in
appearance as a man, he humbled himself.* Phil. 2:5, 8

1. See, a - mid the win - ter's snow, born for us on earth be - low,
2. Lo, with - in a man - ger lies he who built the star - ry skies:
3. Say, ye ho - ly shep- herds, say— what's your joy - ful news to - day?
4. "As we watched at dead of night, lo, we saw a won-drous light;

see the ten - der Lamb ap - pears, prom- ised from e - ter - nal years.
he who, throned in height sub - lime, sits a - mid the cher - u - bim.
Where- fore have ye left your sheep on the lone - ly moun - tain steep?
an - gels sing - ing, 'Peace on earth,' told us of the Sav - ior's birth."

REFRAIN

Hail, thou ev - er - bless - ed morn! Hail, re - demp - tion's hap - py dawn!

Sing through all Je - ru - sa - lem, Christ is born in Beth - le - hem.

5. Sacred infant, all divine,
   what a tender love was thine,
   thus to come from highest bliss
   down to such a world as this!

6. Teach, O teach us, holy child,
   by thy face so meek and mild,
   teach us to resemble thee,
   in thy sweet humility.

Edward Caswall, 1851

SEE AMID THE WINTER'S SNOW 7.7.7.7.ref.
John Goss. 1870

It Came upon the Midnight Clear

An angel of the Lord appeared to them, and the glory of the Lord shone around them.
Luke 2:9

1. It came up-on the mid-night clear, that glo-rious song of old,
2. Still through the clo-ven skies they come, with peace-ful wings un-furled,
3. And ye, be-neath life's crush-ing load, whose forms are bend-ing low,
4. For lo, the days are has-t'ning on, by proph-et bards fore-told,

from an-gels bend-ing near the earth to touch their harps of gold:
and still their heav'n-ly mu-sic floats o'er all the wea-ry world:
who toil a-long the climb-ing way with pain-ful steps and slow,
when with the ev-er-cir-cling years comes round the age of gold;

"Peace on the earth, good will to men, from heav'n's all-gra-cious King";
a-bove its sad and low-ly plains they bend on hov-'ring wing,
look now! for glad and gold-en hours come swift-ly on the wing:
when peace shall o-ver all the earth its an-cient splen-dors fling,

the world in sol-emn still-ness lay to hear the an-gels sing.
and ev-er o'er its Ba-bel sounds the bless-ed an-gels sing.
O rest be-side the wea-ry road and hear the an-gels sing.
and the whole world give back the song which now the an-gels sing.

Edmund H. Sears, 1850

CAROL C.M.D.
Richard S. Willis. 1850

201 O Little Town of Bethlehem

Bethlehem Ephrathah, though you are small ... out of you will come for me one who will be ruler over Israel, whose origins are from of old, from ancient times. Mic. 5:2

1. O lit - tle town of Beth - le - hem, how still we see thee lie;
2. For Christ is born of Mar - y; and gath - ered all a - bove,
3. How si - lent - ly, how si - lent - ly, the won - drous gift is giv'n!
4. O ho - ly child of Beth - le - hem, de - scend to us, we pray;

a - bove thy deep and dream-less sleep the si - lent stars go by:
while mor - tals sleep, the an - gels keep their watch of won-d'ring love.
So God im - parts to hu - man hearts the bless - ings of his heav'n.
cast out our sin and en - ter in; be born in us to - day.

yet in thy dark streets shin - eth the ev - er - last - ing Light;
O morn - ing stars, to - geth - er pro - claim the ho - ly birth!
No ear may hear his com - ing, but in this world of sin,
We hear the Christ - mas an - gels the great glad tid - ings tell;

the hopes and fears of all the years are met in thee to - night.
And prais - es sing to God the King, and peace to men on earth.
where meek souls will re - ceive him still, the dear Christ en - ters in.
O come to us, a - bide with us, our Lord Em - man - u - el.

Phillips Brooks, 1868

ST. LOUIS C.M.D.irreg.
Lewis H. Redner. 1868

O Little Town of Bethlehem

Bethlehem Ephrathah, though you are small ... out of you will come for me one who will be ruler over Israel, whose origins are from of old, from ancient times. Mic. 5:2

1. O lit - tle town of Beth - le - hem, how still we see thee lie;
2. For Christ is born of Mar - y; and gath - ered all a - bove,
3. How si - lent - ly, how si - lent - ly, the won - drous gift is giv'n!
4. O ho - ly child of Beth - le - hem, de - scend to us, we pray;

a - bove thy deep and dream - less sleep the si - lent stars go by:
while mor - tals sleep, the an - gels keep their watch of won - d'ring love.
So God im - parts to hu - man hearts the bless - ings of his heav'n.
cast out our sin and en - ter in; be born in us to - day.

yet in thy dark streets shin - eth the ev - er - last - ing Light;
O morn - ing stars, to - geth - er pro - claim the ho - ly birth!
No ear may hear his com - ing, but in this world of sin,
We hear the Christ - mas an - gels the great glad tid - ings tell;

the hopes and fears of all the years are met in thee to - night.
And prais - es sing to God the King, and peace to men on earth.
where meek souls will re - ceive him still, the dear Christ en - ters in.
O come to us, a - bide with us, our Lord Em - man - u - el.

Phillips Brooks, 1868

CHRISTMAS CAROL C.M.D.irreg.
Walford Davies, 1869–1941

203 Hark! the Herald Angels Sing

A great company of the heavenly host [was] praising God and saying, "Glory to God in the highest, and on earth peace to men on whom his favor rests." Luke 2:13, 14

1. Hark! the her - ald an - gels sing, "Glo - ry to the new - born King;
2. Christ, by high - est heav'n a - dored, Christ, the ev - er - last - ing Lord!
3. Hail the heav'n - born Prince of Peace! Hail the Sun of Righ - teous - ness!

peace on earth, and mer - cy mild, God and sin - ners rec - on - ciled!"
Late in time be - hold him come, off - spring of the Vir - gin's womb.
Light and life to all he brings, ris'n with heal - ing in his wings.

Joy - ful, all ye na - tions, rise, join the tri - umph of the skies;
Veiled in flesh the God - head see; hail th'in - car - nate De - i - ty,
Mild he lays his glo - ry by, born that man no more may die,

with th'an - gel - ic host pro - claim, "Christ is born in Beth - le - hem!"
pleased as man with men to dwell, Je - sus, our Em - man - u - el.
born to raise the sons of earth, born to give them sec - ond birth.

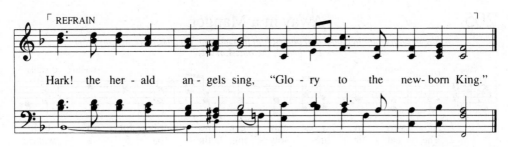

┌ REFRAIN ┐

Hark! the her - ald an - gels sing, "Glo - ry to the new- born King."

Charles Wesley, 1739, 1753; alt.

MENDELSSOHN 7.7.7.7.D.ref.
Felix Mendelssohn-Bartholdy, 1840
Arr. by William H. Cummings, 1856

Away in a Manger

204

*She wrapped him in cloths and placed him in a manger, because there was no room
for them in the inn.* Luke 2:7

1. A - way in a man - ger, no crib for a bed, the lit - tle Lord
2. The cat - tle are low - ing, the ba - by a - wakes, but lit - tle Lord
3. Be near me, Lord Je - sus, I ask thee to stay close by me for -

Je - sus laid down his sweet head; the stars in the bright sky looked
Je - sus no cry - ing he makes; I love thee, Lord Je - sus! Look
ev - er, and love me, I pray; bless all the dear chil - dren in

down where he lay, the lit - tle Lord Je - sus, a - sleep on the hay.
down from the sky, and stay by my cra - dle till morn - ing is nigh.
thy ten - der care, and fit us for heav - en, to live with thee there.

Anon., Philadelphia, 1885, 1892

MUELLER 11.11.11.11.
James R. Murray, 1887

205 Away in a Manger

She wrapped him in cloths and placed him in a manger, because there was no room for them in the inn. Luke 2:7

1. A - way in a man - ger, no crib for a bed,
2. The cat - tle are low - ing, the ba - by a - wakes,
3. Be near me, Lord Je - sus, I ask thee to stay

the lit - tle Lord Je - sus laid down his sweet head;
but lit - tle Lord Je - sus no cry - ing he makes;
close by me for - ev - er, and love me, I pray;

the stars in the bright sky looked down where he lay,
I love thee, Lord Je - sus! Look down from the sky,
bless all the dear chil - dren in thy ten - der care.

the lit - tle Lord Je - sus, a - sleep on the hay.
and stay by my cra - dle till morn - ing is nigh.
and fit us for heav - en, to live with thee there.

Anon., Philadelphia, 1885, 1892

CRADLE SONG 11.11.11.11.
William J. Kirkpatrick, 1895

Brightest and Best of the Sons of the Morning 206

We saw his star in the east and have come to worship him. Matt. 2:2

1. Bright - est and best of the sons of the morn-ing, dawn on our
2. Cold on his cra - dle the dew - drops are shin - ing; low lies his
3. Say, shall we yield him, in cost - ly de - vo - tion, o - dors of
4. Vain - ly we of - fer each am - ple ob - la - tion, vain - ly with
5. Bright - est and best of the sons of the morn-ing, dawn on our

dark - ness and lend us your aid; Star of the East, the ho - ri -
head with the beasts of the stall; an - gels a - dore him in slum -
E - dom and of - f'rings di - vine, gems of the moun - tain and pearls
gifts would his fa - vor se - cure; rich - er by far is the heart's
dark - ness and lend us your aid; Star of the East, the ho - ri -

zon a - dorn - ing, guide where our in - fant Re - deem - er is laid.
ber re - clin - ing, Mak - er and Mon - arch and Lord o - ver all.
of the o - cean, myrrh from the for - est or gold from the mine?
ad - o - ra - tion; dear - er to God are the prayers of the poor.
zon a - dorn - ing, guide where our in - fant Re - deem - er is laid.

Reginald Heber, 1811
Alt. 1961, mod.

MORNING STAR 11.10.11.10.
James P. Harding, 1892

207   Good Christian Men, Rejoice

Today in the town of David a Savior has been born to you; he is Christ the Lord.
Luke 2:11

1. Good Chris - tian men, re - joice, with heart and soul and voice;
2. Good Chris - tian men, re - joice, with heart and soul and voice;
3. Good Chris - tian men, re - joice, with heart and soul and voice;

give ye heed to what we say: Je - sus Christ is born to - day;
now ye hear of end- less bliss: Je - sus Christ was born for this!
now ye need not fear the grave: Je - sus Christ was born to save!

earth and heav'n be - fore him bow, and he is in the man- ger now.
He hath o - pened heav - en's door, and man is bless - ed ev - er- more.
Calls you one and calls you all to gain his ev - er - last - ing hall.

Christ is born to - day! Christ is born to - day!
Christ was born for this! Christ was born for this!
Christ was born to save! Christ was born to save!

Medieval Latin carol
Tr. by John Mason Neale, 1853; alt.
Alt. 1961

IN DULCI JUBILO 6.6.7.7.7.8.5.5.
German melody,14th cent.
Arr. by W. D., 1918

O Come, All Ye Faithful

208

Let's go to Bethlehem and see this thing that has happened, which the Lord has told us about. Luke 2:15

1. O come, all ye faith - ful, joy - ful and tri - um - phant,
2. God of God, Light of Light;
3. Sing, choirs of an - gels, sing in ex - ul - ta - tion,
4. Yea, Lord, we greet thee, born this hap - py morn - ing:

O come ye, O come ye to Beth - le - hem; come and be - hold him
lo, he ab - hors not the Vir - gin's womb: ver - y God, be -
sing, all ye cit - i - zens of heav'n a - bove; glo - ry to God
Je - sus, to thee be all glo - ry giv'n; Word of the Fa - ther,

REFRAIN

born the King of an - gels;
got - ten, not cre - a - ted;   O come, let us a - dore him, O come, let
in the high - est;
late in flesh ap - pear - ing;

us a - dore him, O come, let us a - dore him, Christ the Lord.

Latin hymn
Attr. to John Francis Wade, 1751
Tr. by Frederick Oakeley, 1841; alt.

ADESTE FIDELES 6.6.10.5.6.ref.
John Francis Wade's *Cantus Diversi*, 1751

209   Christians, Awake, Salute the Happy Morn

An angel of the Lord appeared to them, and the glory of the Lord shone around them.
Luke 2:9

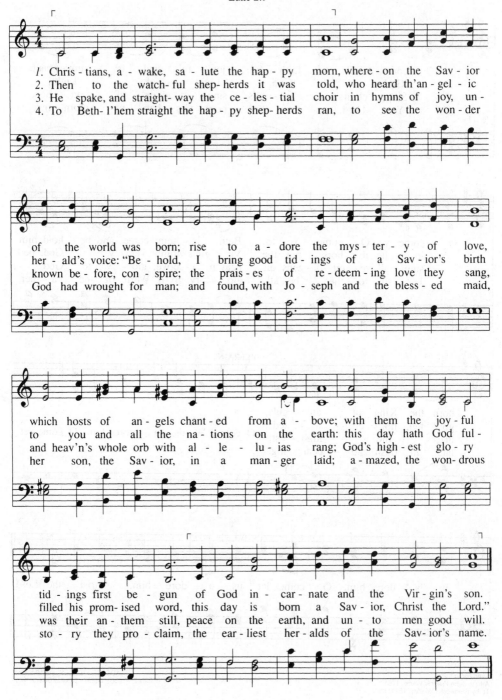

1. Chris - tians, a - wake, sa - lute the hap - py morn, where - on the Sav - ior
2. Then to the watch- ful shep- herds it was told, who heard th'an - gel - ic
3. He spake, and straight- way the ce - les - tial choir in hymns of joy, un -
4. To Beth- l'hem straight the hap - py shep- herds ran, to see the won - der

of the world was born; rise to a - dore the mys - ter - y of love,
her - ald's voice: "Be - hold, I bring good tid - ings of a Sav - ior's birth
known be - fore, con - spire; the prais - es of re - deem - ing love they sang,
God had wrought for man; and found, with Jo - seph and the bless - ed maid,

which hosts of an - gels chant - ed from a - bove; with them the joy - ful
to you and all the na - tions on the earth: this day hath God ful -
and heav'n's whole orb with al - le - lu - ias rang; God's high - est glo - ry
her son, the Sav - ior, in a man - ger laid; a - mazed, the won - drous

tid - ings first be - gun of God in - car - nate and the Vir - gin's son.
filled his prom - ised word, this day is born a Sav - ior, Christ the Lord."
was their an - them still, peace on the earth, and un - to men good will.
sto - ry they pro - claim, the ear - liest her - alds of the Sav - ior's name.

5. Let us, like these good shepherds, then employ
   our grateful voices to proclaim the joy;
   trace we the babe, who hath retrieved our loss,
   from his poor manger to his bitter cross;
   treading his steps, assisted by his grace,
   till man's first heav'nly state again takes place.

6. Then may we hope, th'angelic throngs among.
   to sing, redeemed, a glad triumphal song;
   he that was born upon this joyful day
   around us all his glory shall display;
   saved by his love, incessant we shall sing
   eternal praise to heav'n's almighty King.

John Byrom, 1749; alt.

YORKSHIRE 10.10.10.10.10.10.
John Wainwright, 1750

Silent Night! Holy Night!

210

*They hurried off and found Mary and Joseph, and the baby, who was lying
in the manger. Luke 2:16*

1. Si - lent night! Ho - ly night! All is calm, all is bright round yon
2. Si - lent night! Ho - ly night! Shep- herds quake at the sight! Glo - ries
3. Si - lent night! Ho - ly night! Son of God, love's pure light ra - diant
4. Si - lent night! Ho - ly night! Won - drous star, lend thy light; with the

vir - gin moth - er and child. Ho - ly in - fant, so ten - der and mild,
stream from heav- en a - far, heav'n - ly hosts sing al - le - lu - ia;
beams from thy ho - ly face, with the dawn of re - deem - ing grace,
an - gels let us sing al - le - lu - ia to our King;

sleep in heav - en - ly peace, sleep in heav - en - ly peace.
Christ, the Sav - ior, is born! Christ, the Sav - ior, is born!
Je - sus, Lord, at thy birth, Je - sus, Lord, at thy birth.
Christ, the Sav - ior, is born! Christ, the Sav - ior, is born!

Joseph Mohr, 1818
Tr. ca. 1850

STILLE NACHT Irreg.
Franz Gruber. 1818

211 God Rest You Merry, Gentlemen

Do not be afraid. I bring you good news of great joy that will be for all the people.
Luke 2:10

1. God rest you mer - ry, gen - tle - men, let noth - ing you dis - may,
2. From God our heav'n - ly Fa - ther, a bless - ed an - gel came;
3. "Fear not, then," said the an - gel, "let noth - ing you af - fright;
4. The shep- herds at those tid - ings re - joic - ed much in mind,

re - mem - ber Christ our Sav - ior was born on Christ - mas day,
and un - to cer - tain shep - herds brought tid - ings of the same:
this day is born a Sav - ior of a pure vir - gin bright,
and left their flocks a - feed - ing, in tem - pest, storm, and wind:

to save us all from Sa - tan's pow'r when we were gone a - stray;
how that in Beth - le - hem was born the Son of God by name.
to free all those who trust in him from Sa- tan's pow'r and might."
and went to Beth - le - hem straight- way, the Son of God to find.

REFRAIN

O tid - ings of com - fort and joy, com - fort and joy,

O tid - ings of com - fort and joy.

English carol, 18th cent.

GOD REST YOU MERRY 8.6.8.6.8.6.ref.
English melody, 18th cent.

Within a Crib My Savior Lay

212

This is love: not that we loved God, but that he loved us and sent his Son as
an atoning sacrifice for our sins. 1 John 4:10

1. With - in a crib my Sav - ior lay, a wood - en man - ger filled with hay, come down for love on Christ - mas Day: all glo - ry be to Je - sus!
2. Up - on a cross my Sav - ior died, to ran - som sin - ners, cru - ci - fied, his lov - ing arms still o - pen wide: all glo - ry be to Je - sus!
3. A vic - tor's crown my Sav - ior won, his work of love and mer - cy done, the Fa - ther's high - as - cend - ed Son: all glo - ry be to Je - sus!

Timothy Dudley-Smith, 1968

LORD OF LOVE 8.8.8.7.
Norman L. Warren, b. 1934

213

What Child Is This

Where is the one who has been born king of the Jews? Matt. 2:2

1. What child is this, who, laid to rest, on Mar - y's lap is sleep - ing?
2. Why lies he in such mean es - tate, where ox and ass are feed - ing?
3. So bring him in - cense, gold, and myrrh; come, peas - ant, king, to own him;

Whom an - gels greet with an - thems sweet, while shep-herds watch are keep - ing?
Good Chris - tian, fear; for sin - ners here the si - lent Word is plead - ing.
the King of kings sal - va - tion brings, let lov - ing hearts en-throne him.

This, this is Christ the King, whom shep - herds guard and an - gels sing:
Nails, spear, shall pierce him through; the cross be borne for me, for you:
Raise, raise the song on high, the vir - gin sings her lul - la - by:

haste, haste to bring him laud, the babe, the son of Mar - y.
hail, hail the Word made flesh, the babe, the son of Mar - y.
joy, joy for Christ is born, the babe, the son of Mar - y.

Traditional English carol
Adapted by William C. Dix, ca. 1865

GREENSLEEVES 8.7.8.7.ref.
English melody, 16th cent.

Angels We Have Heard on High

Glory to God in the highest, and on earth peace to men on whom his favor rests.
Luke 2:14

1. An-gels we have heard on high, sweet-ly sing-ing o'er the plains,
2. Shep-herds, why this ju-bi-lee? Why your joy-ous strains pro-long?
3. Come to Beth-le-hem and see him whose birth the an-gels sing;

and the moun-tains in re-ply ech-o back their joy-ous strains.
Say what may the tid-ings be, which in-spire your heav'n-ly song?
come, a-dore on bend-ed knee Christ the Lord, the new-born King.

REFRAIN

Glo - - - - - ri-a in ex-cel-sis De-o,

glo - - - - - ri-a in ex-cel-sis De-o.

Traditional French carol

GLORIA 7.7.7.7.ref.
Traditional French melody
Arr. by Edward S. Barnes, 1937

215 While by the Sheep We Watched at Night

With joy you will draw water from the wells of salvation. Is. 12:3

1. While by the sheep we watched at night, glad tid-ings brought an
2. There shall be born, so he did say, in Beth - le - hem a
3. There shall the child lie in a stall, this child who shall re -
4. This gift of God we'll cher - ish well, that ev - er joy our

REFRAIN — *f* / *p* echo

an - gel bright.
child to - day.
deem us all. How great our joy! Great our joy!
hearts shall fill.

f / *p* echo / *f*

Joy, joy, joy! Joy, joy, joy! Praise we the Lord in

echo — *p*

heav'n on high! Praise we the Lord in heav'n on high!

German carol
Trans. anon.

JUNGST Irreg.
Traditional German melody
Arr. by Hugo Jungst, ca. 1890

Infant Holy, Infant Lowly

He is Lord of lords and King of kings—and with him will be his called, chosen and faithful followers. Rev. 17:14

1. In - fant ho - ly, in - fant low - ly, for his bed a cat - tle stall;
2. Flocks were sleep-ing: shep-herds keep- ing vig - il till the morn- ing new

ox - en low - ing, lit - tle know- ing Christ, the babe, is Lord of all.
saw the glo - ry, heard the sto - ry, tid- ings of a gos- pel true.

Swift are wing - ing an - gels sing - ing, no- els ring- ing, tid- ings bring- ing:
Thus re - joic - ing, free from sor - row, prais- es voic- ing, greet the mor- row:

Christ the babe is Lord of all. Christ the babe is Lord of all.
Christ the babe was born for you. Christ the babe was born for you.

Polish carol
Paraphrased by Edith M. G. Reed, ca. 1925

W ZLOBIE LEZY 8.7.8.7.8.8.7.
Traditional Polish melody
Arr. in *The Kingsway Carol Book*

217 All My Heart This Night Rejoices

The Word became flesh and made his dwelling among us. We have seen his glory.
John 1:14

1. All my heart this night re-joic - es as I hear far and near
2. Forth to - day the Con-qu'ror go - eth, who the foe, sin and woe,
3. Shall we still dread God's dis-plea - sure, who, to save, free - ly gave
4. He be - comes the Lamb that tak - eth sin a - way and for aye
5. Hark! a voice from yon-der man - ger, soft and sweet, doth en-treat:

sweet - est an - gel voic - es. "Christ is born," their choirs are sing - ing
death and hell, o'er - throw-eth. God is man, man to de - liv - er;
• his most cher-ished Trea-sure? To re - deem us, he hath giv - en
full a - tone-ment mak - eth. For our life his own he ten - ders;
"Flee from woe and dan - ger. Breth-ren, from all ills that grieve you,

till the air ev - 'ry - where now with joy is ring - ing.
his dear Son now is one with our blood for - ev - er.
• his own Son from the throne of his might in heav - en.
and our race, by his grace, meet for glo - ry ren - ders.
you are freed; all you need I will sure - ly give you."

6. Come, then, banish all your sadness,
one and all, great and small;
come with songs of gladness.
Love him who with love is glowing;
hail the star, near and far
light and joy bestowing.

7. Dearest Lord, thee will I cherish.
Though my breath fail in death,
yet I shall not perish,
but with thee abide forever
there on high, in that joy
which can vanish never.

Paul Gerhardt, 1653
Tr. by Catherine Winkworth, 1858; alt.

WARUM SOLLT' ICH MICH DENN GRAMEN 8.3.3.6.8.3.3.6.
Johann G. Ebeling, 1666

Angels, from the Realms of Glory

They saw the child with his mother Mary, and they bowed down and worshiped him.
Matt. 2:11

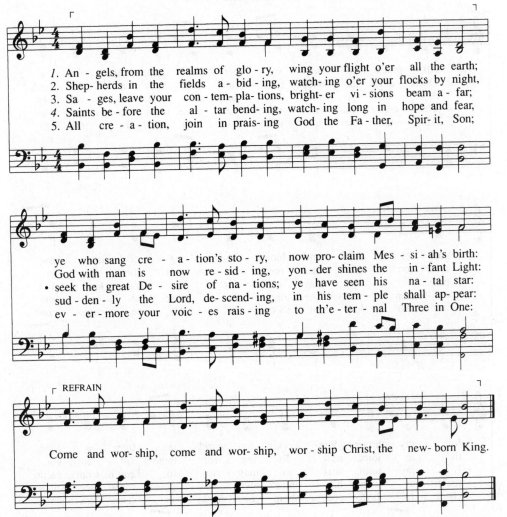

1. An - gels, from the realms of glo - ry, wing your flight o'er all the earth;
2. Shep- herds in the fields a - bid - ing, watch- ing o'er your flocks by night,
3. Sa - ges, leave your con - tem- pla - tions, bright- er vi - sions beam a - far;
4. Saints be - fore the al - tar bend- ing, watch- ing long in hope and fear,
5. All cre - a - tion, join in prais- ing God the Fa - ther, Spir- it, Son;

ye who sang cre - a - tion's sto - ry, now pro- claim Mes - si - ah's birth:
God with man is now re - sid - ing, yon- der shines the in - fant Light:
seek the great De - sire of na - tions; ye have seen his na - tal star:
sud - den - ly the Lord, de- scend- ing, in his tem - ple shall ap- pear:
ev - er- more your voic - es rais- ing to th'e - ter - nal Three in One:

REFRAIN

Come and wor- ship, come and wor- ship, wor - ship Christ, the new- born King.

James Montgomery, 1816, 1825

REGENT SQUARE 8.7.8.7.8.7.
Henry Smart, 1867

219

All Praise to Thee, Eternal Lord

You know the grace of our Lord Jesus Christ, that though he was rich, yet for your sakes he became poor. 2 Cor. 8:9

1. All praise to thee, e - ter - nal Lord, clothed in a garb of flesh and blood; choos - ing a man - ger for thy throne, while worlds on worlds are thine a - lone.
2. Once did the skies be - fore thee bow; a vir - gin's arms con - tain thee now: an - gels who did thee re - joice now lis - ten for thine in - fant voice.
3. A lit - tle child, thou art our guest, that wea - ry ones in thee may rest; for - lorn and low - ly is thy birth, that we may rise to heav'n from earth.
4. Thou com - est in the dark - some night to make us chil - dren of the light, to make us, in the realms di - vine, like thine own an - gels round thee shine.
5. All this for us thy love hath done; by this to thee our love is won: for this we tune our cheer - ful lays, and shout our thanks in cease - less praise.

Martin Luther, 1524
Tr. in *Sabbath Hymn Book*, 1858

CANONBURY L.M.
Robert Schumann, 1839; arr.

From Heaven High I Come to You

The angel said to them, "Do not be afraid. I bring you good news of great joy that will be for all the people." Luke 2:10

1. "From heav - en high I come to you, I bring you
2. "To you this night is born a child of Mar - y,
3. "This is the Christ, our God and Lord, who in all
4. "These are the to - kens ye shall mark: the swad - dling

tid - ings good and new; glad tid - ings of great
chos - en vir - gin mild; this lit - tle child, of
need shall aid af - ford; he will him - self your
clothes and man - ger dark; there ye shall find the

joy I bring, where - of I now will say and sing.
low - ly birth, shall be the joy of all the earth.
Sav - ior be from all your sins to set you free.
in - fant laid by whom the heav'ns and earth were made."

5. Now let us all with gladsome cheer
   go with the shepherds and draw near
   to see the precious Gift of God,
   who hath his own dear Son bestowed.

6. Welcome to earth, thou noble guest,
   through whom the sinful world is blest!
   In my distress thou com'st to me;
   what thanks shall I return to thee?

Martin Luther, 1535
Tr. by Catherine Winkworth, 1855, alt.
Alt. 1961

VOM HIMMEL HOCH L.M.
Attr. to Martin Luther
V. Schumann's *Geistliche Lieder*, 1539

221 Lo, How a Rose E'er Blooming

A shoot will come up from the stump of Jesse; from his roots a Branch will bear fruit.
Is. 11:1

1. Lo, how a rose e'er bloom - ing from ten - der
2. I - sa - iah 'twas fore - told it, the rose I
3. The shep - herds heard the sto - ry, pro - claimed by
4. This flow'r, whose fra - grance ten - der with sweet - ness
5. O Sav - ior, child of Mar - y, who felt our

stem hath sprung, of Jes - se's lin - eage com - ing,
have in mind; with Mar - y we be - hold it,
an - gels bright, how Christ, the Lord of glo - ry,
fills the air, dis - pels with glo - rious splen - dor
hu - man woe; O Sav - ior, King of glo - ry,

as men of old have sung. It came, a flow'r - et bright,
the vir - gin moth - er kind. To show God's love a - right
was born on earth this night. To Beth - le - hem they sped
the dark - ness ev - 'ry - where. True man, yet ver - y God;
who dost our weak - ness know, bring us at length, we pray,

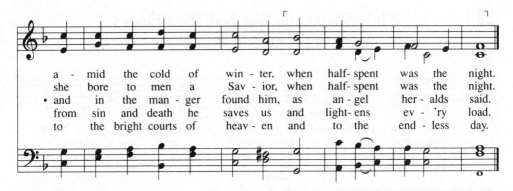

a - mid the cold of win - ter, when half-spent was the night.
she bore to men a Sav - ior, when half-spent was the night.
• and in the man - ger found him, as an - gel her - alds said.
from sin and death he saves us and light- ens ev - 'ry load.
to the bright courts of heav - en and to the end - less day.

German hymn, ca. 1500
St. 1–2 tr. by Theodore Baker, 1894
St. 3–4 tr. by Harriett R. Spaeth, 1875
St. 5 tr. by John C. Mattes, 1914

ES IST EIN' ROS' ENTSPRUNGEN 7.6.7.6.6.7.6.
German melody, 15th cent.
Arr. by Michael Praetorius, 1609; alt.

While Shepherds Watched Their Flocks 222

There were shepherds living out in the fields nearby, keeping watch over their flocks at night. Luke 2:8

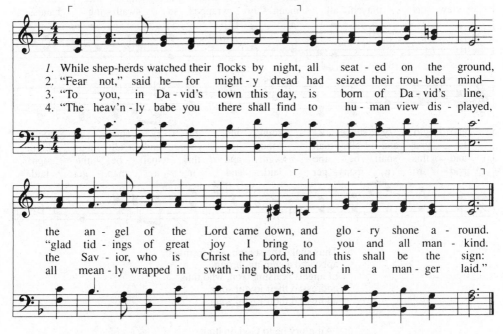

1. While shep-herds watched their flocks by night, all seat - ed on the ground,
2. "Fear not," said he— for might - y dread had seized their trou- bled mind—
3. "To you, in Da - vid's town this day, is born of Da - vid's line,
4. "The heav'n - ly babe you there shall find to hu - man view dis - played,

the an - gel of the Lord came down, and glo - ry shone a - round.
"glad tid - ings of great joy I bring to you and all man - kind.
the Sav - ior, who is Christ the Lord, and this shall be the sign:
all mean - ly wrapped in swath - ing bands, and in a man - ger laid."

5. Thus spake the seraph, and forthwith
   appeared a shining throng
   of angels praising God, who thus
   addressed their joyful song:

6. "All glory be to God on high,
   and to the earth be peace;
   good will henceforth, from heav'n to men,
   begin and never cease!"

Nahum Tate, 1700

WINCHESTER OLD C.M.
T. Este's *The Whole Booke of Psalmes*, 1592; alt. 1990

223 While Shepherds Watched Their Flocks

There were shepherds living out in the fields nearby, keeping watch over their flocks at night. Luke 2:8

1. While shep-herds watched their flocks by night, all seat-ed on the ground, the an-gel of the Lord came down, and glo-ry shone a-round, and glo-ry shone a-round.

2. "Fear not," said he— for might-y dread had seized their trou-bled mind— "glad tid-ings of great joy I bring to you and all man-kind, to you and all man-kind.

3. "To you, in Da-vid's town this day, is born of Da-vid's line, the Sav-ior, who is Christ the Lord, and this shall be the sign, and this shall be the sign:

4. "The heav'n-ly babe you there shall find to hu-man view dis-played, all mean-ly wrapped in swath-ing bands, and in a man-ger laid, and in a man-ger laid."

5. Thus spake the seraph, and forthwith
appeared a shining throng
of angels praising God, who thus
addressed their joyful song,
addressed their joyful song:

6. "All glory be to God on high,
and to the earth be peace;
good will henceforth, from heav'n to men,
begin and never cease,
begin and never cease!"

Nahum Tate, 1700

CHRISTMAS C.M.rep.
From George Frederick Handel, *Siroe*, 1728
Arr. by Lowell Mason, 1821

Go, Tell It on the Mountain

224

*When they had seen him, they spread the word concerning what had been told them
about this child.* Luke 2:17

(Ref.) Go, tell it on the moun-tain, o-ver the hills and ev-ery-where;
go, tell it on the moun-tain that Je-sus Christ is born.

1. While shep-herds kept their watch-ing o'er si-lent flocks by night, be-
2. The shep-herds feared and trem-bled when, lo! a-bove the earth rang
3. Down in a low-ly man-ger our hum-ble Christ was born, and

hold, through-out the heav-ens there shone a ho-ly light.
out the an-gel cho-rus that hailed our Sav-ior's birth.
God sent us sal-va-tion that bless-ed Christ-mas morn.

Spiritual

GO TELL IT Irreg.
Spiritual

225   Once in Royal David's City

You will find a baby wrapped in cloths and lying in a manger. Luke 2:12

1. Once in roy - al Da - vid's cit - y stood a low - ly cat - tle shed,
2. He came down to earth from heav - en who is God and Lord of all,
3. And through all his won - drous child - hood he would hon - or and o - bey,
4. And our eyes at last shall see him, through his own re - deem - ing love;
5. Not in that poor low - ly sta - ble, with the ox - en stand - ing by,

where a moth - er laid her ba - by in a man - ger for his bed:
and his shel - ter was a sta - ble, and his cra - dle was a stall:
• love and watch the low - ly maid - en in whose gen - tle arms he lay:
for that child so dear and gen - tle is our Lord in heav'n a - bove,
we shall see him, but in heav - en, set at God's right hand on high;

Mar - y was that moth - er mild, Je - sus Christ her lit - tle child.
with the poor, and mean, and low - ly, lived on earth our Sav - ior ho - ly.
• Chris- tian chil - dren all must be mild, o - be - dient, good as he.
and he leads his chil- dren on to the place where he is gone.
when like stars his chil- dren crowned all in white shall wait a - round.

Cecil Frances Alexander, 1848

IRBY 8.7.8.7.7.7.
Henry J. Gauntlett, 1849

As with Gladness Men of Old

226

When they saw the star, they were overjoyed. Matt. 2:10

1. As with glad-ness men of old did the guid-ing star be-hold;
2. As with joy-ful steps they sped to that low-ly cra-dle-bed,
3. As they of-fered gifts most rare at that cra-dle rude and bare;
4. Ho-ly Je-sus, ev-'ry day keep us in the nar-row way;
5. In the heav'n-ly coun-try bright need they no cre-at-ed light;

as with joy they hailed its light, lead-ing on-ward, beam-ing bright;
there to bend the knee be-fore him whom heav'n and earth a-dore;
so may we with ho-ly joy, pure, and free from sin's al-loy,
and when earth-ly things are past, bring our ran-somed souls at last
thou its light, its joy, its crown, thou its sun which goes not down;

so, most gra-cious God, may we ev-er-more be led to thee.
so may we with will-ing feet ev-er seek thy mer-cy seat.
all our cost-liest trea-sures bring, Christ, to thee, our heav'n-ly King.
where they need no star to guide, where no clouds thy glo-ry hide.
there for-ev-er may we sing al-le-lu-ias to our King.

William Chatterton Dix, 1860
Alt. 1961

DIX 7.7.7.7.7.7.
Conrad Kocher, 1838
Arr. by William H. Monk, 1861

227 On Christmas Night All Christians Sing

The angel said to them, "Do not be afraid. I bring you good news of great joy that will be for all the people." Luke 2:10

1. On Christ-mas night all Chris-tians sing, to hear the news the an-gels bring; on Christ-mas night all Chris-tians sing, to hear the news the an-gels bring: news of great joy, news of great mirth, news of our mer-ci-ful King's birth.

2. Then why should men on earth be sad, since our Re-deem-er made us glad; then why should men on earth be sad, since our Re-deem-er made us glad, when from our sin he set us free, all for to gain our lib-er-ty.

3. When sin de-parts be-fore Your grace, then life and health come in its place; when sin de-parts be-fore Your grace, then life and health come in its place; an-gels and men with joy may sing, all for to see the new-born King.

4. All out of dark-ness we have light which made the an-gels sing this night; all out of dark-ness we have light, which made the an-gels sing this night: "Glo-ry to God and peace to men, now and for - ev-er-more. A - men."

Traditional English carol
Mod.

SUSSEX CAROL 8.8.8.8.8.8.
Traditional English carol
Arr. by Ralph Vaughan Williams, 1919

Saw You Never, in the Twilight

The star they had seen in the east went ahead of them until it stopped over the place
where the child was. Matt. 2:9

1. Saw you nev - er, in the twi - light, when the sun had left the skies,
2. Heard you nev - er of the sto - ry how they crossed the des - ert wild,
3. Know ye not that low - ly ba - by was the bright and morn - ing Star?

up in heav'n the clear stars shin - ing through the gloom, like sil - ver eyes?
jour - neyed on by plain and moun - tain, till they found the ho - ly child?
He who came to light the Gen - tiles and the dark - ened isles a - far?

So of old the wise men, watch - ing, saw a lit - tle strang - er star,
How they o - pened all their trea - sure, kneel - ing to that in - fant King;
And we, too, may seek his cra - dle; there our hearts' best trea - sures bring:

and they knew the King was giv - en, and they fol - lowed it from far.
gave the gold and fra - grant in - cense, gave the myrrh in of - fer - ing?
love and faith and true de - vo - tion for our Sav - ior, God, and King.

Cecil Frances Alexander, 1853

CHARTRES 8.7.8.7.D.
French melody, 15th cent.
Arr. by Charles Wood; alt. 1990

229 Gentle Mary Laid Her Child

She gave birth to her firstborn, a son. She wrapped him in cloths and placed him in a manger. Luke 2:7

1. Gen - tle Mar - y laid her child low - ly in a man - ger;
2. An - gels sang a - bout his birth, wise men sought and found him;
3. Gen - tle Mar - y laid her child low - ly in a man - ger;

there he lay, the Un - de - filed, to the world a strang - er.
heav - en's star shone bright - ly forth, glo - ry all a - round him.
he is still the Un - de - filed, but no more a strang - er.

Such a babe in such a place, can he be the Sav - ior?
Shep - herds saw the won - drous sight, heard the an - gels sing - ing;
Son of God of hum - ble birth, beau - ti - ful the sto - ry;

Ask the saved of all the race who have found his fa - vor.
all the plains were lit that night, all the hills were ring - ing.
praise his name in all the earth, hail the King of glo - ry!

Joseph Simpson Cook, 1919

TEMPUS ADEST FLORIDUM 7.6.7.6.D.
Piae Cantiones, 1582
Arr. by Ernest MacMillan, 1930

Thou Who Wast Rich beyond All Splendor

Our Lord Jesus Christ ... was rich, yet for your sakes he became poor, so that you through his poverty might become rich. 2 Cor. 8:9

1. Thou who wast rich be - yond all splen - dor, all for love's sake be-
cam - est poor; thrones for a man - ger didst sur - ren - der,
sap - phire - paved courts for sta - ble floor. Thou who wast rich be-
yond all splen - dor, all for love's sake be - cam - est poor.

2. Thou who art God be - yond all prais - ing, all for love's sake be-
cam - est man; stoop - ing so low, but sin - ners rais - ing,
heav'n- ward by thine e - ter - nal plan. Thou who art God be-
yond all prais - ing, all for love's sake be - cam - est man.

3. Thou who art love be - yond all tell - ing, Sav - ior and King, we
wor - ship thee. Em - man - u - el, with - in us dwell - ing,
make us what thou wouldst have us be. Thou who art love be-
yond all tell - ing, Sav - ior and King, we wor - ship thee.

Frank Houghton, 1894–1972

QUELLE EST CETTE ODEUR AGREABLE 9.8.9.8.9.8.
French carol melody
Arr. by Charles H. Kitson, 1930

231
Lovely Child, Holy Child

They saw the child with his mother Mary, and they bowed down and worshiped him.
Then they opened their treasures and presented him with gifts. Matt. 2:11

1. Love-ly child, ho-ly child, gen-tle, mild, un-de-filed;
2. Child of light, born to-night, our de-light, prom-ise bright;
3. Rest your head, sweet-est head; gifts we'll spread at your bed.
4. To this boy, our great joy, we em-ploy hymns of joy;

in-fant King, fair-est King, gifts we'll bring and an-thems sing:
child so fair: see him there; now de-clare him ev-'ry-where:
Je-sus Lord, be a-dored, may this word now be out-poured:
child so fair: see him there; now de-clare him ev-'ry-where:

Al-le-lu-ia, al-le-lu-ia.

Al-le-lu-ia, al-le-lu-ia!

O Jesus Sweet, O Jesus Mild

232

Being found in appearance as a man, he humbled himself and became obedient to death—even death on a cross! Phil. 2:8

1. O Je - sus sweet, O Je - sus mild, your Fa - ther's
2. O Je - sus sweet, O Je - sus mild, your birth the
3. O Je - sus sweet, O Je - sus mild, we seek to

will you have ful - filled. From heav'n a - bove to
world with hope has filled. Your death has ran - somed
do what you have willed. All that we have comes

earth you came, and born as man you took our
our lost race, for on the cross you took our
from a - bove; Lord, keep us walk - ing in your

name. O Je - sus sweet, O Je - sus mild.
place. O Je - sus sweet, O Je - sus mild.
love. O Je - sus sweet, O Je - sus mild.

Samuel Scheidt, 1650
Tr. by Mark E. Hunt, 1976; alt. 1990
Text © 1978, InterVarsity Christian Fellowship. Used by permission.

O JESULEIN SÜSS 8.8.8.8.8.
Johann Sebastian Bach, 1685–1750

233   To Us a Child of Hope Is Born

To us a child is born, to us a son is given, and the government will be on his shoulders.
Is. 9:6

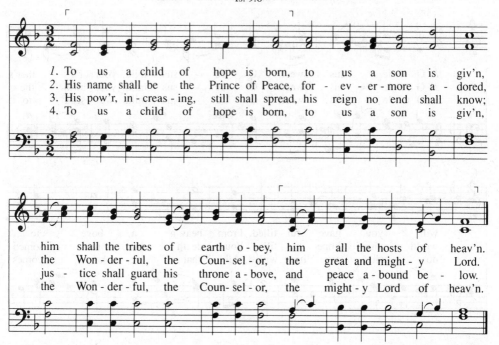

1. To us a child of hope is born, to us a son is giv'n,
2. His name shall be the Prince of Peace, for - ev - er - more a - dored,
3. His pow'r, in - creas - ing, still shall spread, his reign no end shall know;
4. To us a child of hope is born, to us a son is giv'n,

him shall the tribes of earth o - bey, him all the hosts of heav'n.
the Won - der - ful, the Coun - sel - or, the great and might - y Lord.
jus - tice shall guard his throne a - bove, and peace a - bound be - low.
the Won - der - ful, the Coun - sel - or, the might - y Lord of heav'n.

John Morison, 1781; alt.

I DO BELIEVE C.M.
Traditional English melody

234   Tell Me the Story of Jesus

He explained to them what was said in all the Scriptures concerning himself.
Luke 24:27

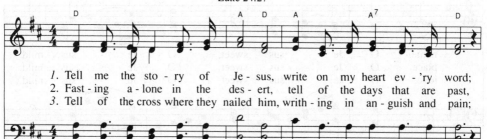

1. Tell me the sto - ry of Je - sus, write on my heart ev - 'ry word;
2. Fast - ing a - lone in the des - ert, tell of the days that are past,
3. Tell of the cross where they nailed him, writh - ing in an - guish and pain;

tell   me   the sto - ry   most   pre - cious, sweet- est that ev – er   was heard.
how   for   our sins   he   was tempt - ed,   yet   was tri - um - phant at   last.
tell   of   the grave where they laid him,   tell   how   he   liv - eth   a – gain.

Tell   how   the   an - gels,   in   cho - rus, sang as   they wel- comed his birth,
Tell   of   the years of his   la - bor,   tell   of   the sor - row   he   bore;
Love   in   that sto - ry   so   ten - der, clear - er than ev - er   I   see:

"Glo - ry   to God   in   the   high- est! Peace and good tid - ings "to   earth."
he   was de- spised and af - flict - ed, home- less, re - ject - ed, and poor.
stay,   let   me weep while you whis- per; love paid the ran - som for   me.

REFRAIN

Tell   me   the sto - ry   of   Je - sus, write on   my heart ev - 'ry word;

tell   me   the sto - ry   most   pre - cious, sweet- est that ev – er   was heard.

Fanny J. Crosby, 1880

STORY OF JESUS 8.7.8.7.D.ref.
John R. Sweney, 1880

235

All Glory, Laud, and Honor

"Hosanna!" "Blessed is he who comes in the name of the Lord!" "Blessed is the King of Israel!" John 12:13

1. All glo - ry, laud, and hon - or to thee, Re - deem - er, King,
2. The peo - ple of the He - brews with palms be - fore thee went;
3. Thou didst ac - cept their prais - es; ac - cept the prayers we bring,

to whom the lips of chil - dren made sweet ho - san - nas ring!
our praise and prayer and an - thems be - fore thee we pre - sent:
who in all good de - light - est, thou good and gra - cious King!

Thou art the King of Is - rael, thou Da - vid's roy - al Son,
to thee, be - fore thy pas - sion, they sang their hymns of praise;
All glo - ry, laud, and hon - or to thee, Re - deem - er, King,

who in the Lord's name com - est, the King and bless - ed One!
to thee, now high ex - alt - ed, our mel - o - dy we raise.
to whom the lips of chil - dren made sweet ho - san - nas ring!

Theodulph of Orleans, ca. 820
Tr. by John Mason Neale, 1854; alt.

ST. THEODULPH 7.6.7.6.D.
Melchior Teschner, ca. 1615

When His Salvation Bringing

236

"Hosanna to the Son of David!" "Blessed is he who comes in the name of the Lord!"
"Hosanna in the highest!" Matt. 21:9

1. When his sal - va - tion bring - ing, to Zi - on Je - sus came,
2. And since the Lord re - tain - eth his love for chil - dren still,
3. For should we fail pro - claim - ing our great Re - deem - er's praise,

the chil - dren all stood sing - ing ho - san - na to his name:
though now as King he reign - eth on Zi - on's heav'n - ly hill,
the stones, our si - lence sham - ing, would their ho - san - nas raise.

nor did their zeal of - fend him, but as he rode a - long,
we'll flock a - round his ban - ner who sits up - on his throne,
But shall we on - ly ren - der the trib - ute of our words?

he let them still at - tend him, and smiled to hear their song.
and cry a - loud, "Ho - san - na to Da - vid's roy - al Son!"
No, while our hearts are ten - der, they too shall be the Lord's.

John King, 1830

TOURS 7.6.7.6.D.
Berthold Tours, 1872

237 Ride On, Ride On in Majesty!

Say to the Daughter of Zion, "See, your king comes to you, gentle and riding on a donkey." Matt. 21:5

1. Ride on, ride on in maj - es - ty! Hark! all the
2. Ride on, ride on in maj - es - ty! In low - ly
3. Ride on, ride on in maj - es - ty! The wing - ed
4. Ride on, ride on in maj - es - ty! Your last and
5. Ride on, ride on in maj - es - ty! In low - ly

tribes ho - san - na cry; O Sav - ior meek, pur -
pomp ride on to die: O Christ, your tri - umphs
squad - rons of the sky look down with sad and
fierc - est strife is nigh; the Fa - ther on his
pomp ride on to die; bow your meek head to

sue your road with palms and scat - tered gar - ments strowed.
now be - gin o'er cap - tive death and con - quered sin.
won - d'ring eyes to see th'ap - proach- ing sac - ri - fice.
sap - phire throne ex - pects his own a - noint - ed Son.
mor - tal pain, then take, O God, your pow'r and reign.

Henry H. Milman, 1827; alt.
Mod.

ST. DROSTANE L.M.
John B. Dykes, 1862

My Dear Redeemer and My Lord

238

Whoever claims to live in him must walk as Jesus did. 1 John 2:6

1. My dear Redeemer and my Lord, I read my
2. Such was your truth, and such your zeal, such def-'rence
3. Cold mountains and the midnight air witnessed the
4. Be now my pattern; make me bear more of your

duty in your Word; but in your life the
to your Father's will, such love, and meekness
fervor of your prayer; the desert your temp-
gracious image here: then God the Judge shall

law appears drawn out in living characters.
so divine, I would transcribe and make them mine.
tations knew, your conflict and your vic-t'ry too.
own my name amongst the fol-l'wers of the Lamb.

Isaac Watts, 1709
Alt. 1990, mod.

FEDERAL STREET L.M.
Henry K. Oliver, 1832

239

Who Is This, So Weak and Helpless

He was in the world, and though the world was made through him, the world did not recognize him. John 1:10

1. Who is this, so weak and help-less, child of low-ly He-brew maid,
2. Who is this, a Man of Sor-rows, walk-ing sad-ly life's hard way,
3. Who is this? Be-hold him shed-ding drops of blood up-on the ground!
4. Who is this that hangs there dy-ing while the rude world scoffs and scorns,

rude-ly in a sta-ble shel-tered, cold-ly in a man-ger laid?
home-less, wea-ry, sigh-ing, weep-ing o-ver sin and Sa-tan's sway?
Who is this, de-spised, re-ject-ed, mocked, in-sult-ed, beat-en, bound?
num-bered with the mal-e-fac-tors, torn with nails, and crowned with thorns?

'Tis the Lord of all cre-a-tion, who this won-drous path has trod;
'Tis our God, our glo-rious Sav-ior, who a-bove the star-ry sky
'Tis our God, who gifts and grac-es on his church is pour-ing down;
'Tis our God who lives for-ev-er 'mid the shin-ing ones on high,

he is God from ev-er-last-ing, and to ev-er-last-ing God.
is for us a place pre-par-ing, where no tear can dim the eye.
who shall smite in ho-ly ven-geance all his foes be-neath his throne.
in the glo-rious gold-en cit-y, reign-ing ev-er-last-ing-ly.

William Walsham How, 1823–1897
Alt. 1990, mod.

EIFIONYDD 8.7.8.7.D.
John Ambrose Lloyd, 1815–1874

The King of Glory Comes

240

Lift up your heads, O you gates; be lifted up, you ancient doors, that the King of glory may come in. Ps. 24:7

(Ref.) The King of glo - ry comes, the na - tion re - joic - es.

O - pen the gates be - fore him, lift up your voic - es.

1. Who is the King of glo - ry? What shall we call him?
2. In all of Gal - i - lee, in cit - y or vil - lage,
3. He gave his life for us, the pledge of sal - va - tion.
4. He con - quered sin and death; he tru - ly has ris - en.

He is Im - man - u - el, the prom - ised of a - ges.
he goes a - mong his peo - ple, cur - ing their ill - ness.
He took up - on him - self the sin of the na - tions.
And he will share with us his heav - en - ly king - dom.

Based on Psalm 24
Willard F. Jabusch, 1966

PROMISED ONE 12.12.ref.
Israeli folk song
Arr. by John Ferguson, 1973

241   Thou Dost Reign on High

Our Lord Jesus Christ ... was rich, yet for your sakes he became poor, so that you
through his poverty might become rich. 2 Cor. 8:9

1. Thou dost reign on high with a king - ly crown, yet thou
2. Heav- en's arch - es rang when the an - gels sang, pro -
3. The fox - es found rest, and the birds their nest, in the
4. Thou cam - est, O Lord, with the liv - ing word that should
5. When heav'n's arch - es shall ring, and her choirs shall sing, at thy

cam - est to earth for me, and in Beth - le- hem's home was there
claim - ing thy roy - al de - gree; but of low - ly birth didst thou
• shade of the for - est tree; but thy couch was the sod, O thou
set thy peo - ple free; but with mock - ing scorn, and with
com - ing to vic - to - ry, let thy voice call me home, say - ing,

found no room for thy ho - ly na - tiv - i - ty: O
come to earth, and in great hu - mil - i - ty: O
• Son of God, in the des - erts of Gal - i - lee: O
crown of thorn, they bore thee to Cal - va - ry: O
"Yet there is room, there is room at my side for thee." And my

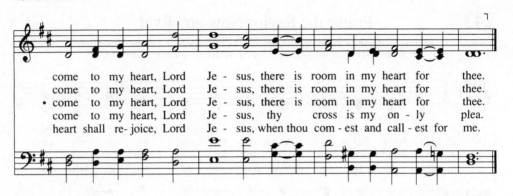

come to my heart, Lord Je - sus, there is room in my heart for thee.
come to my heart, Lord Je - sus, there is room in my heart for thee.
• come to my heart, Lord Je - sus, there is room in my heart for thee.
come to my heart, Lord Je - sus, thy cross is my on - ly plea.
heart shall re- joice, Lord Je - sus, when thou com - est and call - est for me.

Emily E. S. Elliott, 1864; alt.
Alt. 1961

MARGARET Irreg.
T. Richard Matthews, 1876

Not All the Blood of Beasts 242

It is impossible for the blood of bulls and goats to take away sins. Heb. 10:4

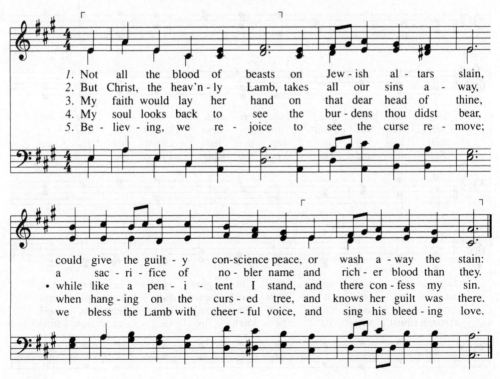

1. Not all the blood of beasts on Jew - ish al - tars slain,
2. But Christ, the heav'n - ly Lamb, takes all our sins a - way,
3. My faith would lay her hand on that dear head of thine,
4. My soul looks back to see the bur - dens thou didst bear,
5. Be - liev - ing, we re - joice to see the curse re - move;

could give the guilt - y con-science peace, or wash a - way the stain:
a sac - ri - fice of no - bler name and rich - er blood than they.
• while like a pen - i - tent I stand, and there con - fess my sin.
when hang - ing on the curs - ed tree, and knows her guilt was there.
we bless the Lamb with cheer - ful voice, and sing his bleed - ing love.

Isaac Watts, 1709
Alt. 1961

FESTAL SONG S.M.
William H. Walter, 1894

243 Praise the Savior Now and Ever

That by his death he might destroy him who holds the power of death—that is, the
devil—and free those who all their lives were held in slavery. Heb. 2:14, 15

1. Praise the Sav - ior now and ev - er; praise him, all be -
2. Man's work fail - eth, Christ's a - vail - eth; he is all our
3. Sin's bond sev - ered, we're de - liv - ered; Christ has bruised the
4. For his fa - vor, praise for - ev - er un - to God the

neath the skies; pros - trate ly - ing, suf - f'ring, dy - ing
righ - teous - ness; he, our Sav - ior, has for - ev - er
ser - pent's head; death no lon - ger is the stron - ger;
Fa - ther sing; praise the Sav - ior, praise him ev - er,

on the cross, a sac - ri - fice. Vic - t'ry gain - ing,
set us free from dire dis - tress. Through his mer - it
hell it - self is cap - tive led. Christ has ris - en
Son of God, our Lord and King. Praise the Spir - it;

life ob - tain - ing, now in glo - ry he doth rise.
we in - her - it light and peace and hap - pi - ness.
from death's pris - on; o'er the tomb he light has shed.
through Christ's mer - it he doth us sal - va - tion bring.

Venantius H. C. Fortunatus, ca. 530–609
Tr. by Augustus Nelson, 1863–1949

UPP, MIN TUNGA 4.4.7.4.4.7.4.4.7.
Koralbok, 1697

He Was Wounded for Our Transgressions

244

He was pierced for our transgressions, he was crushed for our iniquities; the punish-
ment that brought us peace was upon him, and by his wounds we are healed. Is. 53:5

1. He was wound-ed for our trans-gres-sions, he bore our
2. He was num-bered a-mong trans-gres-sors, we did es-
3. We had wan-dered, we all had wan-dered far from the
4. Who can num-ber his gen-er-a-tion? Who shall de-

sins in his bod-y on the tree; for our guilt he gave us
teem him for-sak-en by his God; as our sac-ri-fice he
fold of "the Shep-herd of the sheep"; but he sought us where we
clare all the tri-umphs of his cross? Mil-lions dead now live a-

peace, from our bond-age gave re-lease, and with his
died, that the law be sat-is-fied, and all our
were, on the moun-tains bleak and bare, and brought us
gain, myr-iads fol-low in his train! Vic-to-rious

stripes, and with his stripes, and with his stripes our souls are healed.
sin, and all our sin, and all our sin was laid on him.
home, and brought us home, and brought us safe-ly home to God.
Lord, vic-to-rious Lord, vic-to-rious Lord and com-ing King!

Thomas O. Chisholm, 1941

OAK PARK Irreg.
Merrill Dunlop, 1941; alt. 1990

245 As Jacob with Travel Was Weary One Day

He had a dream in which he saw a stairway resting on the earth, with its top reaching to heaven, and the angels of God were ascending and descending on it. Gen. 28:12

1. As Ja - cob with trav - el was wea - ry one day, at
2. This lad - der is long, it is strong and well made, has stood
3. Come, let us as - cend! All may climb it who will; for the
4. And when we ar - rive at the ha - ven of rest, we shall

night on a stone for a pil - low he lay; he saw in a
hun - dreds of years and is not yet de - cayed; man - y mil - lions have
an - gels of Ja - cob are guard - ing it still: and re - mem - ber, each
hear the glad words, "Come up hith - er, ye blest, here are re - gions of

vi - sion a lad - der so high, that its foot was on
climbed it and reached Si - on's hill, and thou - sands by
step that by faith we pass o'er, some proph - et or
light, here are man - sions of bliss." Oh, who would not

REFRAIN

earth and its top in the sky.
faith are climb - ing it still.
mar - tyr hath trod it be - fore. Al - le - lu - ia to Je - sus, who
climb such a lad - der as this?

died on the tree, and hath raised up a lad - der of mer - cy for

me, and hath raised up a lad - der of mer - cy for me.

Traditional English carol

JACOB'S LADDER 11.11.11.11.ref.
Arr. by John Stainer, 1871; alt. 1990

Man of Sorrows! What a Name

246

He was despised and rejected by men, a man of sorrows, and familiar with suffering.
Is. 53:3

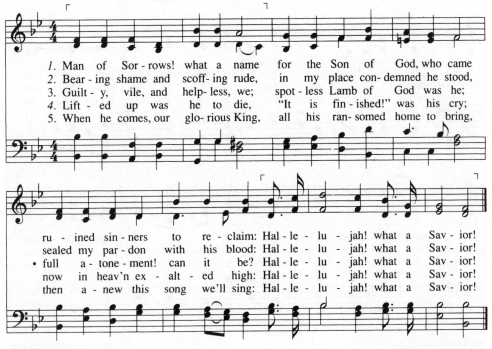

1. Man of Sor - rows! what a name for the Son of God, who came
2. Bear - ing shame and scoff- ing rude, in my place con- demned he stood,
3. Guilt - y, vile, and help- less, we; spot - less Lamb of God was he;
4. Lift - ed up was he to die, "It is fin - ished!" was his cry;
5. When he comes, our glo- rious King, all his ran- somed home to bring,

ru - ined sin - ners to re - claim: Hal - le - lu - jah! what a Sav - ior!
sealed my par - don with his blood: Hal - le - lu - jah! what a Sav - ior!
• full a - tone - ment! can it be? Hal - le - lu - jah! what a Sav - ior!
now in heav'n ex - alt - ed high: Hal - le - lu - jah! what a Sav - ior!
then a - new this song we'll sing: Hal - le - lu - jah! what a Sav - ior!

Philip P. Bliss, 1875

HALLELUJAH! WHAT A SAVIOR! 7.7.7.8.
Philip P. Bliss, 1875

247 O Sacred Head, Now Wounded

He was pierced for our transgressions, he was crushed for our iniquities. Is. 53:5

1. O sacred Head, now wounded, with grief and shame weighed down;
2. What thou, my Lord, hast suffered was all for sinners' gain:
3. What language shall I borrow to thank thee, dearest Friend,

now scornfully surrounded with thorns, thine only crown;
mine, mine was the transgression, but thine the deadly pain.
for this, thy dying sorrow, thy pity without end?

O sacred Head, what glory, what bliss till now was thine!
Lo, here I fall, my Savior! 'Tis I deserve thy place;
O make me thine forever; and should I fainting be,

Yet, though despised and gory, I joy to call thee mine.
look on me with thy favor, vouchsafe to me thy grace.
Lord, let me never, never outlive my love to thee.

Bernard of Clairvaux, 1091–1153
Tr. by Paul Gerhardt, 1656
Tr. by James W. Alexander, 1830

PASSION CHORALE 7.6.7.6.D.
Hans Leo Hassler, 1601
Arr. by Johann Sebastian Bach, 1729

Ah, Holy Jesus, How Hast Thou Offended   248

*Surely he took up our infirmities and carried our sorrows, yet we considered him
stricken by God, smitten by him, and afflicted.* Is. 53:4

1. Ah, ho - ly Je - sus, how hast thou of - fend - ed,
that man to judge thee hath in hate pre - tend - ed? By foes de -
rid - ed, by thine own re - ject - ed, O most af - flict - ed.

2. Who was the guilt - y who brought this up - on thee?
A - las, my trea - son, Je - sus, hath un - done thee. 'Twas I, Lord
Je - sus, I it was de - nied thee: I cru - ci - fied thee.

3. Lo, the Good Shep - herd for the sheep is of - fered;
the slave hath sin - ned, and the Son hath suf - fered: for man's a -
tone - ment, while he noth - ing heed - eth, God in - ter - ced - eth.

4. For me, kind Je - sus, was thine in - car - na - tion,
thy mor - tal sor - row, and thy life's ob - la - tion: thy death of
an - guish and thy bit - ter pas - sion, for my sal - va - tion.

5. There - fore, kind Je - sus, since I can - not pay thee,
I do a - dore thee, and will ev - er pray thee, think on thy
pit - y and thy love un - swerv - ing, not my de - serv - ing.

Johann Heermann, 1630
Tr. in *Yattendon Hymnal*, 1899

HERZLIEBSTER JESU 11.11.11.5.
Johann Crüger, 1640

249   'Tis Midnight; and on Olive's Brow

Jesus went out as usual to the Mount of Olives. Luke 22:39

1. 'Tis mid-night; and on Ol-ive's brow the star is
2. 'Tis mid-night; and, from all re-moved, Em-man-uel
3. 'Tis mid-night; and, for oth-ers' guilt, the Man of
4. 'Tis mid-night; from the heav'n-ly plains is borne the

dimmed that late-ly shone: 'tis mid-night; in the
wres-tles lone with fears: e'en the dis-ci-ple
Sor-rows weeps in blood: yet he that hath in
song that an-gels know: un-heard by mor-tals

gar-den now the suf-f'ring Sav-ior prays a-lone.
that he loved heeds not his Mas-ter's grief and tears.
an-guish knelt is not for-sak-en by his God.
are the strains that sweet-ly soothe the Sav-ior's woe.

William B. Tappan, 1822

OLIVE'S BROW L.M.
William B. Bradbury, 1853

Throned upon the Awful Tree

My God, my God, why have you forsaken me? Mark 15:34

1. Throned up - on the aw - ful tree, King of grief, I watch with thee.
   Dark - ness veils thine an - guished face: none its lines of woe can trace:
   none can tell what pangs un - known hold thee si - lent and a - lone.

2. Si - lent through those three dread hours, wres - tling with the e - vil pow'rs,
   left a - lone with hu - man sin, gloom a - round thee and with - in,
   till th'ap - point - ed time is nigh, till the Lamb of God may die.

3. Hark, that cry that peals a - loud up- ward through the whelm- ing cloud!
   Thou, the Fa - ther's on - ly Son, thou, his own A - noint - ed One,
   thou dost ask him— can it be?— "Why hast thou for - sak - en me?"

4. Lord, should fear and an - guish roll dark - ly o'er my sin - ful soul,
   thou, who once wast thus be - reft that thine own might ne'er be left,
   teach me by that bit - ter cry in the gloom to know thee nigh.

John Ellerton, 1875

ARFON 7.7.7.7.7.7.
Traditional Welsh melody

251 Beneath the Cross of Jesus

Each man will be like a shelter from the wind and a refuge from the storm, like streams
of water in the desert and the shadow of a great rock in a thirsty land. Is. 32:2

1. Be - neath the cross of Je - sus I fain would take my stand,
2. Up - on the cross of Je - sus mine eye at times can see
3. I take, O cross, thy shad - ow for my a - bid - ing place:

the shad - ow of a might - y Rock with - in a wea - ry land;
the ver - y dy - ing form of One who suf - fered there for me:
I ask no oth - er sun - shine than the sun - shine of his face;

a home with - in the wil - der - ness, a rest up - on the way,
and from my strick - en heart with tears two won - ders I con - fess,
con - tent to let the world go by, to know no gain nor loss;

from the burn - ing of the noon - tide heat and the bur - den of the day.
the won - ders of re - deem - ing love and my un - wor - thi - ness.
my sin - ful self my on - ly shame, my glo - ry all the cross.

Elizabeth C. Clephane, 1872
Alt. 1990

ST. CHRISTOPHER 7.6.8.6.8.6.8.6.
Frederick C. Maker, 1881

When I Survey the Wondrous Cross

252

May I never boast except in the cross of our Lord Jesus Christ, through which the world has been crucified to me, and I to the world. Gal. 6:14

1. When I sur - vey the won - drous cross on which the
2. For - bid it, Lord, that I should boast, save in the
3. See, from his head, his hands, his feet, sor - row and
4. Were the whole realm of na - ture mine, that were a

Prince of glo - ry died, my rich - est gain I
death of Christ my God: all the vain things that
love flow min - gled down: did e'er such love and
pres - ent far too small; love so a - maz - ing,

count but loss, and pour con - tempt on all my pride.
charm me most, I sac - ri - fice them to his blood.
sor - row meet, or thorns com - pose so rich a crown?
so di - vine, de - mands my soul, my life, my all.

Isaac Watts, 1707, 1709

HAMBURG L.M.
Gregorian chant
Arr. by Lowell Mason, 1824

253   There Is a Fountain Filled with Blood

On that day a fountain will be opened to the house of David and the inhabitants
of Jerusalem, to cleanse them from sin and impurity. Zech. 13:1

1. There is a foun - tain filled with blood, drawn from Im - man - uel's veins;
2. The dy - ing thief re - joiced to see that foun- tain in his day;
3. E'er since by faith I saw the stream your flow - ing wounds sup - ply,
4. Then in a no - bler, sweet - er song I'll sing your pow'r to save,
5. Dear dy - ing Lamb, your pre - cious blood shall nev - er lose its pow'r,

and sin - ners, plunged be - neath that flood, lose all their guilt - y stains:
and there have I, as vile as he, washed all my sins a - way:
re - deem - ing love has been my theme, and shall be till I die:
when this poor lisp- ing, stam- m'ring tongue lies si - lent in the grave:
till all the ran - somed church of God be saved to sin no more:

lose all their guilt - y stains, lose all their guilt - y stains;
washed all my sins a - way, washed all my sins a - way;
and shall be till I die, and shall be till I die;
lies si - lent in the grave, lies si - lent in the grave;
be saved to sin no more, be saved to sin no more;

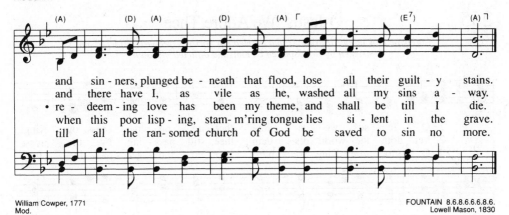

and   sin - ners, plunged be - neath that flood, lose   all   their guilt - y   stains.
and   there have I,   as   vile   as   he, washed all   my   sins   a - way.
• re - deem - ing love has   been   my   theme, and   shall   be   till   I   die.
when   this   poor lisp - ing, stam- m'ring tongue lies   si - lent   in   the   grave.
till   all   the ran- somed church of God be   saved to   sin   no   more.

William Cowper, 1771
Mod.

FOUNTAIN 8.6.8.6.6.6.8.6.
Lowell Mason, 1830

Alas! and Did My Savior Bleed   254

He was pierced for our transgressions, he was crushed for our iniquities. Is. 53:5

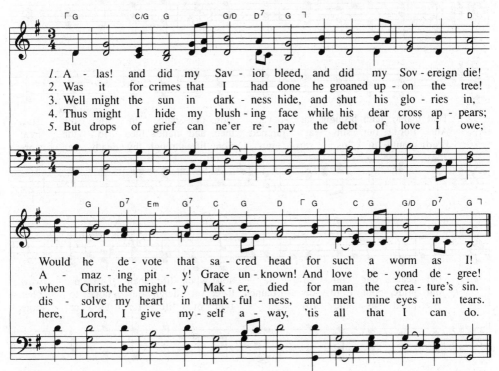

1. A - las!   and did my Sav - ior bleed, and did my Sov - ereign die!
2. Was it   for crimes that I   had done he groaned up - on   the   tree!
3. Well might the sun   in dark - ness hide, and shut his glo - ries in,
4. Thus might I   hide my blush - ing face while his dear cross ap - pears;
5. But drops of   grief can ne'er re - pay the debt of   love I   owe;

Would he   de - vote that sa - cred head for   such   a   worm as   I!
A -   maz - ing pit - y! Grace un - known! And love be - yond de - gree!
• when Christ, the might - y Mak - er,   died for   man the crea - ture's sin.
dis - solve my heart in thank - ful - ness, and melt mine eyes in   tears.
here, Lord, I   give my - self a - way, 'tis all   that I   can   do.

Isaac Watts, 1707
Alt. 1961

MARTYRDOM C.M.
Hugh Wilson, ca. 1800
Arr. by Robert A. Smith, 1825

255   O Jesus, We Adore Thee

Surely he took up our infirmities and carried our sorrows, yet we considered him
stricken by God, smitten by him, and afflicted. Is. 53:4

1. O Je - sus, we a - dore thee, up - on the cross, our King!
2. Yet doth the world dis - dain thee, still pass - ing by the cross;
3. O glo - rious King, we bless thee, no lon - ger pass thee by;

We bow our hearts be - fore thee, thy gra - cious name we sing.
Lord, may our hearts re - tain thee; all else we count but loss.
O Je - sus, we con - fess thee, the Son en - throned on high.

That name hath brought sal - va - tion, that name in life our stay,
Ah, Lord, our sins ar - raigned thee, and nailed thee to the tree:
Lord, grant to us re - mis - sion; life through thy death re - store;

our peace, our con - so - la - tion, when life shall fade a - way.
our pride, our Lord, dis - dained thee; yet deign our hope to be.
yea, grant us the fru - i - tion of life for - ev - er - more.

Arthur T. Russell, 1851

MEIRIONYDD 7.6.7.6.D.
Welsh hymn melody
William Lloyd, 1840; alt. 1990

There Is a Green Hill Far Away

Jesus also suffered outside the city gate to make the people holy through his own blood.
Let us, then, go to him outside the camp, bearing the disgrace he bore. Heb. 13:12, 13

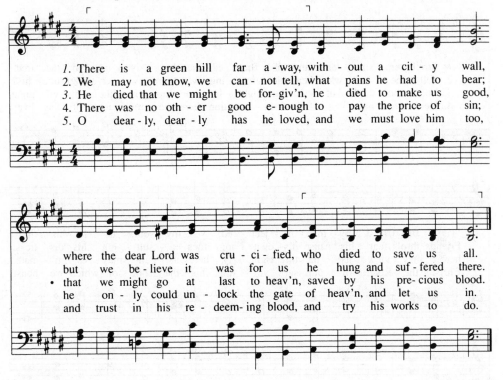

1. There   is   a   green hill   far   a - way, with - out   a   cit - y   wall,
2. We   may not know, we   can - not tell, what   pains he   had   to   bear;
3. He   died that we might   be   for- giv'n, he   died   to   make   us   good,
4. There was   no   oth - er   good   e- nough to   pay   the price of   sin;
5. O   dear - ly,   dear - ly   has   he loved, and   we must love him   too,

where   the dear Lord was   cru - ci - fied, who   died   to   save   us   all.
but   we   be - lieve   it   was   for   us   he   hung and   suf - fered   there.
that   we might   go   at   last   to heav'n, saved by   his   pre - cious   blood.
he   on - ly   could un - lock   the   gate   of heav'n, and   let   us   in.
and   trust   in   his   re - deem- ing blood, and   try   his works to   do.

Cecil Frances Alexander, 1848

MEDITATION C.M.
John H. Gower. 1890

257 Stricken, Smitten, and Afflicted

We considered him stricken by God, smitten by him, and afflicted. Is. 53:4

1. Strick-en, smit-ten, and af-flict-ed, see him dy-ing on the tree!
2. Tell me, ye who hear him groan-ing, was there ev-er grief like his?
3. Ye who think of sin but light-ly nor sup-pose the e-vil great
4. Here we have a firm foun-da-tion, here the ref-uge of the lost;

'Tis the Christ by man re-ject-ed; yes, my soul, 'tis he, 'tis he!
Friends thro' fear his cause dis-own-ing, foes in-sult-ing his dis-tress;
here may view its na-ture right-ly, here its guilt may es-ti-mate.
Christ's the Rock of our sal-va-tion, his the name of which we boast.

'Tis the long-ex-pect-ed Proph-et, Da-vid's son, yet Da-vid's Lord;
man-y hands were raised to wound him, none would in-ter-pose to save;
Mark the sac-ri-fice ap-point-ed, see who bears the aw-ful load;
Lamb of God, for sin-ners wound-ed, sac-ri-fice to can-cel guilt!

by his Son God now has spo-ken: 'tis the true and faith-ful Word.
but the deep-est stroke that pierced him was the stroke that Jus-tice gave.
'tis the Word, the Lord's A-noint-ed, Son of Man and Son of God.
None shall ev-er be con-found-ed who on him their hope have built.

Thomas Kelly, 1804
Alt. 1961

O MEIN JESU, ICH MUSS STERBEN 8.7.8.7.D.
Geistliche Volkslieder, Paderborn, 1850

Sweet the Moments, Rich in Blessing

258

Blessed are they whose transgressions are forgiven, whose sins are covered. Rom. 4:7

1. Sweet the moments, rich in blessing, which before the cross I spend, life and health and
peace pos-sess-ing from the sin-ner's dy-ing Friend.

2. Here I rest, in won-der view-ing all my
sins on Je-sus laid, here I see re-
demp-tion flow-ing from the sac-ri-fice he made.

3. Here I find the dawn of heav-en, while upon the cross I gaze, see my tres-pass-
es for-giv-en, and my songs of tri-umph raise.

4. O that near the cross a-bid-ing, I may
to the Sav-ior cleave, naught with him my
heart di-vid-ing, all for him con-tent to leave.

James Allen, 1757
Alt. by Walter Shirley, 1770

CROSS OF JESUS 8.7.8.7.
From John Stainer, *The Crucifixion*, 1887

259 Hark! the Voice of Love and Mercy

Jesus said, "It is finished." With that, he bowed his head and gave up his spirit.
John 19:30

1. Hark! the voice of love and mer - cy sounds a- loud from Cal - va - ry;
2. "It is fin - ished!" O what plea - sure do these pre - cious words af- ford;
3. Fin - ished all the types and shad- ows of the cer - e - mo - nial law;
4. Tune your harps a - new, ye ser - aphs, join to sing the glo- rious theme;

see, it rends the rocks a - sun - der, shakes the earth, and veils the sky:
heav'n- ly bless - ings, with- out mea - sure, flow to us from Christ the Lord:
fin - ished all that God had prom- ised; death and hell no more shall awe:
all in earth, and all in heav - en, join to praise Em - man- uel's name:

"It is fin - ished! It is fin - ished! It is fin - ished!"
"It is fin - ished! It is fin - ished! It is fin - ished!"
"It is fin - ished! It is fin - ished! It is fin - ished!"
Al - le - lu - ia! Al - le - lu - ia! Al - le - lu - ia!

Hear the dy - ing Sav - ior cry; hear the dy - ing Sav- ior cry.
Saints the dy - ing words re - cord; saints the dy - ing words re - cord.
Saints, from hence your com - fort draw; saints, from hence your com- fort draw.
Glo - ry to the bleed- ing Lamb! Glo - ry to the bleed- ing Lamb!

Jonathan Evans, 1784; alt.

BRYN CALFARIA 8.7.8.7.4.4.4.7.7.
William Owen. 1852

Were You There?

It was the third hour when they crucified him. Mark 15:25

1. Were you there when they cru-ci-fied my Lord? (Were you there?)
2. Were you there when they nailed him to the tree? (Were you there?)
3. Were you there when they pierced him in the side? (Were you there?)
4. Were you there when they laid him in the tomb? (Were you there?)
5. Were you there when he rose up from the dead? (Were you there?)

Were you there when they cru-ci-fied my Lord? (Were you there?)
Were you there when they nailed him to the tree? (Were you there?)
• Were you there when they pierced him in the side? (Were you there?)
Were you there when they laid him in the tomb? (Were you there?)
Were you there when he rose up from the dead? (Were you there?)

Oh!.............. Some-times it caus-es me to trem-ble, trem-ble,
(5.) Some-times I feel like shout-ing glo-ry, glo-ry,

trem-ble. Were you there when they cru-ci-fied my Lord? (Were you there?)
trem-ble. Were you there when they nailed him to the tree? (Were you there?)
• trem-ble. Were you there when they pierced him in the side? (Were you there?)
trem-ble. Were you there when they laid him in the tomb? (Were you there?)
glo-ry! Were you there when he rose up from the dead? (Were you there?)

Spiritual

WERE YOU THERE? Irreg.
Spiritual

261 What Wondrous Love Is This

How great is the love the Father has lavished on us, that we should be called
children of God! 1 John 3:1

1. What won-drous love is this, O my soul, O my soul, what
2. To God and to the Lamb, I will sing, I will sing, to
3. And when from death I'm free, I'll sing on, I'll sing on, and

won-drous love is this, O my soul! What won-drous love is
God and to the Lamb, I will sing; to God and to the
when from death I'm free, I'll sing on; and when from death I'm

this that caused the Lord of bliss to bear the dread-ful curse for my
Lamb, who is the great I AM, while mil-lions join the theme, I will
free, I'll sing and joy-ful be, and through e-ter-ni-ty I'll sing

soul, for my soul, to bear the dread-ful curse for my soul!
sing, I will sing, while mil-lions join the theme, I will sing!
on, I'll sing on, and through e-ter-ni-ty I'll sing on!

American folk hymn

WONDROUS LOVE 12.9.12.9.
The Southern Harmony, 1835

O Come and Mourn with Me Awhile

262

And when Jesus had cried out again in a loud voice, he gave up his spirit. Matt. 27:50

1. O come and mourn with me awhile; O come ye
2. Sev'n times he spake, sev'n words of love; and all three
3. O break, O break, hard heart of mine! Thy weak self-
4. A bro - ken heart, a fount of tears, ask, and they
5. O love of God! O sin of man! In this dread

to the Sav - ior's side; O come, to - geth - er let us mourn:
hours his si - lence cried for mer - cy on the souls of men:
love and guilt - y pride his Pi - late and his Ju - das were:
will not be de - nied; a bro - ken heart love's cra - dle is:
act your strength is tried, and vic - to - ry re - mains with love:

REFRAIN

Je - sus, our Lord, is cru - ci - fied!

Frederick W. Faber, 1814–1863

ST. CROSS L.M.
John B. Dykes, 1823–1876

263

Lift High the Cross

I, when I am lifted up from the earth, will draw all men to myself. John 12:32

Unison

(Ref.) Lift high the cross, the love of Christ pro - claim,

till all the world a - dore his sa - cred name.

Fine

1. Come, breth - ren, fol - low where our Sav - ior trod,
2. Led on their way by this tri - um - phant sign,
3. O Lord, once lift - ed on the glo - rious tree,
4. Thy king - dom come, that earth's de - spair may cease
5. For thy blest cross which doth for us a - tone,

D.C.

our King vic - to - rious, Christ, the Son of God.
the hosts of God in con - qu'ring ranks com - bine.
• as thou hast prom - ised, draw men un - to thee.
be - neath the shad - ow of its heal - ing peace.
cre - a - tion's prais - es rise be - fore thy throne.

George W. Kitchin, 1887
Rev. by Michael R. Newbolt, 1916; alt. 1990
Text and tune © 1974, Hope Publishing Co. All rights reserved. Used by permission.

CRUCIFER Irreg.,ref.
Sydney H. Nicholson, 1916

Jesus, Keep Me near the Cross

264

May I never boast except in the cross of our Lord Jesus Christ. Gal. 6:14

1. Je - sus, keep me near the cross; there a pre - cious foun - tain,
2. Near the cross, a trem- bling soul, love and mer - cy found me;
3. Near the cross! O Lamb of God, bring its scenes be - fore me;
4. Near the cross I'll watch and wait, hop - ing, trust - ing ev - er,

free to all— a heal - ing stream— flows from Cal - v'ry's moun - tain.
there the Bright and Morn - ing Star shed its beams a - round me.
help me walk from day to day with its sha - dow o'er me.
till I reach the gold - en strand just be - yond the riv - er.

REFRAIN

In the cross, in the cross, be my glo - ry ev - er;

till my rap - tured soul shall find rest be - yond the riv - er.

Fanny J. Crosby, 1869

NEAR THE CROSS 7.6.7.6.ref.
William H. Doane. 1869

265 Come, Ye Faithful, Raise the Strain

I will sing to the LORD, for he is highly exalted. Ex. 15:1

1. Come, ye faith-ful, raise the strain of tri-um-phant glad-ness;
2. 'Tis the spring of souls to-day; Christ hath burst his pris-on,
3. Now the queen of sea-sons, bright with the day of splen-dor,
4. Nei-ther might the gates of death, nor the tomb's dark por-tal,

God hath brought his Is-ra-el in-to joy from sad-ness;
and from three days' sleep in death as a sun hath ris-en;
with the roy-al feast of feasts, comes its joy to ren-der;
nor the watch-ers, nor the seal hold thee as a mor-tal:

loosed from Pha-raoh's bit-ter yoke Ja-cob's sons and daugh-ters;
all the win-ter of our sins, long and dark, is fly-ing
comes to glad Je-ru-sa-lem, who with true af-fec-tion
but to-day a-midst thine own thou didst stand, be-stow-ing

led them with un-moist-ened foot through the Red Sea wa-ters.
from his light, to whom we give laud and praise un-dy-ing.
wel-comes in un-wea-ried strains Je-sus' res-ur-rec-tion.
thine own peace, which ev-er-more pass-eth hu-man know-ing.

John of Damascus, 8th cent.
Tr. by John Mason Neale, 1853; alt.

TEMPUS ADEST FLORIDUM 7.6.7.6.D.
Piae Cantiones, 1582
Arr. by Ernest MacMillan, 1930

Come, Ye Faithful, Raise the Strain

266

I will sing to the LORD, for he is highly exalted. Ex. 15:1

1. Come, ye faith - ful, raise the strain of tri - um - phant glad - ness;
2. 'Tis the spring of souls to - day; Christ hath burst his pris - on,
3. Now the queen of sea - sons, bright with the day of splen - dor,
4. Nei - ther might the gates of death, nor the tomb's dark por - tal,

God hath brought his Is - ra - el in - to joy from sad - ness;
and from three days' sleep in death, as a sun hath ris - en;
with the roy - al feast of feasts, comes its joy to ren - der;
nor the watch - ers, nor the seal hold thee as a mor - tal:

loosed from Pha - raoh's bit - ter yoke Ja - cob's sons and daugh - ters;
all the win - ter of our sins, long and dark, is fly - ing
comes to glad Je - ru - sa - lem, who with true af - fec - tion
but to - day a - midst thine own thou didst stand, be - stow - ing

led them with un - moist - ened foot through the Red Sea wa - ters.
from his light, to whom we give laud and praise un - dy - ing.
wel - comes in un - wea - ried strains Je - sus' res - ur - rec - tion.
thine own peace, which ev - er - more pass - eth hu - man know - ing.

John of Damascus, 8th cent.
Tr. by John Mason Neale, 1853; alt.

ST. KEVIN 7.6.7.6.D.
Arthur S. Sullivan, 1872

267 The Day of Resurrection!

Suddenly Jesus met them. "Greetings," he said. Matt. 28:9

1. The day of res - ur - rec - tion! Earth, tell it out a - broad;
2. Our hearts be pure from e - vil, that we may see a - right
3. Now let the heav'ns be joy - ful, let earth her song be - gin;

the Pass - o - ver of glad - ness, the Pass - o - ver of God.
the Lord in rays e - ter - nal of res - ur - rec - tion light;
let the round world keep tri - umph, and all that is there - in;

From death to life e - ter - nal, from this world to the sky,
and lis - tening to his ac - cents, may hear, so calm and plain,
in - vis - i - ble and vis - i - ble, their notes let all things blend,

our Christ hath brought us o - ver with hymns of vic - to - ry.
his own "All hail!" and hear - ing, may raise the vic - tor strain.
for Christ the Lord hath ris - en, our joy that hath no end.

John of Damascus, 8th cent.
Tr. by John Mason Neale, 1862; alt.

LANCASHIRE 7.6.7.6.D.
Henry Smart, 1836; alt. 1990

Welcome, Happy Morning!

268

Christ has indeed been raised from the dead, the firstfruits of those who have fallen asleep. 1 Cor. 15:20

1. "Wel - come, hap - py morn - ing!" age to age shall say:
2. Mak - er and Re - deem - er, life and health of all,
3. Thou, of life the au - thor, death didst un - der - go,
4. Loose the souls long pris - oned, bound with Sa - tan's chain;

hell to - day is van - quished; heav'n is won to - day.
thou, from heav'n be - hold - ing hu - man na - ture's fall,
tread the path of dark - ness, sav - ing strength to show;
thine that now are fall - en raise to life a - gain;

Lo! the Dead is liv - ing, God for - ev - er - more!
of the Fa - ther's God - head true and on - ly Son,
come then, True and Faith - ful, now ful - fil thy word,
show thy face in bright - ness, bid the na - tions see;

Him, their true Cre - a - tor, all his works a - dore.
man - hood to de - liv - er, man - hood didst put on.
'tis thine own third morn - ing; rise, O bur - ied Lord.
bring a - gain our day - light; day re - turns with thee.

Venantius H. C. Fortunatus, ca. 530–609
Tr. by John Ellerton, 1868
Alt. 1961

NOEL NOUVELET 6.5.6.5.D.
Traditional French melody
Arr. by Martin Shaw, 1875–1958

269

Welcome, Happy Morning!

*Christ has indeed been raised from the dead, the firstfruits of those who have
fallen asleep.* 1 Cor. 15:20

1. "Wel- come, hap - py morn - ing!" age to age shall say: hell to-
2. Mak - er and Re - deem - er, life and health of all, thou, from
3. Thou, of life the au - thor, death didst un - der - go, tread the
4. Loose the souls long pris - oned, bound with Sa - tan's chain; thine that

day is van-quished; heav'n is won to - day. Lo! the Dead is liv - ing,
heav'n be - hold - ing hu - man na - ture's fall, of the Fa - ther's God- head
path of dark - ness, sav- ing strength to show; come then, True and Faith- ful,
now are fal - len raise to life a - gain; show thy face in bright- ness,

God for - ev - er - more! Him, their true Cre - a - tor,
true and on - ly Son, man - hood to de - liv - er,
now ful - fil thy word, 'tis thine own third morn - ing;
bid the na - tions see; bring a - gain our day - light;

REFRAIN

all his works a - dore.
man- hood didst put on. "Wel- come, hap- py morn- ing!" age to age shall say:
rise, O bur - ied Lord.
day re - turns with thee.

hell to-day is van - quished, heav'n is won to - day.

Venantius H. C. Fortunatus, ca. 530–609
Tr. by John Ellerton, 1868
Alt. 1961

ST. ALBAN 6.5.6.5.D.ref.
Franz Josef Haydn, 1774
Arr. by John B. Dykes, 1868

Good Christian Men, Rejoice and Sing! 270

*With great power the apostles continued to testify to the resurrection of the
Lord Jesus.* Acts 4:33

1. Good Chris - tian men, re - joice and sing! Now is the tri - umph
2. The Lord of life is ris'n for aye; bring flow'rs of song to
3. Praise we in songs of vic - to - ry that love, that life which
4. Your name we bless, O ris - en Lord, and sing to - day with

of our King! To all the world glad news we bring:
strew his way; let all man - kind re - joice and say:
can - not die, and sing with hearts up - lift - ed high:
one ac - cord the life laid down, the life re - stored:

Al - le - lu - ia! Al - le - lu - ia! Al - le - lu - ia!

Cyril A. Alington, 1931
Mod.

GELOBT SEI GOTT 8.8.8.al.
Melchior Vulpius, 1609

271

Sing, Choirs of New Jerusalem

I heard a loud voice in heaven say: "Now have come the salvation and the power and the kingdom of our God, and the authority of his Christ." Rev. 12:10

1. Sing, choirs of new Je - ru - sa - lem, your
2. For Ju - dah's Li - on burst his chains and
3. Tri - um - phant in his glo - ry now— to
4. All glo - ry to the Fa - ther be, all

sweet - est notes em - ploy, your sweet - est notes em - ploy
crushed the ser - pent's head, and crushed the ser - pent's head;
him all pow'r is giv'n, to him all pow'r is giv'n;
glo - ry to the Son, all glo - ry to the Son,

the pas - chal vic - to - ry to hymn
Christ cries a - loud through death's do - mains
to him in one com - mu - nion bow
all glo - ry to the Spir - it be

in songs of ho - ly joy,
to wake th'im - pris - oned dead,
all saints in earth and heav'n,
while end - less a - ges run,

in songs of ho - ly joy, in songs of ho -
to wake th'im - pris - oned dead, to wake th'im - pris -
all saints in earth and heav'n, all saints in earth
while end - less a - ges run, while end - less a -

in songs of ho - ly joy,
to wake th'im - pris - oned dead,
all saints in earth and heav'n,
while end - less a - ges run,

ly joy, in songs of ho -
oned dead, to wake th'im - pris -
and heav'n, all saints in earth
ges run, while end less a -

in songs of ho - ly joy!
to wake th'im - pris - oned dead.
all saints in earth and heav'n.
while end - less a - ges run.

ly joy, in songs of ho - ly joy!
oned dead, to wake th'im - pris - oned dead.
and heav'n, all saints in earth and heav'n.
ges run, while end - less a - ges run.

Fulbert of Chartres, ca. 975–1028
Tr. by Robert Campbell, 1850; alt.

LYNGHAM C.M.rep.
Thomas Jarman, ca. 1803

272

O Sons and Daughters, Let Us Sing!

He is not here; he has risen! Luke 24:6

1. O sons and daugh - ters, let us sing! The King of
2. That Eas - ter morn at break of day, the faith - ful
3. An an - gel clad in white they see, who sat and
4. That night th'a - pos - tles met in fear; a - midst them

heav'n, the glo - rious King, o'er death to - day rose tri - umph - ing.
wom - en went their way to seek the tomb where Je - sus lay.
spake un - to the three, "Your Lord doth go to Gal - i - lee."
came their Lord most dear, and said, "My peace be on all here."

Al - le - lu - ia! Al - le - lu - ia!

5. When Thomas first the tidings heard,
   how they had seen the risen Lord,
   he doubted the disciples' word.
   (Alleluias)

6. "My pierced side, O Thomas, see;
   my hands, my feet, I show to thee;
   not faithless, but believing be."
   (Alleluias)

7. No longer Thomas then denied;
   he saw the feet, the hands, the side;
   "Thou art my Lord and God," he cried.
   (Alleluias)

8. How blest are they who have not seen,
   and yet whose faith hath constant been;
   for they eternal life shall win.
   (Alleluias)

9. On this most holy day of days,
   to God your hearts and voices raise
   in laud and jubilee and praise.
   (Alleluias)

Jean Tisserand, ca. 1490
Tr. by John Mason Neale, 1851

O FILII ET FILIAE 8.8.8.al.
French melody, 17th cent.

Jesus Christ Is Risen Today

273

Go quickly and tell his disciples: "He has risen from the dead." Matt. 28:7

1. Je - sus Christ is ris'n to - day, Al - le - lu - ia!
2. Hymns of praise then let us sing Al - le - lu - ia!
3. But the pains which he en - dured, Al - le - lu - ia!
4. Sing we to our God a - bove Al - le - lu - ia!

our tri - um - phant ho - ly day, Al - le - lu - ia!
un - to Christ our heav'n - ly King, Al - le - lu - ia!
our sal - va - tion have pro - cured; Al - le - lu - ia!
praise e - ter - nal as his love; Al - le - lu - ia!

who did once up - on the cross Al - le - lu - ia!
who en - dured the cross and grave, Al - le - lu - ia!
now a - bove the sky he's King, Al - le - lu - ia!
praise him, all ye heav'n - ly host, Al - le - lu - ia!

Unison

suf - fer to re - deem our loss. Al - le - lu - ia!
sin - ners to re - deem and save. Al - le - lu - ia!
where the an - gels ev - er sing. Al - le - lu - ia!
Fa - ther, Son, and Ho - ly Ghost. Al - le - lu - ia!

St. 1, anon.
St. 2-3, Arnold's *Compleat Psalmodist*, 1740
St. 4, Charles Wesley, 1740; alt.

LLANFAIR 7.7.7.7.al.
Robert Williams, 1817

274 Thine Be the Glory

Thanks be to God! He gives us the victory through our Lord Jesus Christ. 1 Cor. 15:57

1. Thine be the glo - ry, ris - en, con - qu'ring Son; end - less is the
2. Lo! Je - sus meets us, ris - en from the tomb; lov - ing - ly he
3. No more we doubt thee, glo - rious Prince of life; life is naught with -

vic - t'ry thou o'er death hast won; an - gels in bright rai - ment
greets us, scat - ters fear and gloom; let the church with glad - ness,
out thee: aid us in our strife; make us more than con - qu'rors,

rolled the stone a - way, kept the fold - ed grave - clothes,
hymns of tri - umph sing, for her Lord now liv - eth,
thro' thy death - less love: bring us safe thro' Jor - dan

REFRAIN

where thy bod - y lay.
death hath lost its sting. Thine be the glo - ry, ris - en, con - qu'ring Son;
to thy home a - bove.

end - less   is   the   vic - t'ry   thou o'er   death   hast   won.

Edmond Budry, 1884
Tr. by Richard B. Hoyle, 1923
Text · 1923, World Student Christian Federation. Used by permission.

MACCABAEUS 10.11.11.11.ref.
From George Frederick Handel, *Judas Maccabaeus*, 1747

The Strife Is O'er, the Battle Done   275

Did not the Christ have to suffer these things and then enter his glory? Luke 24:26

Al - le - lu - ia! Al - le - lu - ia! Al - le - lu - ia!

1. The strife is   o'er,   the bat - tle done; the vic - to - ry   of   life is
2. The pow'rs of   death have done their worst, but Christ their   le - gions hath dis-
3. The three sad   days have quick - ly sped; he ris - es   glo - rious from the
4. He closed the   yawn - ing gates of hell; the bars from heav'n's high   por - tals
5. Lord, by the   stripes which wound- ed thee, from death's dread sting thy   ser - vants

won;   the   song   of   tri - umph   has   be - gun.   Al - le - lu - ia!
persed: let   shouts   of   ho - ly   joy   out - burst.   Al - le - lu - ia!
• dead: all   glo - ry   to   our   ris - en Head!   Al - le - lu - ia!
fell: let   hymns of   praise   his   tri - umphs tell.   Al - le - lu - ia!
free,   that   we   may   live   and   sing   to thee.   Al - le - lu - ia!

Latin hymn
Tr. by Francis Pott, 1861

PALESTRINA 8.8.8.al.
Giovanni P. da Palestrina, 1591; arr.

276 Up from the Grave He Arose

An angel of the Lord came down from heaven and, going to the tomb, rolled back the stone and sat on it. Matt. 28:2

1. Low in the grave he lay— Je - sus, my Sav - ior,
2. Vain - ly they watch his bed— Je - sus, my Sav - ior;
3. Death can - not keep his prey— Je - sus, my Sav - ior;

wait - ing the com - ing day— Je - sus, my Lord.
vain - ly they seal the dead— Je - sus, my Lord.
he tore the bars a - way— Je - sus, my Lord.

REFRAIN
Faster

Up from the grave he a - rose, He a - rose!

with a might - y tri - umph o'er his foes. He a - rose!

He a - rose a vic - tor from the dark do - main, and he
lives for - ev - er with his saints to reign. He a - rose! He a - rose!
He a - rose! He a - rose! Hal - le - lu - jah! Christ a - rose!

Robert Lowry, 1874

CHRIST AROSE 11.10.ref.
Robert Lowry, 1874

277   Christ the Lord Is Risen Today

Thanks be to God! He gives us the victory through our Lord Jesus Christ. 1 Cor. 15:57

1. "Christ the Lord is ris'n to-day," Al - - le - lu - ia!
2. Vain the stone, the watch, the seal; Al - - le - lu - ia!
3. Lives a-gain our glo-rious King; Al - - le - lu - ia!
4. Soar we now where Christ has led, Al - - le - lu - ia!

sons of men and an-gels say; Al - - le - lu - ia!
Christ has burst the gates of hell: Al - - le - lu - ia!
where, O death, is now thy sting? Al - - le - lu - ia!
fol-l'wing our ex - alt - ed Head; Al - - le - lu - ia!

raise your joys and tri-umphs high; Al - - le - lu - ia!
death in vain for-bids his rise; Al - - le - lu - ia!
Once he died, our souls to save; Al - - le - lu - ia!
made like him, like him we rise; Al - - le - lu - ia!

sing ye heav'ns, and earth, re - ply. Al - - le - lu - ia!
Christ has o - pened par - a - dise. Al - - le - lu - ia!
where thy vic - to - ry, O grave? Al - - le - lu - ia!
ours the cross, the grave, the skies, Al - - le - lu - ia!

5. Hail, the Lord of earth and heav'n! *Alleluia!*
Praise to thee by both be giv'n; *Alleluia!*
thee we greet triumphant now; *Alleluia!*
hail, the Resurrection, thou! *Alleluia!*

Charles Wesley, 1739

EASTER HYMN 7.7.7.7.al.
Lyra Davidica, 1708; alt.

That Easter Day with Joy Was Bright 278

The disciples were overjoyed when they saw the Lord. John 20:20

1. That Eas - ter day with joy was bright: the sun shone
2. His ris - en flesh with ra - diance glowed, his wound - ed
3. O Je - sus, King of gen - tle - ness, do thou thy -
4. O Lord of all, with us a - bide in this, our

out with fair - er light when to their long - ing
hands and feet he showed; those scars their sol - emn
self our hearts pos - sess, that we may give thee
joy - ful Eas - ter - tide; from ev - 'ry weap - on

eyes re - stored, th'a - pos - tles saw their ris - en Lord.
wit - ness gave that Christ was ris - en from the grave.
all our days the will - ing trib - ute of our praise.
death can wield thine own re - deemed for - ev - er shield.

Early medieval Latin hymn
Tr. in *Hymns Ancient and Modern*, 1861; alt.

PUER NOBIS NASCITUR L.M.
Melody adapted by Michael Praetorius, 1609
Arr. by George R. Woodward, 1910

279 Christ Jesus Lay in Death's Strong Bands

God raised him from the dead, freeing him from the agony of death, because it was impossible for death to keep its hold on him. Acts 2:24

1. Christ Je - sus lay in death's strong bands, for our of - fens - es giv - en;
2. It was a strange and dread- ful strife when life and death con - tend - ed;
3. Here the true Pas - chal Lamb we see, whom God so free - ly gave us;
4. So let us keep the fes - ti - val where - to the Lord in - vites us;
5. Then let us feast this joy - ful day on Christ, the Bread of heav - en;

but now at God's right hand he stands and brings us life from heav - en;
the vic - to - ry re - mained with life, the reign of death was end - ed;
he died on the ac - curs - ed tree— so strong his love!— to save us.
Christ is him - self the joy of all, the sun that warms and lights us.
the Word of grace hath purged a - way the old and e - vil leav - en.

there - fore let us joy - ful be and sing to God right thank - ful - ly
Ho - ly Scrip - ture plain - ly saith that death is swal- lowed up by death,
See, his blood doth mark our door; faith points to it, death pass - es o'er,
By his grace he doth im - part e - ter - nal sun - shine to the heart;
Christ a - lone our souls will feed, he is our meat and drink in - deed;

loud songs of hal - le - lu - jah. Hal - le - lu - jah!
his sting is lost for - ev - er. Hal - le - lu - jah!
• and Sa - tan can - not harm us. Hal - le - lu - jah!
the night of sin is end - ed. Hal - le - lu - jah!
faith lives up - on no oth - er. Hal - le - lu - jah!

Martin Luther, 1524, cento
Tr. by Richard Massie, 1854; alt.
Alt. 1961

CHRIST LAG IN TODESBANDEN 8.7.8.7.7.8.7.4.
Medieval melody
Arr. by Johann Walther, 1524

Christ Is Risen from the Dead 280

Christ has indeed been raised from the dead.... For as in Adam all die, so in Christ all
will be made alive. 1 Cor. 15:20, 22

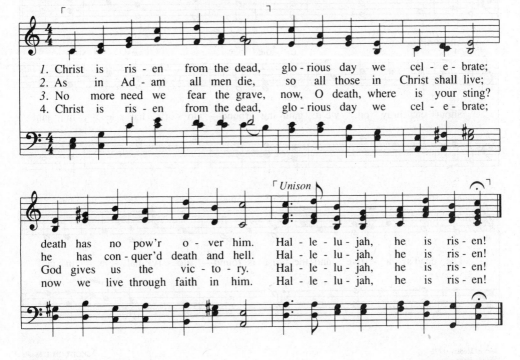

1. Christ is ris - en from the dead, glo - rious day we cel - e - brate;
2. As in Ad - am all men die, so all those in Christ shall live;
3. No more need we fear the grave, now, O death, where is your sting?
4. Christ is ris - en from the dead, glo - rious day we cel - e - brate;

Unison

death has no pow'r o - ver him. Hal - le - lu - jah, he is ris - en!
he has con - quer'd death and hell. Hal - le - lu - jah, he is ris - en!
God gives us the vic - to - ry. Hal - le - lu - jah, he is ris - en!
now we live through faith in him. Hal - le - lu - jah, he is ris - en!

Margaret Bowdler, 1973

CHRIST IS RISEN 7.7.7.8.
Norman Warren, b. 1934

281 I Know That My Redeemer Lives—Glory, Hallelujah!

I know that my Redeemer lives. Job 19:25

1. I know that my Re - deem - er lives— glo - ry, hal - le - lu - jah!
2. He lives, he lives, who once was dead— glo - ry, hal - le - lu - jah!
3. He lives to bless me with his love— glo - ry, hal - le - lu - jah!
4. He lives, all glo - ry to his name!— glo - ry, hal - le - lu - jah!

What com - fort this sweet sen - tence gives— glo - ry, hal - le - lu - jah!
He lives, my ev - er - last - ing Head— glo - ry, hal - le - lu - jah!
He lives to plead for me a - bove— glo - ry, hal - le - lu - jah!
He lives, my Je - sus, still the same— glo - ry, hal - le - lu - jah!

REFRAIN

Shout on, pray on, we're gain - ing ground— glo - ry, hal - le - lu - jah!

The dead's a - live and the lost is found— glo - ry, hal - le - lu - jah!

Samuel Medley, 1775
Refrain, anon.

SHOUT ON C.M.ref.
American folk hymn, 19th cent.; alt. 1990

Lift Up, Lift Up Your Voices Now

282

Having disarmed the powers and authorities, he made a public spectacle of them,
triumphing over them by the cross. Col. 2:15

1. Lift up, lift up your voic - es now; the whole wide
2. In vain with stone the cave they barred; in vain the
3. He binds in chains the an - cient foe; a count - less
4. And all he did, and all he bare, he gives us

world re - joic - es now: the Lord has tri - umphed
watch kept ward and guard: ma - jes - tic from the
host he frees from woe, and heav'n's high por - tal
as our own to share; and hope and joy and

glo - rious - ly, the Lord shall reign vic - to - rious - ly.
spoil - ed tomb, in pomp of tri - umph Christ is come.
o - pen flies, for Christ has ris'n, and man shall rise.
peace be - gin, for Christ has won, and man shall win.

5. O Victor, aid us in the fight,
   and lead through death to realms of light:
   we safely pass where thou hast trod;
   in thee we die to rise to God.

6. Thy flock, from sin and death set free,
   glad alleluias raise to thee;
   and ever with the heav'nly host
   praise Father, Son, and Holy Ghost.

John Mason Neale, 1854, cento
Mod.

WALTHAM L.M.
J. Baptiste Calkin, 1872

283

Alleluia! Alleluia!

Christ has indeed been raised from the dead, the firstfruits of those who have fallen asleep. 1 Cor. 15:20

1. Al - le - lu - ia! Al - le - lu - ia! Hearts to
2. Christ is ris - en, Christ the first - fruits of the
3. Al - le - lu - ia! Al - le - lu - ia! Glo - ry

heav'n and voic - es raise; sing to God a
ho - ly har - vest field, which will all its
be to God on high; al - le - lu - ia

hymn of glad - ness, sing to God a hymn of praise:
full a - bun - dance at his sec - ond com - ing yield:
to the Sav - ior, who has won the vic - to - ry;

he who on the cross a vic - tim for the
then the gold - en ears of har - vest will their
al - le - lu - ia to the Spir - it, fount of

world's sal - va - tion bled, Je - sus Christ, the
heads be - fore him wave, rip - ened by his
love and sanc - ti - ty. Al - le - lu - ia!

King of glo - ry, now is ris - en from the dead.
glo - rious sun - shine from the fur - rows of the grave.
Al - le - lu - ia to the Tri - une Maj - es - ty.

Christopher Wordsworth, 1862
Alt. 1961

EBENEZER (or TON-Y-BOTEL) 8.7.8.7.D.
Thomas John Williams, 1890

284

This Joyful Eastertide

If Christ has not been raised, our preaching is useless and so is your faith. 1 Cor. 15:14

1. This joy - ful Eas - ter - tide, a - way with sin and
2. My flesh in hope shall rest, and for a sea - son
3. Death's flood has lost its chill, since Je - sus crossed the

sor - - row! My Love, the Cru - ci - fied,
slum - - ber, till trump from east to west
riv - - er; lov - er of souls, from ill

has sprung to life this mor - - row.
shall wake the dead in num - - ber.
my pass - ing soul de - liv - - er.

REFRAIN

Had Christ, that once was slain, ne'er burst his three-day prison, our faith had been in vain: but now has Christ a-
ris - en, a - ris - en, a - ris - en,
a - ris - - - - - - en!

George R. Woodward, 1894
Alt. 1990, mod.

VRUCHTEN 6.7.6.7.ref.
Joachim Oudaen's *David's Psalmen*, 1685
Arr. by Charles Wood, 1866–1926

285

Jesus, Lord, Redeemer

*Were not our hearts burning within us while he talked with us on the road and opened
the Scriptures to us?* Luke 24:32

1. Je - sus, Lord, Re - deem - er, once for sin - ners slain,
2. Faith - ful ones, com - mun - ing toward the close of day,
3. In the up - per cham - ber, where the ten in fear

cru - ci - fied in weak - ness, raised in pow'r, to reign,
des - o - late and wea - ry, met you in the way.
gath - ered sad and trou - bled, there you did ap - pear.

dwell - ing with the Fa - ther, end - less in your days,
So, when sun is set - ting, come to us and show
So, O Lord, this eve - ning, bid our sor - rows cease;

un - to you be glo - ry, hon - or, bless - ing, praise.
all the truth; and in us make our hearts to glow.
breath - ing on us, Sav - ior, say, "I give you peace."

Patrick Miller Kirkland, b. 1857
Mod.

KING'S WESTON 6.5.6.5.D.
Ralph Vaughan Williams, 1925

Worship Christ, the Risen King!

286

He is not here; he has risen, just as he said. Matt. 28:6

1. Rise, O church, and lift your voic-es, Christ has con-quered death and hell.
2. See the tomb where death had laid him, emp-ty now, its mouth de-clares:
3. Hear the earth pro-test and trem-ble, see the stone re-moved with pow'r;
4. Doubt may lift its head to mur-mur, scoff-ers mock and sin-ners jeer;
5. We ac-claim your life, O Je-sus, now we sing your vic-to-ry;

Sing as all the earth re-joic-es; res-ur-rec-tion an-thems swell.
"Death and I could not con-tain him, for the throne of life he shares."
all hell's min-ions may as-sem-ble, but can-not with-stand his hour.
but the truth pro-claims a won-der thought-ful hearts re-ceive with cheer.
sin or hell may seek to seize us, but your con-quest keeps us free.

Come and wor-ship, come and wor-ship, wor-ship Christ, the ris-en King!
Come and wor-ship, come and wor-ship, wor-ship Christ, the ris-en King!
He has con-quered, he has con-quered, Christ the Lord, the ris-en King!
He is ris-en, he is ris-en, now re-ceive the ris-en King!
Stand in tri-umph, stand in tri-umph, wor-ship Christ, the ris-en King!

Jack W. Hayford, 1986

REGENT SQUARE 8.7.8.7.8.7.
Henry T. Smart, 1867

287 Morning Sun

Early on the first day of the week, while it was still dark, Mary Magdalene went to the tomb and saw that the stone had been removed from the entrance. John 20:1

1. On the first day of the week, Mar - y came, the
2. Hid - ing in that se - cret room, his dis - ci - ples
3. Then at last on the moun - tain - top, an - gels told them,

grave to seek; Je - sus met her
full of gloom and sor - row, sud - den - ly the
"You should stop your cry - ing, Je - sus Christ will

by the way on that first res - ur - rec - tion day!
Lord ap - peared, "Death is con - quered— dry your tears!"
come a - gain; what a glad re - u - nion then!"

James C. Ward, 1975

MUSIC ANNO DOMINI 7.7.7.7.ref.
James C. Ward, 1975

288 Jesus Christ Has Triumphed Now

He is not here; he has risen, just as he said. Matt. 28:6

1. Je - sus Christ has tri - umphed now— res - ur - rec - tion!
2. God has raised him from the dead— res - ur - rec - tion!
3. Once for all he set us free— res - ur - rec - tion!

He has con - quered death with pow'r— res - ur - rec - tion!
Ris - en our vic - to - rious Head— res - ur - rec - tion!
We shall live e - ter - nal - ly— res - ur - rec - tion!

(1.) Come see the tomb is bare— res - ur - rec - tion!
(2.) Christ died, but rose to reign— res - ur - rec - tion!

John F. Wilson, 1974, 1990

RESURRECTION (WILSON) Irreg.
John F. Wilson, 1974

289
A Hymn of Glory Let Us Sing

Why do you stand here looking into the sky? This same Jesus ... will come back in the same way you have seen him go into heaven. Acts 1:11

1. A hymn of glo-ry let us sing; new songs thro'-out the world shall
2. The ho-ly ap-os-tol-ic band up-on the Mount of Ol-ives
3. To whom the an-gels, draw-ing nigh: "Why stand and gaze up-on the
4. "A-gain shall ye be-hold him so as ye to-day have seen him

ring: Al-le-lu-ia! Al-le-lu-ia! Christ, by a road be-fore un-
stand; Al-le-lu-ia! Al-le-lu-ia! and with his fol-low-ers they
sky?" Al-le-lu-ia! Al-le-lu-ia! "This is the Sav-ior," thus they
go, Al-le-lu-ia! Al-le-lu-ia! in glo-rious pomp as-cend-ing

trod, as-cend-eth to the throne of God.
see Je-sus' re-splen-dent maj-es-ty.
say, "this is his no-ble tri-umph day." Al-le-lu-ia! Al-le-
high, up to the por-tals of the sky."

lu-ia! Al-le-lu-ia! Al-le-lu-ia! Al-le-lu-ia!

The Venerable Bede, 673–735
Tr. by Benjamin Webb, 1854; alt.
Tune from the *English Hymnal* by permission of Oxford University Press.

LASST UNS ERFREUEN L.M.al.
Geistliche Kirchengesänge, Cologne, 1623

Hail the Day That Sees Him Rise

290

Lift up your heads, O you gates; be lifted up, you ancient doors, that the King of glory may come in. Ps. 24:7

1. Hail the day that sees him rise Al - le - lu - ia!
2. There for him high tri - umph waits; Al - le - lu - ia!
3. See, he lifts his hands a - bove! Al - le - lu - ia!
4. Lord, be - yond our mor - tal sight, Al - le - lu - ia!

to his throne a - bove the skies; Al - le - lu - ia!
lift your heads, e - ter - nal gates, Al - le - lu - ia!
See, he shows the prints of love! Al - le - lu - ia!
raise our hearts to reach thy height; Al - le - lu - ia!

Christ, the Lamb for sin - ners giv'n, Al - le - lu - ia!
he hath con - quered death and sin, Al - le - lu - ia!
Hark! his gra - cious lips be - stow Al - le - lu - ia!
there thy face un - cloud - ed see, Al - le - lu - ia!

Unison

en - ters now the high - est heav'n. Al - le - lu - ia!
take the King of glo - ry in! Al - le - lu - ia!
bless - ings on his church be - low. Al - le - lu - ia!
find our heav'n of heav'ns in thee! Al - le - lu - ia!

Charles Wesley, 1739

LLANFAIR 7.7.7.7.al.
Robert Williams. 1817

291   See, the Conqueror Mounts in Triumph

When you ascended on high, you led captives in your train. Ps. 68:18

1. See, the Con-qu'ror mounts in tri-umph; see the King in roy - al state,
2. Who is this that comes in glo - ry, with the trump of ju - bi - lee?
3. You have raised our hu - man na - ture in the clouds to God's right hand;

rid - ing on the clouds, his char - iot, to his heav'n-ly pal - ace gate:
Lord of bat - tles, God of ar - mies, he has gained the vic - to - ry;
there we sit in heav'n - ly plac - es, there with you in glo - ry stand:

Hark! the choirs of an - gel voic - es joy - ful al - le - lu - ias sing,
he who on the cross did suf - fer, he who from the grave a - rose,
Je - sus reigns, a-dored by an - gels, man with God is on the throne;

and the por - tals high are lift - ed to re - ceive their heav'n-ly King.
he has van-quished sin and Sa - tan, he by death has spoiled his foes.
might - y Lord, in your as - cen - sion we by faith be - hold our own.

Christopher Wordsworth, 1862
Mod.

RUSTINGTON 8.7.8.7.D.
C. Hubert H. Parry, 1897

Who Shall Ascend the Mountain of the Lord 292

Who may ascend the hill of the LORD? Who may stand in his holy place? He who has clean hands and a pure heart. Ps. 24:3, 4

Unison

1. Who shall as - cend the moun- tain of the Lord, to search the
2. One King a - lone, whose hands and heart are pure, one Ser- vant
3. He on - ly can as- cend to God's right hand who first came
4. Be - fore the clouds re- ceive the King on high, a cross lifts
5. He shall as - cend the moun- tain of the Lord, the King of

mys - ter - y in heav - en stored, the knowl-edge of the Ho - ly
of the Lord with pur- pose sure, can en - ter in that glo - ry
• down as his high mer - cy planned; true God and man has earth and
up his form a - gainst the sky; the Fram- er of the worlds has
glo - ry, whose own blood out- poured paid that dear price that mer - cy

st. 1-4   *st. 5*

One a- dored? Al - le - lu - ia!
to en- dure. Al - le - lu - ia!
• heav- en spanned. Al - le - lu - ia!
come to die. Al - le - lu - ia!
did af- ford. Al - le - lu - ia!

Based on Psalm 24
Edmund P. Clowney, 1987
Text © 1990, Edmund P. Clowney. All rights reserved. Used by permission.

ENGELBERG 10.10.10.4.
Charles V. Stanford, 1904

293

Golden Harps Are Sounding

Christ ... entered heaven itself, now to appear for us in God's presence. Heb. 9:24

1. Gold-en harps are sound-ing, an-gel voic-es ring, pearl-y gates are
o-pened, o-pened for the King: Christ, the King of glo-ry, Je-sus,
King of love, is gone up in tri-umph to his throne a-bove.

2. He who came to save us, he who bled and died, now is crowned with
glo-ry at his Fa-ther's side. Nev-er-more to suf-fer, nev-er-
more to die, Je-sus, King of glo-ry, is gone up on high.

3. Pray-ing for his chil-dren in that bless-ed place, call-ing them to
glo-ry, send-ing them his grace; his bright home pre-par-ing, faith-ful
ones, for you; Je-sus ev-er liv-eth, ev-er lov-eth too.

REFRAIN

All his work is end-ed, joy-ful-ly we sing;

Je - sus hath as - cend - ed: glo - ry to our King!

Frances R. Havergal, 1871

HERMAS 6.5.6.5.D.ref.
Frances R. Havergal, 1871

The Golden Gates Are Lifted Up

294

I am going there to prepare a place for you. John 14:2

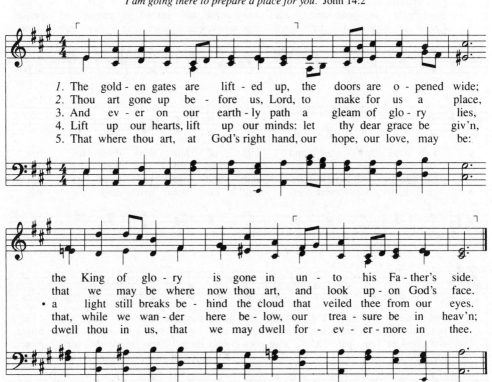

1. The gold - en gates are lift - ed up, the doors are o - pened wide;
2. Thou art gone up be - fore us, Lord, to make for us a place,
3. And ev - er on our earth - ly path a gleam of glo - ry lies,
4. Lift up our hearts, lift up our minds: let thy dear grace be giv'n,
5. That where thou art, at God's right hand, our hope, our love, may be:

the King of glo - ry is gone in un - to his Fa - ther's side.
that we may be where now thou art, and look up - on God's face.
a light still breaks be - hind the cloud that veiled thee from our eyes.
that, while we wan - der here be - low, our trea - sure be in heav'n;
dwell thou in us, that we may dwell for - ev - er - more in thee.

Cecil Frances Alexander, 1852, 1858

MIRFIELD C.M.
Arthur Cottman. 1872

295 Crown Him with Many Crowns

On his head are many crowns. Rev. 19:12

1. Crown him with man - y crowns, the Lamb up - on his throne;
2. Crown him the Lord of love; be - hold his hands and side,
3. Crown him the Lord of peace; whose pow'r a scep - ter sways
4. Crown him the Lord of years, the Po - ten - tate of time;

hark! how the heav'n - ly an - them drowns all mu - sic but its own:
rich wounds, yet vis - i - ble a - bove, in beau - ty glo - ri - fied:
from pole to pole, that wars may cease, ab - sorbed in prayer and praise:
Cre - a - tor of the roll - ing spheres, in - ef - fa - bly sub - lime:

a - wake, my soul, and sing of him who died for thee,
no an - gel in the sky can ful - ly bear that sight,
his reign shall know no end; and round his pierc - ed feet
all hail, Re - deem - er, hail! for thou hast died for me:

and hail him as thy match - less King through all e - ter - ni - ty.
but down - ward bends his burn - ing eye at mys - ter - ies so bright.
fair flow'rs of par - a - dise ex - tend their fra - grance ev - er sweet.
thy praise shall nev - er, nev - er fail through - out e - ter - ni - ty.

Matthew Bridges, 1851

DIADEMATA S.M.D.
George J. Elvey, 1868

All Hail the Power of Jesus' Name!

296

God exalted him to the highest place and gave him the name that is above every name.
Phil. 2:9

1. All hail the pow'r of Je - sus' name! Let an - gels pros - trate fall;
2. Crown him, ye mar - tyrs of your God, who from his al - tar call;
3. Ye seed of Is - rael's cho - sen race, ye ran - somed of the fall,
4. Sin - ners, whose love can ne'er for - get the worm- wood and the gall,

bring forth the roy - al di - a - dem, and crown him Lord of all;
ex - tol the Stem of Jes - se's rod, and crown him Lord of all;
hail him who saves you by his grace, and crown him Lord of all;
go, spread your tro - phies at his feet, and crown him Lord of all;

bring forth the roy - al di - a - dem, and crown him Lord of all.
ex - tol the Stem of Jes - se's rod, and crown him Lord of all.
hail him who saves you by his grace, and crown him Lord of all.
go, spread your tro - phies at his feet, and crown him Lord of all.

5. Let ev'ry kindred, ev'ry tribe,
   on this terrestrial ball,
   to him all majesty ascribe.
   and crown him Lord of all;
   to him all majesty ascribe,
   and crown him Lord of all.

6. O that with yonder sacred throng
   we at his feet may fall;
   we'll join the everlasting song,
   and crown him Lord of all;
   we'll join the everlasting song,
   and crown him Lord of all.

St. 1–5, Edward Perronet, 1779; alt.
St. 6, John Rippon, 1787

CORONATION C.M. rep.
Oliver Holden, 1793

297   All Hail the Power of Jesus' Name!

God exalted him to the highest place and gave him the name that is above every name.
Phil. 2:9

1. All hail the pow'r of Je - sus' name! Let an - gels pros-trate fall,
2. Crown him, ye mar - tyrs of your God, who from his al - tar call,
3. Ye seed of Is - rael's cho - sen race, ye ran - somed of the fall,
4. Sin - ners, whose love can ne'er for - get the worm- wood and the gall,

let an - gels pros-trate fall; bring forth the roy - al di - a - dem,
who from his al - tar call; ex - tol the Stem of Jes - se's rod,
ye ran - somed of the fall, hail him who saves you by his grace,
the worm- wood and the gall, go, spread your tro - phies at his feet,

REFRAIN

and crown . . . . him, crown him,
and crown him, crown him, crown him, crown him, crown him,

crown . . . .

crown him, crown him, and crown him Lord of all!

. . . . him.   and crown him

5. Let ev'ry kindred, ev'ry tribe
   on this terrestrial ball,
   on this terrestrial ball,
   to him all majesty ascribe,
   (Refrain)

6. O that with yonder sacred throng
   we at his feet may fall,
   we at his feet may fall!
   We'll join the everlasting song,
   (Refrain)

St. 1–5, Edward Perronet, 1779; alt.
St. 6, John Rippon, 1787

DIADEM 8.6.6.8.ref.
James Ellor, 1838

The Head That Once Was Crowned with Thorns   298

God has made this Jesus, whom you crucified, both Lord and Christ. Acts 2:36

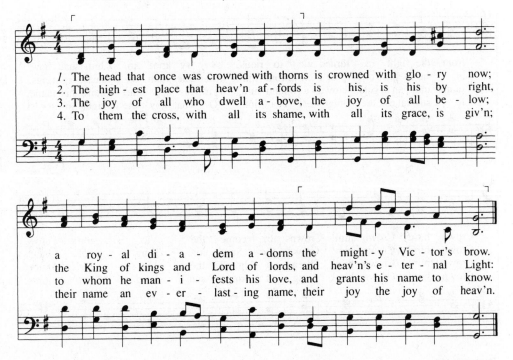

1. The head that once was crowned with thorns is crowned with glo - ry now;
2. The high - est place that heav'n af - fords is his, is his by right,
3. The joy of all who dwell a - bove, the joy of all be - low;
4. To them the cross, with all its shame, with all its grace, is giv'n;

a roy - al di - a - dem a - dorns the might - y Vic - tor's brow.
the King of kings and Lord of lords, and heav'n's e - ter - nal Light:
to whom he man - i - fests his love, and grants his name to know.
their name an ev - er - last - ing name, their joy the joy of heav'n.

5. They suffer with their Lord below,
   they reign with him above;
   their profit and their joy to know
   the myst'ry of his love.

6. The cross he bore is life and health,
   though shame and death to him;
   his people's hope, his people's wealth,
   their everlasting theme.

Thomas Kelly, 1820

ST. MAGNUS C.M.
Attr. to Jeremiah Clarke, 1701

299 Look, Ye Saints, the Sight Is Glorious

God exalted him to the highest place and gave him the name that is above every name.
Phil. 2:9

1. Look, ye saints, the sight is glo-rious: see the Man of Sor-rows now;
2. Crown the Sav-ior, an-gels, crown him; rich the tro-phies Je-sus brings;
3. Sin-ners in de-ri-sion crowned him, mock-ing thus the Sav-ior's claim;
4. Hark! those bursts of ac-cla-ma-tion! Hark! those loud tri-um-phant chords!

from the fight re-turned vic-to-rious, ev-'ry knee to him shall bow.
in the seat of pow'r en-throne him, while the vault of heav-en rings.
saints and an-gels crowd a-round him, own his ti-tle, praise his name.
Je-sus takes the high-est sta-tion; O what joy the sight af-fords!

Crown him! Crown him! Crowns be-come the Vic-tor's brow.
Crown him! Crown him! Crown the Sav-ior King of kings.
Crown him! Crown him! Spread a-broad the Vic-tor's fame!
Crown him! Crown him! King of kings and Lord of lords.

Thomas Kelly, 1809

CORONAE 8.7.8.7.4.7.
William H. Monk. 1871

Blessing and Honor and Glory and Power

300

Worthy is the Lamb, who was slain, to receive power and wealth and wisdom and strength and honor and glory and praise! Rev. 5:12

1. Bless - ing and hon - or and glo - ry and pow - er,
wis - dom and rich - es and strength ev - er - more
give ye to him who our bat - tle hath won,
whose are the king - dom, the crown, and the throne.

2. Sound - eth the heav'n of the heav'ns with his name;
ring - eth the earth with his glo - ry and fame;
o - cean and moun - tain, stream, for - est, and flow - er
ech - o his prais - es and tell of his pow - er.

3. Ev - er as - cend - eth the song and the joy;
ev - er de - scend - eth the love from on high;
bless - ing and hon - or and glo - ry and praise—
this is the theme of the hymns that we raise.

4. Give we the glo - ry and praise to the Lamb;
take we the robe and the harp and the palm;
sing we the song of the Lamb that was slain,
dy - ing in weak - ness, but ris - ing to reign.

Horatius Bonar, 1866; alt.

O QUANTA QUALIA 10.10.10.10.
La Feillée's *Méthode du plain-chant,* 1808

Tune from the *Revised Church Hymnary* by permission of Oxford University Press.

301 Join All the Glorious Names

God exalted him to the highest place and gave him the name that is above every name.
Phil. 2:9

1. Join all the glo - rious names of wis - dom, love, and pow'r,
2. Great Proph - et of my God, my tongue would bless thy name:
3. Je - sus, my great High Priest, of - fered his blood and died;
4. Thou art my Coun - sel - or, my pat - tern, and my Guide,
5. My Sav - ior and my Lord, my Con - qu'ror and my King,

that ev - er mor - tals knew, that an - gels ev - er bore: all are too
by thee the joy - ful news of our sal - va - tion came, the joy - ful
my guilt - y con - science seeks no sac - ri - fice be - side: his pow'r - ful
and thou my Shep - herd art; O keep me near thy side; nor let my
thy scep - ter and thy sword, thy reign - ing grace, I sing: thine is the

poor to speak his worth, too poor to set my Sav - ior forth.
news of sins for - giv'n, of hell sub - dued and peace with heav'n.
blood did once a - tone and now it pleads be - fore the throne.
feet e'er turn a - stray to wan - der in the crook - ed way.
pow'r; be - hold I sit in will - ing bonds be - neath thy feet.

Isaac Watts, 1707

DARWALL 6.6.6.6.8.8.
John Darwall, 1770

Come, Christians, Join to Sing

Come, let us sing for joy to the LORD. Ps. 95:1

302

1. Come, Chris-tians, join to sing   Al - le - lu - ia!   A - men!
2. Come, lift your hearts on high,   Al - le - lu - ia!   A - men!
3. Praise yet our Christ a - gain,   Al - le - lu - ia!   A - men!

loud praise to Christ our King;   Al - le - lu - ia!   A - men!
let prais - es fill the sky;   Al - le - lu - ia!   A - men!
life shall not end the strain;   Al - le - lu - ia!   A - men!

let all, with heart and voice,   be - fore his throne re - joice;
he is our Guide and Friend;   to us he'll con - de - scend;
on heav - en's bliss - ful shore,   his good - ness we'll a - dore,

praise is his gra-cious choice.   Al - le - lu - ia!   A - men!
his love shall nev - er end.   Al - le - lu - ia!   A - men!
sing - ing for - ev - er - more,   "Al - le - lu - ia!   A - men!"

Christian H. Bateman, 1843

MADRID 6.6.6.6.D.
Traditional Spanish melody
Arr. by David Evans, 1927

303
Blessed Jesus, at Your Word

Lord, to whom shall we go? You have the words of eternal life. John 6:68

1. Bless - ed Je - sus, at your word we are gath - ered
2. All our knowl - edge, sense, and sight lie in deep - est
3. Glo - rious Lord, your - self im - part, Light of light, from
4. Fa - ther, Son, and Ho - ly Ghost, praise to you and

all to hear you; let our hearts and souls be stirred
dark - ness shroud - ed, till your Spir - it breaks our night
God pro - ceed - ing; o - pen now our ears and heart,
ad - o - ra - tion! Grant that we your Word may trust

now to seek and love and fear you, by your teach - ings,
with the beams of truth un - cloud - ed. You a - lone to
help us by your Spir - it's plead - ing; hear the cry your
and ob - tain true con - so - la - tion, while we here be -

sweet and ho - ly, drawn from earth to love you sole - ly.
God can win us; you must work all good with - in us.
peo - ple rais - es, hear and bless our prayers and prais - es.
low must wan - der, till we sing your prais - es yon - der.

St. 1–3, Tobias Clausnitzer, 1663; st. 4, anon., 1707
St. 1–3 tr. by Catherine Winkworth, 1858; st. 4 trans. anon.; alt. 1990, mod.

LIEBSTER JESU 7.8.7.8.8.8.
Johann R. Ahle, 1664

I Heard the Voice of Jesus Say

Come to me, all you who are weary and burdened, and I will give you rest. Matt. 11:28

1. I heard the voice of Je - sus say, "Come un - to me and rest;
2. I heard the voice of Je - sus say, "Be - hold, I free - ly give
3. I heard the voice of Je - sus say, "I am this dark world's Light;

lay down, O wea - ry one, lay down your head up - on my breast."
the liv - ing wa - ter; thirst - y one, stoop down and drink, and live."
look un - to me, your morn shall rise, and all your day be bright."

I came to Je - sus as I was, wea - ry and worn and sad;
I came to Je - sus, and I drank of that life - giv - ing stream;
I looked to Je - sus and I found in him my Star, my Sun;

I found in him a rest - ing place, and he has made me glad.
my thirst was quenched, my soul re - vived, and now I live in him.
and in that light of life I'll walk, till trav'l - ing days are done.

Horatius Bonar, 1846
Alt. 1990. mod.

VOX DILECTI C.M.D.
John B. Dykes, 1868

305 Arise, My Soul, Arise

He is able to save completely those who come to God through him, because he always lives to intercede for them. Heb. 7:25

Charles Wesley, 1742
Alt. 1961, mod.

LENOX 6.6.6.6.8.8.8.
Louis Edson, 1782

Jesus, My Great High Priest

306

When Christ came as high priest ... he entered the Most Holy Place once for all by his own blood, having obtained eternal redemption. Heb. 9:11, 12

1. Je - sus, my great High Priest, of - fered his blood and died;
   my guilt - y con - science seeks no sac - ri - fice be - side. His
   pow'r - ful blood did once a - tone, and now it pleads be - fore the throne.

2. To this dear Sure - ty's hand will I com - mit my cause;
   he an - swers and ful - fils his Fa - ther's bro - ken laws. Be -
   hold my soul at free - dom set; my Sure - ty paid the dread - ful debt.

3. My Ad - vo - cate ap - pears for my de - fense on high;
   the Fa - ther bows his ears and lays his thun - der by. Not
   all that hell or sin can say shall turn his heart, his love, a - way.

4. Should all the hosts of death and pow'rs of hell un - known
   put their most dread - ful forms of rage and mis - chief on, I
   shall be safe, for Christ dis - plays his con-qu'ring pow'r and guard - ian grace.

Isaac Watts, 1709, cento
Alt. 1961

BEVAN 6.6.6.6.8.8.
John Goss, 1853

307

Nothing but the Blood

The blood of Jesus, his Son, purifies us from all sin. 1 John 1:7

Robert Lowry, 1876

PLAINFIELD 7.8.7.8.ref.
Robert Lowry, 1876

Jesus Paid It All

308

*Though your sins are like scarlet, they shall be as white as snow; though they are red
as crimson, they shall be like wool.* Is. 1:18

1. I hear the Sav-ior say, "Your strength in-deed is small,
2. Lord, now in-deed I find your power, and yours a-lone,
3. For noth-ing good have I where-by your grace to claim—
4. And when, be-fore the throne, I stand in him com-plete,

child of weak-ness, watch and pray, find in me your all in all."
can change the lep-er's spots, and melt the heart of stone.
I'll wash my gar-ments white in the blood of Cal-v'ry's Lamb.
"Je-sus died my soul to save," my lips shall still re-peat.

REFRAIN

Je-sus paid it all, all to him I owe;

sin had left a crim-son stain, he washed it white as snow.

Elvina M. Hall, 1865; mod.

ALL TO CHRIST 6.6.7.7.ref.
John T. Grape, 1868

309 Rejoice, the Lord Is King

After he had provided purification for sins, he sat down at the right hand of the
Majesty in heaven. Heb. 1:3

1. Re - joice, the Lord is King: your Lord and King a - dore! Re-
2. Je - sus the Sav - ior reigns, the God of truth and love; when
3. His king - dom can - not fail, he rules o'er earth and heav'n; the
4. He sits at God's right hand till all his foes sub - mit, and
5. Re - joice in glo - rious hope! Our Lord, the Judge, shall come, and

joice, give thanks, and sing, and tri - umph ev - er - more.
he had purged our stains, he took his seat a - bove.
keys of death and hell are to our Je - sus giv'n. Lift up your
bow to his com - mand, and fall be- neath his feet.
take his ser - vants up to their e - ter - nal home.

REFRAIN

heart, lift up your voice! Re - joice, a - gain I say, re - joice!

Charles Wesley, 1746; alt.

ARTHUR'S SEAT 6.6.6.6.8.8.
John Goss, 1800–1880
Arr. by Uzziah C. Burnap, 1874

Rejoice, the Lord Is King

310

After he had provided purification for sins, he sat down at the right hand of the Majesty in heaven. Heb. 1:3

1. Re - joice, the Lord is King: your Lord and King a - dore! Re -
2. Je - sus the Sav - ior reigns, the God of truth and love; when
3. His king - dom can - not fail, he rules o'er earth and heav'n; the
4. He sits at God's right hand till all his foes sub - mit, and
5. Re - joice in glo - rious hope! Our Lord, the Judge, shall come, and

joice, give thanks, and sing, and tri - umph ev - er - more.
he had purged our stains, he took his seat a - bove.
keys of death and hell are to our Je - sus giv'n. Lift up your
bow to his com - mand, and fall be - neath his feet.
take his ser - vants up to their e - ter - nal home.

REFRAIN

heart, lift up your voice! Re - joice, a - gain I say, re - joice!

Charles Wesley, 1746; alt.

DARWALL 6.6.6.6.8.8.
John Darwall, 1770

311 Hail to the Lord's Anointed

In his days the righteous will flourish; prosperity will abound till the moon is no more.
Ps. 72:7

1. Hail to the Lord's A - noint - ed, great Da - vid's great - er Son!
2. He comes with com - fort speed - y to those who suf - fer wrong;
3. He shall come down like show - ers up - on the fruit - ful earth;
4. O'er ev - 'ry foe vic - to - rious, he on his throne shall rest,

Hail, in the time ap - point - ed, his reign on earth be - gun!
to help the poor and need - y, and bid the weak be strong;
and love, joy, hope, like flow - ers, spring in his path to birth;
from age to age more glo - rious, all - bless - ing and all - blessed;

He comes to break op - pres - sion, to set the cap - tive free,
to give them songs for sigh - ing, their dark - ness turn to light,
be - fore him on the moun - tains shall peace, the her - ald, go;
the tide of time shall nev - er his cov - e - nant re - move;

to take a - way trans - gres - sion, and rule in eq - ui - ty.
whose souls, con- demned and dy - ing, were pre - cious in his sight.
and righ - teous - ness, in foun - tains, from hill to val - ley flow.
his name shall stand for - ev - er— that name to us is Love.

Based on Psalm 72
James Montgomery, 1821, 1828; alt. 1990

AURELIA 7.6.7.6.D.
Samuel S. Wesley, 1864

O God, Your Judgments Give the King

312

Endow the king with your justice, O God, the royal son with your righteousness.
Ps. 72:1

1. O God, your judg-ments give the King, his son your righ-teous-ness;
2. The peo-ple's poor ones he shall judge, the need-y's chil-dren bless;
3. His large and great do-min-ion shall from sea to sea ex-tend;
4. Now bless-ed be the Lord our God, the God of Is-ra-el,

with right he shall your peo-ple judge, your poor with up-right-ness.
and he will break in piec-es those who would the poor op-press.
it from the Riv-er shall reach forth to earth's re-mot-est end.
for he a-lone does won-drous works in glo-ry that ex-cel.

And then the moun-tains shall bring forth to all the peo-ple peace;
The just shall flour-ish in his days, and pros-per in his reign;
Yea, kings shall all be-fore him bow, all na-tions shall o-bey;
And bless-ed be his glo-rious name to all e-ter-ni-ty.

the hills be-cause of righ-teous-ness their bless-ing shall in-crease.
and while the moon en-dures he shall a-bun-dant peace main-tain.
he'll save the need-y when they cry, the poor who have no stay.
The whole earth let his glo-ry fill; a-men, so let it be.

Psalm 72:1–4, 7, 8, 11, 18, 19
Reformed Presbyterian *Book of Psalms*, 1940
Alt. 1990, mod.

OSTEND C.M.D.
Lowell Mason, 1792–1872
Arr. by Wilfred G. Clelland, 1958

313

Unto My Lord Jehovah Said

*The LORD says to my Lord: "Sit at my right hand until I make your enemies
a footstool for your feet." Ps. 110:1*

1. Un - to my Lord Je - ho - vah said, "At my right hand I
2. Your saints, to greet your day of might, in ho - ly rai - ment
3. The Lord at your right hand shall bring on rul - ers des - o -

throne you, till at your feet, in tri - umph laid, your foes their
mus - ter; as dew - drops in the morn - ing light your youths a -
la - tion; the Lord shall smite each hea - then king, and judge each

rul - er own you." From Zi - on shall Je - ho - vah send your
round you clus - ter. Je - ho - vah swore and made de - cree, "You,
reb - el na - tion. He, swift - ly march - ing in his wrath, shall

scep - ter, till be - fore you bend the knees of proud re - bel - lion.
King of Righ - teous - ness, shall be a roy - al priest for - ev - er."
quaff the brook up - on his path, and lift his head in glo - ry.

Psalm 110
Irish Psalter, 1898; mod.

ELBING 8.7.8.7.8.8.7.
Peter Sohren. 1668; alt. 1990

O Wherefore Do the Nations Rage

314

Why do the nations conspire and the peoples plot in vain? Ps. 2:1

1. O where - fore do the na - tions rage, and kings and
2. Their strength is weak - ness in the sight of him who
3. By God's de - cree his Son re - ceives the na - tions
4. Be wise, ye rul - ers of the earth, and serve the
5. De - lay not, lest his an - ger rise, and ye should

rul - ers strive in vain, a - gainst the Lord of
sits en - throned a - bove; he speaks, and judg - ments
for his her - i - tage; the con - qu'ring Christ su -
Lord with god - ly fear; with rev - 'rent joy con -
per - ish in your way; lo, all that put their

earth and heav'n to o - ver - throw Mes - si - ah's reign?
fall on them who tempt his wrath and scorn his love.
preme shall reign as King of kings, from age to age.
fess the Son while yet in mer - cy he is near.
trust in him are blest in - deed, and blest al - way.

From Psalm 2
The Psalter, 1912; alt. 1990

SAXONY L.M.
Spangenberg's *Gesangbuch*, 1568; alt. 1990

315   He Walks among the Golden Lamps

Among the lampstands was someone "like a son of man." Rev. 1:13

1. He walks a-mong the gold - en lamps on feet like bur - nished
2. And in his hand the sev - en stars and from his mouth a
3. More ra - diant than the sun at noon, who was, and is to

bronze; his hair as snows of win - ter white, his
sword; his voice the thun - der of the seas; all
be: who was, from ev - er - last - ing days; who

eyes with fire a - flame and bright; his glo - rious
crea - tures bow to his de - crees, who holds the
lives, the Lord of all our ways; to him be

robe of seam - less light sur - pass - ing Sol - o - mon's.
ev - er - last - ing keys and reigns as sov - 'reign Lord.
maj - es - ty and praise for all e - ter - ni - ty.

Timothy Dudley-Smith, 1972

REVELATION 8.6.8.8.8.6.
Noël Tredinnick, 1973

The Mighty God, the Lord

316

The Mighty One, God, the LORD, speaks and summons the earth. Ps. 50:1

1. The might - y God, the Lord, hath spo - ken un - to all;
   from ris - ing to the set - ting sun, he un - to earth doth call.
   From Zi - on, his own hill, where per - fect beau - ty dwells,
   Je - ho - vah hath his glo - ry shown, in bright - ness that ex - cels.

2. Our God shall sure - ly come, and si - lence shall not keep;
   be - fore him fire shall waste, and storms tem - pes - tuous round him sweep.
   He to the heav'ns a - bove shall then send forth his call,
   and like - wise to the earth, that he may judge his peo - ple all:

3. "To - geth - er let my saints un - to me gath - ered be,
   those that by sac - ri - fice have made a cov - e - nant with me."
   Then shall the heav'ns de - clare his righ - teous - ness a - broad;
   be - cause the Lord him - self is judge, yea, none is judge, but God.

Psalm 50:1–6
Based on *Scottish Psalter*, 1650

DIADEMATA S.M.D.
George J. Elvey, 1868

317 Wake, Awake, for Night Is Flying

Here's the bridegroom! Come out to meet him! Matt. 25:6

1. "Wake, a - wake, for night is fly - ing," the watch - men on the heights are cry - ing, "a - wake, Je - ru - sa - lem, at last!" Mid - night hears the wel - come voic - es, and at the thrill - ing cry re - joic - es: "Come forth, ye vir - gins, night is past!

2. Zi - on hears the watch - men sing - ing, and all her heart with joy is spring - ing; she wakes, she ris - es from her gloom: for her Lord comes down all - glo - rious, the strong in grace, in truth vic - to - rious; her Star is ris'n, her Light is come!

3. Now let all the heav'ns a - dore thee, and men and an - gels sing be - fore thee, with harp and cym - bal's clear - est tone; of one pearl each shin - ing por - tal, where we are with the choir im - mor - tal of an - gels round thy daz - zling throne;

The Bride-groom comes; a - wake, your lamps with glad - ness take;
Ah, come, thou bless - ed Lord, O Je - sus, Son of God,
nor eye hath seen, nor ear hath yet at - tained to hear

al - le - lu - ia! And for his mar - riage
al - le - lu - ia! We fol - low till the
what there is ours; but we re - joice, and

feast pre - pare, for you must go to meet him there."
halls we see where thou hast bid us sup with thee.
sing to thee our hymn of joy e - ter - nal - ly.

Philipp Nicolai, 1599
Tr. by Catherine Winkworth, 1858, 1863

WACHET AUF 8.9.8.8.9.8.6.6.4.8.8.
Philipp Nicolai, 1599
Arr. by Johann Sebastian Bach, 1731

318   Lo! He Comes with Clouds Descending

Look, he is coming with the clouds, and every eye will see him. Rev. 1:7

1. Lo! he comes with clouds de - scend - ing, once for fa - vored
2. Ev - 'ry eye shall now be - hold him, robed in dread - ful
3. Ev - 'ry is - land, sea, and moun - tain, heav'n and earth, shall
4. Now Re - demp - tion, long ex - pect - ed, see in sol - emn

sin - ners slain; thou - sand thou - sand saints at - tend - ing
maj - es - ty; those who set at naught and sold him,
flee a - way; all who hate him must, con - found - ed,
pomp ap - pear! All his saints, by man re - ject - ed,

swell the tri - umph of his train. Al - le - lu - ia!
pierced, and nailed him to the tree, deep - ly wail - ing,
hear the trump pro - claim the day: Come to judg - ment!
now shall meet him in the air. Al - le - lu - ia!

Al - le - lu - ia! God ap - pears on earth to reign.
deep - ly wail - ing, shall the true Mes - si - ah see.
Come to judg - ment! Come to judg - ment, come a - way!
Al - le - lu - ia! See the day of God ap - pear!

5. Yea, amen! let all adore thee,
high on thine eternal throne;
Savior, take the pow'r and glory,
claim the kingdom for thine own:
O come quickly, O come quickly;
alleluia! come, Lord, come.

St. 1–2, 5, Charles Wesley, 1758
St. 3–4, John Cennick, 1752
Alt. by Martin Madan, 1760

HOLYWOOD 8.7.8.7.8.7.
John Francis Wade's *Cantus Diversi*, 1751

Day of Judgment! Day of Wonders!   319

The trumpet will sound, the dead will be raised. 1 Cor. 15:52

1. Day of judg - ment! Day of won - ders! Hark! the trum - pet's
2. See the Judge, our na - ture wear - ing, clothed in maj - es -
3. At his call the dead a - wak - en, rise to life from
4. But to those who have con - fess - ed, loved and served the

aw - ful sound, loud - er than a thou- sand thun- ders, shakes the vast cre -
ty di - vine; you who long for his ap - pear - ing then shall say, "This
earth and sea; all the pow'rs of na - ture, shak - en by his looks, pre -
Lord be - low, he will say, "Come near, ye bless - ed, see the king- dom

a - tion round. How the sum - mons will the sin - ner's heart con - found!
God is mine!" Gra - cious Sav - ior, own me in that day as thine.
pare to flee. Care - less sin - ner, what will then be - come of thee?
I be - stow; you for - ev - er shall my love and glo - ry know."

John Newton, 1774

ST. AUSTIN 8.7.8.7.4.7.
Gregorian chant
Arr. in the *Bristol Tune Book*. 1876

320 Rejoice, All Ye Believers

Here's the bridegroom! Come out to meet him! Matt. 25:6

1. Re - joice, all ye be - liev - ers, and let your lights ap - pear;
2. See that your lamps are burn - ing; re - plen - ish them with oil;
3. Ye saints, who here in pa - tience your cross and suf - f'rings bore,
4. Our hope and ex - pec - ta - tion, O Je - sus, now ap - pear;

the eve - ning is ad - vanc - ing, and dark - er night is near:
and wait for your sal - va - tion, the end of earth - ly toil.
shall live and reign for - ev - er, when sor - row is no more:
a - rise, thou sun so longed for, o'er this be - night - ed sphere.

the Bride - groom is a - ris - ing, and soon he draw - eth nigh;
The watch - ers on the moun - tain pro - claim the Bride - groom near;
a - round the throne of glo - ry the Lamb ye shall be - hold,
With hearts and hands up - lift - ed, we plead, O Lord, to see

up, pray, and watch, and wres - tle: at mid - night comes the cry.
go meet him as he com - eth, with al - le - lu - ias clear.
in tri - umph cast be - fore him your di - a - dems of gold.
the day of earth's re - demp - tion that brings us un - to thee.

Laurentius Laurenti, 1700
Tr. by Sarah B. Findlater, 1854

LANCASHIRE 7.6.7.6.D.
Henry Smart, 1836; alt. 1990

Great God, What Do I See and Hear!

321

*The Lord himself will come down from heaven, with a loud command, with the voice
of the archangel and with the trumpet call of God. 1 Thess. 4:16*

1. Great God, what do I see and hear! The end of things cre-
2. The dead in Christ shall first a - rise, at the last trum - pet's
3. But sin - ners, filled with guilt - y fears, be - hold his wrath pre-
4. Great God, what do I see and hear! The end of things cre-

at - ed! The Judge of man - kind doth ap - pear on clouds of
sound - ing, caught up to meet him in the skies, with joy their
vail - ing; for they shall rise, and find their tears and sighs are
at - ed! The Judge of man - kind doth ap - pear on clouds of

glo - ry seat - ed! The trum - pet sounds; the graves re - store the
Lord sur - round - ing; no gloom - y fears their souls dis - may; his
un - a - vail - ing: the day of grace is past and gone; trem-
glo - ry seat - ed! Be - neath his cross I view the day when

dead which they con - tained be - fore: pre - pare, my soul, to meet him.
pres - ence sheds e - ter - nal day on those pre - pared to meet him.
bling they stand be - fore the throne, all un - pre - pared to meet him.
heav'n and earth shall pass a - way, and thus pre - pare to meet him.

St. 1, anon., 1802
St. 2-4, William B. Collyer, 1812
Alt. by Thomas Cotterill, 1820

LUTHER'S HYMN 8.7.8.7.8.8.7.
Martin Luther, 1483–1546
Arr. in Klug's *Geistliche Lieder*, 1535

322
O Quickly Come, Dread Judge of All

Behold, I am coming soon! My reward is with me. Rev. 22:12

1. O quick-ly come, dread Judge of all; for, aw-ful though thine ad-vent be, all shad-ows from the truth will fall, and false-hood die, in sight of thee: O quick-ly come, for doubt and fear like clouds dis-solve when thou art near.

2. O quick-ly come, great King of all; reign all a-round us and with-in; let sin no more our souls en-thral, let pain and sor-row die with sin: O quick-ly come, for thou a-lone canst make thy scat-tered peo-ple one.

3. O quick-ly come, true Life of all, for death is might-y all a-round; on ev-'ry home his shad-ows fall, on ev-'ry heart his mark is found: O quick-ly come, for grief and pain can nev-er cloud thy glo-rious reign.

4. O quick-ly come, sure Light of all, for gloom-y night broods o'er our way; and weak-ly souls be-gin to fall with wear-y watch-ing for the day: O quick-ly come, for round thy throne no eye is blind, no night is known.

Lawrence Tuttiett, 1854

MELITA 8.8.8.8.8.8.
John B. Dykes, 1861

Ten Thousand Times Ten Thousand

323

Many angels, numbering ... ten thousand times ten thousand ... sang: "Worthy is the Lamb, who was slain, to receive power." Rev. 5:11, 12

1. Ten thou-sand times ten thou-sand in spar-kling rai-ment bright,
the ar-mies of the ran-somed saints throng up the steeps of light:
'tis fin-ished, all is fin-ished, their fight with death and sin:
fling o-pen wide the gold-en gates, and let the vic-tors in.

2. What rush of al-le-lu-ias fills all the earth and sky!
What ring-ing of a thou-sand harps be-speaks the tri-umph nigh!
O day, for which cre-a-tion and all its tribes were made;
O joy, for all its for-mer woes a thou-sand-fold re-paid!

3. O then what rap-tured greet-ings on Ca-naan's hap-py shore;
what knit-ting sev-ered friend-ships up where part-ings are no more!
Then eyes with joy shall spar-kle, that brimmed with tears of late;
or-phans no lon-ger fa-ther-less, nor wid-ows des-o-late.

4. Bring near thy great sal-va-tion, thou Lamb for sin-ners slain;
fill up the roll of thine e-lect, then take thy pow'r and reign:
ap-pear, De-sire of na-tions, thine ex-iles long for home;
show in the heav'ns thy prom-ised sign; thou Prince and Sav-ior, come.

Henry Alford, 1867

ALFORD 7.6.8.6.D.
John B. Dykes, 1875

324 Christ Is Coming!

We wait for the blessed hope—the glorious appearing of our great God and Savior,
Jesus Christ. Titus 2:13

1. Christ is com-ing! Let cre-a-tion from her groans and tra-vail cease; let the glo-rious proc-la-ma-tion hope re-store and faith in-crease: Christ is com-ing! Christ is com-ing! Come, thou bless-ed Prince of Peace.

2. Earth can now but tell the sto-ry of thy bit-ter cross and pain; she shall yet be-hold thy glo-ry, when thou com-est back to reign: Christ is com-ing! Christ is com-ing! Let each heart re-peat the strain.

3. Long thine ex-iles have been pin-ing, far from rest, and home, and thee: but, in heav'n-ly ves-tures shin-ing, they their lov-ing Lord shall see: Christ is com-ing! Christ is com-ing! Haste the joy-ous ju-bi-lee.

4. With that bless-ed hope be-fore us, let no harp re-main un-strung; let the might-y ad-vent cho-rus on-ward roll from tongue to tongue: "Christ is com-ing! Christ is com-ing! Come, Lord Je-sus, quick-ly come!"

John Ross Macduff, 1853

NEANDER 8.7.8.7.8.7.
Joachim Neander, 1680; alt. 1990

When He Cometh, When He Cometh

325

"They will be mine," says the LORD Almighty, "in the day when I make up my treasured possession." Mal. 3:17

1. When he com - eth, when he com - eth to make up his jew - els,
2. He will gath - er, he will gath - er the gems for his king - dom,
3. Lit - tle chil - dren, lit - tle chil - dren who love their Re - deem - er,

all his jew - els, pre - cious jew - els, his loved and his own.
all the pure ones, all the bright ones, his loved and his own.
are the jew - els, pre - cious jew - els, his loved and his own.

REFRAIN

Like the stars of the morn - ing, his bright crown a - dorn - ing,

they shall shine in their beau - ty, bright gems for his crown.

William O. Cushing, 1823–1903

JEWELS 8.6.8.5.ref.
George Frederick Root, 1820–1895

326 Thou Art Coming, O My Savior

Look, he is coming with the clouds, and every eye will see him. Rev. 1:7

1. Thou art com - ing, O my Sav - ior, thou art com - ing,
2. Thou art com - ing, thou art com - ing; we shall meet thee
3. O the joy to see thee reign - ing, thee, my own be -

O my King, in thy beau - ty all re - splen - dent,
on thy way, we shall see thee, we shall know thee,
lov - ed Lord! Ev - 'ry tongue thy name con - fess - ing,

in thy glo - ry all tran - scen - dent; well may we re -
we shall bless thee, we shall show thee all our hearts could
wor - ship, hon - or, glo - ry, bless - ing brought to thee with

joice and sing: com - ing! in the o - p'ning east
nev - er say: what an an - them that will be,
glad ac - cord; thee, my Mas - ter and my Friend,

her - ald bright - ness slow - ly swells; com - ing! O my
ring - ing out our love to thee, pour - ing out our
vin - di - cat - ed and en - throned; un - to earth's re -

glo - rious Priest, hear we not thy gold - en bells?
rap - ture sweet at thine own all - glo - rious feet.
mot - est end glo - ri - fied, a - dored, and owned.

Frances Havergal, 1872

BEVERLEY 8.7.8.8.7.7.7.7.7.
William H. Monk, 1875

327

One Day He's Coming

*Christ was sacrificed once to take away the sins of many people; and he will appear
a second time, not to bear sin, but to bring salvation.* Heb. 9:28

1. One day when heav - en was filled with his prais - es,
2. One day they led him up Cal - va - ry's moun - tain,
3. One day they left him a - lone in the gar - den,
4. One day the grave could con - ceal him no lon - ger,
5. One day the trum - pet will sound for his com - ing,

one day when sin was as black as could be,
one day they nailed him to die on the tree;
• one day he rest - ed, from suf - fer - ing free;
one day the stone rolled a - way from the door;
one day the skies with his glo - ries will shine;

Je - sus came forth to be born of a vir - gin—
suf - fer - ing an - guish, de - spised and re - ject - ed:
• an - gels came down o'er his tomb to keep vig - il;
then he a - rose, o - ver death he had con - quered;
won - der - ful day, my be - lov - ed ones bring - ing;

dwelt a - mongst men, my ex - am - ple is he!
bear - ing our sins, my Re - deem - er is he!
• hope of the hope - less, my Sav - ior is he!
now is as - cend - ed, my Lord ev - er - more!
glo - ri - ous Sav - ior, this Je - sus is mine!

REFRAIN

Liv - ing, he loved me; dy - ing, he saved me; bur - ied, he

car - ried my sins far a - way; ris - ing, he jus - ti - fied

free - ly, for - ev - er: one day he's com - ing— O glo - ri - ous day!

J. Wilbur Chapman, 1910

CHAPMAN 11.10.11.10.ref.
Charles H. Marsh, 1910

328 My Lord, What a Mourning

The stars will fall from the sky ... and all the nations of the earth will mourn.
Matt. 24:29, 30

(Ref.) My Lord, what a mourn-ing, my Lord, what a mourn-ing,

my Lord, what a mourn-ing, when the stars be-gin to fall.

1. You'll hear the trum-pet sound, to wake the na-tions un-der-ground,
2. You'll hear the sin-ners mourn, to wake the na-tions un-der-ground,
3. You'll hear the Chris-tians shout, to wake the na-tions un-der-ground,
4. You'll hear the an-gels sing, to wake the na-tions un-der-ground,

look-ing to my God's right hand, when the stars be-gin to fall.

Spiritual

MOURNING 6.8.7.7.ref.
Spiritual
Arr. by Josephine Carradine Dixon, 1960

Come, O Creator Spirit Blest

329

*In him you too are being built together to become a dwelling in which God lives
by his Spirit. Eph. 2:22*

1. Come, O Cre - a - tor Spir - it blest, and in our
2. You are the Com - for - ter, we cry, sent to the
3. Bring - ing from heav'n our sev'n - fold dow'r, sign of our
4. Make our dull minds with rap - ture glow, let hu - man

hearts take up your rest; Spir - it of grace, with
earth from God Most High, foun - tain of life and
God's right hand of pow'r, O bless - ed Spir - it,
hearts with love o'er - flow; and when our fee - ble

heav'n - ly aid come to the souls whom you have made.
fire of love, and our a - noint - ing from a - bove.
prom - ised long, your com - ing wakes the heart to song.
flesh would fail, may your im - mor - tal strength pre - vail.

5. Far from our souls the foe repel,
   grant us in peace henceforth to dwell;
   ill shall not come, nor harm betide,
   if only you will be our guide.

6. Show us the Father, Holy One,
   help us to know th'eternal Son;
   Spirit divine, forevermore
   you will we trust and you adore.

Latin, 10th cent.
Trans. cento; mod.

GRACE CHURCH L.M.
Ignaz J. Pleyel, 1815; arr.

330
Holy Ghost, Dispel Our Sadness

The kingdom of God is ... righteousness, peace and joy in the Holy Spirit. Rom. 14:17

1. Ho - ly Ghost, dis - pel our sad - ness, pierce the clouds of sin - ful night;
2. From that height which knows no mea - sure, as a gra - cious show'r de - scend;
3. Come, O best of all do - na - tions God can give or we im - plore;

come, O source of sweet- est glad - ness, breathe your life and spread your light.
bring - ing down the rich - est trea - sure man can wish or God can send.
hav - ing your sweet con- so - la - tions we need wish for noth - ing more.

Lov - ing Spir - it, God of peace, great dis - trib - u - tor of grace,
Heav'n - ly Glo - ry, shin - ing down from the Fa - ther and the Son,
Come with unc - tion and with pow'r, on our souls your grac - es show'r;

rest up - on this con - gre - ga - tion; hear, O hear our sup - pli - ca - tion.
grant us your il - lu - mi - na - tion; rest up - on this con - gre - ga - tion.
au - thor of the new cre - a - tion, make our hearts your hab - i - ta - tion.

Paul Gerhardt, 1648
Tr. by John Christian Jacobi, 1725,
  and Augustus M. Toplady, 1776; alt. 1990, mod.

PSALM 42 (COBLENTZ) 8.7.8.7.7.7.8.8.
Louis Bourgeois, 1551

Come, O Come, Thou Quickening Spirit

331

I will ask the Father, and he will give you another Counselor to be with you forever—
the Spirit of truth. John 14:16, 17

1. Come, O come, thou quick - 'ning Spir - it, God from all e -
ter - ni - ty! May thy pow - er nev - er fail us;
dwell with - in us con - stant - ly. Then shall truth and
life and light ban - ish all the gloom of night.

2. Grant our hearts in full - est mea - sure wis - dom, coun - sel,
pu - ri - ty, that we ev - er may be seek - ing
on - ly that which pleas - eth thee. Let thy knowl - edge
spread and grow, work - ing er - ror's o - ver - throw.

3. Show us, Lord, the path of bless - ing; when we tres - pass
on our way, cast, O Lord, our sins be - hind thee
and be with us day by day. Should we stray, O
Lord, re - call; work re - pen - tance when we fall.

4. Ho - ly Spir - it, strong and might - y, thou who mak - est
all things new, make thy work with - in us per - fect
and the e - vil foe sub - due. Grant us weap - ons
for the strife and with vic - t'ry crown our life.

Heinrich Held, ca. 1664
Tr. by Charles W. Schaeffer, 1866; alt.; alt. 1961

LUX PRIMA 8.7.8.7.7.7.
Charles F. Gounod, 1872

332 Come, Holy Spirit, Heavenly Dove

God has poured out his love into our hearts by the Holy Spirit, whom he has given us.
Rom. 5:5

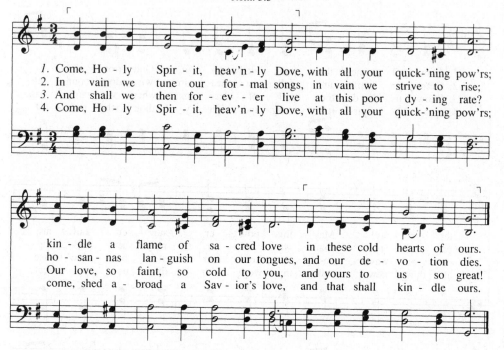

1. Come, Ho - ly Spir - it, heav'n - ly Dove, with all your quick-'ning pow'rs;
2. In vain we tune our for - mal songs, in vain we strive to rise;
3. And shall we then for - ev - er live at this poor dy - ing rate?
4. Come, Ho - ly Spir - it, heav'n - ly Dove, with all your quick-'ning pow'rs;

kin - dle a flame of sa - cred love in these cold hearts of ours.
ho - san - nas lan - guish on our tongues, and our de - vo - tion dies.
Our love, so faint, so cold to you, and yours to us so great!
come, shed a - broad a Sav - ior's love, and that shall kin - dle ours.

Isaac Watts, 1707
Mod.

ST. AGNES C.M.
John B. Dykes, 1866

333 Gracious Spirit, Dove Divine

You did not receive a spirit that makes you a slave again to fear, but you received the Spirit of sonship. Rom. 8:15

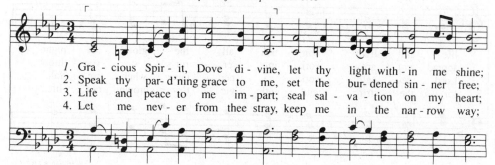

1. Gra - cious Spir - it, Dove di - vine, let thy light with - in me shine;
2. Speak thy par - d'ning grace to me, set the bur - dened sin - ner free;
3. Life and peace to me im - part; seal sal - va - tion on my heart;
4. Let me nev - er from thee stray, keep me in the nar - row way;

all my guilt-y fears re-move, fill me full of heav'n and love.
lead me to the Lamb of God, wash me in his pre-cious blood.
breathe thy-self in-to my breast, ear-nest of im-mor-tal rest.
fill my soul with joy di-vine, keep me, Lord, for-ev-er thine.

John Stocker, 1777

MERCY 7.7.7.7.
Louis M. Gottschalk, 1867; arr.

Breathe on Me, Breath of God   334

He breathed on them and said, "Receive the Holy Spirit." John 20:22

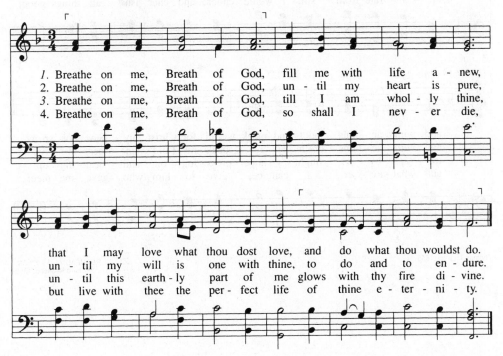

1. Breathe on me, Breath of God, fill me with life a-new,
2. Breathe on me, Breath of God, un-til my heart is pure,
3. Breathe on me, Breath of God, till I am whol-ly thine,
4. Breathe on me, Breath of God, so shall I nev-er die,

that I may love what thou dost love, and do what thou wouldst do.
un-til my will is one with thine, to do and to en-dure.
un-til this earth-ly part of me glows with thy fire di-vine.
but live with thee the per-fect life of thine e-ter-ni-ty.

Edwin Hatch, 1878

TRENTHAM S.M.
Robert Jackson, 1888

335

Gracious Spirit, Dwell with Me

*I will put my Spirit in you and move you to follow my decrees and be careful
to keep my laws. Ezek. 36:27*

1. Gra - cious Spir - it, dwell with me: I my - self would gra - cious be;
2. Truth - ful Spir - it, dwell with me: I my - self would truth - ful be;
3. Might - y Spir - it, dwell with me: I my - self would might - y be;
4. Ho - ly Spir - it, dwell with me: I my - self would ho - ly be;

and with words that help and heal would thy life in mine re - veal;
and with wis - dom kind and clear let thy life in mine ap - pear;
might - y so as to pre - vail where un - aid - ed man must fail;
sep - a - rate from sin, I would choose and cher - ish all things good,

and with ac - tions bold and meek would for Christ my Sav - ior speak.
and with ac - tions broth - er - ly speak my Lord's sin - cer - i - ty.
ev - er by a might - y hope press - ing on and bear - ing up.
and what - ev - er I can be, give to him who gave me thee!

Thomas T. Lynch, 1855

REDHEAD 76 7.7.7.7.7.7.
Richard Redhead. 1853

Spirit, Strength of All the Weak

336

I pray that ... he may strengthen you with power through his Spirit in your inner being.
Eph. 3:16

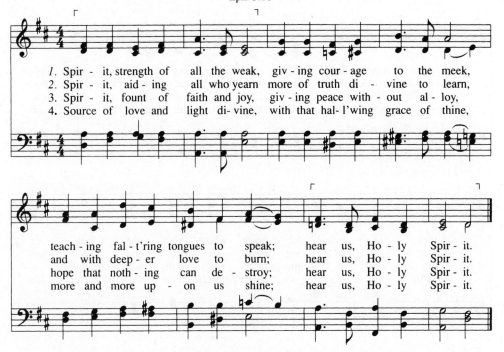

1. Spir - it, strength of all the weak, giv - ing cour - age to the meek,
2. Spir - it, aid - ing all who yearn more of truth di - vine to learn,
3. Spir - it, fount of faith and joy, giv - ing peace with - out al - loy,
4. Source of love and light di - vine, with that hal - l'wing grace of thine,

teach - ing fal - t'ring tongues to speak; hear us, Ho - ly Spir - it.
and with deep - er love to burn; hear us, Ho - ly Spir - it.
hope that noth - ing can de - stroy; hear us, Ho - ly Spir - it.
more and more up - on us shine; hear us, Ho - ly Spir - it.

5. Holy, loving, as thou art,
   come and live within our heart,
   never from us to depart;
   hear us, Holy Spirit.

6. May we soon, from sin set free,
   where thy work may perfect be,
   Jesus' face with rapture see;
   hear us, Holy Spirit.

Thomas Benson Pollock, 1836–1896

GOWER'S LITANY 7.7.7.6.
John Henry Gower, 1891

337   O Spirit of the Living God

I will pour out my Spirit on all people. Acts 2:17

1. O Spirit of the living God, in all thy
plenitude of grace, where-e'er the foot of
man hath trod, descend on our apostate race.

2. Give tongues of fire and hearts of love to preach the
reconciling word; give pow'r and unction
from above, when-e'er the joyful sound is heard.

3. Be darkness, at thy coming, light; confusion,
order in thy path; souls without strength inspire
with might; bid mercy triumph over wrath.

4. O Spirit of the Lord, prepare all the round
earth her God to meet; breathe thou abroad like
morning air, till hearts of stone begin to beat.

5. Baptize the nations; far and nigh
the triumphs of the cross record;
the name of Jesus glorify,
till every kindred call him Lord.

6. God from eternity hath willed
all flesh shall his salvation see:
so be the Father's love fulfilled,
the Savior's sufferings crowned through thee.

James Montgomery, 1823

MENDON L.M.
Traditional German melody
Arr. by Samuel Dyer, 1828

Spirit of God, Descend upon My Heart

338

Since we live by the Spirit, let us keep in step with the Spirit. Gal. 5:25

1. Spir - it of God, de - scend up - on my heart; wean it from
2. I ask no dream, no proph - et ec - sta - sies, no sud- den
3. Hast thou not bid us love thee, God and King? All, all thine
4. Teach me to feel that thou art al - ways nigh; teach me the
5. Teach me to love thee as thine an - gels love, one ho - ly

earth, through all its puls - es move; stoop to my weak - ness,
rend - ing of the veil of clay, no an - gel vis - i -
own, soul, heart, and strength and mind. I see thy cross— there
strug- gles of the soul to bear, to check the ris - ing
pas - sion fill - ing all my frame; the bap - tism of the

might - y as thou art, and make me love thee as I ought to love.
tant, no o - p'ning skies; but take the dim - ness of my soul a - way.
teach my heart to cling: O let me seek thee, and O let me find.
doubt, the reb - el sigh; teach me the pa - tience of un - an- swered prayer.
heav'n - de- scend- ed Dove, my heart an al - tar, and thy love the flame.

George Croly, 1854

MORECAMBE 10.10.10.10.
Frederick C. Atkinson. 1870

339 For Your Gift of God the Spirit

You were marked in him with a seal, the promised Holy Spirit, who is a deposit guaranteeing our inheritance. Eph. 1:13, 14

1. For your gift of God the Spir - it, pow'r to make our lives a-new,
2. He who in cre - a - tion's dawn-ing brood-ed on the life-less deep,
3. He, him-self the liv - ing Au - thor, wakes to life the sa - cred Word,
4. He, the might-y God, in-dwells us; his to strength-en, help, em-pow'r;

pledge of life and hope of glo - ry, Sav - ior, we would wor-ship you.
still a - cross our na - ture's dark-ness moves to wake our souls from sleep,
reads with us its ho - ly pa - ges and re - veals our ris - en Lord.
his to o - ver - come the tempt - er, ours to call in dan-ger's hour.

Crown - ing gift of res - ur - rec - tion sent from your as - cend - ed throne,
moves to stir, to draw, to quick - en, thrusts us through with sense of sin;
He it is who works with-in us, teach - ing reb - el hearts to pray,
In his strength we dare to bat - tle all the rag - ing hosts of sin,

full - ness of the ver - y God - head, come to make your life our own.
brings to birth and seals and fills us— sav - ing Ad - vo - cate with - in.
he whose ho - ly in - ter - ces - sions rise for us both night and day.
and by him a - lone we con - quer foes with-out and foes with - in.

5. Father, grant your Holy Spirit
in our hearts may rule today,
grieved not, quenched not, but unhindered,
work in us his sovereign way.
Fill us with your holy fullness,
God the Father, Spirit, Son;
in us, through us, then, forever,
shall your perfect will be done.

Margaret Clarkson, 1984

BLAENWERN 8.7.8.7.D.
Williams P. Rowlands, 1905

Come, Dearest Lord, Descend and Dwell 340

That Christ may dwell in your hearts through faith. Eph. 3:17

1. Come, dear - est Lord, de - scend and dwell by faith and
2. Come, fill our hearts with in - ward strength; make our en -
3. Now to the God whose pow'r can do more than our

love in ev - 'ry breast; then shall we know and
larg - ed souls pos - sess and learn the height, and
thoughts or wish - es know, be ev - er - last - ing

taste and feel the joys that can - not be ex - pressed.
breadth, and length of your un - mea - sur - a - ble grace.
hon - ors done by all the church, through Christ his Son.

Isaac Watts, 1709
Mod.

FEDERAL STREET L.M.
Henry K. Oliver, 1832

341 O Breath of Life, Come Sweeping through Us

Will you not revive us again, that your people may rejoice in you? Ps. 85:6

1. O Breath of life, come sweep-ing through us, re - vive your
2. O Wind of God, come bend us, break us, till hum - bly
3. O Breath of love, come breathe with - in us, re - new - ing
4. O Heart of Christ, once bro - ken for us, 'tis there we
5. Re - vive us, Lord! Is zeal a - bat - ing while har - vest

church with life and pow'r; O Breath of Life, come, cleanse, re -
we con - fess our need; then in your ten - der - ness re -
• thought and will and heart; come, Love of Christ, a - fresh to
find our strength and rest; our bro - ken, con - trite hearts now
fields are vast and white? Re - vive us, Lord, the world is

new us, and fit your church to meet this hour.
make us, re - vive, re - store, for this we plead.
• win us, re - vive your church in ev - ery part.
so - lace, and let your wait - ing church be blest.
wait - ing, e - quip your church to spread the light.

Bessie P. Head, ca. 1914
Mod.

SPIRITUS VITAE 9.8.9.8.
Mary J. Hammond, ca. 1920

Christ Is Made the Sure Foundation

342

The Sovereign LORD says: "See, I lay a stone in Zion, a tested stone, a precious
cornerstone for a sure foundation." Is. 28:16

1. Christ is made the sure foun-da-tion, Christ the head and cor-ner-stone,
2. All that ded-i-cat-ed cit-y, dear-ly loved of God on high,
3. To this tem-ple, where we call thee, come, O Lord of hosts, to-day:
4. Here vouch-safe to all thy ser-vants what they ask of thee to gain,
5. Laud and hon-or to the Fa-ther, laud and hon-or to the Son,

cho-sen of the Lord and pre-cious, bind-ing all the church in one;
in ex-ul-tant ju-bi-la-tion pours per-pet-ual mel-o-dy;
• with thy wont-ed lov-ing-kind-ness hear thy peo-ple as they pray;
what they gain from thee for-ev-er with the bless-ed to re-tain,
laud and hon-or to the Spir-it, ev-er Three and ev-er One,

ho-ly Zi-on's help for-ev-er, and her con-fi-dence a-lone.
God the One in Three a-dor-ing in glad hymns e-ter-nal-ly.
• and thy full-est ben-e-dic-tion shed with-in its walls al-way.
and here-af-ter in thy glo-ry ev-er-more with thee to reign.
One in might, and One in glo-ry, while un-end-ing a-ges run.

Latin, 7th cent.
Tr. by John Mason Neale, 1851
Alt. in *Hymns Ancient and Modern*, 1861

REGENT SQUARE 8.7.8.7.8.7.
Henry Smart, 1876

343 Christ Is Made the Sure Foundation

The Sovereign LORD says: "See, I lay a stone in Zion, a tested stone, a precious cornerstone for a sure foundation." Is. 28:16

1. Christ is made the sure foun - da - tion, Christ the head and
2. All that ded - i - cat - ed cit - y, dear - ly loved of
3. To this tem - ple, where we call thee, come, O Lord of
4. Here vouch - safe to all thy ser - vants what they ask of

cor - ner - stone, cho - sen of the Lord and pre - cious, bind - ing
God on high, in ex - ul - tant ju - bi - la - tion pours per -
hosts, to - day: with thy wont - ed lov - ing - kind - ness hear thy
thee to gain, what they gain from thee for - ev - er with the

all the church in one; ho - ly Zi - on's help for -
pet - ual mel - o - dy; God the One in Three a -
peo - ple as they pray; and thy full - est ben - e -
bless - ed to re - tain, and here - af - ter in thy

ev - er, and her con - fi - dence a - lone.
dor - ing in glad hymns e - ter - nal - ly.
dic - tion shed with - in its walls al - way.
glo - ry ev - er - more with thee to reign.

5. Laud and honor to the Father,
    laud and honor to the Son,
    laud and honor to the Spirit,
    ever Three and ever One,
    One in might, and One in glory,
    while unending ages run.

Latin, 7th cent.
Tr. by John Mason Neale, 1851
Alt. in *Hymns Ancient and Modern*, 1861

WESTMINSTER ABBEY 8.7.8.7.8.7.
Henry Purcell, 1659–1695
Arr. by Ernest Hawkins, 1802–1868; alt. 1990

O 'Twas a Joyful Sound to Hear   344

I rejoiced with those who said to me, "Let us go to the house of the Lord." Ps. 122:1

1. O   'twas a   joy - ful   sound to   hear our   tribes de - vout - ly say,
2. At   Sa - lem's courts we   must ap - pear with   our   as - sem - bled pow'rs
3. O   pray we   then   for Sa - lem's peace; for they shall pros- p'rous be,
4. May peace with - in   thy   sa - cred   walls a   con - stant guest be found;

"Up,   Is - rael! to   the   tem - ple   haste, and keep your fes - tal   day."
in   strong and beau - teous or - der ranged, like her   u - nit - ed tow'rs.
thou   ho - ly   cit - y   of   our   God, who bear true love   to   thee.
with   plen - ty   and   pros-per - i - ty   thy   pal - ac - es   be crowned.

5. For my dear brethren's sake, and friends
    no less than brethren dear,
    I'll pray: "May peace in Salem's tow'rs
    a constant guest appear."

6. But most of all I'll seek thy good,
    and ever wish thee well,
    for Zion and the temple's sake,
    where God vouchsafes to dwell.

Psalm 122
Tate and Brady's *New Version*, 1696, 1698
Tune by permission of Oxford University Press.

OSWALD'S TREE C.M.
H. Walford Davies, 1869–1941

345 Glorious Things of Thee Are Spoken

Glorious things are said of you, O city of God. Ps. 87:3

1. Glo - rious things of thee are spo - ken, Zi - on, cit - y of our God;
2. See, the streams of liv - ing wa - ters, spring-ing from e - ter - nal love,
3. Round each hab - i - ta - tion hov -'ring, see the cloud and fire ap - pear
4. Sav - ior, if of Zi - on's cit - y I, through grace, a mem - ber am,

he whose word can - not be bro - ken formed thee for his own a - bode:
well sup - ply thy sons and daugh-ters, and all fear of want re - move:
for a glo - ry and a cov-'ring, show- ing that the Lord is near:
let the world de - ride or pit - y, I will glo - ry in thy name:

on the Rock of A - ges found- ed, what can shake thy sure re - pose?
who can faint, while such a riv - er ev - er flows their thirst t'as-suage?—
thus de - riv - ing from their ban - ner light by night and shade by day,
fad - ing is the world-ling's plea- sure, all his boast- ed pomp and show;

With sal - va - tion's walls sur- round- ed, thou may'st smile at all thy foes.
grace which, like the Lord, the giv - er, nev - er fails from age to age.
safe they feed up - on the man - na which he gives them when they pray.
sol - id joys and last - ing trea- sure none but Zi - on's chil- dren know.

John Newton, 1779

AUSTRIAN HYMN 8.7.8.7.D.
Franz Joseph Haydn, 1797

Hail to the Brightness of Zion's Glad Morning! 346

Arise, shine, for your light has come, and the glory of the LORD rises upon you....
Nations will come to your light, and kings to the brightness of your dawn. Is. 60:1, 3

1. Hail to the bright-ness of Zi - on's glad morn - ing!
2. Hail to the bright-ness of Zi - on's glad morn - ing!
3. Lo, in the des - ert rich flow - ers are spring - ing,
4. See, from all lands, from the isles of the o - cean,

Joy to the lands that in dark - ness have lain!
Long by the proph - ets of Is - rael fore - told!
streams ev - er co - pious are glid - ing a - long;
praise to Je - ho - vah as - cend - ing on high;

Hushed be the ac - cents of sor - row and mourn - ing;
Hail to the mil - lions from bond - age re - turn - ing!
loud from the moun - tain - tops ech - oes are ring - ing,
fall'n are the en - gines of war and com - mo - tion,

Zi - on in tri - umph be - gins her mild reign.
Gen - tiles and Jews the blest vi - sion be - hold.
wastes rise in ver - dure and min - gle in song.
shouts of sal - va - tion are rend - ing the sky.

Thomas Hastings, 1831

WESLEY 11.10.11.10.
Lowell Mason, 1830

347

The Church's One Foundation

Christ Jesus himself as the chief cornerstone. Eph. 2:20

1. The church-'s one foun - da - tion is Je - sus Christ, her Lord;
2. E - lect from ev - 'ry na - tion, yet one o'er all the earth,
3. Though with a scorn - ful won - der men see her sore op - pressed,
4. The church shall nev - er per - ish! Her dear Lord to de - fend,

she is his new cre - a - tion by wa - ter and the Word:
her char - ter of sal - va - tion one Lord, one faith, one birth;
by schis - ms rent a - sun - der, by her - e - sies dis - tressed,
to guide, sus - tain, and cher - ish, is with her to the end;

from heav'n he came and sought her to be his ho - ly bride;
one ho - ly name she bless - es, par - takes one ho - ly food,
yet saints their watch are keep - ing, their cry goes up, "How long?"
though there be those that hate her, and false sons in her pale,

with his own blood he bought her, and for her life he died.
and to one hope she press - es, with ev - 'ry grace en - dued.
And soon the night of weep - ing shall be the morn of song.
a - gainst or foe or trai - tor she ev - er shall pre - vail.

5. 'Mid toil and tribulation,
   and tumult of her war,
   she waits the consummation
   of peace forevermore;
   till with the vision glorious
   her longing eyes are blest,
   and the great church victorious
   shall be the church at rest.

6. Yet she on earth hath union
   with God the Three in One,
   and mystic sweet communion
   with those whose rest is won:
   O happy ones and holy!
   Lord, give us grace that we,
   like them, the meek and lowly,
   on high may dwell with thee.

Samuel J. Stone, 1866

AURELIA 7.6.7.6.D.
Samuel S. Wesley, 1864

Jesus, with Thy Church Abide

348

The church of the living God, the pillar and foundation of the truth. 1 Tim. 3:15

1. Je - sus, with thy church a - bide, be her Sav - ior, Lord, and Guide,
2. Keep her life and doc - trine pure; grant her pa - tience to en - dure,
3. May she one in doc - trine be, one in truth and char - i - ty,
4. May she guide the poor and blind, seek the lost un - til she find,

while on earth her faith is tried: we be - seech thee, hear us.
trust - ing in thy prom - ise sure: we be - seech thee, hear us.
win - ning all to faith in thee: we be - seech thee, hear us.
and the bro - ken - heart - ed bind: we be - seech thee, hear us.

5. Save her love from growing cold,
   make her watchmen strong and bold,
   fence her round, thy peaceful fold:
   we beseech thee, hear us.

6. May her lamp of truth be bright,
   bid her bear aloft its light
   through the realms of heathen night:
   we beseech thee, hear us.

7. Arm her soldiers with the cross,
   brave to suffer toil or loss,
   counting earthly gain but dross:
   we beseech thee, hear us.

8. May she holy triumphs win,
   overthrow the hosts of sin,
   gather all the nations in:
   we beseech thee, hear us.

Thomas Benson Pollock, 1871
Alt. in *Hymns Ancient and Modern*, 1875

GOWER'S LITANY 7.7.7.6.
John Henry Gower, 1891

349   O Thou Who the Shepherd of Israel Art

Hear us, O Shepherd of Israel, you who lead Joseph like a flock. Ps. 80:1

1. O thou who the Shep-herd of Is-ra-el art, give ear to our
2. In E-phraim's, Ma-nas-seh's, and Ben-ja-min's sight, O come thou and
3. From E-gypt's dark bor-der a vine thou didst take; de-stroy-ing the
4. The axe hews it down; it is burned in the fire; they per-ish, re-
5. No more shall we wan-der, de-light-ing in shame; re-vive us, O

1. pray'r and thy fa-vor im-part; thou lead-er of Jo-seph, thou
2. save us; a-wake in thy might. O God, give us fa-vor, re-
3. hea-then didst room for it make. Where plant-ed it grew at thy
4. buked in thy ter-ri-ble ire. O lay then thy hand on the
5. Lord, we will call on thy name. O Lord God of hosts, us re-

1. guide of his way, 'mid cher-u-bim dwell-ing, thy glo-ry dis-play.
2. store to thy grace; and then we shall live in the light of thy face.
3. sov-'reign com-mand, with roots deep-ly set and boughs fill-ing the land.
4. Man of thy might, the Son of Man made to stand strong in thy sight.
5. store to thy grace; and then we shall live in the light of thy face.

Psalm 80:1–3, 8, 9, 16–19
Associate Reformed Presbyterian *Psalter*, 1931

JOANNA (or ST. DENIO) 11.11.11.11.
Traditional Welsh hymn melody

Zion Stands by Hills Surrounded

350

As the mountains surround Jerusalem, so the LORD surrounds his people both now
and forevermore. Ps. 125:2

1. Zi - on stands by hills sur - round - ed, Zi - on, kept by pow'r di - vine;
2. Ev - 'ry hu - man tie may per - ish; friend to friend un - faith - ful prove;
3. In the fur - nace God may prove thee, thence to bring thee forth more bright,

all her foes shall be con - found - ed, though the world in arms com - bine.
moth- ers cease their own to cher - ish; heav'n and earth at last re - move;
but can nev - er cease to love thee; thou art pre - cious in his sight.

Hap - py Zi - on, what a fa - vored lot is thine!
but no chang - es can at - tend Je - ho - vah's love,
God is with thee— God, thine ev - er - last - ing light,

Hap - py Zi - on, what a fa - vored lot is thine!
but no chang - es can at - tend Je - ho - vah's love.
God is with thee— God, thine ev - er - last - ing light.

Thomas Kelly, 1806

ZION 8.7.8.7.4.7.rep.
Thomas Hastings, 1830

351 Built on the Rock the Church Doth Stand

On this rock I will build my church, and the gates of Hades will not overcome it.
Matt. 16:18

1. Built on the rock the church doth stand, e - ven when
2. Sure - ly in tem - ples made with hands God, the Most
3. We are God's house of liv - ing stones, built for his
4. Yet in this house, an earth - ly frame, Je - sus his
5. Now we may gath - er with our King e'en in the

stee - ples are fall - ing; crum - bled have spires in
High, is not dwell - ing; high in the heav'ns his
• own hab - i - ta - tion; he fills our hearts, his
chil - dren is bless - ing; high - er we come to
low - li - est dwell - ing; prais - es to him we

ev - ery land, bells still are chim - ing and call - ing:
tem - ple stands, all earth - ly tem - ples ex - cel - ling.
• hum - ble thrones, grant - ing us life and sal - va - tion.
praise his name, faith in our Sav - ior con - fess - ing.
there may bring, his won - drous mer - cy forth - tell - ing.

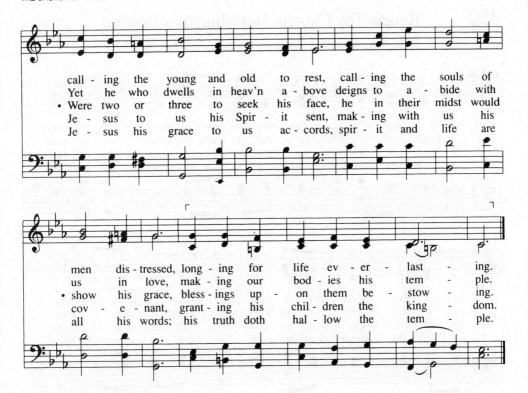

call - ing the young and old to rest, call - ing the souls of
Yet he who dwells in heav'n a - bove deigns to a - bide with
• Were two or three to seek his face, he in their midst would
Je - sus to us his Spir - it sent, mak - ing with us his
Je - sus his grace to us ac - cords, spir - it and life are

men dis - tressed, long - ing for life ev - er - last - ing.
us in love, mak - ing our bod - ies his tem - ple.
• show his grace, bless - ings up - on them be - stow - ing.
cov - e - nant, grant - ing his chil - dren the king - dom.
all his words; his truth doth hal - low the tem - ple.

Nicolai F. S. Grundtvig, 1837
Tr. by Carl Doving, 1909
Rev. by Fred C. M. Hansen, ca. 1927

KIRKEN DEN ER ET 8.8.8.8.8.8.8.8.
Ludvig M. Lindeman, 1840

352 Renew Thy Church, Her Ministries Restore

I hold this against you: You have forsaken your first love. Rev. 2:4

1. Re - new thy church, her min - is - tries re - store: both to serve
2. Teach us thy Word, re - veal its truth di - vine; on our path
3. Teach us to pray, for thou art ev - er near; thy still voice
4. Teach us to love, with strength of heart and mind, ev - ery- one,

and a - dore. Make her a - gain as salt through-out the land,
let it shine. Tell of thy works, thy might - y acts of grace;
let us hear. Our souls are rest - less till they rest in thee:
all man-kind. Break down old walls of prej - u - dice and hate;

and as light from a stand. 'Mid som - ber shad - ows
from each page show thy face. As thou hast loved us,
this our glad des - ti - ny. Be - fore thy pres - ence
leave us not to our fate. As thou hast loved and

of the night, where greed and ha - tred spread their blight,
sent thy Son, and our sal - va - tion now is won,
keep us still, that we may find for us thy will
giv'n thy life to end hos - til - i - ty and strife,

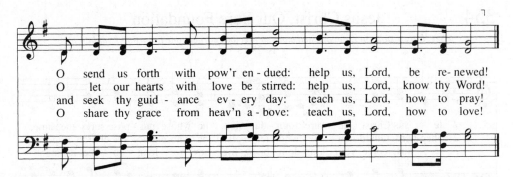

O send us forth with pow'r en-dued: help us, Lord, be re-newed!
O let our hearts with love be stirred: help us, Lord, know thy Word!
and seek thy guid-ance ev-ery day: teach us, Lord, how to pray!
O share thy grace from heav'n a-bove: teach us, Lord, how to love!

Kenneth Lorne Cober, 1960

ALL IS WELL 10.6.10.6.8.8.8.6.
J. T. White's *The Sacred Harp*, 1844

I Love Thy Kingdom, Lord 353

I love the house where you live, O LORD, the place where your glory dwells. Ps. 26:8

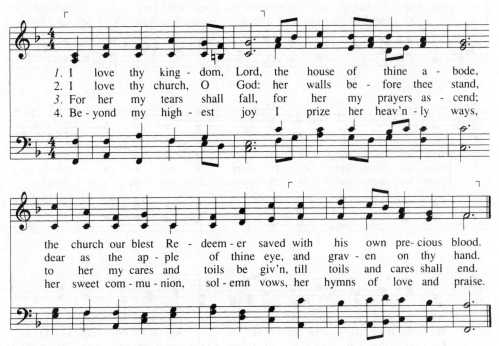

1. I love thy king-dom, Lord, the house of thine a-bode,
2. I love thy church, O God: her walls be-fore thee stand,
3. For her my tears shall fall, for her my prayers as-cend;
4. Be-yond my high-est joy I prize her heav'n-ly ways,

the church our blest Re-deem-er saved with his own pre-cious blood.
dear as the ap-ple of thine eye, and grav-en on thy hand.
to her my cares and toils be giv'n, till toils and cares shall end.
her sweet com-mu-nion, sol-emn vows, her hymns of love and praise.

5. Jesus, thou Friend divine,
   our Savior and our King,
   thy hand from ev'ry snare and foe
   shall great deliv'rance bring.

6. Sure as thy truth shall last,
   to Zion shall be giv'n
   the brightest glories earth can yield,
   and brighter bliss of heav'n.

Timothy Dwight, 1800

ST. THOMAS S.M.
Aaron Williams, 1763

354 Jesus Christ, Our Sure Foundation

See, I lay a stone in Zion, a tested stone, a precious cornerstone for a sure foundation.
Is. 28:16

1. Je - sus Christ, our sure foun - da - tion, he whose pur - pose stays the same,
2. Shep-herd, Guard-ian, he who teach- es, on whose grace the church de-pends,
3. Je - sus, come, your king-dom bring- ing, how we long to see its sight!

build - ing for him - self a na - tion, giv - ing those he calls his name.
tend - ing it through his - t'ry's reach- es, and will keep it to the end.
Ev - 'ry saint, Christ's prais- es sing- ing, stands be - fore th'e - ter- nal Light.

Praise we now and ev - er-more, Je - sus we a - dore!
Praise we now and ev - er-more, Je - sus we a - dore!
Praise we now and ev - er-more, Je - sus we a - dore!

God has giv'n to us sal - va - tion, Je - sus Christ has borne our blame.
He who from the first did seek us, Sav - ior, Rul - er, Guide, and Friend.
Ex - al - ta - tion ev - er ring - ing, Christ, our King, re - turn in might.

Mark Hunt, 1976

OAKBROOK 8.7.8.7.7.5.8.7.
Hughes M. Huffman, 1970

Text © 1976, assigned to InterVarsity Christian Fellowship. Tune © 1970, assigned to InterVarsity Christian Fellowship. Used by permission.

We Are God's People

355

We are his people, the sheep of his pasture. Ps. 100:3

Unison

1. We are God's peo - ple, the cho - sen of the Lord, born of his
2. We are God's loved ones, the Bride of Christ our Lord, for we have
3. We are the Bod - y of which the Lord is Head, called to o -
4. We are a tem - ple, the Spir - it's dwell - ing place, formed in great

Spir - it, es - tab - lished by his Word; our cor - ner - stone is
known it, the love of God out - poured; now let us learn how
bey him, now ris - en from the dead; he wills us be a
weak - ness, a cup to hold God's grace; we die a - lone, for

Christ a - lone, and strong in him we stand: O let us live trans -
to re - turn the gift of love once giv'n: O let us share each
fam - i - ly, di - verse yet tru - ly one: O let us give our
on its own each mem - ber los - es fire: yet joined in one the

par - ent - ly, and walk heart to heart and hand in hand.
joy and care, and live with a zeal that pleas - es heav'n.
gifts to God, and so shall his work on earth be done.
flame burns on to give warmth and light, and to in - spire.

Bryan Jeffery Leech, 1976

SYMPHONY 11.11.8.6.8.9.
From Johannes Brahms, *Symphony No. 1 in C Minor,* 1876
Arr. by Fred Bock, 1976

356　　　　　How Beautiful the Sight

How good and pleasant it is when brothers live together in unity! Ps. 133:1

1. How beau - ti - ful the sight of breth - ren who a - gree
2. 'Tis like the dew that fills the cups of Her - mon's flow'rs;
3. For there the Lord com - mands bless- ings, a bound- less store,

in friend - ship to u - nite, and bonds of char - i - ty; 'tis
or Zi - on's fruit - ful hill, bright with the drops of show'rs, when
from his un - spar - ing hands, yea, life for - ev - er - more: thrice

like the pre - cious oint- ment, shed o'er all his robes, from Aar - on's head.
min- gling o - dors breathe a- round, and glo - ry rests on all the ground.
hap - py they who meet a - bove to spend e - ter - ni - ty in love!

Psalm 133
James Montgomery, 1771–1854

ST. GODRIC 6.6.6.6.8.8.
John B. Dykes, 1823–1876

Let Our Choir New Anthems Raise

Be faithful, even to the point of death, and I will give you the crown of life. Rev. 2:10

1. Let our choir new an-thems raise, wake the morn with glad - ness;
2. Nev - er flinched they from the flame, from the tor - ture nev - er;
3. Faith they had that knew not shame, love that could not lan- guish;

God him - self to joy and praise turns the mar - tyrs' sad - ness:
vain the foe - man's sharp - est aim, Sa - tan's best en - deav - or:
and e - ter - nal hope o'er - came mo - men - tar - y an - guish.

bright the day that won their crown, o - pened heav'n's bright por - tal,
for by faith they saw the land decked in all its glo - ry,
Up and fol - low, Chris - tian men! Press through toil and sor - row;

as they laid the mor - tal down and put on th'im - mor - tal.
where tri - um - phant now they stand with the vic - tor's sto - ry.
spurn the night of fear and then, O the glo - rious mor - row!

Joseph the Hymnographer, ca. 800–883.
Tr. and arr. by John Mason Neale, 1862; alt.

ST. KEVIN 7.6.7.6.D.
Arthur S. Sullivan, 1872

358

For All the Saints

They will rest from their labor, for their deeds will follow them. Rev. 14:13

1. For all the saints who from their la - bors rest,
2. Thou wast their rock, their for - tress, and their might;
3. O may thy sol - diers faith - ful, true, and bold,
4. The gold - en eve - ning bright- ens in the west;
5. But lo! there breaks a yet more glo - rious day;
6. From earth's wide bounds, from o - cean's far - thest coast,

who thee by faith be - fore the world con - fessed,
thou, Lord, their Cap - tain in the well - fought fight;
fight as the saints who no - bly fought of old,
soon, soon to faith - ful war - riors comes their rest;
the saints tri - um - phant rise in bright ar - ray;
through gates of pearl streams in the count - less host,

thy name, O Je - sus, be for - ev - er blest.
and win with them the dark - ness drear, their one true light.
sweet is the calm of par - a - dise the blest.
the King of glo - ry pass - es on his way.
sing - ing to Fa - ther, Son, and Ho - ly Ghost.

Al - le - lu - ia! Al - le - lu - ia!

William Walsham How, 1864, 1875

SINE NOMINE 10.10.10.al.
Ralph Vaughan Williams, 1906

Tune from the *English Hymnal* by permission of Oxford University Press.

Blest Be the Tie That Binds 359

You are all one in Christ Jesus. Gal. 3:28

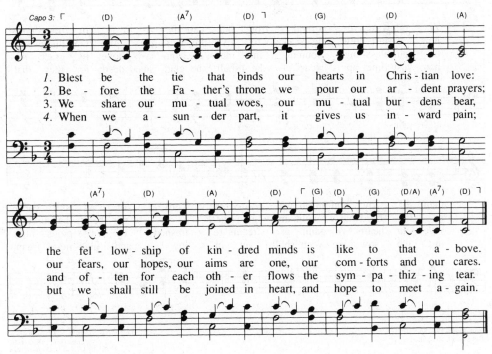

1. Blest be the tie that binds our hearts in Chris - tian love:
2. Be - fore the Fa - ther's throne we pour our ar - dent prayers;
3. We share our mu - tual woes, our mu - tual bur - dens bear,
4. When we a - sun - der part, it gives us in - ward pain;

the fel - low - ship of kin - dred minds is like to that a - bove.
our fears, our hopes, our aims are one, our com - forts and our cares.
and of - ten for each oth - er flows the sym - pa - thiz - ing tear.
but we shall still be joined in heart, and hope to meet a - gain.

5. This glorious hope revives
   our courage by the way,
   while each in expectation lives,
   and longs to see the day.

6. From sorrow, toil and pain,
   and sin, we shall be free;
   and perfect love and friendship reign
   through all eternity.

John Fawcett, 1782

DENNIS S.M.
Hans G. Nägeli, 1773–1836
Arr. by Lowell Mason, 1845

360 When in His Might the Lord

When the LORD brought back the captives to Zion, we were like men who dreamed.
Ps. 126:1

1. When in his might the Lord a - rose to set us free, and
2. The na - tions saw with fear the might of God dis - played, when
3. A - gain re - fresh us, Lord, with your re - viv - ing love, and
4. Al - though with bit - ter tears the sow - er bears his seed, when

Zi - on was re - stored from her cap - tiv - i - ty, in trans - ports
he at last drew near to give his peo - ple aid; great things for
be your bless - ing poured in mer - cy from a - bove; by grace re -
har - vest time ap - pears he shall be glad in - deed; for they that

then of joy and mirth we praised the Lord of all the earth.
us the Lord has wrought, and glad - ness to our hearts has brought.
vive our hearts a - gain, as streams re - freshed by co - pious rain.
in the sow - ing weep shall yet in joy and glad - ness reap.

From Psalm 126
The Psalter, 1912; mod.

ARTHUR'S SEAT 6.6.6.6.8.8.
John Goss, 1800–1880
Arr. by Uzziah C. Burnap, 1874

O Praise Ye the Lord

361

Praise the LORD. Sing to the LORD a new song, his praise in the assembly of the saints. Ps. 149:1

1. O praise ye the Lord and sing a new song,
2. With tim - brel and harp and joy - ful ac - claim,
3. In glo - ry ex - ult, ye saints of the Lord;
4. For this is his word: his saints shall not fail,

a - mid all his saints his prais - es pro - long;
with glad - ness and mirth, sing praise to his name;
with songs in the night high prais - es ac - cord;
but o - ver the earth their pow'r shall pre - vail;

the praise of their Mak - er his peo - ple shall sing,
for God in his peo - ple his plea - sure doth seek,
go forth in his ser - vice, be strong in his might
all king - doms and na - tions shall yield to their sway.

and chil - dren of Zi - on re - joice in their King.
with robes of sal - va - tion he cloth - eth the meek.
to con - quer all e - vil and stand for the right.
To God give the glo - ry and praise him for aye.

From Psalm 149
The Psalter, 1912

LAUDATE DOMINUM 10.10.11.11.
C. Hubert H. Parry, 1894

362   O People Blest, Whose Sons in Youth

Blessed are the people whose God is the LORD. Ps. 144:15

1. O peo - ple blest, whose sons in youth, in stur - dy strength and
2. O peo - ple blest, when flock and field their rich, a - bun - dant
3. O hap - py peo - ple, fa - vored land, to whom the Lord with

no - ble truth, like plants in vig - or spring; whose daugh-ters fair, a
in - crease yield, and bless - ings mul - ti - ply; when plen - ty all thy
lib - 'ral hand has thus his good - ness shown; yea, sure - ly is that

queen - ly race, are like the cor - ner - stones that grace
chil - dren share, and no in - vad - ing foe is there,
peo - ple blest by whom Je - ho - vah is con - fessed

the pal - ace of a king, the pal - ace of a king.
and no dis - tress - ful cry, and no dis - tress - ful cry.
to be their God a - lone, to be their God a - lone.

From Psalm 144:12–15
The Psalter, 1912; alt. 1961

SHORTLE 8.8.6.D.rep.
Charles G. Goodrich, 1905

We Gather Together

I will instruct you and teach you in the way you should go; I will counsel you and watch over you. Ps. 32:8

1. We gath - er to - geth - er to ask the Lord's bless - ing;
   he chas - tens and has - tens his will to make known;
   the wick - ed op - press - ing now cease from dis - tress - ing:
   sing prais - es to his name; he for - gets not his own.

2. Be - side us to guide us, our God with us join - ing,
   or - dain - ing, main - tain - ing his king - dom di - vine;
   so from the be - gin - ning the fight we were win - ning:
   thou, Lord, wast at our side: all glo - ry be thine!

3. We all do ex - tol thee, thou lead - er tri - um - phant,
   and pray that thou still our de - fend - er wilt be.
   Let thy con - gre - ga - tion en - dure thro' trib - u - la - tion:
   thy name be ev - er prais'd! O Lord, make us free!

Netherlands folk hymn
Tr. by Theodore Baker, 1917
Alt. 1990

KREMSER 12.11.12.11.
Adrianus Valerius's *Nederlandtsch Gedenckclank*, 1626
Arr. by Edward Kremser, 1877

364   Let Children Hear the Mighty Deeds

O my people, hear my teaching; listen to the words of my mouth. Ps. 78:1

1. Let chil - dren hear the might - y deeds which God per - formed of old;
2. He bids us make his glo - ries known, his works of pow'r and grace;
3. Our lips shall tell them to our sons, and they a - gain to theirs;
4. Thus shall they learn in God a - lone their hope se - cure - ly stands,

which in our youn - ger years we saw, and which our fa - thers told.
and we'll con - vey his won - ders down through ev - 'ry ris - ing race.
that gen - er - a - tions yet un - born may teach them to their heirs.
that they may ne'er for - get his works, but prac - tice his com - mands.

From Psalm 78:1–7
Isaac Watts, 1719

DUNDEE C.M.
Scottish Psalter, 1615

Unless the Lord the House Shall Build

365

Unless the LORD builds the house, its builders labor in vain. Ps. 127:1

1. Un - less the Lord the house shall build, the wea - ry
2. In vain you rise ere morn - ing break, and late your
3. Lo, chil - dren are a great re - ward, a gift from
4. And blest the man whose age is cheered by stal - wart

build - ers toil in vain; un - less the Lord the
night - ly vig - ils keep, and of the bread of
God in ver - y truth; with ar - rows is his
sons and daugh - ters fair; no en - e - mies by

cit - y shield, the guards a use - less watch main - tain.
toil par - take; God gives to his be - lov - ed sleep.
quiv - er stored who joys in chil - dren of his youth.
him are feared, no lack of love, no want of care.

From Psalm 127
The Psalter, 1912

ABENDS L.M.
Herbert S. Oakeley, 1874

366 My People, Give Ear, Attend to My Word

O my people, hear my teaching; listen to the words of my mouth. Ps. 78:1

1. My people, give ear, attend to my word,
in parables new deep truths shall be heard;
the wonderful story our fathers made known
to children succeeding by us must be shown.

2. Instructing our sons we gladly record
the praises, the works, the might of the Lord,
for he has commanded that what he has done
be passed in tradition from father to son.

3. Let children thus learn from history's light
to hope in our God and walk in his sight,
the God of their fathers to fear and obey,
and ne'er like their fathers to turn from his way.

4. The story be told, to warn and restrain,
of hearts that were hard, rebellious, and vain,
of soldiers who faltered when battle was near,
who kept not God's cov'nant nor walked in his fear.

5. God's wonderful works to them he had shown,
   his marvelous deeds their fathers had known;
   he made for their pathway the waters divide,
   his glorious pillar of cloud was their guide.

6. Unharmed through the sea, where perished their foe,
   he caused them with ease and safety to go;
   his holy land gaining, in peace they were brought
   to dwell in the mountain the Lord's hand had bought.

7. He gave them the land, a heritage fair;
   the nations that dwelt in wickedness there
   he drove out before them with great overthrow,
   and gave to his people the tents of the foe.

8. His servant he called, a shepherd of sheep,
   from tending his flock, the people to keep;
   so David, their shepherd, with wisdom and might
   protected and fed them and led them aright.

From Psalm 78
The Psalter, 1912

HANOVER (CROFT) 10.10.11.11.
William Croft, 1708

The Lord Will Come and Not Be Slow 367

He comes to judge ... the world in righteousness and the peoples in his truth.
Ps. 96:13

1. The Lord will come and not be slow, his foot-steps can-not err;
2. Truth from the earth, like to a flow'r, shall bud and blos-som then,
3. Rise, God, and judge the earth in might, this wick-ed earth re-dress;
4. For great you are, and won-ders great by your strong hand are done:

be-fore him righ-teous-ness shall go, his roy-al har-bin-ger.
and jus-tice, from her heav'n-ly bow'r, look down on mor-tal men.
for you are he who shall by right the na-tions all pos-sess.
you in your ev-er-last-ing seat re-main the Lord a-lone.

John Milton, 1608–1684
Alt. 1990. mod.

ST. MAGNUS C.M.
Attr. to Jeremiah Clarke, 1701

368 The Ends of All the Earth Shall Hear

*All the ends of the earth will remember and turn to the Lord, and all the families
of the nations will bow down before him.* Ps. 22:27

1. The ends of all the earth shall hear and turn un-to the
2. For his the king-dom, his of right, he rules the na-tions
3. Both rich and poor, both bond and free, shall wor-ship him on

Lord in fear; all kin-dreds of the earth shall own
by his might; all earth to him her hom-age brings,
bend-ed knee, and chil-dren's chil-dren shall pro-claim

REFRAIN

and wor-ship him as God a-lone.
the Lord of Lords, the King of kings. All earth to him
the glo-rious hon-or of his name.

her hom-age brings, the Lord of lords, the King of kings.

From Psalm 22:27–30
The Psalter, 1912

VISION L.M.ref.
William H. Doane, 1832–1916; alt. 1990

Shout, for the Blessed Jesus Reigns

They will bring all your brothers, from all the nations, to my holy mountain in Jerusalem. Is. 66:20

1. Shout, for the bless - ed Je - sus reigns; through dis - tant
2. He calls his cho - sen from a - far, they all at
3. Gen - tiles and Jews his laws o - bey; na - tions re -
4. O may his ho - ly church in - crease, his Word and
5. Loud hal - le - lu - jahs to the Lamb, from all be -

lands his tri - umphs spread; and sin - ners, freed from
Zi - on's gates ar - rive; those who were dead in
mote their of - f'rings bring, and un - con - strained their
Spir - it still pre - vail, while an - gels cel - e -
low, and all a - bove! In loft - y songs ex -

end - less pains, own him their Sav - ior and their Head.
sin be - fore by sov - ereign grace are made a - live.
hom - age pay to their ex - alt - ed God and King.
brate his praise, and saints his grow - ing glo - ries hail.
alt his name, in songs as last - ing as his love.

Benjamin Beddome, 1769

TRURO L.M.
Psalmodia Evangelica, 1789

370 Revive Thy Work, O Lord

I stand in awe of your deeds, O LORD. Renew them in our day, in our time
make them known. Hab. 3:2

1. Re - vive thy work, O Lord, thy might - y arm make bare;
2. Re - vive thy work, O Lord, dis - turb this sleep of death;
3. Re - vive thy work, O Lord, cre - ate soul - thirst for thee;
4. Re - vive thy work, O Lord, ex - alt thy pre - cious name;
5. Re - vive thy work, O Lord, give Pen - te - cos - tal show'rs;

speak with the voice that wakes the dead, and make thy peo - ple hear.
quick - en the smoul-d'ring em - bers now by thine al - might - y breath.
and hun- g'ring for the Bread of Life O may our spir - its be.
and, by the Ho - ly Ghost, our love for thee and thine in - flame.
the glo - ry shall be all thine own, the bless- ing, Lord, be ours.

Albert Midlane, 1858

FESTAL SONG S.M.
William H. Walter, 1894

O Lord of Hosts, How Lovely

371

How lovely is your dwelling place, O LORD Almighty! Ps. 84:1

1. O Lord of Hosts, how love-ly the place where thou dost dwell!
2. Blest who thy house in-hab-it, they ev-er give thee praise;
3. O hear, Lord God of Ja-cob, to me an an-swer yield;
4. Our sun and shield, Je-ho-vah, will grace and glo-ry give;

Thy tab-er-na-cles ho-ly in pleas-ant-ness ex-cel.
blest all whom thou dost strength-en, who love the sa-cred ways.
the face of thine a-noint-ed, be-hold, O God, our shield.
no good will he de-ny them that up-right-ly do live.

My soul is long-ing, faint-ing, Je-ho-vah's courts to see;
So they from strength un-wea-ried go for-ward un-to strength,
One day ex-cels a thou-sand if spent thy courts with-in;
O God of hosts, Je-ho-vah, how blest is ev-'ry-one

my heart and flesh are cry-ing, O liv-ing God, for thee.
till they ap-pear in Zi-on be-fore the Lord at length.
I'll choose thy thresh-old, rath-er than dwell in tents of sin.
who con-fi-dence re-pos-es on thee, O Lord, a-lone.

From Psalm 84
Associate Reformed Presbyterian *Psalter*, 1931; alt. 1961

LLANGLOFFAN 7.6.7.6.D.
Welsh hymn melody
David Evans's *Hymnau a Thonau*, 1865

372 Praise Waits for Thee in Zion

Praise awaits you, O God, in Zion; to you our vows will be fulfilled. Ps. 65:1

1. Praise waits for thee in Zi - on; all men shall wor - ship there
2. How blest the man thou call - est and bring - est near to thee,
3. O God of our sal - va - tion, since thou dost love the right,
4. Thy might sets fast the moun - tains; strength girds thee ev - er - more

and pay their vows be - fore thee, O God who hear - est prayer.
that in thy courts for - ev - er his dwell - ing place may be;
thou wilt an an - swer send us in won - drous deeds of might.
to calm the rag - ing peo - ples and still the o - cean's roar.

Our sins rise up a - gainst us, pre - vail - ing day by day,
he shall with - in thy tem - ple be sat - is - fied with grace,
In all earth's hab - i - ta - tions, on all the bound - less sea,
Thy maj - es - ty and great - ness are through all lands con - fess'd,

but thou wilt show us mer - cy and take their guilt a - way.
and filled with all the good - ness of thy most ho - ly place.
man finds no sure re - li - ance, no peace, a - part from thee.
and joy on earth thou send - est a - far from east to west.

5. To bless the earth thou sendest from thine abundant store
   the waters of the springtime, enriching it once more.
   The seed by thee provided is sown o'er hill and plain,
   and thou with gentle showers dost bless the springtime grain.

6. The year with good thou crownest, the earth thy mercy fills,
   the wilderness is fruitful, and joyful are the hills;
   with corn the vales are covered, the flocks in pastures graze;
   all nature joins in singing a joyful song of praise.

From Psalm 65
The Psalter, 1912

NYLAND 7.6.7.6.D.
Traditional Finnish melody
Arr. by David Evans, 1927

Tune from the *Revised Church Hymnary* by permission of Oxford University Press.

Within Your Temple, Lord

373

Within your temple, O God, we meditate on your unfailing love. Ps. 48:9

1. With - in your tem - ple, Lord, we on your mer - cies dwell; far
2. Let Zi - on's mount re - joice, let Ju - dah's daugh - ters praise the
3. The tow'rs of Zi - on tell, her pal - ac - es sur - vey, mark

as your name is known, there does your praise ex - cel: your
Lord with cheer - ful voice, for judg - ment he dis - plays; go
all her bul - warks well, and to your chil - dren say: "This

prais - es sound through ev - 'ry land, and right your scep - ter shall com - mand.
round the walls on Zi - on's mount, go round her splen - dors to re - count.
God for - ev - er shall a - bide, ev'n un - to death, our God and guide."

From Psalm 48:9–14
United Presbyterian *Book of Psalms,* 1871; alt. 1961, mod.

ST. JOHN 6.6.6.6.8.8.
Congregational Church Music, 1853

374

Arise, O Lord Our God, Arise

Arise, O LORD, and come to your resting place, you and the ark of your might.
Ps. 132:8

1. A - rise, O Lord our God, a - rise and
2. Your gra - cious cov - 'nant, Lord, ful - fil, turn
3. Your Zi - on you have cho - sen, Lord, and
4. "I will a - bun - dant - ly pro - vide for

en - ter now in - to your rest; O let this house be
not a - way from us your face; es - tab - lish here Mes -
you have said, "I love her well, this is my con - stant
Zi - on's good," the Lord has said. "I will sup - ply her

your a - bode, for - ev - er with your pres - ence blest.
si - ah's throne and let him reign with - in this place.
rest - ing place, and here will I de - light to dwell."
dai - ly need and sat - tis - fy her poor with bread."

From Psalm 132
The Psalter, 1912
Alt. 1990, mod.

HERR JESU CHRIST L.M.
Pensum Sacrum, Görlitz, 1648
Arr. by Johann Sebastian Bach, 1685–1750

Lord of the Worlds Above

Blessed are those who dwell in your house; they are ever praising you. Ps. 84:4

1. Lord of the worlds a - bove, how pleas - ant and how fair
2. O hap - py souls that pray where God ap - points to hear!
3. They go from strength to strength, through this dark vale of tears,
4. God is our sun and shield, our light and our de - fense;

the dwell - ings of thy love, thine earth - ly tem - ples, are: to
O hap - py men that pay their con - stant ser - vice there! They
till each ar - rives at length, till each in heav'n ap - pears: O
with gifts his hands are filled; we draw our bless - ings thence. Thrice

thine a - bode my heart as - pires, with warm de - sires to see my God.
praise thee still; and hap - py they that love the way to Zi - on's hill.
glo - rious seat, when God, our King, shall thith - er bring our will - ing feet!
hap - py he, O God of hosts, whose spir - it trusts a - lone in thee.

From Psalm 84
Isaac Watts, 1719; alt.

EASTVIEW 6.6.6.6.8.8.
J. V. Lee, 1959

376   Open Now Thy Gates of Beauty

One thing I ask of the LORD, this is what I seek: that I may dwell in the house of the
LORD all the days of my life, to gaze upon the beauty of the LORD. Ps. 27:4

1. O - pen now thy gates of beau - ty, Zi - on, let me en - ter there,
2. Lord, my God, I come be - fore thee, come thou al - so un - to me;
3. Here thy praise is glad - ly chant - ed, here thy seed is du - ly sown;
4. Thou my faith in - crease and quick- en, let me keep thy gift di - vine,
5. Speak, O God, and I will hear thee, let thy will be done in- deed;

where my soul in joy - ful du - ty waits for him who an- swers prayer.
where we find thee and a - dore thee, there a heav'n on earth must be.
let my soul, where it is plant- ed, bring forth pre- cious sheaves a - lone,
how - so - e'er temp - ta - tions thick- en; may thy Word still o'er me shine
may I un - dis - turbed draw near thee while thou dost thy peo - ple feed.

Oh, how bless - ed is this place, filled with so - lace, light, and grace!
To my heart, O en - ter thou, let it be thy tem - ple now!
so that all I hear may be fruit - ful un - to life in me.
as my guid - ing star through life, as my com - fort in my strife.
Here of life the foun - tain flows, here is balm for all our woes.

Benjamin Schmolck, 1732, cento
Tr. by Catherine Winkworth, 1863; alt.

NEANDER 8.7.8.7.7.7.
Joachim Neander, 1680; alt. 1990

Jesus, Where'er Your People Meet

377

Where two or three come together in my name, there am I with them. Matt. 18:20

1. Je - sus, where - e'er your peo - ple meet, there they be -
2. For you, with - in no walls con - fined, are dwell - ing
3. Dear Shep - herd of your cho - sen few, your for - mer
4. Here may we prove the pow'r of prayer to strength - en
5. Lord, we are few, but you are near; nor short your

hold your mer - cy seat; where - e'er they seek you, you are
in the hum - ble mind; such ev - er bring you where they
mer - cies here re - new; here to our wait - ing hearts pro -
faith and sweet - en care, to teach our faint de - sires to
arm, nor deaf your ear; O rend the heav'ns, come quick - ly

found, and ev - 'ry place is hal - lowed ground.
come, and go - ing, take you to their home.
claim the sweet - ness of your sav - ing name.
rise, and bring all heav'n be - fore our eyes.
down, and make a thou - sand hearts your own.

William Cowper, 1769
Alt. 1990, mod.

WARRINGTON L.M.
Ralph Harrison, 1784

378   Here, O My Lord, I See Thee Face to Face

I am the living bread that came down from heaven. John 6:51

1. Here, O my Lord, I see thee face to face; here would I touch and handle things unseen, here grasp with firmer hand th'eternal grace, and all my weariness upon thee lean.

2. Here would I feed upon the bread of God, here drink with thee the royal wine of heav'n; here would I lay aside each earthly load, here taste afresh the calm of sin forgiv'n.

3. This is the hour of banquet and of song; this is the heav'nly table spread for me: here let me feast, and, feasting, still prolong the brief, bright hour of fellowship with thee.

4. I have no help but thine, nor do I need another arm save thine to lean upon: it is enough, my Lord, enough indeed; my strength is in thy might, thy might alone.

5. Mine is the sin, but thine the righteousness; mine is the guilt, but thine the cleansing blood; here is my robe, my refuge, and my peace, thy blood, thy righteousness, O Lord my God.

Horatius Bonar, 1855

MORECAMBE 10.10.10.10.
Frederick C. Atkinson, 1870

Lord Jesus Christ, Be Present Now

379

Let us come before him with thanksgiving and extol him with music and song. Ps. 95:2

1. Lord Jesus Christ, be present now, our hearts in true devotion bow, your Spirit send with grace divine, and let your truth within us shine.

2. Unseal our lips to sing your praise, our souls to you in worship raise, make strong our faith, increase our light, that we may know your name aright:

3. Until we join the hosts that cry, "Holy are you, O Lord Most High!" And in the light of that blest place for e'er behold you face to face.

4. Glory to God the Father, Son, and Holy Spirit, Three in One! To you, O blessed Trinity, be praise throughout eternity!

Anon., 1651
Tr. by Catherine Winkworth, 1863; alt.
Mod.

HERR JESU CHRIST L.M.
Pensum Sacrum, Görlitz, 1648
Arr. by Johann Sebastian Bach, 1685–1750

380 Father, Again in Jesus' Name We Meet

*Who is a God like you, who pardons sin ...? You do not stay angry forever but delight
to show mercy. Mic. 7:18*

1. Fa - ther, a - gain in Je - sus' name we meet,
2. O we would bless you for your cease - less care,
3. A - las, un - wor - thy of your bound - less love,
4. O by that name in whom all ful - ness dwells,

and bow in pen - i - tence be - neath your feet:
and all your works from day to day de - clare:
too oft with care - less feet from you we rove;
O by that love which ev - 'ry love ex - cels,

a - gain to you our fee - ble voic - es raise,
is not our life with hour - ly mer - cies crowned?
but now, en - cour - aged by your voice, we come,
O by that blood so free - ly shed for sin,

to sue for mer - cy, and to sing your praise.
Does not your arm en - cir - cle us a - round?
re - turn - ing sin - ners to a Fa - ther's home.
o - pen blest mer - cy's gate and take us in.

Lucy E. G. Whitmore, 1824; alt.
Mod.

LONGWOOD 10.10.10.10.
Joseph Barnby, 1872

Brethren, We Have Met to Worship

381

I will rain down bread from heaven for you. Ex. 16:4

1. Breth-ren, we have met to wor-ship and a-dore the Lord our God;
2. Breth-ren, see poor sin-ners round you slum-b'ring on the brink of woe;
3. Sis-ters, will you join and help us? Mo-ses' sis-ter aid-ed him;
4. Let us love our God su-preme-ly, let us love each oth-er too;

will you pray with all your pow-er, while we try to preach the Word?
death is com-ing, hell is mov-ing— can you bear to let them go?
will you help the trem-bling mourn-ers who are strug-gling hard with sin?
let us love and pray for sin-ners till our God makes all things new.

All is vain un-less the Spir-it of the Ho-ly One comes down;
See our fa-thers and our moth-ers and our chil-dren sink-ing down;
Tell them all a-bout the Sav-ior— tell them that he will be found;
Then he'll call us home to heav-en, at his ta-ble we'll sit down;

breth-ren, pray, and ho-ly man-na will be show-ered all a-round.
breth-ren, pray, and ho-ly man-na will be show-ered all a-round.
sis-ters, pray, and ho-ly man-na will be show-ered all a-round.
Christ will gird him-self and serve us with sweet man-na all a-round.

Attr. to George Atkins, 19th cent.

HOLY MANNA 8.7.8.7.D.
Attr. to William Moore, 1825

382

God Himself Is with Us

The LORD is in his holy temple; let all the earth be silent before him. Hab. 2:20

1. God him - self is with us: let us now a - dore him,
2. God him - self is with us: hear the harps re - sound - ing!
3. O thou fount of bless - ing, pu - ri - fy my spir - it;

and with awe ap - pear be - fore him. God is in his tem - ple—
See the crowds the throne sur - round - ing! "Ho - ly, ho - ly, ho - ly"—
trust - ing on - ly in thy mer - it, like the ho - ly an - gels

all with - in keep si - lence, pros - trate lie with
hear the hymn as - cend - ing, an - gels, saints, their
who be - hold thy glo - ry, may I cease - less -

deep - est rev - 'rence. Him a - lone God we own,
voic - es blend - ing! Bow thine ear to us here:
ly a - dore thee, and in all, great and small,

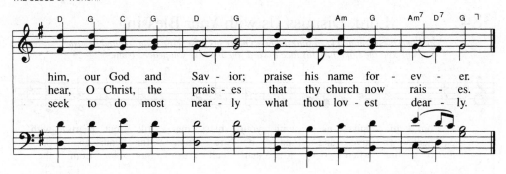

him,   our God and   Sav - ior;   praise his name for - ev -   er.
hear,   O Christ, the   prais - es   that   thy church now rais -   es.
seek to do most   near - ly   what thou lov - est   dear -   ly.

Gerhard Tersteegen, 1729
Tr. by Frederick W. Foster and John Miller, 1789; alt.

WUNDERBARER KÖNIG 6.6.8.6.6.8.3.3.6.6.
Joachim Neander, 1680; alt. 1990

Almighty God, Your Word Is Cast   383

The one who received the seed that fell on good soil is the man who hears the word and understands it. He produces a crop. Matt. 13:23

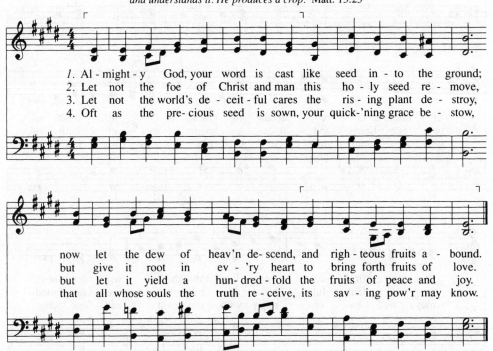

1. Al - might - y   God, your word is cast like seed in - to the ground;
2. Let not   the foe of Christ and man this ho - ly seed re - move,
3. Let not   the world's de - ceit - ful cares the ris - ing plant de - stroy,
4. Oft as   the pre - cious seed is sown, your quick - 'ning grace be - stow,

now let the dew of heav'n de - scend, and righ - teous fruits a - bound.
but give it root in ev - 'ry heart to bring forth fruits of love.
but let it yield a hun - dred - fold the fruits of peace and joy.
that all whose souls the truth re - ceive, its sav - ing pow'r may know.

John Cawood, 1819

DUNFERMLINE C.M.
Scottish Psalter, 1615

384 Lord, Dismiss Us with Your Blessing

The LORD bless you and keep you; the LORD make his face shine upon you and be gracious to you; the LORD turn his face toward you and give you peace. Num. 6:24–26

1. Lord, dis - miss us with your bless - ing; fill our hearts with
2. Thanks we give and ad - o - ra - tion for your gos - pel's
3. So that when your love shall call us, Sav - ior, from the

joy and peace; let us each, your love pos - sess - ing,
joy - ful sound: may the fruits of your sal - va - tion
world a - way, let no fear of death ap - pall us,

tri - umph in re - deem - ing grace: O re - fresh us,
in our hearts and lives a - bound: ev - er faith - ful,
glad your sum - mons to o - bey: may we ev - er,

O re - fresh us, trav - 'ling through this wil - der - ness.
ev - er faith - ful, to the truth may we be found;
may we ev - er reign with you in end - less day.

Attr. to John Fawcett, 1773; alt.
St. 3 recast by Godfrey Thring; mod.

SICILIAN MARINERS 8.7.8.7.8.7.
Sicilian melody, 18th cent.; arr.

God Be with You Till We Meet Again

385

I commit you to God and to the word of his grace, which can build you up. Acts 20:32

Unison

1. God be with you till we meet a - gain;
2. God be with you till we meet a - gain;
3. God be with you till we meet a - gain;
4. God be with you till we meet a - gain;

Harmony

by his coun - sels guide, up - hold you, with his sheep se-
'neath his wings pro - tect - ing hide you, dai - ly man - na
when life's per - ils thick con - found you, put his lov - ing
keep love's ban - ner float - ing o'er you, smite death's threat- 'ning

Unison

cure - ly fold you: God be with you till we meet a - gain.
still pro - vide you: God be with you till we meet a - gain.
arms a - round you: God be with you till we meet a - gain.
wave be - fore you: God be with you till we meet a - gain.

Jeremiah E. Rankin, 1880

RANDOLPH Irreg.
Ralph Vaughan Williams, 1906

Tune from the *English Hymnal* by permission of Oxford University Press.

386 God Be with You Till We Meet Again

I commit you to God and to the word of his grace, which can build you up. Acts 20:32

1. God be with you till we meet again; by his
2. God be with you till we meet again; 'neath his
3. God be with you till we meet again; when life's
4. God be with you till we meet again; keep love's

coun - sels guide, up - hold you, with his sheep se - cure - ly
wings pro - tect - ing hide you, dai - ly man - na still pro -
per - ils thick con - found you, put his lov - ing arms a -
ban - ner float - ing o'er you, smite death's threat-'ning wave be -

fold you: God be with you till we meet a - gain.
vide you: God be with you till we meet a - gain.
round you: God be with you till we meet a - gain.
fore you: God be with you till we meet a - gain.

REFRAIN

Till we meet, till we meet, till we meet at Je - sus' feet; till we

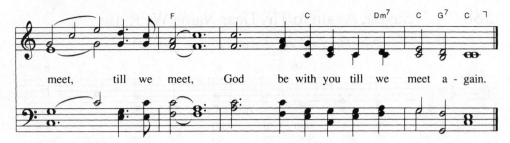

meet, till we meet, God be with you till we meet a - gain.

Jeremiah E. Rankin, 1880

GOD BE WITH YOU 9.8.8.9.ref.
William G. Tomer, 1880

Now May He Who from the Dead 387

May the God of peace, who ... brought back from the dead our Lord Jesus ... equip you
with everything good for doing his will. Heb. 13:20, 21

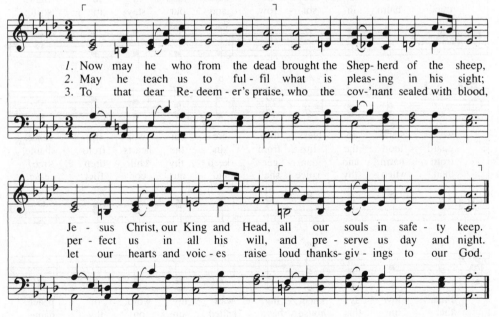

1. Now may he who from the dead brought the Shep-herd of the sheep,
2. May he teach us to ful - fil what is pleas- ing in his sight;
3. To that dear Re - deem - er's praise, who the cov-'nant sealed with blood,

Je - sus Christ, our King and Head, all our souls in safe - ty keep.
per - fect us in all his will, and pre - serve us day and night.
let our hearts and voic - es raise loud thanks- giv - ings to our God.

John Newton, 1779

MERCY 7.7.7.7.
Louis M. Gottschalk, 1867: arr.

388 Savior, Again to Thy Dear Name We Raise

Peace I leave with you; my peace I give you. John 14:27

1. Sav - ior, a - gain to thy dear name we raise
2. Grant us thy peace up - on our home - ward way;
3. Grant us thy peace, Lord, through the com - ing night;
4. Grant us thy peace through - out our earth - ly life,

with one ac - cord our part - ing hymn of praise;
with thee be - gan, with thee shall end the day;
turn thou for us its dark - ness in - to light;
our balm in sor - row, and our stay in strife;

we stand to bless thee ere our wor - ship cease;
guard thou the lips from sin, the hearts from shame,
from harm and dan - ger keep thy chil - dren free,
then, when thy voice shall bid our con - flict cease,

then, low - ly kneel - ing, wait thy word of peace.
that in this house have called up - on thy name.
for dark and light are both a - like to thee.
call us, O Lord, to thine e - ter - nal peace.

John Ellerton, 1866, 1868

ELLERS 10.10.10.10.
Edward J. Hopkins, 1869

This Is the Day the Lord Has Made

389

This is the day the LORD has made; let us rejoice and be glad in it. Ps. 118:24

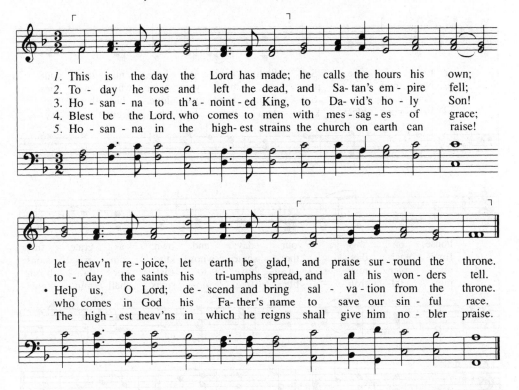

1. This is the day the Lord has made; he calls the hours his own;
2. To - day he rose and left the dead, and Sa- tan's em - pire fell;
3. Ho - san - na to th'a - noint - ed King, to Da- vid's ho - ly Son!
4. Blest be the Lord, who comes to men with mes - sag - es of grace;
5. Ho - san - na in the high- est strains the church on earth can raise!

let heav'n re - joice, let earth be glad, and praise sur - round the throne.
to - day the saints his tri- umphs spread, and all his won - ders tell.
Help us, O Lord; de - scend and bring sal - va - tion from the throne.
who comes in God his Fa- ther's name to save our sin - ful race.
The high - est heav'ns in which he reigns shall give him no - bler praise.

Based on Psalm 118
Isaac Watts, 1719

ARLINGTON C.M.
Thomas A. Arne, 1762
Arr. by Ralph Harrison, 1784

390 Lord of the Sabbath, Hear Us Pray

The Son of Man is Lord of the Sabbath. Matt. 12:8

1. Lord of the Sabbath, hear us pray, in this your house, on this your day; and own, as grateful sacrifice, the songs which from your temple rise.

2. Now met to pray and bless your name, whose mercies flow each day the same, whose kind compassions never cease, we seek instruction, pardon, peace.

3. Your earthly Sabbaths, Lord, we love, but there's a nobler rest above; to that our laboring souls aspire with ardent hope and strong desire.

4. In your blest kingdom we shall be from every mortal trouble free; no sighs shall mingle with the songs resounding from immortal tongues;

5. No rude alarms of raging foes;
no cares to break the long repose;
no midnight shade, no waning moon,
but sacred, high, eternal noon.

6. O long-expected day, begin,
dawn on these realms of woe and sin!
Break, morn of God, upon our eyes;
and let the world's true Sun arise!

Philip Doddridge, 1737
Alt. by Thomas Cotterill, 1819, and others; mod.

GERMANY L.M.
William Gardiner's *Sacred Melodies*, 1815

Safely through Another Week

"From one New Moon to another and from one Sabbath to another, all mankind will come and bow down before me," says the LORD. Is. 66:23

1. Safe - ly through an - oth - er week God has brought us on our way;
2. While we pray for par - d'ning grace, through the dear Re - deem - er's name,
3. Here we come thy name to praise, let us feel thy pres - ence near;
4. May thy gos - pel's joy - ful sound con - quer sin - ners, com - fort saints;

let us now a bless - ing seek, wait - ing in his courts to - day;
show thy rec - on - cil - ing face; take a - way our sin and shame;
may thy glo - ry meet our eyes, while we in thy house ap - pear:
may the fruits of grace a - bound, bring re - lief for all com - plaints:

day of all the week the best, em - blem of e - ter - nal rest,
from our world - ly cares set free, may we rest this day in thee,
here af - ford us, Lord, a taste of our ev - er - last - ing feast,
thus may all our Sab - baths prove, till we join the church a - bove,

day of all the week the best, em - blem of e - ter - nal rest.
from our world - ly cares set free, may we rest this day in thee.
here af - ford us, Lord, a taste of our ev - er - last - ing feast.
thus may all our Sab - baths prove, till we join the church a - bove.

John Newton, 1774; alt.

SABBATH 7.7.7.7.7.7.
Lowell Mason. 1824; alt. 1990

392

O Day of Rest and Gladness

If you call the Sabbath a delight and the Lord's holy day honorable ... then you will find your joy in the Lord. Is. 58:13, 14

1. O day of rest and glad-ness, O day of joy and light,
2. On you, at the cre - a - tion, the light first had its birth;
3. You are a port pro - tect - ed from storms that round us rise,
4. To - day on wea - ry na - tions the heav'n - ly man - na falls;
5. New grac - es ev - er gain - ing from this our day of rest,

O balm of care and sad-ness, most beau - ti - ful, most bright,
on you, for our sal - va - tion, Christ rose from depths of earth;
• a gar - den in - ter - sect - ed with streams of par - a - dise;
to ho - ly con - vo - ca - tions the sil - ver trum - pet calls,
we reach the rest re - main - ing to spir - its of the blest.

on you the high and low - ly, through a - ges joined in tune,
on you our Lord, vic - to - rious, the Spir - it sent from heav'n;
• you are a cool - ing foun - tain in life's dry, drea - ry sand;
where gos - pel light is glow - ing with pure and ra - diant beams,
To Ho - ly Ghost be prais - es, to Fa - ther, and to Son;

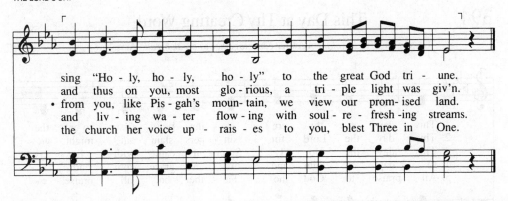

sing "Ho - ly, ho - ly, ho - ly" to the great God tri - une.
and thus on you, most glo - rious, a tri - ple light was giv'n.
• from you, like Pis - gah's moun - tain, we view our prom - ised land.
and liv - ing wa - ter flow - ing with soul - re - fresh -ing streams.
the church her voice up - rais - es to you, blest Three in One.

Christopher Wordsworth, 1862
Mod.

MENDEBRAS 7.6.7.6.D.
Traditional German melody
Arr. by Lowell Mason, 1839

Come, Let Us Join with One Accord 393

There remains, then, a Sabbath-rest for the people of God. Heb. 4:9

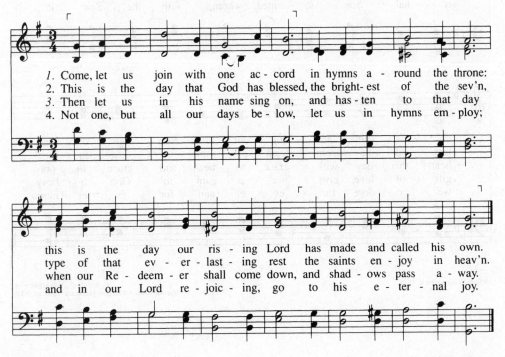

1. Come, let us join with one ac - cord in hymns a - round the throne:
2. This is the day that God has blessed, the bright-est of the sev'n,
3. Then let us in his name sing on, and has -ten to that day
4. Not one, but all our days be - low, let us in hymns em - ploy;

this is the day our ris - ing Lord has made and called his own.
type of that ev - er - last - ing rest the saints en - joy in heav'n.
when our Re - deem - er shall come down, and shad - ows pass a - way.
and in our Lord re - joic - ing, go to his e - ter - nal joy.

Charles Wesley, 1763
Mod.

BEATITUDO C.M.
John B. Dykes, 1875

394 This Day at Thy Creating Word

On the first day of the week we came together to break bread. Acts 20:7

1. This day at thy cre - at - ing word first o'er the
2. This day the Lord for sin - ners slain in might vic -
3. This day the Ho - ly Spir - it came with fi - ery
4. O day of light and life and grace, from earth - ly
5. All praise to God the Fa - ther be, all praise, e -

earth the light was poured: O Lord, this day up -
to - rious rose a - gain: O Je - sus, may we
• tongues of clo - ven flame: O Spir - it, fill our
toil sweet rest - ing place, thy hal - lowed hours, blest
ter - nal Son, to thee, whom, with the Spir - it,

on us shine and fill our souls with light di - vine.
rais - ed be from death of sin to life in thee!
• hearts this day with grace to hear and grace to pray.
gift of love, give we a - gain to God a - bove.
we a - dore for - ev - er and for - ev - er - more.

William Walsham How, 1871

WINCHESTER NEW L.M.
Musikalisches Handbuch, Hamburg, 1690; alt. 1990

Awake, My Soul, and with the Sun

395

I will awaken the dawn. I will praise you, O Lord, among the nations. Ps. 57:8, 9

1. A - wake, my soul, and with the sun your dai - ly
2. By in - fluence of the light di - vine let your own
3. All praise to you, who safe have kept, and have re -
4. Lord, I my vows to you re - new, dis - perse my
5. Praise God from whom all bless - ings flow; praise him, all

stage of du - ty run: shake off dull sloth, and
light to oth - ers shine; re - flect all heav'n's pro -
• freshed me whilst I slept: grant, Lord, when I from
sins as morn - ing dew; guard my first springs of
crea - tures here be - low; praise him a - bove, ye

joy - ful rise to pay your morn - ing sac - ri - fice.
pi - tious rays in ar - dent love and cheer - ful praise.
• death shall wake, I may of end - less light par - take.
thought and will, and with your - self my spir - it fill.
heav'n - ly host: praise Fa - ther, Son, and Ho - ly Ghost.

Thomas Ken, 1695, 1709
Mod.

MORNING HYMN L.M.
François H. Barthélémon, 1791

396 Come, My Soul, Thou Must Be Waking

Awake, my soul!... I will awaken the dawn. I will praise you, O Lord,
among the nations. Ps. 57:8, 9

1. Come, my soul, thou must be wak-ing; now is break-ing o'er the
2. Thou too hail the light re-turn-ing; read-y burn-ing be the
3. Pray that he may pros-per ev-er each en-deav-or, when thine
4. Think that he thy ways be-hold-eth; he un-fold-eth ev-er-y
5. On-ly God's free gifts a-buse not, light re-fuse not, but his

earth an-oth-er day: come to him who made this splen-dor;
in-cense of thy pow'rs; for the night is safe-ly end-ed,
aim is good and true; but that he may ev-er thwart thee,
fault that lurks with-in; ev-ery stain of shame glossed o-ver
Spir-it's voice o-bey; thou with him shalt dwell, be-hold-ing

see thou ren-der all thy fee-ble pow'rs can pay.
God hath tend-ed with his care thy help-less hours.
and con-vert thee, when thou e-vil wouldst pur-sue.
can dis-cov-er, and dis-cern each deed of sin.
light en-fold-ing all things in un-cloud-ed day.

F. R. L. von Canitz, 1700
Tr. by Henry J. Buckoll, 1841; alt.

HAYDN 8.4.7.8.4.7.
Franz Joseph Haydn, 1791; arr.

Light of Light, Enlighten Me

With you is the fountain of life; in your light we see light. Ps. 36:9

1. Light of light, en - light - en me, now a - new the day is dawn- ing;
2. Fount of all our joy and peace, to thy liv - ing wa - ters lead me;
3. Kin - dle thou the sac - ri - fice, that up - on my lips is ly - ing;
4. Let me with my heart to - day, "Ho - ly, ho - ly, ho - ly" sing- ing,
5. Hence all care, all van - i - ty, for the day to God is ho - ly;

sun of grace, the shad - ows flee; bright- en thou my Sab - bath morn- ing;
thou from earth my soul re - lease, and with grace and mer - cy feed me;
• clear the shad - ows from mine eyes, that, from ev - ery er - ror fly - ing,
rapt a - while from earth a - way, all my soul to thee up- spring- ing,
come, thou glo - rious Maj - es - ty, deign to fill this tem - ple low- ly;

with thy joy - ous sun - shine blest, hap - py is my day of rest.
bless thy Word, that it may prove rich in fruits that thou dost love.
• no strange fire may in me glow that thine al - tar doth not know.
have a fore - taste in - ly giv'n how they wor - ship thee in heav'n.
naught to - day my soul shall move, sim - ply rest - ing in thy love.

Benjamin Schmolck, 1714
Tr. by Catherine Winkworth, 1858

HINCHMAN 7.8.7.8.7.7.
Uzziah C. Burnap, 1869

398 Christ, Whose Glory Fills the Skies

The rising sun will come to us from heaven to shine on those living in darkness.
Luke 1:78, 79

1. Christ, whose glo - ry fills the skies, Christ, the true, the
2. Dark and cheer - less is the morn un - ac - com - pa -
3. Vis - it, then, this soul of mine; pierce the gloom of

on - ly Light, Sun of Righ - teous - ness, a - rise,
nied by thee; joy - less is the day's re - turn
sin and grief; fill me, Ra - dian - cy di - vine;

tri - umph o'er the shades of night; Day - spring from on
till thy mer - cy's beams I see; till they in - ward
scat - ter all my un - be - lief; more and more thy -

high, be near; Day - star, in my heart ap - pear.
light im - part, glad my eyes, and warm my heart.
self dis - play, shin - ing to the per - fect day.

Charles Wesley, 1740

LUX PRIMA 7.7.7.7.7.7.
Charles F. Gounod, 1872

Lord, As the Day Begins

399

In the morning, O LORD, you hear my voice; in the morning I lay my requests before you and wait in expectation. Ps. 5:3

1. Lord, as the day be-gins lift up our hearts in praise;
2. Christ be in work and skill, serv - ing each oth - er's need;
3. Grant us the Spir - it's strength, teach us to walk his way;
4. Now as the day be-gins make it the best of days;

take from us all our sins, guard us in all our ways:
Christ be in thought and will, Christ be in word and deed:
so bring us all at length safe to the close of day:
take from us all our sins, guard us in all our ways:

our ev - ery step di - rect and guide that Christ in all be glo - ri - fied!
our minds be set on things a - bove in joy and peace, in faith and love.
from hour to hour sus - tain and bless, and let our song be thank - ful - ness.
our ev - ery step di - rect and guide that Christ in all be glo - ri - fied!

Timothy Dudley-Smith, 1980

SAMUEL 6.6.6.6.8.8.
Arthur S. Sullivan, 1874

400 O Bless Our God with One Accord

Praise the LORD, all you servants of the LORD who minister by night in the house of the LORD. Ps. 134:1

1. O bless our God with one ac - cord, ye faith - ful
2. Lift up your hands, in prayer draw nigh un - to his
3. Je - ho - vah bless thee from a - bove, from Zi - on

ser - vants of the Lord, who in his house do
sanc - tu - ar - y high; bless ye the Lord, kneel
in his bound - less love, our God, who heav'n and

stand by night; and praise him there with all your might.
at his feet, and wor - ship him with rev - erence meet.
earth did frame; blest be his great and ho - ly name.

From Psalm 134
Lambertus J. Lamberts, 1928

OLD HUNDREDTH L.M.
Louis Bourgeois's *Genevan Psalter*, 1551

All Praise to Thee, My God, This Night

401

I will lie down and sleep in peace, for you alone, O LORD, make me
dwell in safety. Ps. 4:8

1. All praise to thee, my God, this night, for all the
bless - ings of the light; keep me, O keep me,
King of kings, be - neath thine own al - might - y wings.

2. For - give me, Lord, for thy dear Son, the ills that
I this day have done; that with the world, my -
self, and thee, I, ere I sleep, at peace may be.

3. O may my soul on thee re - pose, and with sweet
sleep mine eye - lids close; sleep that may me more
vig - 'rous make to serve my God when I a - wake.

4. When in the night I sleep - less lie, my soul with
heav'n - ly thoughts sup - ply; let no ill dreams dis -
turb my rest, no pow'rs of dark - ness me mo - lest.

5. O when shall I in endless day
forever chase dark sleep away,
and hymns with the supernal choir
incessant sing, and never tire!

6. Praise God from whom all blessings flow;
praise him, all creatures here below;
praise him above, ye heav'nly host:
praise Father, Son, and Holy Ghost.

Thomas Ken, 1695, 1709

TALLIS' CANON L.M.
Thomas Tallis, ca. 1567

402 Abide with Me: Fast Falls the Eventide

This is how we know that he lives in us: We know it by the Spirit he gave us.
1 John 3:24

1. A - bide with me: fast falls the e - ven - tide; the dark - ness
2. Swift to its close ebbs out life's lit - tle day; earth's joys grow
3. I need thy pres - ence ev - ery pass - ing hour; what but thy
4. I fear no foe, with thee at hand to bless: ills have no
5. Hold thou thy cross be - fore my clos - ing eyes; shine through the

deep - ens; Lord, with me a - bide: when oth - er help - ers fail, and
dim, its glo - ries pass a - way; change and de - cay in all a -
grace can foil the tempt - er's pow'r? Who like thy - self my guide and
weight, and tears no bit - ter - ness. Where is death's sting? where, grave, thy
gloom, and point me to the skies: heav'n's morn - ing breaks, and earth's vain

com - forts flee, help of the help - less, O a - bide with me.
round I see; O thou who chang - est not, a - bide with me.
stay can be? Through cloud and sun - shine, O a - bide with me.
vic - to - ry? I tri - umph still, if thou a - bide with me.
shad - ows flee: in life, in death, O Lord, a - bide with me.

Henry F. Lyte, 1847

EVENTIDE (MONK) 10.10.10.10.
William H. Monk. 1861

Savior, Breathe an Evening Blessing

You will not fear the terror of night. Ps. 91:5

1. Sav - ior, breathe an eve - ning bless - ing, ere re -
2. Though de - struc - tion walk a - round us, though the
3. Though the night be dark and drea - ry, dark - ness
4. Should swift death this night o'er - take us, and our

pose our spir - its seal; sin and want we come con -
ar - row past us fly, an - gel guards from thee sur -
can - not hide from thee; thou art he who, nev - er
couch be - come our tomb, may the morn in heav'n a -

fess - ing: thou canst save, and thou canst heal.
round us; we are safe if thou art nigh.
wea - ry, watch - est where thy peo - ple be.
wake us, clad in light and death - less bloom.

James Edmeston, 1820

EVENING PRAYER 8.7.8.7.
George C. Stebbins, 1878

404 Sun of My Soul, Thou Savior Dear

Even the darkness will not be dark to you; the night will shine like the day, for darkness is as light to you. Ps. 139:12

1. Sun of my soul, thou Sav - ior dear, it is not night if thou be near; O may no earth - born cloud a - rise to hide thee from thy ser - vant's eyes.

2. When the soft dews of kind - ly sleep my wea - ry eye - lids gent - ly steep, be my last thought, how sweet to rest for - ev - er on my Sav - ior's breast.

3. A - bide with me from morn till eve, for with - out thee I can - not live; a - bide with me when night is nigh, for with - out thee I dare not die.

4. If some poor wan - d'ring child of thine have spurned to - day the voice di - vine, now, Lord, the gra - cious work be - gin; let him no more lie down in sin.

5. Watch by the sick; enrich the poor
with blessings from thy boundless store;
be every mourner's sleep tonight,
like infant's slumbers, pure and light.

6. Come near and bless us when we wake,
ere through the world our way we take,
till in the ocean of thy love
we lose ourselves in heav'n above.

John Keble, 1820

HURSLEY L.M.
Katholisches Gesangbuch, Vienna, ca. 1774; alt.

God, That Madest Earth and Heaven

405

By day the LORD directs his love, at night his song is with me—a prayer to the God of my life. Ps. 42:8

1. God, that mad-est earth and heav-en, dark-ness and light,
2. And when morn a-gain shall call us to run life's way,
3. Guard us wak-ing, guard us sleep-ing; and when we die,

who the day for toil hast giv-en, for rest the night;
may we still, what-e'er be-fall us, thy will o-bey.
may we, in thy might-y keep-ing, all peace-ful lie:

may thine an-gel-guards de-fend us, slum-ber sweet thy mer-cy send us,
From the pow'r of e-vil hide us, in the nar-row path-way guide us,
when the last dread trump shall wake us, do not thou, O God, for-sake us,

ho-ly dreams and hopes at-tend us, this live-long night.
nor thy smile be e'er de-nied us, the live-long day.
but to reign in glo-ry take us, with thee on high.

St. 1, Reginald Heber, 1827
St. 2, William Mercer, 1864
St. 3, Richard Whately, 1787–1863

AR HYD Y NOS 8.4.8.4.8.8.8.4.
Traditional Welsh melody
Arr. by L. O. Emerson, 1906

406
Now the Day Is Over

When you lie down, you will not be afraid; when you lie down, your sleep
will be sweet. Prov. 3:24

1. Now the day is o - ver, night is draw - ing nigh,
2. Je - sus, give the wea - ry calm and sweet re - pose;
3. Grant to lit - tle chil - dren vi - sions bright of thee;
4. Com - fort ev - 'ry suf - f'rer watch - ing late in pain;

shad - ows of the eve - ning steal a - cross the sky.
with thy ten - d'rest bless - ing may our eye - lids close.
guard the sail - ors, toss - ing on the deep blue sea.
those who plan some e - vil from their sin re - strain.

5. Through the long night watches
    may thine angels spread
    their white wings above me,
    watching round my bed.

6. Glory to the Father,
    glory to the Son,
    and to thee, blest Spirit,
    whilst all ages run.

Sabine Baring-Gould, 1865

MERRIAL 6.5.6.5.
Joseph Barnby, 1868

The Day You Gave Us, Lord, Is Ended

407

From the rising of the sun to the place where it sets, the name of the LORD is
to be praised. Ps. 113:3

1. The day you gave us, Lord, is end - ed, the dark - ness
2. We thank you that your church, un - sleep - ing while earth rolls
3. As o'er each con - ti - nent and is - land the dawn leads
4. The sun, that bids us rest, is wak - ing our breth - ren
5. So be it, Lord; your throne shall nev - er, like earth's proud

falls at your be - hest; to you our morn - ing hymns as -
on - ward in - to light, through all the world her watch is
• on an - oth - er day, the voice of prayer is nev - er
'neath the west - ern sky, and hour by hour fresh lips are
em - pires, pass a - way: but stand, and rule, and grow for -

cend - ed, your praise shall hal - low now our rest.
keep - ing, and rests not now by day or night.
• si - lent, nor dies the strain of praise a - way.
mak - ing your won - drous do - ings heard on high.
ev - er, till all your crea - tures own your sway.

John Ellerton, 1870
Alt. 1990, mod.

ST. CLEMENT 9.8.9.8.
Clement C. Scholefield, 1874

408 Day Is Dying in the West

Holy, holy, holy is the LORD Almighty; the whole earth is full of his glory. Is. 6:3

1. Day is dy - ing in the west; heav'n is touch - ing
2. While the deep - 'ning shad - ows fall, Light of light, on
3. And when fad - ing from our sight, pass the stars, the

earth with rest; wait and wor - ship while the night
whom we call through the glo - ry and the grace
day, the night, Lord of glo - ry, on our eyes

sets her eve - ning lamps a - light through all the sky.
of the stars that veil thy face, our hearts as - cend.
let e - ter - nal morn - ing rise and shad - ows end.

REFRAIN

Ho - ly, ho - ly, ho - ly, Lord God of hosts! Heav'n and earth are

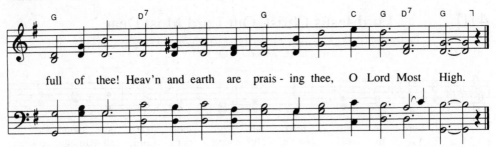

full of thee! Heav'n and earth are prais-ing thee, O Lord Most High.

Mary A. Lathbury, 1877
Alt. 1961

EVENING PRAISE 7.7.7.7.4.ref.
William F. Sherwin, 1877

Softly Now the Light of Day

409

By day the LORD directs his love, at night his song is with me—a prayer to the God of my life. Ps. 42:8

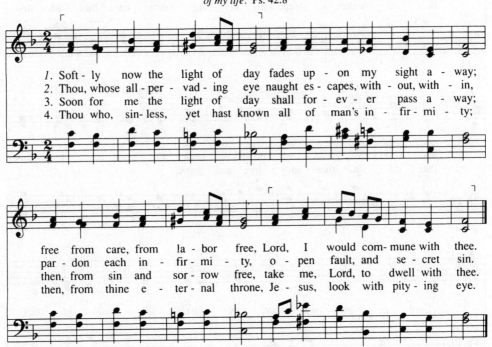

1. Soft-ly now the light of day fades up-on my sight a-way;
2. Thou, whose all-per-vad-ing eye naught es-capes, with-out, with-in,
3. Soon for me the light of day shall for-ev-er pass a-way;
4. Thou who, sin-less, yet hast known all of man's in-fir-mi-ty;

free from care, from la-bor free, Lord, I would com-mune with thee.
par-don each in-fir-mi-ty, o-pen fault, and se-cret sin.
then, from sin and sor-row free, take me, Lord, to dwell with thee.
then, from thine e-ter-nal throne, Je-sus, look with pity-ing eye.

George W. Doane, 1824

SEYMOUR 7.7.7.7.
Carl Maria von Weber, 1826; arr.

410 Lord Jesus Christ, Our Lord Most Dear

If you belong to Christ, then you are Abraham's seed, and heirs according
to the promise. Gal. 3:29

1. Lord Jesus Christ, our Lord most dear, as thou wast once an infant here, so give this child of thine, we pray, thy grace and blessing day by day.
2. As in thy heav'nly kingdom, Lord, all things obey thy sacred word, do thou thy mighty succor give, and shield this child by morn and eve. O holy Jesus, Lord divine, we pray thee guard this child of thine.
3. Their watch let angels round him keep wher-e'er he be, awake, asleep; thy saving grace on him bestow that he in thee may live and grow.

REFRAIN

O holy Jesus, Lord divine, we pray thee guard this child of thine.

Heinrich of Laufenberg, 15th cent.
Tr. by Catherine Winkworth, 1869; alt. 1961

ST. CHRYSOSTOM 8.8.8.8.8.8.
Joseph Barnby, 1872

Shine Thou upon Us, Lord

411

Preach the Word. 2 Tim. 4:2

1. Shine thou up-on us, Lord, true light of men, to-day,
2. Breathe thou up-on us, Lord, thy Spir-it's liv-ing flame,
3. Speak thou for us, O Lord, in all we say of thee;
4. Live thou with-in us, Lord; thy mind and will be ours;

and through the writ-ten Word thy ver-y self dis-play,
that so with one ac-cord our lips may tell thy name.
ac-cord-ing to thy Word let all our teach-ing be,
be thou be-lov'd, a-dored, and served with all our pow'rs,

that so from hearts which burn with gaz-ing on thy face
Give thou the hear-ing ear, fix thou the wan-d'ring thought,
that so thy lambs may know their own true Shep-herd's voice,
that so our lives may teach thy chil-dren what thou art,

thy lit-tle ones may learn the won-ders of thy grace.
that those we teach may hear the great things thou hast wrought.
wher-e'er he leads them go, and in his love re-joice.
and plead, by more than speech, for thee with ev-'ry heart.

John Ellerton, 1881

LEONI 6.6.8.4.D.
Jewish melody
Arr. by Meyer Lyon, 1770

412   See Israel's Gentle Shepherd Stand

He took the children in his arms, put his hands on them and blessed them. Mark 10:16

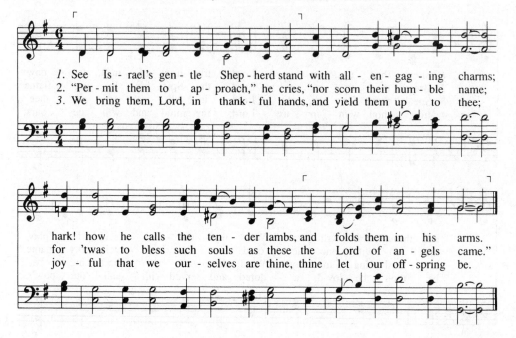

1. See Is - rael's gen - tle Shep - herd stand with all - en - gag - ing charms;
2. "Per - mit them to ap - proach," he cries, "nor scorn their hum - ble name;
3. We bring them, Lord, in thank - ful hands, and yield them up to thee;

hark! how he calls the ten - der lambs, and folds them in his arms.
for 'twas to bless such souls as these the Lord of an - gels came."
joy - ful that we our - selves are thine, thine let our off - spring be.

Philip Doddridge, 1755

SOHO C.M.
Joseph Barnby, 1881

413   Our Children, Lord, in Faith and Prayer

The promise is for you and your children. Acts 2:39

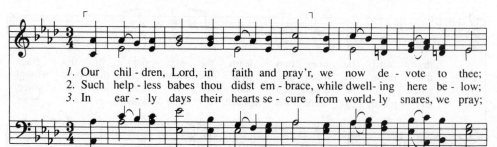

1. Our chil - dren, Lord, in faith and pray'r, we now de - vote to thee;
2. Such help - less babes thou didst em - brace, while dwell - ing here be - low;
3. In ear - ly days their hearts se - cure from world - ly snares, we pray;

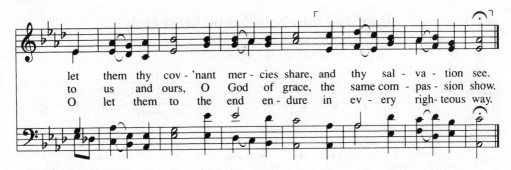

let them thy cov - 'nant mer - cies share, and thy sal - va - tion see.
to us and ours, O God of grace, the same com - pas - sion show.
O let them to the end en - dure in ev - ery righ - teous way.

Thomas Haweis, 1808; alt.

ARMENIA C.M.
Sylvanus B. Pond, 1792–1871
Arr. by Austin C. Lovelace, 1964

Tune arr. © 1964, Abingdon Press. Reprinted from the *Book of Hymns* by permission.

Dear Lord, Today Our Child   414

Sons are a heritage from the LORD, *children a reward from him.* Ps. 127:3

1. Dear Lord, to - day our child, an her - i - tage from thee,
2. Dear Lord, to - day our child, sweet to - ken of thy love,
3. Dear Lord, to - day our child, rich trea - sure of thy grace,
4. Dear Lord, to - day our child, a gra - cious gift of thine,
5. Dear Lord, to - day our child, the fruit of God-blessed seed,

we bring in faith and claim for him thy prom - ise free.
we bring in - to thy church for bless - ings from a - bove.
we bring, up - on his brow the sign and seal to place.
we bring to set a - part, bap - tized in name di - vine.
we bring to thee to ask for help in ev - 'ry need.

Calvin A. Busch, 1954

SECOND PARISH 6.6.6.6.
Calvin A. Busch, 1954
Arr. by Esther J. Roskamp, 1960

415

Baptized into Your Name Most Holy

We were therefore buried with him through baptism into death in order that ... we too
may live a new life. Rom. 6:4

1. Bap - tized in - to your name most ho - ly, O Fa - ther,
2. My lov - ing Fa - ther, me you've tak - en for - e'er to
3. And I have vowed to fear and love you, and to o -
4. My faith - ful God, your Word fails nev - er, your cov - 'nant

Son, and Ho - ly Ghost, I claim a place, though weak and low - ly,
be your child and heir; my faith - ful Sav - ior, me you've giv - en
bey you, Lord, a - lone; be - cause the Ho - ly Spir - it moved me,
sure - ly will a - bide; oh, cast me not a - way for - ev - er,

a - mong your seed, your cho - sen host. Bur - ied with Christ and
your righ - teous, ho - ly life to share; O Ho - ly Spir - it,
I dared to pledge my - self your own, re - nounc - ing sin to
should I trans - gress it on my side! Though I have oft my

dead to sin: your Spir - it e'er shall live with - in.
you will be a com - fort, guide, and help to me.
keep the faith and war with e - vil un - to death.
soul de - filed, in love for - give, re - store your child.

5. Yes, all I am and love most dearly
I offer now, O Lord, to you.
Oh, let me make my vows sincerely,
and what I say, help me to do.
Let naught within me, naught I own,
serve any will but yours alone.

6. And never let my purpose falter,
O Father, Son, and Holy Ghost,
but keep me faithful to your altar,
till you shall call me from my post.
So unto you I live and die
and praise you evermore on high.

Johann J. Rambach, 1723
Tr. by Catherine Winkworth, 1863
Rev. in *Lutheran Book of Worship*, 1978; alt. 1990

NEUMARK 9.8.9.8.8.8.
Georg Neumark, 1657

Gracious Savior, Gentle Shepherd 416

He tends his flock like a shepherd: He gathers the lambs in his arms and carries them
close to his heart. Is. 40:11

1. Gra - cious Sav - ior, gen - tle Shep - herd, our lit - tle ones are dear to thee;
2. Ten - der Shep - herd, nev - er leave them, from thy fold to go a - stray;
3. Let thy ho - ly Word in - struct them: fill their minds with heav'n - ly light;
4. Cleanse their hearts from sin - ful fol - ly in the stream thy love sup - plied;

gath - ered with thine arms and car - ried in thy bo - som may they be
by thy look of love di - rect - ed, may they walk the nar - row way;
let thy love and grace con - strain them to ap - prove what - e'er is right,
min - gled streams of blood and wa - ter flow - ing from thy wound - ed side:

sweet - ly, gent - ly, safe - ly tend - ed, from all want and dan - ger free.
thus di - rect them, and pro - tect them, lest they fall an eas - y prey.
take thine eas - y yoke and wear it, and to prove thy bur - den light.
and to heav'n - ly pas - tures lead them, where thine own still wa - ters glide.

Jane E. Leeson, 1842
Adapted by John Keble, 1857; alt. 1961

DISMISSAL 8.7.8.7.8.7.
William L. Viner, 1845

417 A Little Child the Savior Came

Let the little children come to me, and do not hinder them, for the kingdom of God
belongs to such as these. Mark 10:14

1. A lit - tle child the Sav - ior came, the Might - y
2. He who, a lit - tle child, be - gan the life di -
3. We bring them, Lord, and with the sign of sprin - kled
4. O give thine an - gels charge, good Lord, them safe - ly
5. O thou, who by an in - fant's tongue dost hear thy

God was still his name; and an - gels wor - shiped
vine to show to man, pro - claims from heav'n the
wa - ter name them thine: their souls with sav - ing
in thy way to guard; thy bless - ing on their
per - fect glo - ry sung, may these, with all the

as he lay the seem - ing in - fant of a day.
mes - sage free: "Let lit - tle chil - dren come to me."
grace en - dow; bap - tize them with thy Spir - it now.
lives com - mand, and write their names up - on thy hand.
heav'n - ly host, praise Fa - ther, Son, and Ho - ly Ghost.

William Robertson, 1861

ANGELUS L.M.
Heilige Seelenlust, Breslau, 1657

O King Eternal, Sovereign Lord

418

God said to Abraham, "As for you, you must keep my covenant, you and your descendants after you for the generations to come." Gen. 17:9

1. O King e-ter-nal, sov-ereign Lord,
2. Through a-ges long your cov-enant stands,
3. Great God, from whom all bless-ings spring,
4. By word and wa-ter we con-fess
5. Bap-tize this child with plen-teous grace;

we gath-er now with one ac-cord, in mem-ory
our names are grav-en on your hands. And for this
whose eyes see ev-ery pre-cious thing, this babe in
the great-ness of your faith-ful-ness, in that our
set him a-part be-fore your face; that he may

of your faith-ful Word, giv'n long a-go.
child your law com-mands this sign we show.
faith and love we bring, with hearts a-glow.
chil-dren you will bless: your love they know.
choose a-mong his race with Christ to go.

William Fitch, 1911–1982

ALMSGIVING 8.8.8.4.
John B. Dykes, 1865

419 In Your Arms, Lord Jesus Christ

He took the children in his arms, put his hands on them and blessed them. Mark 10:16

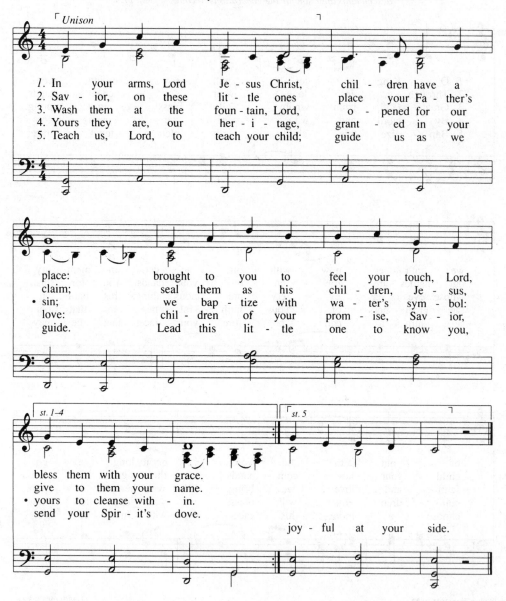

Unison

1. In your arms, Lord Je - sus Christ, chil - dren have a
2. Sav - ior, on these lit - tle ones place your Fa - ther's
3. Wash them at the foun - tain, Lord, o - pened for our
4. Yours they are, our her - i - tage, grant - ed in your
5. Teach us, Lord, to teach your child; guide us as we

place: brought to you to feel your touch, Lord,
claim; seal them as his chil - dren, Je - sus,
• sin; we bap - tize with wa - ter's sym - bol:
love: chil - dren of your prom - ise, Sav - ior,
guide. Lead this lit - tle one to know you,

st. 1–4

st. 5

bless them with your grace.
give to them your name.
• yours to cleanse with - in.
send your Spir - it's dove.

joy - ful at your side.

Edmund P. Clowney, 1985

LISTENING 6.5.6.5.
Norman L. Warren, 1969

At the Lamb's High Feast We Sing

420

Christ, our Passover lamb, has been sacrificed. 1 Cor. 5:7

1. At the Lamb's high feast we sing praise to our vic - to - rious King,
2. Where the pas - chal blood is poured, death's dark an - gel sheathes his sword;
3. Might - y vic - tim from the sky, pow'rs of hell be - neath thee lie;

who has washed us in the tide flow - ing from his pierc - ed side;
Is - rael's hosts tri - um - phant go through the wave that drowns the foe.
death is con - quered in the fight, thou hast brought us life and light:

praise we him whose love di - vine gives his sa - cred blood for wine,
Praise we Christ, whose blood was shed, pas - chal vic - tim, pas - chal bread;
hymns of glo - ry and of praise, ris - en Lord, to thee we raise;

gives his bod - y for the feast, Christ the vic - tim, Christ the priest.
with sin - cer - i - ty and love eat we man - na from a - bove.
ho - ly Fa - ther, praise to thee, with the Spir - it, ev - er be.

Latin hymn, 6th cent.
Tr. by Robert Campbell, 1849; alt.

ST. GEORGE'S, WINDSOR 7.7.7.7.D.
George J. Elvey, 1859

421 Soul, Adorn Yourself with Gladness

"Let us rejoice and be glad and give him glory! For the wedding of the Lamb has come."
… "Blessed are those who are invited to the wedding supper of the Lamb!" Rev. 19:7, 9

1. Soul, a-dorn your-self with glad - ness, leave the gloom - y haunts of sad - ness,
2. Has - ten as a bride to meet him, ea - ger - ly and glad-ly greet him.
3. Now in faith I hum-bly pon - der o - ver this sur-pass-ing won - der
4. Je - sus, source of last-ing plea - sure, tru - est friend and dear-est trea - sure,

come in - to the day-light's splen - dor, there with joy your prais-es ren - der.
There he stands al - read - y knock- ing; quick - ly, now, your gate un - lock - ing,
that the bread of life is bound-less though the souls it feeds are count-less;
peace be - yond all un - der - stand - ing, joy in - to all life ex - pand - ing:

Bless the One whose grace un - bound-ed this a - maz - ing ban-quet found-ed;
o - pen wide the fast-closed por - tal, say - ing to the Lord im - mor - tal:
with the choic - est wine of heav - en Christ's own blood to us is giv - en.
hum-bly now, I bow be - fore you, love in-car - nate, I a - dore you;

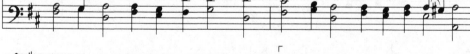

he, though heav'n-ly, high, and ho - ly, deigns to dwell with you most low - ly.
"Come, and leave your loved one nev - er; dwell with - in my heart for - ev - er."
Oh, most glo - rious con - so - la - tion, pledge and seal of my sal - va - tion,
wor - thi - ly let me re - ceive you, and, so fa-vored, nev- er leave you.

Johann Franck, 1649
Tr. by Catherine Winkworth, 1858; alt.
Rev. in *Lutheran Book of Worship*, 1978

SCHMÜCKE DICH L.M.D.
Johann Crüger, 1649

'Twas on That Night When Doomed to Know

422

The Lord Jesus, on the night he was betrayed, took bread. 1 Cor. 11:23

1. 'Twas on that night when doomed to know the ea - ger
2. And af - ter thanks and glo - ry giv'n to him that
3. "My bro - ken bod - y thus I give for you, for
4. Then in his hands the cup he raised, and God a -

rage of ev - ery foe, that night in which he
rules in earth and heav'n, that sym - bol of his
all. Take, eat, and live. And oft the sa - cred
new he thanked and praised, while kind - ness in his

was be - trayed, the Sav - ior of the world took bread;
flesh he broke, and thus to all his fol - l'wers spoke:
rite re - new that brings my sav - ing love to view."
bo - som glowed, and from his lips sal - va - tion flowed.

5. "My blood I thus pour forth," he cries,
   "to cleanse the soul in sin that lies;
   in this the covenant is sealed,
   and heav'n's eternal grace revealed.

6. "With love to man this cup is fraught;
   let all partake the sacred draught;
   through latest ages let it pour,
   in mem'ry of my dying hour."

John Morison, 1781

ROCKINGHAM OLD L.M.
Arr. by Edward Miller, 1790

423 According to Thy Gracious Word

Do this in remembrance of me. Luke 22:19

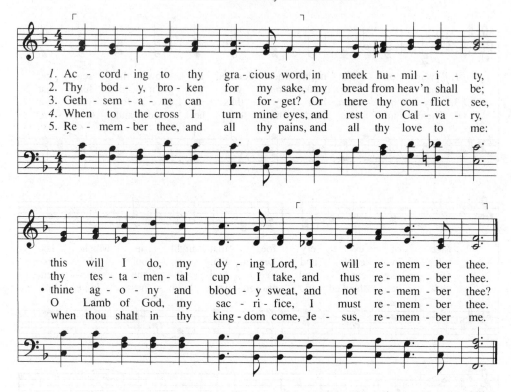

1. Ac - cord - ing to thy gra - cious word, in meek hu - mil - i - ty,
2. Thy bod - y, bro - ken for my sake, my bread from heav'n shall be;
3. Geth - sem - a - ne can I for - get? Or there thy con - flict see,
4. When to the cross I turn mine eyes, and rest on Cal - va - ry,
5. Re - mem - ber thee, and all thy pains, and all thy love to me:

this will I do, my dy - ing Lord, I will re - mem - ber thee.
thy tes - ta - men - tal cup I take, and thus re - mem - ber thee.
• thine ag - o - ny and blood - y sweat, and not re - mem - ber thee?
O Lamb of God, my sac - ri - fice, I must re - mem - ber thee.
when thou shalt in thy king - dom come, Je - sus, re - mem - ber me.

James Montgomery, 1825

DALEHURST C.M.
Arthur Cottman, 1874

424 Shepherd of Souls, Refresh and Bless

Our forefathers ... all ate the same spiritual food and drank the same spiritual drink;
for they drank from the spiritual rock ... and that rock was Christ. 1 Cor. 10:1–4

1. Shep - herd of souls, re - fresh and bless your cho - sen pil - grim flock
2. Hun - gry and thirst - y, faint and weak, as you when here be - low,
3. We would not live by bread a - lone, but by that Word of grace,
4. Be known to us in break- ing bread, but do not then de - part;
5. There sup with us in love di - vine; your bod - y and your blood,

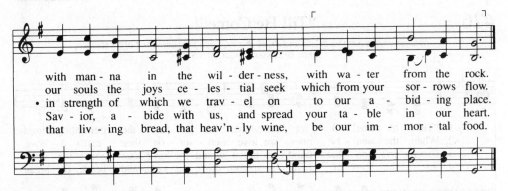

with man - na in the wil - der - ness, with wa - ter from the rock.
our souls the joys ce - les - tial seek which from your sor - rows flow.
• in strength of which we trav - el on to our a - bid - ing place.
Sav - ior, a - bide with us, and spread your ta - ble in our heart.
that liv - ing bread, that heav'n - ly wine, be our im - mor - tal food.

St. 1–3, anon.
St. 4–5, James Montgomery, 1825; mod.

ST. AGNES C.M.
John B. Dykes, 1866

Bread of the World in Mercy Broken

425

My flesh is real food and my blood is real drink. John 6:55

1. Bread of the world in mer - cy bro - ken, wine of the
2. Look on the heart by sor - row bro - ken, look on the

soul in mer - cy shed, by whom the words of life were
tears by sin - ners shed; and be thy feast to us the

spo - ken, and in whose death our sins are dead,
to - ken that by thy grace our souls are fed.

Reginald Heber, 1827

EUCHARISTIC HYMN 9.8.9.8.
John S. B. Hodges, 1869

426   "Till He Come"!

Whenever you eat this bread and drink this cup, you proclaim the Lord's death
until he comes. 1 Cor. 11:26

1. "Till he come"! O let the words lin - ger on the trem-bling chords;
2. When the wea - ry ones we love en - ter on their rest a - bove,
3. Clouds and con - flicts round us press: would we have one sor - row less?
4. See, the feast of love is spread, drink the wine, and break the bread:

let the lit - tle while be - tween in their gold - en light be seen;
seems the earth so poor and vast, all our life - joy o - ver-cast?
All the sharp- ness of the cross, all that tells the world is loss,
sweet me - mo - rials, till the Lord call us round his heav'n - ly board;

let us think how heav'n and home lie be - yond that "Till he come."
Hush, be ev - ery mur- mur dumb: it is on - ly till he come.
death and dark - ness, and the tomb, on - ly whis - per, "Till he come."
some from earth, from glo - ry some, sev - ered on - ly till he come.

Edward H. Bickersteth, 1862

REDHEAD 76 7.7.7.7.7.7.
Richard Redhead, 1853

Amidst Us Our Beloved Stands

427

Jesus came and stood among them and said ..., "Put your finger here; see my hands."
John 20:26, 27

1. A - midst us our Be - lov - ed stands, and bids us
   view his pierc - ed hands; points to the wound - ed
   feet and side, blest em - blems of the Cru - ci - fied.

2. What food lux - u - rious loads the board, when at his
   ta - ble sits the Lord! The wine how rich, the
   bread how sweet, when Je - sus deigns the guests to meet!

3. If now, with eyes de - filed and dim, we see the
   signs, but see not him; O may his love the
   scales dis - place, and bid us see him face to face!

4. O glo - rious Bride - groom of our hearts, your pres - ent
   smile a heav'n im - parts! O lift the veil, if
   veil there be, let ev - ery saint your glo - ry see!

Charles H. Spurgeon, 1866
Alt. 1990, mod.

HAMBURG L.M.
Gregorian chant
Arr. by Lowell Mason, 1824

428

Not Worthy, Lord!

*Father, I have sinned against heaven and against you. I am no longer worthy to be
called your son.* Luke 15:21

1. Not wor-thy, Lord! to gath-er up the crumbs with trem-bling
2. I am not wor-thy to be thought thy child, nor sit the
3. One word from thee, my Lord, one smile, one look, and I could
4. I hear thy voice; thou bidd'st me come and rest; I come, I
5. My praise can on-ly breathe it-self in prayer, my prayer can

hand that from thy ta-ble fall, a wea-ry, heav-y-lad-en
last and low-est at thy board; too long a wan-d'rer and too
face the cold, rough world a-gain; and with that trea-sure in my
kneel, I clasp thy pierc-ed feet; thou bidd'st me take my place, a
on-ly lose it-self in thee; dwell thou for-ev-er in my

sin-ner comes to plead thy prom-ise and o-bey thy call.
oft be-guiled, I on-ly ask one rec-on-cil-ing word.
heart could brook the wrath of dev-ils and the scorn of men.
wel-come guest a-mong thy saints, and of thy ban-quet eat.
heart, and there, Lord, let me sup with thee; sup thou with me.

Edward H. Bickersteth, 1872

COMMUNION 10.10.10.10.
Felix Mendelssohn-Bartholdy, 1835; arr.

Let Thy Blood in Mercy Poured

429

Offer your bodies as living sacrifices, holy and pleasing to God—this is your spiritual act of worship. Rom. 12:1

1. Let thy blood in mer-cy poured, let thy gra-cious
body bro-ken, be to me, O gra-cious Lord,
of thy bound-less love the to-ken.

2. Thou didst die that I might live; bless-ed Lord, thou
cam'st to save me; all that love of God could give,
Je-sus by his sor-rows gave me. Thou didst give thy-

3. By the thorns that crowned thy brow, by the spear wound
and the nail-ing, by the pain and death, I now
claim, O Christ, thy love un-fail-ing.

4. Wilt thou own the gift I bring? All my pen-i-
tence I give thee; thou art my ex-alt-ed King,
of thy match-less love for-give me.

REFRAIN

self for me, now I give my-self to thee.

Greek hymn
Tr. by John Brownlie, 1907

JESUS, MEINE ZUVERSICHT 7.8.7.8.7.7.
Johann Crüger, 1653; arr.

430 I Hunger and I Thirst

Your forefathers ate manna and died, but he who feeds on this bread will live forever.
John 6:58

1. I hun-ger and I thirst; Je - sus, my man - na be;
2. Thou bruised and bro - ken Bread, my life - long needs sup - ply;
3. Thou true life - giv - ing Vine, let me thy sweet - ness prove;
4. Rough paths my feet have trod, since first their course be - gan;
5. For still the des - ert lies my thirst - ing soul be - fore;

ye liv - ing wa - ters, burst out of the rock for me.
as liv - ing souls are fed, O feed me, or I die.
• re - new my life with thine, re - fresh my soul with love.
feed me, thou Bread of God, help me, thou Son of Man.
O liv - ing wa - ters rise with - in me ev - er - more.

John S. B. Monsell, 1866
Alt. 1990

DOLOMITE CHANT 6.6.6.6.
Traditional Austrian melody
Arr. by Joseph Thomas Cooper, 1819–1879; alt. 1990

431 A Parting Hymn We Sing

When they had sung a hymn, they went out to the Mount of Olives. Matt. 26:30

1. A part - ing hymn we sing a - round your ta - ble, Lord;
2. Here have we seen your face, and felt your pres - ence here;
3. We're pur - chased by your blood, by sin no lon - ger led;
4. In self - for - get - ting love be our com - mu - nion shown,

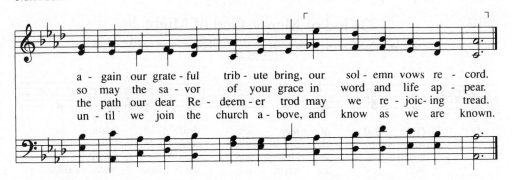

a - gain our grate - ful trib - ute bring, our sol - emn vows re - cord.
so may the sa - vor of your grace in word and life ap - pear.
the path our dear Re - deem - er trod may we re - joic - ing tread.
un - til we join the church a - bove, and know as we are known.

Aaron R. Wolfe, 1858
Mod.

SCHUMANN S.M.
Mason and Webb's *Cantica Laudis*, 1850

We Give Thee But Thine Own
432

Everything comes from you, and we have given you only what comes from your hand.
1 Chron. 29:14

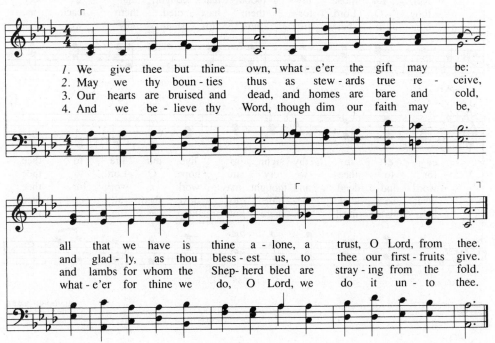

1. We give thee but thine own, what - e'er the gift may be:
2. May we thy boun - ties thus as stew - ards true re - ceive,
3. Our hearts are bruised and dead, and homes are bare and cold,
4. And we be - lieve thy Word, though dim our faith may be,

all that we have is thine a - lone, a trust, O Lord, from thee.
and glad - ly, as thou bless - est us, to thee our first - fruits give.
and lambs for whom the Shep- herd bled are stray - ing from the fold.
what - e'er for thine we do, O Lord, we do it un - to thee.

William Walsham How, 1864

SCHUMANN S.M.
Mason and Webb's *Cantica Laudis*, 1850

433

O God of Mercy, God of Might

Whatever you did for one of the least of these brothers of mine, you did for me.
Matt. 25:40

1. O God of mer - cy, God of might, in
2. And thou who cam'st on earth to die, that
3. Teach us the les - son thou hast taught, to
4. For they are breth - ren, far and wide, since
5. In sick - ness, sor - row, want, or care, what -

love and pit - y in - fi - nite, teach us, as
fall - en man might live there - by, O hear us,
• feel for those thy blood hath bought; that ev - ery
thou, O Lord, for them hast died; then teach us,
e'er it be, 'tis ours to share; may we, when

ev - er in thy sight, to live our life to thee.
for to thee we cry in hope, O Lord, to thee.
• word and deed and thought may work a work for thee.
what - so - e'er be - tide, to love them all in thee.
help is need - ed, there give help as un - to thee.

Godfrey Thring, 1877
Alt. 1961

ELMHURST 8.8.8.6.
Edwin Drewett, 1887

Lord, Thou Lov'st the Cheerful Giver

434

God loves a cheerful giver. 2 Cor. 9:7

1. Lord, thou lov'st the cheer-ful giv-er, who with o-pen heart and hand
2. We are thine, thy mer-cy sought us, found us in death's dread-ful way,
3. Blest by thee with gifts and grac-es, may we heed thy church-'s call;
4. Sav-ior, thou hast free-ly giv-en all the bless-ings we en-joy,

bless-es free-ly, as a riv-er that re-fresh-es all the land.
to the fold in safe-ty brought us, nev-er-more from thee to stray.
glad-ly in all times and plac-es give to thee who giv-est all.
earth-ly store and bread of heav-en, love and peace with-out al-loy;

Grant us then the grace of giv-ing with a spir-it large and free,
Thine own life thou free-ly gav-est as an of-f'ring on the cross
Thou hast bought us, and no lon-ger can we claim to be our own;
hum-bly now we bow be-fore thee, and our all to thee re-sign;

that our life and all our liv-ing we may con-se-crate to thee.
for each sin-ner whom thou sav-est from e-ter-nal shame and loss.
ev-er free and ev-er stron-ger, we shall serve thee, Lord, a-lone.
for the king-dom, pow'r, and glo-ry, are, O Lord, for-ev-er thine.

Robert Murray, 1898

BEECHER 8.7.8.7.D.
John Zundel. 1870: alt. 1990

435 Lord of All Good, We Bring Our Gifts to You

Offer yourselves to God, as those who have been brought from death to life; and offer the parts of your body to him as instruments of righteousness. Rom. 6:13

1. Lord of all good, we bring our gifts to you,
2. We give our minds to un - der - stand your ways;
3. Fa - ther, whose boun - ty all cre - a - tion shows;

pledg - es of love and of - f'rings of our skill;
hands, voic - es, eyes to serve your great de - sign;
Christ, by whose sac - ri - fice our lives are new;

through them ful - fill your pur - pose ev - er true
your flame of love has set our hearts a - blaze:
Spir - it, from whom all life in full - ness flows:

as our whole life is of - fered to your will.
thus for your glo - ry all our pow'rs com - bine.
we give our - selves in grat - i - tude to you!

Albert F. Bayly, 1950; alt.

MORESTEAD 10.10.10.10.
Sydney Watson, 1964

Zion, Founded on the Mountains

436

He has set his foundation on the holy mountain. Ps. 87:1

1. Zi - on, found - ed on the moun - tains, God, thy Mak - er,
2. Hea - then lands and hos - tile peo - ples soon shall come the
3. When the Lord shall count the na - tions, sons and daugh - ters

loves thee well; he has cho - sen thee, most pre - cious,
Lord to know; na - tions born a - gain in Zi - on
he shall see, born to end - less life in Zi - on,

he de - lights in thee to dwell; God's own cit - y, God's own cit - y,
shall the Lord's sal - va - tion show; God Al - might - y, God Al - might - y,
and their joy - ful song shall be: "Bless - ed Zi - on, bless - ed Zi - on,

God's own cit - y, who can all thy glo - ry tell?
God Al - might - y, shall on Zi - on strength be - stow.
bless - ed Zi - on, all our foun - tains are in thee."

From Psalm 87
The Psalter, 1912
Tune arr. from the *Revised Church Hymnary* by permission of Oxford University Press.

CAERSALEM 8.7.8.7.4.4.4.7.
Robert Edwards, 1837

437   O God, to Us Show Mercy

May God be gracious to us and bless us and make his face shine upon us. Ps. 67:1

1. O God, to us show mer - cy and bless us in your grace;
2. O God, let all men praise you, let all the na - tions sing;
3. O God, let peo - ple praise you, let all the na - tions sing,

cause now to shine up - on us the bright - ness of your face;
in ev - 'ry land let prais - es and songs of glad - ness ring;
for earth in rich a - bun - dance to us her fruit shall bring.

that so your way most ho - ly on earth may soon be known,
for you shall judge the peo - ple in truth and righ - teous - ness,
The Lord our God shall bless us, our God shall bless - ing send,

and un - to ev - 'ry peo - ple your sav - ing grace be shown.
and through the earth the na - tions shall your just rule con - fess.
and all the earth shall fear him to its re - mot - est end.

Psalm 67
The Psalter, 1912; alt. 1990, mod.

MEIRIONYDD 7.6.7.6.D.
Welsh hymn melody
William Lloyd, 1840; alt. 1990

All Lands, to God in Joyful Sounds

438

Shout with joy to God, all the earth! Ps. 66:1

1. All lands, to God in joy - ful sounds a - loft your voic - es
   raise; sing forth the hon - or of his name, and glo - rious
   make his praise, and glo - rious make his praise.

2. Say ye to God, "How ter - ri - ble in all thy works art
   thou! To thee thy foes by thy great pow'r shall be con -
   strained to bow, shall be con - strained to bow.

3. "Yea, all the earth shall wor - ship thee, and un - to thee shall
   sing; to thy great name shall songs of joy with loud ho -
   san - nas ring, with loud ho - san - nas ring."

4. O come, be - hold the works of God, his might - y do - ings
   see; in deal - ing with the sons of men most won - der -
   ful is he, most won - der - ful is he.

5. He led in safety through the flood
   the people of his choice,
   he turned the sea to solid ground;
   in him let us rejoice,
   in him let us rejoice.

6. He rules forever by his might,
   his eyes the nations try;
   let not the proud, rebellious ones
   exalt themselves on high,
   exalt themselves on high.

Psalm 66:1–7
The Psalter, 1912

MILES LANE C.M.rep.
William Shrubsole, 1779
Arr. in *The New Christian Hymnal,* 1929

439 Christ Shall Have Dominion

He will rule from sea to sea. Ps. 72:8

1. Christ shall have do - min - ion o - ver land and sea, earth's re - mot - est
2. When the need - y seek him, he will mer - cy show; yea, the weak and
3. Ev - er and for - ev - er shall his name en - dure, long as suns con -
4. Un - to God Al - might - y joy - ful Zi - on sings; he a - lone is

re - gions shall his em - pire be; they that wilds in - hab - it shall their
help - less shall his pit - y know; he will sure - ly save them from op -
tin - ue it shall stand se - cure; and in him for - ev - er all men
glo - rious, do - ing won-drous things. Ev - er - more, ye peo - ple, bless his

wor - ship bring, kings shall ren - der trib - ute, na - tions serve our King.
pres- sion's might, for their lives are pre - cious in his ho - ly sight.
shall be blest, and all na - tions hail him King of kings con - fessed.
glo - rious name, his e - ter - nal glo - ry through the earth pro - claim.

REFRAIN

Christ shall have do - min - ion o - ver land and sea,

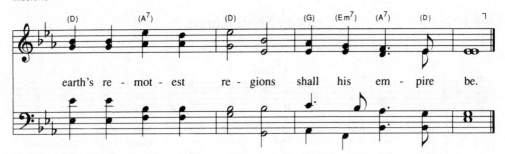

earth's re - mot - est re - gions shall his em - pire be.

From Psalm 72:8–14, 17–19
The Psalter, 1912

ST. GERTRUDE 6.5.6.5.D.ref.
Arthur S. Sullivan, 1871

Ye Christian Heralds, Go Proclaim

440

As you go, preach this message. Matt. 10:7

1. Ye Chris - tian her - alds, go pro - claim sal - va - tion
2. God shield you with a wall of fire, with flam - ing
3. And when our la - bors all are o'er, then we shall

through Em - man - uel's name! To dis - tant climes the
zeal your breasts in - spire, bid rag - ing winds their
meet to part no more, meet with the blood - bought

tid - ings bear, and plant the Rose of Shar - on there.
fu - ry cease, and hush the tem - pests in - to peace.
throng to fall and crown our Je - sus Lord of all.

Bourne H. Draper, 1803; alt.

MISSIONARY CHANT L.M.
Heinrich C. Zeuner, 1832

441 Jesus Shall Reign

He will rule from sea to sea and from the River to the ends of the earth. Ps. 72:8

1. Je - sus shall reign wher - e'er the sun does his suc -
2. To him shall end - less prayer be made, and prais - es
3. Peo - ple and realms of ev - ery tongue dwell on his
4. Bless - ings a - bound wher - e'er he reigns; the pris - 'ner
5. Let ev - ery crea - ture rise and bring pe - cu - liar

ces - sive jour - neys run; his king - dom stretch from shore to
throng to crown his head; his name, like sweet per - fume, shall
love with sweet- est song; and in - fant voic - es shall pro -
leaps to lose his chains, the wea - ry find e - ter - nal
hon - ors to our King; an - gels de - scend with songs a -

shore, till moons shall wax and wane no more.
rise with ev - ery morn - ing sac - ri - fice.
claim their ear - ly bless - ings on his name.
rest, and all the sons of want are blest.
gain, and earth re - peat the loud a - men!

Based on Psalm 72
Isaac Watts, 1719

DUKE STREET L.M.
John Hatton, 1793

Arise, O God

The LORD rises upon you and his glory appears over you. Is. 60:2

1. A - rise, O God, and shine in all thy sav - ing might,
2. Bring dis - tant na - tions near to sing thy glo - rious praise;
3. Send forth thy glo - rious pow'r, that Gen - tiles all may see,
4. To God, the on - ly wise, the one im - mor - tal King,

and pros - per each de - sign to spread thy glo - rious light:
let ev - 'ry peo - ple hear and learn thy ho - ly ways:
and earth pre - sent her store in con - verts born to thee:
let hal - le - lu - jahs rise from ev - 'ry liv - ing thing:

let heal - ing streams of mer - cy flow, that all the earth thy
reign, might - y God, as - sert thy cause, and gov - ern by thy
God, our own God, thy church O bless, and fill the world with
let all that breathe, on ev - 'ry coast, praise Fa - ther, Son, and

truth may know, that all the earth thy truth may know.
righ - teous laws, and gov - ern by thy righ - teous laws.
righ - teous - ness, and fill the world with righ - teous - ness.
Ho - ly Ghost, praise Fa - ther, Son, and Ho - ly Ghost.

William Hurn, 1813; alt.
Alt. 1961

RHOSYMEDRE 6.6.6.6.8.8.8.
John David Edwards, ca. 1840

443   Hark! the Voice of Jesus Crying

The harvest is plentiful, but the workers are few. Luke 10:2

1. Hark! the voice of Je - sus cry - ing, "Who will go and work to - day?
2. If you can - not cross the o - cean, and the hea - then lands ex - plore,
3. If you can - not be a watch - man, stand - ing high on Zi - on's wall,
4. Let none hear you i - dly say - ing, "There is noth - ing I can do,"

Fields are white, and har - vests wait - ing; who will bear the sheaves a - way?"
you can find the hea - then near - er, you can help them at your door.
point - ing out the path to heav - en, of - f'ring life and peace to all,
while the sons of men are dy - ing, and the Mas - ter calls for you:

Loud and long the Mas - ter call - eth, rich re - ward he of - fers free;
If you can - not give your thou - sands, you can give the wid - ow's mite;
with your pray'rs and with your boun - ties you can do what God de - mands;
take the task he gives you glad - ly, let his work your plea - sure be;

who will an - swer, glad - ly say - ing, "Here am I; send me, send me."
and the least you give for Je - sus will be pre - cious in his sight.
you can be like faith - ful Aa - ron, hold - ing up the proph - et's hands.
an - swer quick - ly when he call - eth, "Here am I; send me, send me."

Daniel March, 1868
Alt. 1961

ELLESDIE 8.7.8.7.D.
Attr. to Wolfgang Amadeus Mozart, 1756–1791
Arr. in Joshua Leavitt's *The Christian Lyre*, 1831; rev.

O Zion, Haste, Your Mission High Fulfilling

444

We tell you the good news. Acts 13:32

1. O Zi - on, haste, your mis- sion high ful - fill- ing, to tell to all the
2. Be - hold how man - y thou-sands still are ly - ing, bound in the dark- some
3. Pro - claim to ev - ery peo- ple, tongue, and na - tion that God, in whom they
4. Give of your sons to bear the mes- sage glo - rious; give of your wealth to

world that God is light; that he who made all na - tions is not will - ing
pris - on- house of sin, with none to tell them of the Sav- ior's dy - ing,
live and move, is love: tell how he stooped to save his lost cre - a - tion,
speed them on their way; pour out your soul for them in prayer vic - to- rious;

REFRAIN

one soul should per - ish, lost in shades of night.
or of the life he died for them to win. Pub- lish glad tid - ings,
and died on earth that man might live a - bove.
and all your spend- ing Je - sus will re - pay.

tid - ings of peace; tid - ings of Je - sus, re - demp- tion, and re - lease.

Mary A. Thomson, 1868; alt.

TIDINGS 11.10.11.10.
James Walch. 1875

445

Bring Them In

If a man owns a hundred sheep, and one of them wanders away, will he not leave the ninety–nine ... and go to look for the one that wandered off? Matt. 18:12

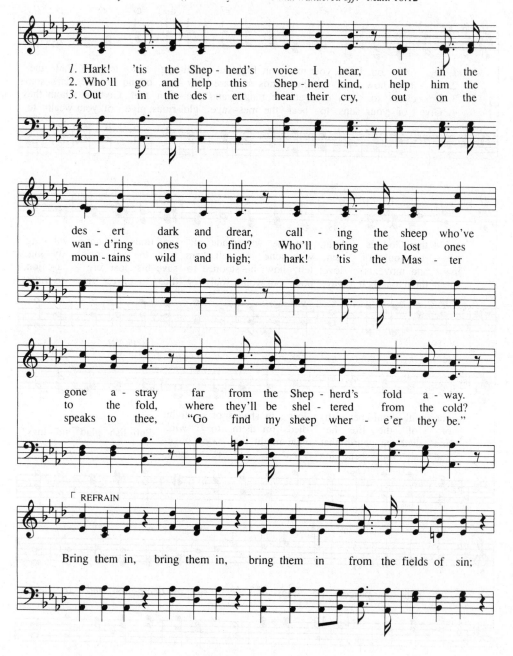

1. Hark! 'tis the Shep - herd's voice I hear, out in the
2. Who'll go and help this Shep - herd kind, help him the
3. Out in the des - ert hear their cry, out on the

des - ert dark and drear, call - ing the sheep who've
wan - d'ring ones to find? Who'll bring the lost ones
moun - tains wild and high; hark! 'tis the Mas - ter

gone a - stray far from the Shep - herd's fold a - way.
to the fold, where they'll be shel - tered from the cold?
speaks to thee, "Go find my sheep wher - e'er they be."

REFRAIN

Bring them in, bring them in, bring them in from the fields of sin;

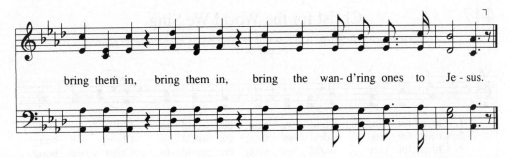

bring them in, bring them in, bring the wan-d'ring ones to Je-sus.

Alexcenah Thomas, 19th cent.

BRING THEM IN L.M.ref.
William A. Ogden, 1841–1897

Fling Out the Banner! Let It Float 446

For those who fear you, you have raised a banner to be unfurled against the bow.
Ps. 60:4

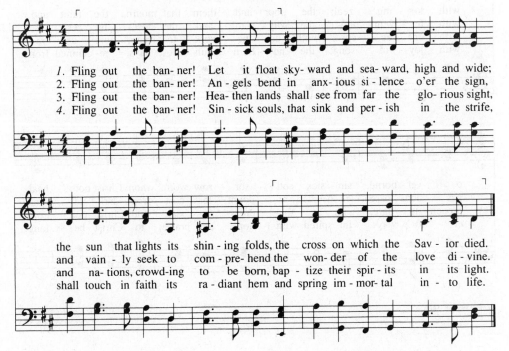

1. Fling out the ban-ner! Let it float sky-ward and sea-ward, high and wide,
2. Fling out the ban-ner! An-gels bend in anx-ious si-lence o'er the sign,
3. Fling out the ban-ner! Hea-then lands shall see from far the glo-rious sight,
4. Fling out the ban-ner! Sin-sick souls, that sink and per-ish in the strife,

the sun that lights its shin-ing folds, the cross on which the Sav-ior died.
and vain-ly seek to com-pre-hend the won-der of the love di-vine.
and na-tions, crowd-ing to be born, bap-tize their spir-its in its light.
shall touch in faith its ra-diant hem and spring im-mor-tal in-to life.

5. Fling out the banner! Let it float
skyward and seaward, high and wide,
our glory, only in the cross;
our only hope, the Crucified!

6. Fling out the banner! Wide and high,
seaward and skyward, let it shine:
nor skill, nor might, nor merit ours;
we conquer only in that sign.

George W. Doane, 1848

WALTHAM L.M.
J. Baptiste Calkin, 1872

447   Christ for the World We Sing

Repentance and forgiveness of sins will be preached in his name to all nations.
Luke 24:47

1. Christ for the world we sing; the world to Christ we bring
2. Christ for the world we sing; the world to Christ we bring
3. Christ for the world we sing; the world to Christ we bring
4. Christ for the world we sing; the world to Christ we bring

with lov - ing zeal; the poor and them that mourn, the faint and
with fer - vent pray'r; the way - ward and the lost, by rest - less
with one ac - cord; with us the work to share, with us re -
with joy - ful song; the new - born souls whose days, re - claimed from

o - ver - borne, sin - sick and sor - row worn, whom Christ doth heal.
pas - sions tossed, re - deemed at count - less cost from dark de - spair.
proach to dare, with us the cross to bear, for Christ our Lord.
er - ror's ways, in - spired with hope and praise, to Christ be - long.

Samuel Wolcott, 1869

ITALIAN HYMN 6.6.4.6.6.6.4.
Felice de Giardini, 1769

We Have Heard the Joyful Sound

448

Proclaim his salvation day after day. Declare his glory among the nations. Ps. 96:2, 3

1. We have heard the joy - ful sound: Je - sus saves! Je - sus saves!
2. Waft it on the roll - ing tide: Je - sus saves! Je - sus saves!
3. Sing a - bove the bat - tle strife, Je - sus saves! Je - sus saves!
4. Give the winds a might - y voice, Je - sus saves! Je - sus saves!

Spread the tid - ings all a - round: Je - sus saves! Je - sus saves!
Tell to sin - ners far and wide: Je - sus saves! Je - sus saves!
By his death and end - less life, Je - sus saves! Je - sus saves!
Let the na - tions now re - joice— Je - sus saves! Je - sus saves!

Bear the news to ev - 'ry land, climb the steeps and cross the waves;
Sing, ye is - lands of the sea; ech - o back, ye o - cean caves;
Sing it soft - ly through the gloom, when the heart for mer - cy craves;
Shout sal - va - tion full and free, high - est hills and deep - est caves;

on - ward! 'tis our Lord's com - mand; Je - sus saves! Je - sus saves!
earth shall keep her ju - bi - lee: Je - sus saves! Je - sus saves!
sing in tri - umph o'er the tomb— Je - sus saves! Je - sus saves!
this our song of vic - to - ry— Je - sus saves! Je - sus saves!

Priscilla J. Owens, 1868

JESUS SAVES 7.6.7.6.7.7.7.6.
William J. Kirkpatrick, 1882

449

We Rest on Thee

We rely on you, and in your name we have come. 2 Chron. 14:11

1. "We rest on thee"— our shield and our de - fend - er!
2. Yea, "in thy name," O Cap - tain of sal - va - tion!
3. "We go" in faith, our own great weak - ness feel - ing,
4. "We rest on thee"— our shield and our de - fend - er!

We go not forth a - lone a - gainst the foe;
In thy dear name, all oth - er names a - bove:
and need - ing more each day thy grace to know:
Thine is the bat - tle, thine shall be the praise

strong in thy strength, safe in thy keep - ing ten - der,
Je - sus our righ - teous - ness, our sure foun - da - tion,
yet from our hearts a song of tri - umph peal - ing,
when pass - ing through the gates of pearl - y splen - dor,

"We rest on thee, and in thy name we go,"
our Prince of glo-ry and our King of love,
"We rest on thee, and in thy name we go,"
vic-tors— we rest with thee, through end-less days,

strong in thy strength, safe in thy keep-ing ten-der,
Je-sus our righ-teous-ness, our sure foun-da-tion,
yet from our hearts a song of tri-umph peal-ing,
when pass-ing through the gates of pearl-y splen-dor,

"We rest on thee, and in thy name we go."
our Prince of glo-ry and our King of love.
"We rest on thee, and in thy name we go."
vic-tors— we rest with thee, through end-less days.

Edith G. Cherry, ca. 1895

FINLANDIA 11.10.11.10.11.10.
Jean Sibelius, 1899; arr.

450

So Send I You

Peace be with you! As the Father has sent me, I am sending you. John 20:21

1. So send I you— by grace made strong to tri - umph o'er hosts of
2. So send I you— to take to souls in bond - age the word of
3. So send I you— my strength to know in weak - ness, my joy in
4. So send I you— to bear my cross with pa - tience, and then one

hell, o'er dark - ness, death, and sin, my name to bear, and in that
truth that sets the cap - tive free, to break the bonds of sin, to
grief, my per - fect peace in pain, to prove my pow'r, my grace, my
day with joy to lay it down, to hear my voice, "Well done, my

name to con - quer— so send I you, my vic - to - ry to win.
loose death's fet - ters— so send I you, to bring the lost to me.
prom - ised pres - ence— so send I you, e - ter - nal fruit to gain.
faith - ful ser - vant— come, share my throne, my king - dom, and my

st. 1–3

st. 4

crown!" "As the Fa - ther hath sent me, so send I you."

Margaret Clarkson, 1954, 1963

SO SEND I YOU 11.10.11.10 ref.
John W. Peterson, 1954

The Sending, Lord, Springs

451

Whom shall I send? And who will go for us? Is. 6:8

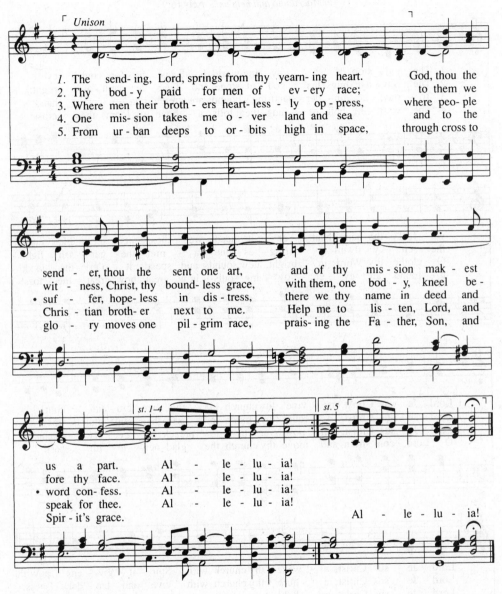

1. The send-ing, Lord, springs from thy yearn-ing heart. God, thou the
2. Thy bod-y paid for men of ev-ery race; to them we
3. Where men their broth-ers heart-less-ly op-press, where peo-ple
4. One mis-sion takes me o-ver land and sea and to the
5. From ur-ban deeps to or-bits high in space, through cross to

send-er, thou the sent one art, and of thy mis-sion mak-est
wit-ness, Christ, thy bound-less grace, with them, one bod-y, kneel be-
suf-fer, hope-less in dis-tress, there we thy name in deed and
Chris-tian broth-er next to me. Help me to lis-ten, Lord, and
glo-ry moves one pil-grim race, prais-ing the Fa-ther, Son, and

st. 1–4   *st. 5*

us a part. Al - le - lu - ia!
fore thy face. Al - le - lu - ia!
word con-fess. Al - le - lu - ia!
speak for thee. Al - le - lu - ia!
Spir-it's grace.   Al - le - lu - ia!

William J. Danker, 1966

Text © 1966, *Christianity Today.* Used by permission.

ENGELBERG 10.10.10.4.
Charles V. Stanford, 1904

452

Macedonia

Paul had a vision of a man of Macedonia standing and begging him, "Come over to Macedonia and help us." Acts 16:9

1. The vi - sion of a dy - ing world is vast be - fore our eyes;
2. The sav - age hugs his god of stone and fears de - scent of night;
3. To - day, as un - der - stand-ing's bounds are stretch'd on ev - ery hand,
4. The warn - ing bell of judg- ment tolls, a - bove us looms the cross;

we feel the heart- beat of its need, we hear its fee - ble cries:
the cit - y dwell- er cring - es lone a - mid the gar - ish light:
O clothe thy Word in bright, new sounds, and speed it o'er the land;
a - round are ev - er - dy - ing souls— how great, how great the loss!

Lord Je - sus Christ, re - vive thy church in this, her cru - cial hour!
Lord Je - sus Christ, a - rouse thy church to see their mute dis - tress!
Lord Je - sus Christ, em - pow - er us to preach by ev - ery means!
O Lord, con - strain and move thy church the glad news to im - part!

Lord Je - sus Christ, a - wake thy church with Spir - it - giv - en pow'r.
Lord Je - sus Christ, e - quip thy church with love and ten - der - ness.
Lord Je - sus Christ, em - bold - en us in near and dis - tant scenes.
And Lord, as thou dost stir thy church, be - gin with - in my heart.

Anne Ortlund, 1966

ALL SAINTS NEW C.M.D.
Henry S. Cutler, 1872

All Authority and Power

453

All authority in heaven and on earth has been given to me. Matt. 28:18

1. All au-thor-i-ty and pow-er, ev-'ry sta-tus
2. All the na-tions owe him wor-ship, ev-'ry tongue shall
3. All the clear com-mands of Je-sus must be heed-ed
4. All the time he will be with us, al-ways, to the

and do-main, now be-longs to him who suf-fered
call him Lord; how are men to call up-on him
and o-beyed; full pro-vi-sion for our weak-ness
end of days, with his own be-liev-ing peo-ple,

our re-demp-tion to ob-tain; an-gels, de-mons,
if his name they have not heard? There-fore go and
in his teach-ing he has made; in the Gos-pel
who keep stead-fast in his ways; God the Fa-ther,

kings and rul-ers, o-ver all shall Je-sus reign!
make dis-ci-ples, preach his gos-pel, spread his word.
words and sym-bols, sav-ing truth to us con-veyed.
Son, and Spir-it, bless us, and to him the praise!

Christopher Idle, 1973

NEANDER 8.7.8.7.8.7.
Joachim Neander, 1680; alt. 1990

454 Our God Is Mighty, Worthy of All Praising

Declare his glory among the nations. Ps. 96:3

Unison

1. Our God is might-y, wor-thy of all prais-ing;
2. Our God is gra-cious, in-fi-nite in mer-cy;
3. Our God is faith-ful; he will work with-in us,
4. Our God is sov-'reign o-ver all cre-a-tion,

sing un-to him a glad, tri-um-phant song;
he bridged the hope-less gulf our sin had made;
ful-fill-ing all the pur-pose he has planned,
and soon his earth shall hear his might-y voice:

he is the Lord, su-preme in earth and heav-en;
he gave his Son to pur-chase our sal-va-tion—
cleans-ing our hearts and fill-ing with his Spir-it,
with shout of joy the King shall come in splen-dor—

to him all strength and maj-es-ty be-long.
in Je-sus Christ we meet God un-a-fraid!
mak-ing us strong to keep his last com-mand.
lift up your hearts, con-fess him, and re-joice!

Margaret Clarkson, 1976

VIOLA 11.10.11.10.ref.
Hughes M. Huffman, 1976

Text © 1976, InterVarsity Press. Assigned 1979 to Hope Publishing Co. All rights reserved. Used by permission. Tune © 1976, Hughes M. Huffman, assigned to InterVarsity Christian Fellowship. Used by permission.

455 And Can It Be That I Should Gain

While we were still sinners, Christ died for us. Rom. 5:8

1. And can it be that I should gain an in - t'rest in the Sav - ior's blood? Died he for me, who caused his pain? For me, who him to death pur - sued? A - maz - ing love!
2. 'Tis mys - t'ry all! Th'Im - mor - tal dies: who can ex - plore his strange de - sign? In vain the first - born ser - aph tries to sound the depths of love di - vine. 'Tis mer - cy all!
3. He left his Fa - ther's throne a - bove (so free, so in - fi - nite his grace!), hum - bled him - self (so great his love!), and bled for all his cho - sen race. 'Tis mer - cy all,
4. Long my im - pris - oned spir - it lay fast bound in sin and na - ture's night; thine eye dif - fused a quick - 'ning ray; I woke, the dun - geon flamed with light; my chains fell off,
5. No con - dem - na - tion now I dread; Je - sus, and all in him, is mine! A - live in him, my liv - ing Head, and clothed in righ - teous - ness di - vine, bold I ap - proach

SALVATION BY GRACE

How can it be that thou, my God, shouldst
Let earth a - dore, let an - gel minds in -
• im - mense and free; for, O my God, it
my heart was free; I rose, went forth, and
th'e - ter - nal throne, and claim the crown, through

die for me?
quire no more. A - maz - ing love! How can it
• found out me.
fol - lowed thee. A - maz - ing love! How
Christ, my own.

REFRAIN

be that thou, my God, shouldst die for me?
can it be that thou, my God,

Charles Wesley, 1738
Alt. 1990

SAGINA L.M.D.
Thomas Campbell, 1825

456 By Grace I'm Saved, Grace Free and Boundless

It is by grace you have been saved, through faith—and this not from yourselves, it is the gift of God—not by works, so that no one can boast. Eph. 2:8, 9

1. By grace I'm saved, grace free and bound - less; my soul, be -
2. By grace! None dare lay claim to mer - it; our works and
3. By grace! O mark this word of prom - ise when you are
4. By grace! This ground of faith is cer - tain; so long as

lieve and doubt it not. Why stag - ger at this word of
con - duct have no worth. God in his love sent our Re -
by your sins op - pressed, when Sa - tan plagues your trou - bled
God is true, it stands. What saints have penned by in - spi -

prom - ise? Has Scrip - ture ev - er false - hood taught? No; then this
deem - er, Christ Je - sus, to this sin - ful earth; his death did
con - science, and when your heart is seek - ing rest. What rea - son
ra - tion, what in his Word our God com - mands, what our whole

word must true re - main: by grace you too shall heav'n ob - tain.
for our sins a - tone, and we are saved by grace a - lone.
can - not com - pre - hend God by his grace to you will send.
faith must rest up - on, is grace a - lone, grace in his Son.

Christian L. Scheidt, 1742, cento
Alt. 1990, mod.

MENTZER 9.8.9.8.8.8.
Johann B. König's *Harmonischer Liederschatz*, 1738

Come, Thou Fount of Every Blessing

457

Samuel ... named it Ebenezer, saying, "Thus far has the LORD helped us." 1 Sam. 7:12

1. Come, thou fount of ev-'ry bless-ing, tune my heart to sing thy grace;
2. Here I raise my Eb-en-e-zer; hith-er by thy help I'm come;
3. O to grace how great a debt-or dai-ly I'm con-strained to be;

streams of mer-cy, nev-er ceas-ing, call for songs of loud-est praise.
and I hope, by thy good plea-sure, safe-ly to ar-rive at home.
let that grace now, like a fet-ter, bind my wan-d'ring heart to thee.

Teach me some me-lo-dious son-net, sung by flam-ing tongues a-bove;
Je-sus sought me when a strang-er, wan-d'ring from the fold of God:
Prone to wan-der—Lord, I feel it—prone to leave the God I love:

praise the mount! I'm fixed up-on it, mount of God's un-chang-ing love.
he, to res-cue me from dan-ger, in-ter-posed his pre-cious blood.
here's my heart, O take and seal it, seal it for thy courts a-bove.

Robert Robinson, 1758

NETTLETON 8.7.8.7.D.
Asahel Nettleton. 1825

458

What Tho' I Cannot Break My Chain

Who then can be saved?... With man this is impossible, but not with God; all things are possible with God. Mark 10:26, 27

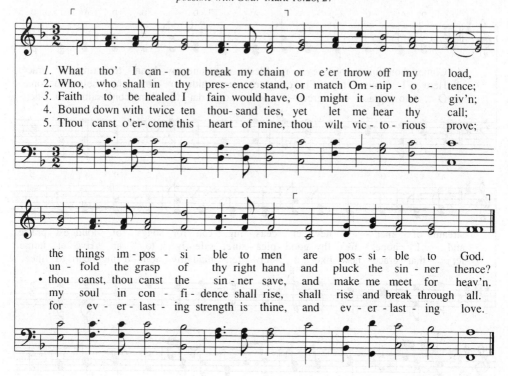

1. What tho' I can-not break my chain or e'er throw off my load,
   the things im-pos - si - ble to men are pos - si - ble to God.
2. Who, who shall in thy pres- ence stand, or match Om - nip - o - tence;
   un - fold the grasp of thy right hand and pluck the sin - ner thence?
3. Faith to be healed I fain would have, O might it now be giv'n;
   • thou canst, thou canst the sin - ner save, and make me meet for heav'n.
4. Bound down with twice ten thou- sand ties, yet let me hear thy call;
   my soul in con - fi - dence shall rise, shall rise and break through all.
5. Thou canst o'er- come this heart of mine, thou wilt vic - to - rious prove;
   for ev - er - last - ing strength is thine, and ev - er - last - ing love.

Augustus M. Toplady, 1740–1778

ARLINGTON C.M.
Thomas A. Arne, 1762
Arr. by Ralph Harrison, 1784

459

I Am Not Skilled to Understand

God exalted him to his own right hand as Prince and Savior. Acts 5:31

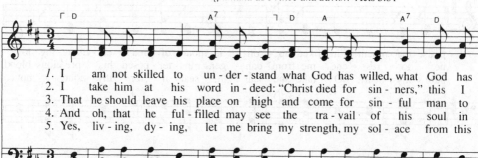

1. I am not skilled to un - der - stand what God has willed, what God has
2. I take him at his word in - deed: "Christ died for sin - ners," this I
3. That he should leave his place on high and come for sin - ful man to
4. And oh, that he ful - filled may see the tra - vail of his soul in
5. Yes, liv - ing, dy - ing, let me bring my strength, my sol - ace from this

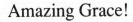

planned; I on-ly know at his right hand is One who is my Sav-ior!
read; for in my heart I find a need of him to be my Sav-ior!
• die, you count it strange? so once did I, be - fore I knew my Sav-ior!
me, and with his work con - tent-ed be, as I with my dear Sav-ior!
spring; that he who lives to be my King once died to be my Sav-ior!

Dora Greenwell, 1873

GREENWELL 8.8.8.7.
William J. Kirkpatrick, 1885

Amazing Grace! 460

Who am I, O LORD God, and what is my family, that you have brought me this far?
1 Chron. 17:16

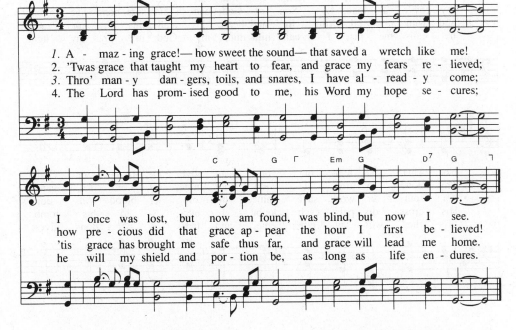

1. A - maz - ing grace!— how sweet the sound— that saved a wretch like me!
2. 'Twas grace that taught my heart to fear, and grace my fears re - lieved;
3. Thro' man - y dan - gers, toils, and snares, I have al - read - y come;
4. The Lord has prom- ised good to me, his Word my hope se - cures;

I once was lost, but now am found, was blind, but now I see.
how pre - cious did that grace ap - pear the hour I first be - lieved!
'tis grace has brought me safe thus far, and grace will lead me home.
he will my shield and por - tion be, as long as life en - dures.

5. And when this flesh and heart shall fail,
and mortal life shall cease,
I shall possess within the veil
a life of joy and peace.

6. When we've been there ten thousand years,
bright shining as the sun,
we've no less days to sing God's praise
than when we've first begun.

St. 1–5, John Newton, 1779
St. 6, *A Collection of Sacred Ballads*, 1790

AMAZING GRACE C.M.
Traditional American melody
Arr. by Edwin O. Excell, 1900

461 Not What My Hands Have Done

He saved us, not because of righteous things we had done, but because of his mercy.
Titus 3:5

1. Not what my hands have done can save my guilt-y soul;
2. Thy work a-lone, O Christ, can ease this weight of sin;
3. Thy grace a-lone, O God, to me can par-don speak;
4. I bless the Christ of God; I rest on love di-vine;
5. I praise the God of grace; I trust his truth and might;

not what my toil-ing flesh has borne can make my spir-it whole.
thy blood a-lone, O Lamb of God, can give me peace with-in.
thy pow'r a-lone, O Son of God, can this sore bond-age break.
and with un-fal-t'ring lip and heart, I call this Sav-ior mine.
he calls me his, I call him mine, my God, my joy, my light.

Not what I feel or do can give me peace with God;
Thy love to me, O God, not mine, O Lord, to thee,
No oth-er work, save thine, no oth-er blood will do;
His cross dis-pels each doubt; I bur-y in his tomb
'Tis he who sav-eth me, and free-ly par-don gives;

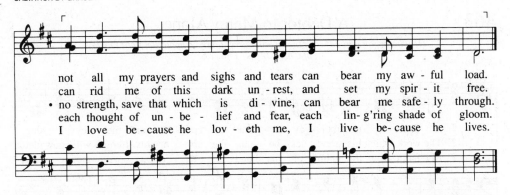

not all my prayers and sighs and tears can bear my aw-ful load.
can rid me of this dark un-rest, and set my spir-it free.
• no strength, save that which is di-vine, can bear me safe-ly through.
each thought of un-be-lief and fear, each lin-g'ring shade of gloom.
I love be-cause he lov-eth me, I live be-cause he lives.

Horatius Bonar, 1861; alt.

LEOMINSTER S.M.D.
George William Martin, 1862
Arr. by Arthur S. Sullivan, 1874

Grace! 'Tis a Charming Sound   462

God ... made us alive with Christ ... in order that in the coming ages he might show the incomparable riches of his grace. Eph. 2:4–7

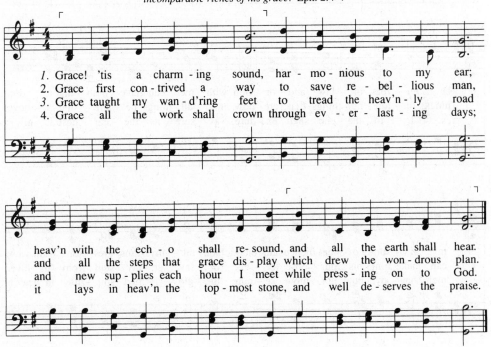

1. Grace! 'tis a charm-ing sound, har-mo-nious to my ear;
2. Grace first con-trived a way to save re-bel-lious man,
3. Grace taught my wan-d'ring feet to tread the heav'n-ly road
4. Grace all the work shall crown through ev-er-last-ing days;

heav'n with the ech-o shall re-sound, and all the earth shall hear.
and all the steps that grace dis-play which drew the won-drous plan.
and new sup-plies each hour I meet while press-ing on to God.
it lays in heav'n the top-most stone, and well de-serves the praise.

Philip Doddridge, 1755
Mod.

ST. MICHAEL S.M.
Genevan Psalter, 1543

463

A Debtor to Mercy Alone

He who began a good work in you will carry it on to completion until the day
of Christ Jesus. Phil. 1:6

1. A debt-or to mer-cy a-lone, of cov-e-nant mer-cy I sing;
2. The work which his good-ness be-gan, the arm of his strength will com-plete;
3. My name from the palms of his hands e-ter-ni-ty will not e-rase;

nor fear, with your righ-teous-ness on, my per-son and of-f'ring to bring.
his prom-ise is yea and a-men, and nev-er was for-feit-ed yet.
im-pressed on his heart it re-mains, in marks of in-del-i-ble grace.

The ter-rors of law and of God with me can have noth-ing to do;
Things fu-ture, nor things that are now, nor all things be-low or a-bove,
Yes, I to the end shall en-dure, as sure as the ear-nest is giv'n;

my Sav-ior's o-be-dience and blood hide all my trans-gres-sions from view.
can make him his pur-pose for-go, or sev-er my soul from his love.
more hap-py, but not more se-cure, the glo-ri-fied spir-its in heav'n.

Augustus M. Toplady, 1740–1778
Mod.

TREWEN L.M.D.
David Emlyn Evans, 1843–1913

I Was a Wandering Sheep

464

We all, like sheep, have gone astray, each of us has turned to his own way; and the LORD has laid on him the iniquity of us all. Is. 53:6

1. I was a wan-d'ring sheep, I did not love the fold;
2. The Shep-herd sought his sheep, the Fa-ther sought his child;
3. Je-sus my Shep-herd is; 'twas he that loved my soul,
4. I was a wan-d'ring sheep, I would not be con-trolled;

I did not love my Shep-herd's voice, I would not be con-trolled.
they fol-lowed me o'er vale and hill, o'er des-erts waste and wild:
'twas he that washed me in his blood, 'twas he that made me whole;
but now I love my Shep-herd's voice, I love, I love the fold.

I was a way-ward child, I did not love my home;
they found me nigh to death, fam-ished and faint and lone;
'twas he that sought the lost, that found the wan-d'ring sheep,
I was a way-ward child, I once pre-ferred to roam;

I did not love my Fa-ther's voice, I loved a-far to roam.
they bound me with the bands of love, they saved the wan-d'ring one.
'twas he that brought me to the fold, 'tis he that still doth keep,
but now I love my Fa-ther's voice, I love, I love his home.

Horatius Bonar, 1843

LEBANON S.M.D.
John Zundel, 1855

465

Marvelous Grace of Our Loving Lord

Where sin increased, grace increased all the more. Rom. 5:20

1. Mar - vel - ous grace of our lov - ing Lord, grace that ex - ceeds our
2. Sin and de - spair like the sea waves cold, threa - ten the soul with
3. Dark is the stain that we can - not hide, what can a - vail to

sin and our guilt, yon - der on Cal - va - ry's mount out - poured,
in - fi - nite loss; grace that is great - er, yes, grace un - told,
wash it a - way? Look! there is flow - ing a crim - son tide;

REFRAIN

there where the blood of the Lamb was spilt. Grace, grace,
points to the Ref - uge, the might - y cross. Mar - vel - ous grace,
whit - er than snow you may be to - day.

God's grace, grace that will par - don and cleanse with - in; grace,
in - fi - nite grace, mar - vel - ous

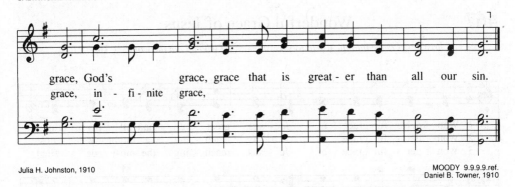

grace, God's   grace, grace that is great - er than all our sin.
grace, in - fi - nite grace,

Julia H. Johnston, 1910

MOODY 9.9.9.9.ref.
Daniel B. Towner, 1910

I Sought the Lord, and Afterward I Knew   466

We love because he first loved us. 1 John 4:19

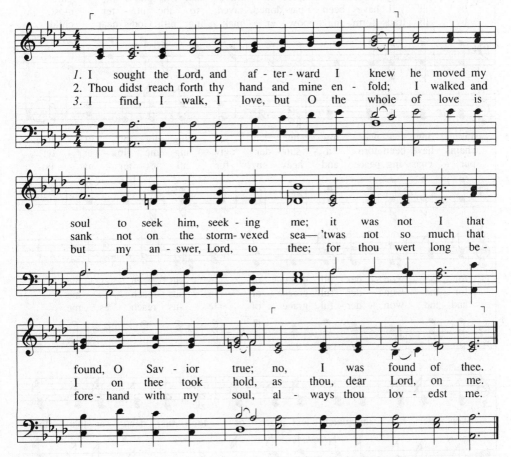

1. I sought the Lord, and af - ter - ward I knew he moved my
2. Thou didst reach forth thy hand and mine en - fold; I walked and
3. I find, I walk, I love, but O the whole of love is

soul to seek him, seek - ing me; it was not I that
sank not on the storm- vexed sea— 'twas not so much that
but my an - swer, Lord, to thee; for thou wert long be -

found, O Sav - ior true; no, I was found of thee.
I on thee took hold, as thou, dear Lord, on me.
fore - hand with my soul, al - ways thou lov - edst me.

Anon., 1878

PEACE 10.10.10.6.
George W. Chadwick, 1893

467 Wonderful Grace of Jesus

Christ Jesus came into the world to save sinners—of whom I am the worst. 1 Tim. 1:15

1. Won - der - ful grace of Je - sus, great - er than all my sin;
2. Won - der - ful grace of Je - sus, reach - ing a might - y host,
3. Won - der - ful grace of Je - sus, reach - ing the most de - filed,

how shall my tongue de - scribe it, where shall its praise be - gin?
by it I have been par - doned, saved to the ut - ter - most,
by its trans - form - ing pow - er, mak - ing him God's dear child,

Tak - ing a - way my bur - den, set - ting my spir - it free;
chains have been torn a - sun - der, giv - ing me lib - er - ty;
pur - chas - ing peace and heav - en, for all e - ter - ni - ty;

for the won - der - ful grace of Je - sus reach - es me.
for the won - der - ful grace of Je - sus reach - es me.
and the won - der - ful grace of Je - sus reach - es me.

REFRAIN

Won - der - ful the match - less grace of Je - sus, deep - er than the

the roll - ing sea;
might - y roll - ing sea; won - der - ful
High - er than the moun - tain,

grace, all - suf - fi - cient for
spark - ling like a foun - tain, all - suf - fi - cient grace for e - ven

me, for e - ven me; broad - er than the scope of my trans -
me;

gres - sions, great - er far than all my sin and shame;

O mag - ni - fy the pre - cious name of Je - sus, praise his name!

Haldor Lillenas, 1918
Alt. 1961

WONDERFUL GRACE Irreg.
Haldor Lillenas, 1918

468
My Faith Has Found a Resting Place

While we were still sinners, Christ died for us. Rom. 5:8

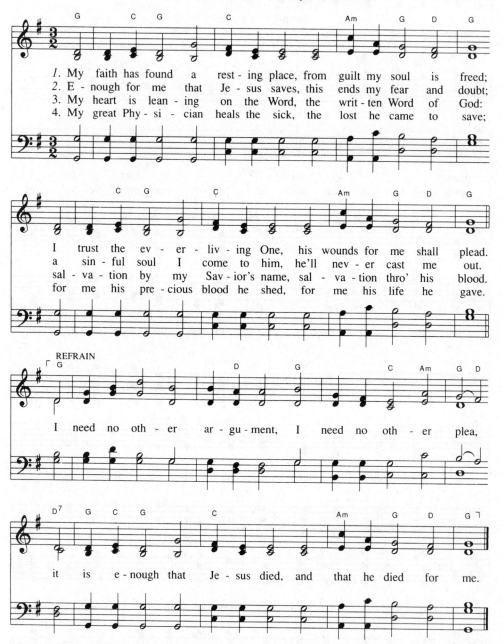

1. My faith has found a rest-ing place, from guilt my soul is freed;
2. E-nough for me that Je-sus saves, this ends my fear and doubt;
3. My heart is lean-ing on the Word, the writ-ten Word of God:
4. My great Phy-si-cian heals the sick, the lost he came to save;

I trust the ev-er-liv-ing One, his wounds for me shall plead.
a sin-ful soul I come to him, he'll nev-er cast me out.
sal-va-tion by my Sav-ior's name, sal-va-tion thro' his blood.
for me his pre-cious blood he shed, for me his life he gave.

REFRAIN

I need no oth-er ar-gu-ment, I need no oth-er plea,

it is e-nough that Je-sus died, and that he died for me.

Lidie H. Edmunds, 1891
Alt. 1990

LANDAS C.M.ref.
André Grétry, 1741–1831
Arr. by William J. Kirkpatrick, 1891

How Sweet and Awesome Is the Place

469

A certain man was preparing a great banquet and invited many guests. Luke 14:16

1. How sweet and awe – some is the place
2. While all our hearts and all our songs
3. "Why was I made to hear your voice,
4. 'Twas the same love that spread the feast

with Christ with – in the doors, while ev – er – last – ing
join to ad – mire the feast, each of us cries, with
and en – ter while there's room, when thou – sands make a
that sweet – ly drew us in; else we had still re –

love dis – plays the choic – est of her stores.
thank – ful tongue, "Lord, why was I a guest?
wretch – ed choice, and rath – er starve than come?"
fused to taste, and per – ished in our sin.

5. Pity the nations, O our God,
   constrain the earth to come;
   send your victorious Word abroad,
   and bring the strangers home.

6. We long to see your churches full,
   that all the chosen race
   may, with one voice and heart and soul,
   sing your redeeming grace.

Isaac Watts, 1707
Alt. 1961, 1990, mod.

ST. COLUMBA C.M.
Old Irish hymn melody; alt. 1990

470
How Vast the Benefits Divine

He chose us in him before the creation of the world to be holy and blameless
in his sight. Eph. 1:4

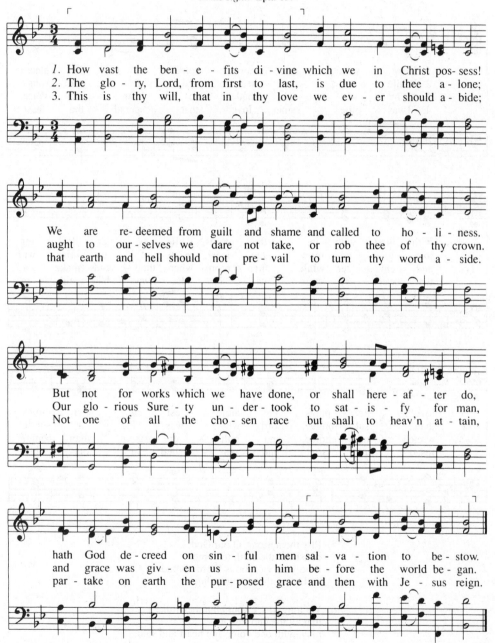

1. How vast the ben - e - fits di - vine which we in Christ pos - sess!
2. The glo - ry, Lord, from first to last, is due to thee a - lone;
3. This is thy will, that in thy love we ev - er should a - bide;

We are re - deemed from guilt and shame and called to ho - li - ness.
aught to our - selves we dare not take, or rob thee of thy crown.
that earth and hell should not pre - vail to turn thy word a - side.

But not for works which we have done, or shall here - af - ter do,
Our glo - rious Sure - ty un - der - took to sat - is - fy for man,
Not one of all the cho - sen race but shall to heav'n at - tain,

hath God de - creed on sin - ful men sal - va - tion to be - stow.
and grace was giv - en us in him be - fore the world be - gan.
par - take on earth the pur - posed grace and then with Je - sus reign.

Augustus M. Toplady, 1774
Alt. 1961

ST. MATTHEW C.M.D.
William Croft, 1708

'Tis Not That I Did Choose Thee

471

You did not choose me, but I chose you. John 15:16

1. 'Tis not that I did choose thee, for, Lord, that could not be;
this heart would still refuse thee, hadst thou not cho-sen me.
Thou from the sin that stained me hast cleansed and set me free;
of old thou hast or-dained me, that I should live to thee.

2. 'Twas sov-'reign mer-cy called me and taught my o-p'ning mind;
the world had else en-thralled me, to heav'n-ly glo-ries blind.
My heart owns none be-fore thee, for thy rich grace I thirst;
this know-ing, if I love thee, thou must have loved me first.

Josiah Conder, 1836

SAVOY CHAPEL 7.6.7.6.D.
John Baptiste Calkin, 1887; alt. 1990

472

Come, Ye Sinners, Poor and Wretched

I have not come to call the righteous, but sinners. Matt. 9:13

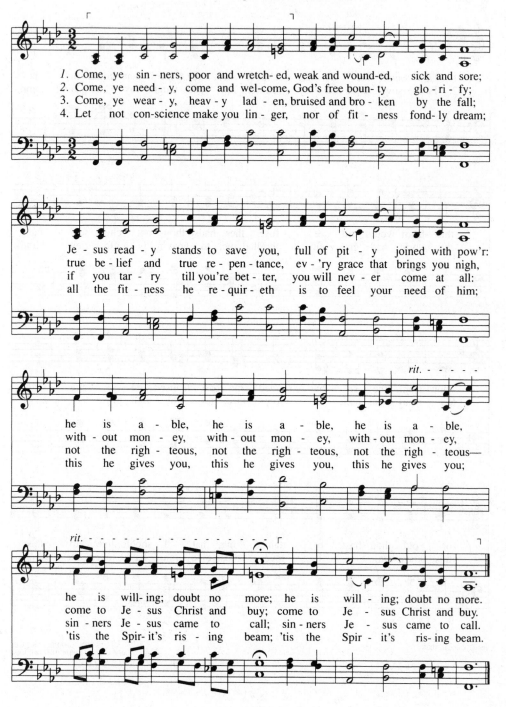

1. Come, ye sin - ners, poor and wretch- ed, weak and wound-ed, sick and sore;
2. Come, ye need - y, come and wel-come, God's free boun- ty glo - ri - fy;
3. Come, ye wear - y, heav - y lad - en, bruised and bro - ken by the fall;
4. Let not con-science make you lin - ger, nor of fit - ness fond- ly dream;

Je - sus read - y stands to save you, full of pit - y joined with pow'r;
true be - lief and true re - pen - tance, ev - 'ry grace that brings you nigh,
if you tar - ry till you're bet - ter, you will nev - er come at all:
all the fit - ness he re - quir - eth is to feel your need of him;

he is a - ble, he is a - ble, he is a - ble,
with - out mon - ey, with - out mon - ey, with - out mon - ey,
not the righ - teous, not the righ - teous, not the righ - teous—
this he gives you, this he gives you, this he gives you;

he is will- ing; doubt no more; he is will - ing; doubt no more.
come to Je - sus Christ and buy; come to Je - sus Christ and buy.
sin - ners Je - sus came to call; sin - ners Je - sus came to call.
'tis the Spir-it's ris - ing beam; 'tis the Spir - it's ris- ing beam.

5. Lo! th'incarnate God, ascended, pleads the merit of his blood;
   venture on him, venture wholly, let no other trust intrude:
   none but Jesus, none but Jesus, none but Jesus
   can do helpless sinners good, can do helpless sinners good.

Joseph Hart, 1759; alt.

BRYN CALFARIA 8.7.8.7.4.4.4.7.7.
William Owen, 1852

Jesus Sinners Doth Receive

473

This man welcomes sinners and eats with them. Luke 15:2

1. "Je - sus sin - ners doth re - ceive": word of sur - est con - so - la - tion;
2. On God's grace we have no claim, yet to us his pledge is giv - en;
3. When a help - less lamb doth stray, af - ter it, the Shep-herd, press - ing
4. Oh, how blest it is to know: were as scar - let my trans-gres - sion,
5. Now my con-science is at peace, from the Law I stand ac - quit - ted;

word all sor - row to re - lieve, word of par - don, peace, sal - va - tion!
he hath sworn by his own name, o - pen are the gates of heav - en.
thro' each dark and dan-g'rous way, brings it back, his own pos-sess - ing
it shall be as white as snow by thy blood and bit - ter pas - sion;
Christ hath pur-chased my re - lease and my ev - ery sin re - mit - ted.

Naught like this can com - fort give: "Je - sus sin - ners doth re - ceive."
Take to heart this word and live: "Je - sus sin - ners doth re - ceive."
Je - sus seeks thee, O be - lieve: "Je - sus sin - ners doth re - ceive."
for these words I now be - lieve: "Je - sus sin - ners doth re - ceive."
Naught re - mains my soul to grieve— "Je - sus sin - ners doth re - ceive."

Erdmann Neumeister, 1718
Trans. composite

JESUS, MEINE ZUVERSICHT 7.8.7.8.7.7.
Johann Crüger, 1653; arr.

474 Blow Ye the Trumpet, Blow!

The LORD has anointed me ... to proclaim the year of the LORD's favor. Is. 61:1, 2

1. Blow ye the trumpet, blow! The gladly solemn sound
2. Jesus, our great High Priest, has full atonement made;
3. Extol the Lamb of God, the sacrificial Lamb;
4. Ye slaves of sin and hell, your liberty receive:

let all the nations know, to earth's remotest bound:
ye weary spirits, rest; ye mournful souls, be glad:
redemption through his blood throughout the world proclaim:
and safe in Jesus dwell, and blest in Jesus live:

REFRAIN

The year of jubilee is come; return, ye ransomed
sinners, home; return, ye ransomed sinners, home.

5. Ye who have sold for naught
   your heritage above,
   receive it back unbought,
   the gift of Jesus' love:
   (Refrain)

6. The gospel trumpet hear,
   the news of heav'nly grace;
   and, saved from earth, appear
   before your Savior's face:
   (Refrain)

Charles Wesley, 1750
Alt. 1961

LENOX 6.6.6.6.ref.
Louis Edson. 1782

Come to the Savior Now

475

Come to me. Matt. 11:28

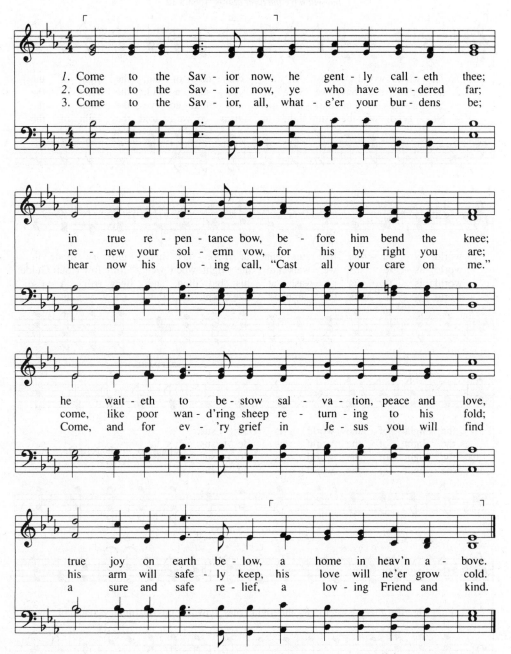

1. Come to the Sav - ior now, he gent - ly call - eth thee;
2. Come to the Sav - ior now, ye who have wan - dered far;
3. Come to the Sav - ior, all, what - e'er your bur - dens be;

in true re - pen - tance bow, be - fore him bend the knee;
re - new your sol - emn vow, for his by right you are;
hear now his lov - ing call, "Cast all your care on me."

he wait - eth to be - stow sal - va - tion, peace and love,
come, like poor wan - d'ring sheep re - turn - ing to his fold;
Come, and for ev - 'ry grief in Je - sus you will find

true joy on earth be - low, a home in heav'n a - bove.
his arm will safe - ly keep, his love will ne'er grow cold.
a sure and safe re - lief, a lov - ing Friend and kind.

John M. Wigner, 1871

INVITATION 6.6.6.6.D.
Frederick C. Maker, 1881

476 The Light of the World Is Jesus

I am the light of the world. Whoever follows me will never walk in darkness,
but will have the light of life. John 8:12

1. The whole world was lost in the dark-ness of sin; the light of the
2. No dark-ness have we who in Je-sus a-bide, the light of the
3. Ye dwell-ers in dark-ness with sin-blind-ed eyes, the light of the
4. No need of the sun-light in heav-en, we're told, the light of the

world is Je-sus; like sun-shine at noon-day his glo-ry shone in,
world is Je-sus; we walk in the light when we fol-low our Guide,
world is Je-sus; go, wash at his bid-ding, and light will a-rise,
world is Je-sus; the Lamb is the light in the Cit-y of Gold,

the light of the world is Je-sus.
the light of the world is Je-sus.
the light of the world is Je-sus. Come to the light, 'tis
the light of the world is Je-sus.

shin-ing for thee; sweet-ly the light has dawned up-on me; once I was

blind, but now I can see; the light of the world is Je - sus.

Philip P. Bliss, 1875

LIGHT OF THE WORLD 11.8.11.8.ref.
Philip P. Bliss, 1875

Are You Weary, Are You Languid 477

Come to me, all you who are weary and burdened, and I will give you rest. Matt. 11:28

1. Are you wea - ry, are you lan - guid, are you sore dis - tress'd?
2. Has he marks to lead me to him, if he be my Guide?
3. Is there di - a - dem, as Mon - arch, that his brow a - dorns?
4. If I find him, if I fol - low, what his prom - ise here?

"Come to me," says One, "and com - ing, be at rest."
"In his feet and hands are wound- prints, and his side."
"Yes, a crown, in ve - ry sure - ty, but of thorns."
"Man - y a sor - row, man - y a la - bor, man - y a tear."

5. If I still hold closely to him,
   what has he at last?
   "Sorrow vanquished, labor ended,
   Jordan passed."

6. If I ask him to receive me,
   will he say me nay?
   "Not till earth and not till heaven
   pass away."

7. Finding, foll'wing, keeping, struggling,
   is he sure to bless?
   "Saints, apostles, prophets, martyrs
   answer yes."

John Mason Neale, 1862; alt.
Alt. 1990, mod.

STEPHANOS 8.5.8.3.
Henry W. Baker, 1868

478

I Love to Tell the Story

Let me tell you what he has done for me. Ps. 66:16

1. I love to tell the sto - ry of un - seen things a - bove,
2. I love to tell the sto - ry; more won - der - ful it seems
3. I love to tell the sto - ry; 'tis pleas - ant to re - peat
4. I love to tell the sto - ry; for those who know it best

of Je - sus and his glo - ry, of Je - sus and his love.
than all the gold - en fan - cies of all our gold - en dreams.
what seems, each time I tell it, more won - der - ful - ly sweet.
seem hun - ger - ing and thirst - ing to hear it, like the rest.

I love to tell the sto - ry, be - cause I know 'tis true;
I love to tell the sto - ry, it did so much for me;
I love to tell the sto - ry, for some have nev - er heard
And when, in scenes of glo - ry, I sing the new, new song,

it   sat - is - fies   my   long - ings   as   noth - ing   else   can   do.
and   that   is   just   the   rea - son   I   tell   it   now   to   thee.
the   mes - sage of   sal - va - tion   from God's own   ho - ly   Word.
'twill   be   the old,   old   sto - ry,   that   I   have loved   so   long.

REFRAIN

I   love   to   tell   the   sto - ry,   'twill   be   my theme in   glo - ry

to   tell   the   old,   old   sto - ry   of   Je - sus   and   his   love.

Katherine Hankey, 1866

I LOVE TO TELL THE STORY 7.6.7.6.D.
William G. Fischer. 1869

479 Softly and Tenderly Jesus Is Calling

He calls his own sheep by name. John 10:3

1. Soft - ly and ten - der - ly Je - sus is call - ing, call - ing for
2. Why should we tar - ry when Je - sus is plead - ing, plead - ing for
3. Time is now fleet - ing, the mo - ments are pass - ing, pass - ing from
4. Oh! for the won - der - ful love he has prom - ised, prom - ised for

you and for me; see, on the por - tals he's wait - ing and watch-ing,
you and for me? Why should we lin - ger and heed not his mer-cies,
you and from me; shad - ows are gath - er - ing, death-beds are com - ing,
you and for me; though we have sinned, he has mer - cy and par - don,

REFRAIN

watch - ing for you and for me.
mer - cies for you and for me? Come home, come home,
com - ing for you and for me. Come home, come home,
par - don for you and for me.

ye who are wea - ry, come home; ear - nest - ly, ten - der - ly,

Je - sus is call - ing, call - ing, O sin - ner, come home!

Will L. Thompson, 1880

THOMPSON 11.7.11.7.ref.
Will L. Thompson, 1880

Come, for the Feast Is Spread

480

Come to me. Matt. 11:28

1. Come, for the feast is spread, hark to the call; come to the
2. Come where the foun - tain flows, riv - er of life; heal - ing for
3. Come to the throne of grace, bold - ly draw near; he who would

Liv - ing Bread, of - fered to all. Come to his house of wine,
all thy woes, doubt - ing, and strife. Mil - lions have been sup - plied,
win the race must tar - ry here. What - e'er thy want may be,

low on his breast re - cline, all that he has is thine; come, sin - ner, come.
no one was e'er de - nied, come to the crim - son tide; come, sin - ner, come.
here is the grace for thee, Je - sus thine on - ly plea; come, Chris - tian, come.

Henry Burton, 1878

SOMETHING FOR JESUS 6.4.6.4.6.6.6.4.
Robert Lowry, 1871

481 Turn Your Eyes upon Jesus

Turn to me and be saved, all you ends of the earth. Is. 45:22

1. O soul, are you wea - ry and trou - bled? No light in the
2. Through death in - to life ev - er - last - ing he passed, and we
3. His Word shall not fail you— he prom - ised; be - lieve him and

dark - ness you see? There's light for a look at the
fol - low him there; o - ver us sin no more hath do -
all will be well: then go to a world that is

Sav - ior, and life more a - bun - dant and free!
min - ion— for more than con - qu'rors we are!
dy - ing, his per - fect sal - va - tion to tell!

THE FREE OFFER OF THE GOSPEL

REFRAIN

Turn your eyes up-on Je - sus, look full in his
won - der - ful face; and the things of earth will grow
strange - ly dim in the light of his glo - ry and grace.

Helen H. Lemmel, 1922

LEMMEL 9.8.9.8.ref.
Helen H. Lemmel, 1922

482

Come unto Me, Ye Weary

Come to me, all you who are weary and burdened, and I will give you rest.
Matt. 11:28

1. "Come un-to me, ye wea-ry, and I will give you rest."
2. "Come un-to me, dear chil-dren, and I will give you light."
3. "Come un-to me, ye faint-ing, and I will give you life."
4. "And who-so-ev-er com-eth I will not cast him out."

O bless-ed voice of Je - sus which comes to hearts op-pressed!
O lov-ing voice of Je - sus which comes to cheer the night!
O peace-ful voice of Je - sus which comes to end our strife!
O pa-tient love of Je - sus which drives a-way our doubt;

It tells of ben-e-dic-tion, of par-don, grace, and peace,
Our hearts were filled with sad-ness, and we had lost our way;
The foe is stern and ea-ger, the fight is fierce and long;
which calls us, ver-y sin-ners, un-wor-thy though we be

of joy that hath no end-ing, of love which can-not cease.
but morn-ing brings us glad-ness, and songs the break of day.
but thou hast made us might-y, and strong-er than the strong.
of love so free and bound-less, to come, dear Lord, to thee!

William C. Dix, 1867

LLANGLOFFAN 7.6.7.6.D.
Welsh hymn melody
David Evans's *Hymnau a Thonau,* 1865

We Sing the Glorious Conquest

483

Meanwhile, Saul was still breathing out murderous threats against the Lord's disciples.
Acts 9:1

1. We sing the glo - rious con - quest be - fore Da - mas - cus gate,
2. O glo - ry most ex - cel - ling, that smote a - cross his path!
3. O Wis - dom or - d'ring all things in or - der strong and sweet,
4. Lord, teach your church the les - son, still in her dark - est hour

when Saul, the church - 's spoil - er, came breath - ing threats and hate;
O light that pierced and blind - ed the zeal - ot in his wrath!
what no - bler spoil was ev - er cast at the vic - tor's feet?
of weak - ness and of dan - ger, to trust your hid - den pow'r:

the rav - 'ning wolf rushed for - ward full ear - ly to the prey;
O voice that spoke un - to him the calm, re - prov - ing word!
What wis - er mas - ter - build - er e'er wrought at your em - ploy
your grace by ways mys - te - rious the wrath of man can bind,

but lo! the Shep - herd met him, and bound him fast to - day.
O love that sought and held him the bond - man of his Lord!
than he, till now so fu - rious your build - ing to de - stroy?
and in your bold - est foe - man your cho - sen saint can find.

John Ellerton, 1871
Alt. 1961, mod.

WOODBIRD 7.6.7.6.D.
Traditional German melody; alt. 1990

484
I Hear Thy Welcome Voice

I have not come to call the righteous, but sinners. Mark 2:17

1. I hear thy wel-come voice that calls me, Lord, to thee
2. Though I come weak and vile, thou dost my strength as-sure;
3. 'Tis Je-sus calls me on to per-fect faith and love,
4. 'Tis Je-sus who con-firms the bless-ed work with-in,
5. And he the wit-ness gives to loy-al hearts and free,

for cleans-ing in thy pre-cious blood that flowed on Cal-va-ry.
thou dost my vile-ness ful-ly cleanse, till spot-less all and pure.
to per-fect hope and peace and trust, for earth and heav'n a-bove.
by add-ing grace to wel-comed grace, where reigned the pow'r of sin.
that ev-'ry prom-ise is ful-filled, if faith but brings the plea.

REFRAIN

I am com-ing, Lord, com-ing now to thee:

wash me, cleanse me, in the blood that flowed on Cal-va-ry.

Lewis Hartsough, 1872
Alt. 1990

WELCOME VOICE S.M.ref.
Lewis Hartsough, 1872

O Thou That Hear'st When Sinners Cry

Create in me a pure heart, O God, and renew a steadfast spirit within me. Ps. 51:10

1. O thou that hear'st when sin - ners cry, though all my crimes be - fore thee lie, be - hold them not with an - gry look, but blot their mem - 'ry from thy book.

2. Cre - ate my na - ture pure with - in, and form my soul a - verse to sin; let thy good Spir - it ne'er de - part, nor hide thy pres - ence from my heart.

3. I can - not live with - out thy light, cast out and ban - ished from thy sight; thy ho - ly joys, my God, re - store, and guard me, that I fall no more.

4. A bro - ken heart, my God, my King, is all the sac - ri - fice I bring; the God of grace will ne'er de - spise a bro - ken heart for sac - ri - fice.

5. My soul lies humbled in the dust,
   and owns thy dreadful sentence just:
   look down, O Lord, with pitying eye,
   and save the soul condemned to die.

6. Then will I teach the world thy ways;
   sinners shall learn thy sovereign grace;
   I'll lead them to my Savior's blood,
   and they shall praise a pard'ning God.

From Psalm 51
Isaac Watts, 1719

HAMBURG L.M.
Gregorian chant
Arr. by Lowell Mason, 1824

486

God, Be Merciful to Me

Have mercy on me, O God, according to your unfailing love. Ps. 51:1

1. God, be mer-ci-ful to me, on thy grace I rest my plea;
2. My trans-gres-sions I con-fess, grief and guilt my soul op-press;
3. I am e-vil, born in sin; thou de-sir-est truth with-in.
4. Bro-ken, hum-bled to the dust by thy wrath and judg-ment just,

plen-teous in com-pas-sion thou, blot out my trans-gres-sions now;
I have sinned a-gainst thy grace and pro-voked thee to thy face;
Thou a-lone my Sav-ior art, teach thy wis-dom to my heart;
let my con-trite heart re-joice and in glad-ness hear thy voice;

wash me, make me pure with-in, cleanse, O cleanse me from my sin.
I con-fess thy judg-ment just, speech-less, I thy mer-cy trust.
make me pure, thy grace be-stow, wash me whit-er than the snow.
from my sins O hide thy face, blot them out in bound-less grace.

5. Gracious God, my heart renew,
   make my spirit right and true;
   cast me not away from thee,
   let thy Spirit dwell in me;
   thy salvation's joy impart,
   steadfast make my willing heart.

6. Sinners then shall learn from me
   and return, O God, to thee;
   Savior, all my guilt remove,
   and my tongue shall sing thy love;
   touch my silent lips, O Lord,
   and my mouth shall praise accord.

From Psalm 51:1–15
The Psalter, 1912

REDHEAD 76 7.7.7.7.7.7.
Richard Redhead, 1853

In Thy Wrath and Hot Displeasure

487

O Lord, do not rebuke me in your anger or discipline me in your wrath. Ps. 38:1

1. In thy wrath and hot dis - plea - sure, chas - ten not thy ser - vant, Lord;
2. With my bur - den of trans - gres - sion heav - y - lad - en, o - ver - borne,
3. Dark - ness gath - ers, foes as - sail me, but I an - swer not a word;
4. I am prone to halt and stum - ble, grief and sor - row dwell with - in,

let thy mer - cy, with - out mea - sure, help and peace to me af - ford.
hum - bled low I make con - fes - sion, for my fol - ly now I mourn.
all my friends de - sert and fail me, on - ly thou my cry hast heard.
shame and guilt my spir - it hum - ble; I am sor - ry for my sin.

Heav - y is my trib - u - la - tion, sore my pun - ish - ment has been;
Weak and wound - ed, I im - plore thee; Lord, to me thy mer - cy show;
Lord, in thee am I con - fid - ing; thou wilt an - swer when I call,
Lord, my God, do not for - sake me, let me know that thou art near,

bro - ken by thine in - dig - na - tion, I am trou - bled by my sin.
all my pray'r is now be - fore thee, all my trou - ble thou dost know.
lest my foes, the good de - rid - ing, tri - umph in thy ser - vant's fall.
un - der thy pro - tec - tion take me, as my Sav - ior now ap - pear.

From Psalm 38
The Psalter, 1912

RUSTINGTON 8.7.8.7.D.
C. Hubert H. Parry, 1897

488

Remember Not, O God

Do not hold against us the sins of the fathers. Ps. 79:8

1. Re - mem - ber not, O God, the sins of long a - go;
2. O Lord, our Sav - ior, help, and glo - ri - fy your name;
3. In your com - pas - sion hear your pris - 'ners' plain - tive sigh,
4. Then, safe with - in your fold, we will ex - alt your name;

in ten - der mer - cy vis - it us, dis - tressed and hum - bled low.
de - liv - er us from all our sins and take a - way our shame.
and in the great - ness of your pow'r save those a - bout to die.
our thank - ful hearts with songs of joy your good - ness will pro - claim.

From Psalm 79:8–13
The Psalter, 1912; mod.

STEEPLE ASHTON S.M.
John Barnard, b. 1948

489

Lord, like the Publican I Stand

The tax collector … beat his breast and said, "God, have mercy on me, a sinner."
Luke 18:13

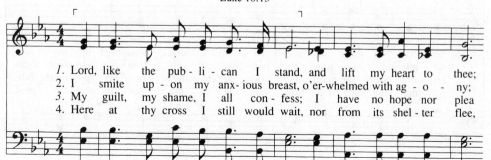

1. Lord, like the pub - li - can I stand, and lift my heart to thee;
2. I smite up - on my anx - ious breast, o'er-whelmed with ag - o - ny;
3. My guilt, my shame, I all con - fess; I have no hope nor plea
4. Here at thy cross I still would wait, nor from its shel - ter flee,

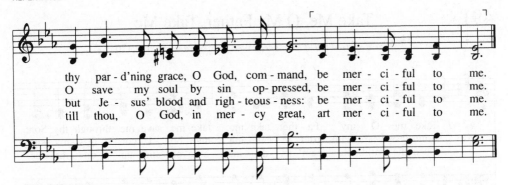

thy par - d'ning grace, O God, com - mand, be mer - ci - ful to me.
O save my soul by sin op - pressed, be mer - ci - ful to me.
but Je - sus' blood and righ - teous - ness: be mer - ci - ful to me.
till thou, O God, in mer - cy great, art mer - ci - ful to me.

Thomas Raffles, 1831

AVONDALE C.M.
Charles H. Gabriel, 1856–1932

Out of the Deep I Call
490

You are a forgiving God, gracious and compassionate, slow to anger and abounding in love. Neh. 9:17

1. Out of the deep I call to thee, O Lord, to thee.
2. Out of the deep I cry, the woe - ful deep of sin,
3. Out of the deep of fear and dread of com - ing shame;
4. Lord, there is mer - cy now, as ev - er was, with thee.

Be - fore thy throne of grace I fall; be mer - ci - ful to me.
of e - vil done in days gone by, of e - vil now with - in;
all night till morn - ing watch is near I plead the pre - cious name.
Be - fore thy throne of grace I bow; be mer - ci - ful to me.

Henry W. Baker, 1868

SOUTHWELL S.M.
William Daman. 1579

491 Take Me, O My Father, Take Me

I have strayed like a lost sheep. Seek your servant. Ps. 119:176

1. Take me, O my Fa-ther, take me; take me, save me, through thy Son;
   that which thou wouldst have me, make me, let thy will in me be done.
   Long from thee my foot-steps stray-ing, thorn-y proved the way I trod;
   wea-ry come I now, and pray-ing, take me to thy love, my God.

2. Fruit-less years with grief re-call-ing, hum-bly I con-fess my sin;
   at thy feet, O Fa-ther, fall-ing, to thy house-hold take me in.
   Free-ly now to thee I prof-fer this re-lent-ing heart of mine;
   free-ly life and soul I of-fer, gift un-wor-thy love like thine.

3. Once the world's Re-deem-er, dy-ing, bore our sins up-on the tree;
   on that sac-ri-fice re-ly-ing, now I look in hope to thee:
   Fa-ther, take me; all for-giv-ing, fold me to thy lov-ing breast;
   in thy love for-ev-er liv-ing I must be for-ev-er blest.

Ray Palmer, 1864

VESPER HYMN 8.7.8.7.D.
Dimitri Bortniansky, 1818
Arr. by John A. Stevenson, 1761–1833; alt. 1990

O Jesus, Thou Art Standing

Here I am! I stand at the door and knock. If anyone hears my voice and opens the door,
I will come in and eat with him, and he with me. Rev. 3:20

1. O Je - sus, thou art stand - ing out - side the fast- closed door,
2. O Je - sus, thou art knock- ing; and lo, that hand is scarred,
3. O Je - sus, thou art plead - ing in ac - cents meek and low,

in low - ly pa - tience wait - ing to pass the thresh - old o'er:
and thorns thy brow en - cir - cle, and tears thy face have marred:
"I died for you, my chil - dren, and will ye treat me so?"

shame on us, Chris - tian broth - ers, his name and sign who bear,
O love that pass - eth knowl - edge, so pa - tient - ly to wait!
O Lord, with shame and sor - row we o - pen now the door;

O shame, thrice shame up - on us, to keep him stand - ing there!
O sin that hath no e - qual, so fast to bar the gate!
dear Sav - ior, en - ter, en - ter, and leave us nev - er - more.

William Walsham How, 1867

ST. EDITH 7.6.7.6.D.
Justin H. Knecht, 1799, and
Edward Husband, 1871

493

We Have Not Known Thee As We Ought

We have acted very wickedly toward you. We have not obeyed the commands, decrees and laws you gave your servant Moses. Neh. 1:7

1. We have not known thee as we ought, nor learned thy
wis-dom, grace, and pow'r; the things of earth have filled our thought,
and tri-fles of the pass-ing hour. Lord, give us light thy
truth to see, and make us wise in know-ing thee.

2. We have not feared thee as we ought, nor bowed be-
neath thine awe-some eye, nor guard-ed deed and word and thought,
re-mem-ber-ing that God was nigh. Lord, give us faith to
know thee near, and grant the grace of ho-ly fear.

3. We have not loved thee as we ought, nor cared that
we are loved by thee; thy pres-ence we have cold-ly sought,
and fee-bly longed thy face to see. Lord, give a pure and
lov-ing heart to feel and own the love thou art.

4. We have not served thee as we ought; a-las! the
du-ties left un-done, the work with lit-tle fer-vor wrought,
the bat-tles lost, or scarce-ly won! Lord, give the zeal, and
give the might, for thee to toil, for thee to fight.

5. When shall we know thee as we ought,
   and fear and love and serve aright!
   When shall we, out of trial brought,
   be perfect in the land of light!
   Lord, may we day by day prepare
   to see thy face, and serve thee there.

Thomas Benson Pollock, 1889
Alt. 1990

ST. CHRYSOSTOM 8.8.8.8.8.8.
Joseph Barnby, 1872

Forgive Our Sins As We Forgive

494

Forgive us our debts, as we also have forgiven our debtors. Matt. 6:12

1. "For - give our sins as we for - give," you taught us,
   Lord, to pray; but you a - lone can give us grace to
   live the words we say, to live the words we say.

2. How can your par - don reach and bless the un - for -
   giv - ing heart that broods on wrongs and will not let old
   bit - ter - ness de - part, old bit - ter - ness de - part?

3. In blaz - ing light your cross re - veals the truth we
   dim - ly know; how small the debts men owe to us; how
   great our debt to you, how great our debt to you.

4. Lord, cleanse the depths with - in our souls, and bid re -
   sent - ment cease; then, rec - on - ciled to God and man our
   lives will spread your peace, our lives will spread your peace.

Rosamond E. Herklots, 1969

DOVE OF PEACE C.M.rep.
American folk tune
Arr. by Austin C. Lovelace, 1977

495 No, Not Despairingly Come I to Thee

If we confess our sins, he is faithful and just and will forgive us our sins and purify us from all unrighteousness. 1 John 1:9

1. No, not despairingly come I to thee;
   no, not distrustingly bend I the knee:
   sin hath gone o - ver me, yet is this still my plea,
   Je - sus hath died.

2. Ah! mine in - iq - ui - ty crim - son has been,
   in - fi - nite, in - fi - nite, sin up - on sin;
   sin of not lov - ing thee, sin of not trust - ing thee,
   in - fi - nite sin.

3. Lord, I con - fess to thee sad - ly my sin;
   all I am tell I thee, all I have been: purge thou my
   sin a - way, wash thou my soul this day;
   Lord, make me clean.

4. Faith - ful and just art thou, for - giv - ing all;
   lov - ing and kind art thou when poor ones call: Lord, let the
   cleans - ing blood, blood of the Lamb of God,
   pass o'er my soul.

5. Then all is peace and light this soul with - in;
   thus shall I walk with thee, the loved Un - seen; lean - ing on
   thee, my God, guid - ed a - long the road,
   noth - ing be - tween.

Horatius Bonar, 1866

KEDRON 6.4.6.4.6.6.4.
Ann B. Spratt, 1866

Kind and Merciful God, We Have Sinned

496

If we confess our sins, he is faithful and just and will forgive us our sins. 1 John 1:9

1. Kind and mer-ci-ful God, we have sinned in your sight, we have all wan-dered far from your way; we have fol-lowed de-sire, we have failed to as-pire to the vir-tue we ought to dis-play.

2. Kind and mer-ci-ful God, we've ne-glect-ed your Word and the truth that would guide us a-right; we have lived in the shade of the dark we have made, when you willed us to walk in the light.

3. Kind and mer-ci-ful God, we have bro-ken your laws and in con-duct have veered from the norm; we have dreamed of the good, but the good that we could we have fre-quent-ly failed to per-form.

4. Kind and mer-ci-ful God, in Christ's death on the cross you pro-vid-ed a cleans-ing from sin; speak the words that for-give that hence-forth we may live by the might of your Spir-it with-in.

5. Kind and mer-ci-ful God, bid us lift up our heads and com-mand us to rise from our knees; may our hearts now be changed and no lon-ger es-tranged, through the pow'r of your par-don and peace.

Bryan Jeffery Leech, 1973

ELFAKER 6.6.9.D.
Traditional Swedish melody
Adapted by Bryan Jeffery Leech

497

I Need Thee, Precious Jesus

Lord, to whom shall we go? You have the words of eternal life. John 6:68

1. I need thee, pre - cious Je - sus, for I am full of sin;
2. I need thee, pre - cious Je - sus, for I am ver - y poor;
3. I need thee, pre - cious Je - sus, and hope to see thee soon,

my soul is dark and guilt - y, my heart is dead with - in.
a strang - er and a pil - grim, I have no earth - ly store.
en - cir - cled with the rain - bow and seat - ed on thy throne.

I need the cleans - ing foun - tain where I can al - ways flee,
I need the love of Je - sus to cheer me on my way,
There, with thy blood- bought chil - dren, my joy shall ev - er be,

the blood of Christ most pre - cious, the sin - ner's per - fect plea.
to guide my doubt - ing foot - steps, to be my strength and stay.
to sing my Je - sus' prais - es, to gaze, O Lord, on thee.

Frederick Whitfield, 1855

MEIRIONYDD 7.6.7.6.D.
Welsh hymn melody
William Lloyd, 1840; alt. 1990

Jesus! What a Friend for Sinners!

A friend of ... "sinners." Matt. 11:19

498

1. Je - sus! what a Friend for sin - ners! Je - sus! lov - er of my soul;
2. Je - sus! what a strength in weak - ness! Let me hide my - self in him;
3. Je - sus! what a help in sor - row! While the bil - lows o'er me roll,
4. Je - sus! what a guide and keep - er! While the tem - pest still is high,
5. Je - sus! I do now re - ceive him, more than all in him I find;

friends may fail me, foes as - sail me, he, my Sav - ior, makes me whole.
tempt - ed, tried, and some - times fail - ing, he, my strength, my vic - t'ry wins.
e - ven when my heart is break - ing, he, my com - fort, helps my soul.
storms a - bout me, night o'er - takes me, he, my pi - lot, hears my cry.
he hath grant - ed me for - give - ness, I am his, and he is mine.

REFRAIN

Hal - le - lu - jah! what a Sav - ior! Hal - le - lu - jah! what a Friend!

Sav - ing, help - ing, keep - ing, lov - ing, he is with me to the end.

J. Wilbur Chapman, 1910

HYFRYDOL 8.7.8.7.D.
Rowland Hugh Pritchard, 1855

499
Rock of Ages, Cleft for Me

That rock was Christ. 1 Cor. 10:4

1. Rock of A - ges, cleft for me, let me hide my - self in thee;
2. Not the la - bors of my hands can ful - fil thy law's de - mands;
3. Noth - ing in my hand I bring, sim - ply to thy cross I cling;
4. While I draw this fleet - ing breath, when mine eye - lids close in death,

let the wa - ter and the blood, from thy riv - en side which flowed,
could my zeal no res - pite know, could my tears for - ev - er flow,
na - ked, come to thee for dress; help - less, look to thee for grace;
when I soar to worlds un - known, see thee on thy judg - ment throne,

be of sin the dou - ble cure, cleanse me from its guilt and pow'r.
all for sin could not a - tone; thou must save, and thou a - lone.
foul, I to the Foun - tain fly; wash me, Sav - ior, or I die.
Rock of A - ges, cleft for me, let me hide my - self in thee.

Augustus M. Toplady, 1776
Alt. by Thomas Cotterill, 1815

TOPLADY 7.7.7.7.7.7.
Thomas Hastings, 1830

Rock of Ages, Cleft for Me

500

That rock was Christ. 1 Cor. 10:4

1. Rock of A - ges, cleft for me, let me hide my -
2. Not the la - bors of my hands can ful - fil thy
3. Noth - ing in my hand I bring, sim - ply to thy
4. While I draw this fleet - ing breath, when mine eye - lids

self in thee; let the wa - ter and the blood, from thy riv - en
law's de-mands; could my zeal no res - pite know, could my tears for -
cross I cling; na - ked, come to thee for dress; help - less, look to
close in death, when I soar to worlds un- known, see thee on thy

side which flowed, be of sin the dou - ble cure, cleanse me from its
ev - er flow, all for sin could not a - tone; thou must save, and
thee for grace; foul, I to the Foun- tain fly; wash me, Sav - ior,
judg - ment throne, Rock of A - ges, cleft for me, let me hide my-

guilt and pow'r.
thou a - lone.
or I die.
self in thee.

Fine

Augustus M. Toplady, 1776
Alt. by Thomas Cotterill, 1815

NEW CITY FELLOWSHIP 7.7.7.7.7.7.
James Ward, 1984

501 Just As I Am, without One Plea

Whoever comes to me I will never drive away. John 6:37

1. Just as I am, without one plea but that thy
blood was shed for me, and that thou bidd'st me
come to thee, O Lamb of God, I come, I come.

2. Just as I am, and waiting not to rid my
soul of one dark blot, to thee, whose blood can
cleanse each spot, O Lamb of God, I come, I come.

3. Just as I am, though tossed about with many a
conflict, many a doubt, fightings and fears with-
in, without, O Lamb of God, I come, I come.

4. Just as I am, poor, wretched, blind; sight, riches,
healing of the mind, yea, all I need, in
thee to find, O Lamb of God, I come, I come.

5. Just as I am, thou wilt receive,
wilt welcome, pardon, cleanse, relieve;
because thy promise I believe,
O Lamb of God, I come, I come.

6. Just as I am, thy love unknown
has broken ev'ry barrier down;
now, to be thine, yea, thine alone,
O Lamb of God, I come, I come.

Charlotte Elliott, 1836

WOODWORTH L.M.
William B. Bradbury, 1849

Just As I Am, without One Plea

502

Whoever comes to me I will never drive away. John 6:37

1. Just as I am, with-out one plea but that thy blood was shed for
   me, and that thou bidd'st me come to thee, O Lamb of God, I come.
2. Just as I am, and wait-ing not to rid my soul of one dark
   blot, to thee, whose blood can cleanse each spot, O Lamb of God, I come.
3. Just as I am, though tossed a-bout with man-y a con-flict, man-y a
   doubt, fight-ings and fears with-in, with-out, O Lamb of God, I come.
4. Just as I am, poor, wretch-ed, blind; sight, rich-es, heal-ing of the
   mind, yea, all I need, in thee to find, O Lamb of God, I come.

REFRAIN

Just as I am, just as I am, just as I am I come.
Just as I am, just as I am I come.
Just as I am, just as I am, just as I am I come.

5. Just as I am, thou wilt receive,
   wilt welcome, pardon, cleanse, relieve;
   because thy promise I believe,
   O Lamb of God, I come.
   (Refrain)

6. Just as I am, thy love unknown
   has broken ev'ry barrier down;
   now, to be thine, yea, thine alone,
   O Lamb of God, I come.
   (Refrain)

Charlotte Elliott, 1836

MAUNDER 8.8.8.6.ref.
From John Henry Maunder (1858–1920), *From Olivet to Calvary*

503 Out of My Bondage, Sorrow, and Night

He has sent me to bind up the brokenhearted, to proclaim freedom for the captives
and release from darkness for the prisoners. Is. 61:1

1. Out of my bond - age, sor - row, and night, Je - sus, I come,
2. Out of my shame - ful fail - ure and loss, Je - sus, I come,
3. Out of un - rest and ar - ro - gant pride, Je - sus, I come,
4. Out of the fear and dread of the tomb, Je - sus, I come,

Je - sus, I come; in - to thy free - dom, glad - ness, and light,
Je - sus, I come; in - to the glo - rious gain of thy cross,
Je - sus, I come; in - to thy bless - ed will to a - bide,
Je - sus, I come; in - to the joy and light of thy home,

Je - sus, I come to thee; out of my sick - ness
Je - sus, I come to thee; out of earth's sor - rows
Je - sus, I come to thee; out of my - self to
Je - sus, I come to thee; out of the depths of

in - to thy health, out of my want and in - to thy wealth,
in - to thy balm, out of life's storms and in - to thy calm,
dwell in thy love, out of de - spair in - to rap - tures a - bove,
ru - in un - told, in - to the peace of thy shel - ter - ing fold,

out of my sin and in - to thy- self, Je - sus, I come to thee.
out of dis - tress to ju - bi- lant psalm, Je - sus, I come to thee.
up - ward for aye on wings like a dove, Je - sus, I come to thee.
ev - er thy glo - rious face to be- hold, Je - sus, I come to thee.

W. T. Sleeper, 1887

JESUS, I COME Irreg.
George C. Stebbins, 1887

I Am Trusting Thee, Lord Jesus 504

I know whom I have believed, and am convinced that he is able to guard what I have entrusted to him for that day. 2 Tim. 1:12

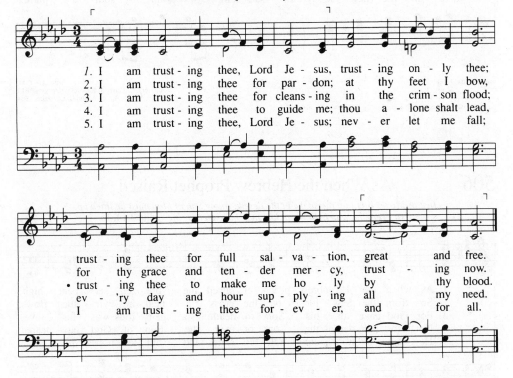

1. I am trust - ing thee, Lord Je - sus, trust - ing on - ly thee;
2. I am trust - ing thee for par - don; at thy feet I bow,
3. I am trust - ing thee for cleans - ing in the crim - son flood;
4. I am trust - ing thee to guide me; thou a - lone shalt lead,
5. I am trust - ing thee, Lord Je - sus; nev - er let me fall;

trust - ing thee for full sal - va - tion, great and free.
for thy grace and ten - der mer - cy, trust - ing now.
trust - ing thee to make me ho - ly by thy blood.
ev - 'ry day and hour sup - ply - ing all my need.
I am trust - ing thee for - ev - er, and for all.

Frances R. Havergal, 1874

BULLINGER 8.5.8.3.
Ethelbert W. Bullinger, 1874

505   I'm Not Ashamed to Own My Lord

I am not ashamed of the gospel, because it is the power of God for the salvation of everyone who believes. Rom. 1:16

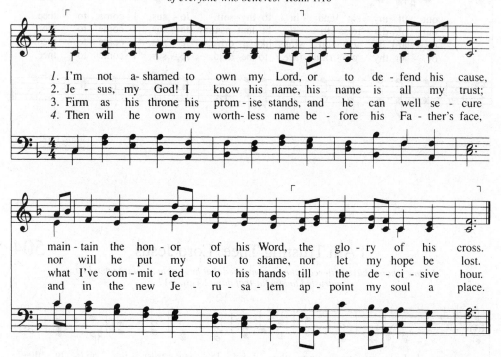

1. I'm not a-shamed to own my Lord, or to de-fend his cause,
2. Je - sus, my God! I know his name, his name is all my trust;
3. Firm as his throne his prom-ise stands, and he can well se - cure
4. Then will he own my worth-less name be - fore his Fa - ther's face,

main - tain the hon - or of his Word, the glo - ry of his cross.
nor will he put my soul to shame, nor let my hope be lost.
what I've com - mit - ted to his hands till the de - ci - sive hour.
and in the new Je - ru - sa - lem ap - point my soul a place.

Isaac Watts, 1709

PISGAH C.M.
Attr. to J. C. Lowry in *Kentucky Harmony,* 1817
Arr. by Austin C. Lovelace, 1964

Tune arr. © 1964, Abingdon Press. Reprinted from *The Book of Hymns* by permission.

506   As When the Hebrew Prophet Raised

Just as Moses lifted up the snake in the desert, so the Son of Man must be lifted up, that everyone who believes in him may have eternal life. John 3:14, 15

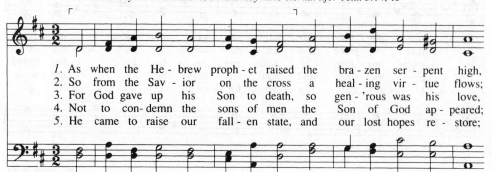

1. As when the He - brew proph - et raised the bra - zen ser - pent high,
2. So from the Sav - ior on the cross a heal - ing vir - tue flows;
3. For God gave up his Son to death, so gen - 'rous was his love,
4. Not to con - demn the sons of men the Son of God ap - peared;
5. He came to raise our fall - en state, and our lost hopes re - store;

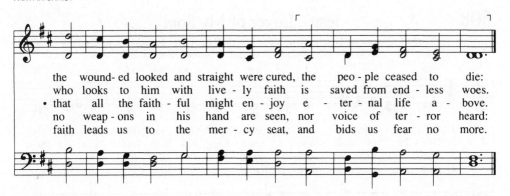

the wound- ed looked and straight were cured, the peo - ple ceased to die:
who looks to him with live - ly faith is saved from end - less woes.
• that all the faith - ful might en - joy e - ter - nal life a - bove.
no weap - ons in his hand are seen, nor voice of ter - ror heard:
faith leads us to the mer - cy seat, and bids us fear no more.

Isaac Watts, 1709
Scottish Paraphrases, 1781

DOWNS C.M.
Lowell Mason, 1832

Approach, My Soul, the Mercy Seat 507

Since we have a great high priest ... let us ... approach the throne of grace
with confidence. Heb. 4:14, 16

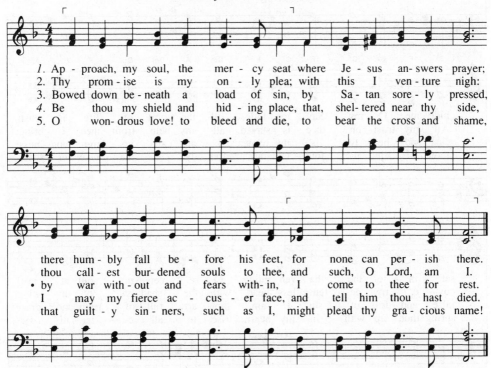

1. Ap - proach, my soul, the mer - cy seat where Je - sus an - swers prayer;
2. Thy prom - ise is my on - ly plea; with this I ven - ture nigh:
3. Bowed down be - neath a load of sin, by Sa - tan sore - ly pressed,
4. Be thou my shield and hid - ing place, that, shel - tered near thy side,
5. O won- drous love! to bleed and die, to bear the cross and shame,

there hum - bly fall be - fore his feet, for none can per - ish there.
thou call - est bur- dened souls to thee, and such, O Lord, am I.
• by war with - out and fears with- in, I come to thee for rest.
I may my fierce ac - cus - er face, and tell him thou hast died.
that guilt - y sin - ners, such as I, might plead thy gra - cious name!

John Newton, 1779

DALEHURST C.M.
Arthur Cottman. 1874

508 Jesus, Lover of My Soul

*Who shall separate us from the love of Christ? Shall trouble or hardship or persecution
or famine or nakedness or danger or sword?* Rom. 8:35

1. Je - sus, lov - er of my soul, let me to thy bo - som fly,
while the near - er wa - ters roll, while the tem - pest still is high:
hide me, O my Sav - ior, hide, till the storm of life is past;
safe in - to the ha - ven guide, O re - ceive my soul at last!

2. Oth - er ref - uge have I none, hangs my help - less soul on thee;
leave, ah! leave me not a - lone, still sup - port and com - fort me!
All my trust on thee is stayed, all my help from thee I bring;
cov - er my de - fense - less head with the shad - ow of thy wing.

3. Thou, O Christ, art all I want; more than all in thee I find;
raise the fall - en, cheer the faint, heal the sick, and lead the blind.
Just and ho - ly is thy name; I am all un - righ - teous - ness;
false and full of sin I am, thou art full of truth and grace.

4. Plen - teous grace with thee is found, grace to cov - er all my sin;
let the heal - ing streams a - bound; make and keep me pure with - in:
thou of life the foun - tain art, free - ly let me take of thee;
spring thou up with - in my heart, rise to all e - ter - ni - ty.

Charles Wesley, 1740

ABERYSTWYTH 7.7.7.7.D.
Joseph Parry, 1879

Jesus, Lover of My Soul

You have been ... a refuge for the needy in his distress, a shelter from the storm and a shade from the heat. Is. 25:4

1. Je - sus, lov - er of my soul, let me to thy bo - som fly,
2. Oth - er ref - uge have I none, hangs my help - less soul on thee;
3. Thou, O Christ, art all I want; more than all in thee I find:
4. Plen - teous grace with thee is found, grace to cov - er all my sin;

while the near - er wa - ters roll, while the tem - pest still is high:
leave, ah! leave me not a - lone, still sup - port and com - fort me!
raise the fall - en, cheer the faint, heal the sick, and lead the blind.
let the heal - ing streams a - bound; make and keep me pure with - in:

hide me, O my Sav - ior, hide, till the storm of life is past;
All my trust on thee is stayed, all my help from thee I bring;
Just and ho - ly is thy name; I am all un - righ - teous - ness;
thou of life the foun - tain art, free - ly let me take of thee;

safe in - to the ha - ven guide, O re - ceive my soul at last!
cov - er my de - fense - less head with the shad - ow of thy wing.
false and full of sin I am, thou art full of truth and grace.
spring thou up with - in my heart, rise to all e - ter - ni - ty.

Charles Wesley, 1740

MARTYN 7.7.7.7.D.
Simeon B. Marsh, 1834
Arr. by Rhys Thomas, 1916

510 Thou Hidden Source of Calm Repose

The peace of God, which transcends all understanding, will guard your hearts and your minds in Christ Jesus. Phil. 4:7

1. Thou hid - den source of calm re - pose, thou all - suf - fi - cient love di - vine, my help and ref - uge from my foes, se - cure I am, if thou art mine: and lo! from sin and grief and shame I hide me, Je - sus, in thy name.

2. Thy might - y name sal - va - tion is, and keeps my hap - py soul a - bove; com - fort it brings, and pow'r and peace and joy and ev - er - last - ing love: to me, with thy dear name, are giv'n par - don and ho - li - ness and heav'n.

3. Je - sus, my all in all thou art; my rest in toil, my ease in pain, the med - i - cine of my bro - ken heart, in war my peace, in loss my gain, my smile be - neath the ty - rant's frown, in shame my glo - ry and my crown:

4. In want my plen - ti - ful sup - ply, in weak - ness my al - might - y pow'r, in bonds my per - fect lib - er - ty, my light in Sa - tan's dark - est hour, my help and stay when - e'er I call, my life in death, my heav'n, my all.

Charles Wesley, 1749

STELLA 8.8.8.8.8.8.
Arr. in *Easy Hymn Tunes,* 1851

Jesus, and Shall It Ever Be

511

If anyone is ashamed of me and my words, the Son of Man will be ashamed of him.
Luke 9:26

1. Je - sus, and shall it ev - er be, a mor - tal
2. A - shamed of Je - sus! soon - er far let eve - ning
3. A - shamed of Je - sus! just as soon let mid - night
4. A - shamed of Je - sus, that dear Friend on whom my

man a - shamed of thee? A - shamed of thee whom
blush to own a star: he sheds the beams of
be a - shamed of noon: 'tis mid - night with my
hopes of heav'n de - pend! No, when I blush, be

an - gels praise, whose glo - ries shine through end - less days!
light di - vine o'er this be - night - ed soul of mine.
soul till he, bright Morn - ing Star, bid dark - ness flee.
this my shame, that I no more re - vere his name.

5. Ashamed of Jesus! yes, I may
   when I've no guilt to wash away,
   no tear to wipe, no good to crave,
   no fears to quell, no soul to save.

6. Till then— nor is my boasting vain—
   till then I boast a Savior slain;
   and O may this my glory be,
   that Christ is not ashamed of me.

Joseph Grigg, 1765
Alt. by Benjamin Francis, 1787

BROOKFIELD L.M.
Thomas B. Southgate, 1855

512   I Lay My Sins on Jesus

*If we confess our sins, he is faithful and just and will forgive us our sins and purify us
from all unrighteousness. 1 John 1:9*

1. I lay my sins on Je - sus, the spot - less Lamb of God;
2. I lay my wants on Je - sus; all ful - ness dwells in him;
3. I rest my soul on Je - sus, this wea - ry soul of mine;
4. I long to be like Je - sus, meek, lov - ing, low - ly, mild;

he bears them all, and frees us from the ac - curs - ed load:
he heals all my dis - eas - es, he doth my soul re - deem:
his right hand me em - brac - es, I on his breast re - cline.
I long to be like Je - sus, the Fa - ther's ho - ly child:

I bring my guilt to Je - sus, to wash my crim - son stains
I lay my griefs on Je - sus, my bur - dens and my cares;
I love the name of Je - sus, Im - man - uel, Christ, the Lord;
I long to be with Je - sus a - mid the heav'n - ly throng,

white in his blood most pre - cious, till not a spot re - mains.
he from them all re - leas - es, he all my sor - rows shares.
like fra - grance on the breez - es his name a - broad is poured.
to sing with saints his prais - es, to learn the an - gels' song.

Horatius Bonar, 1843

COMMEMORATION 7.6.7.6.D.
Bartholomaeus Gesius, 1605
Arr. by Johann Sebastian Bach, 1769: alt. 1990

Blessed Lord, in Thee Is Refuge

My salvation and my honor depend on God; he is my mighty rock, my refuge. Ps. 62:7

1. Bless-ed Lord, in thee is ref-uge, safe-ty for my trem-bling soul;
2. In the past, too, un-be-liev-ing, 'midst the tem-pest I have been,
3. Oh, for trust that brings the tri-umph when de-feat seems strange-ly near;

pow'r to lift my head when droop-ing 'midst the an - gry bil-lows' roll.
and my heart has slow-ly trust-ed what my eyes have nev-er seen.
oh, for faith that chang-es fight-ing in-to vic - t'ry's ring-ing cheer!

I will trust thee, I will trust thee, I will trust thee;
Bless-ed Je - sus, bless-ed Je - sus, bless-ed Je - sus,
Faith tri - um - phant, faith tri - um - phant, faith tri - um - phant,

all my life thou shalt con - trol; all my life thou shalt con - trol.
teach me on thine arm to lean; teach me on thine arm to lean.
know-ing not de - feat nor fear; know-ing not de - feat nor fear.

Herbert Booth

BRYN CALFARIA 8.7.8.7.4.4.4.7.7.
William Owen. 1852

514 For God So Loved the World

For God so loved the world, that he gave his only begotten Son, that whosoever
believeth in him should not perish, but have everlasting life. John 3:16 KJV

1. For God so loved the world   that he   gave .... his
2. For God .... did not send   his ..... Son in - to the world   to
3. He came in - to the world   and he   dwelt a - mong his own; but his

on - ly be - got - ten Son,   that who - so - ev - er be-
bring .... con - dem - na- tion, but rath - er that, through the re-
own, ... they would not re - ceive. But   pow'r to be - come   the .....

lieves in   him   should not per - - ish,
ceiv - ing of him,   men might find true sal - va - tion,
sons of   God he gave to all who be - lieved.

but have life ev - er - last - ing,   have life ev - er - last - ing,
and have life ev - er - last - ing,   have life ev - er - last - ing,
He   gave life ev - er - last - ing;   gave life ev - er - last - ing,

have life ev - er - last - ing, have life ev - er - last - ing.
have life ev - er - last - ing, have life ev - er - last - ing.
his life ev - er - last - ing, his life ev - er - last - ing.

For God so loved the world that he gave his
For God so loved the world that he gave his
For God so loved the world that he gave his

st. 1, 2 | *st. 3* CODA | *rit.*

on - ly be - got - ten Son.
on - ly be - got - ten Son.
on - ly be - got - ten Son, his on - ly be - got - ten

Son, his on - ly be - got - ten Son.

Stuart Dauermann, 1972, 1975

FOR GOD SO LOVED Irreg.
Stuart Dauermann, 1972, 1975; alt. 1990

515 How Lovely Shines the Morning Star!

I am the Root and the Offspring of David, and the bright Morning Star. Rev. 22:16

1. How love-ly shines the Morn-ing Star! The na-tions see and
2. Now rich-ly to my wait-ing heart, O thou, my God, deign
3. Thou, might-y Fa-ther, in thy Son didst love me ere thou

hail a-far the light in Ju-dah shin-ing. Thou Da-vid's son of
to im-part the grace of love un-dy-ing. In thy blest bod-y
hadst be-gun this an-cient world's foun-da-tion. Thy Son hath made a

Ja-cob's race, my bride-groom and my King of grace, for thee my heart is
let me be, e'en as the branch is in the tree, thy life my life sup-
friend of me, and when in spir-it him I see, I joy in trib-u-

pin-ing. Low-ly, ho-ly, great and glo-rious, thou vic-to-rious
ply-ing. Sigh-ing, cry-ing, for the sa-vor of thy fa-vor;
la-tion. What bliss is this! He that liv-eth to me giv-eth

Prince of grac - es, fill - ing all the heav'n-ly plac - es.
rest - ing nev - er till I rest in thee for - ev - er.
life for - ev - er; noth - ing me from him can sev - er.

Philipp Nicolai, 1597
Trans. composite

WIE SCHÖN LEUCHTET DER MORGENSTERN 8.8.7.8.8.7.4.4.4.4.8.
Philipp Nicolai, 1599
Arr. by Johann Sebastian Bach, ca. 1730; alt. 1990

Jesus, I Live to Thee

516

Whether we live or die, we belong to the Lord. Rom. 14:8

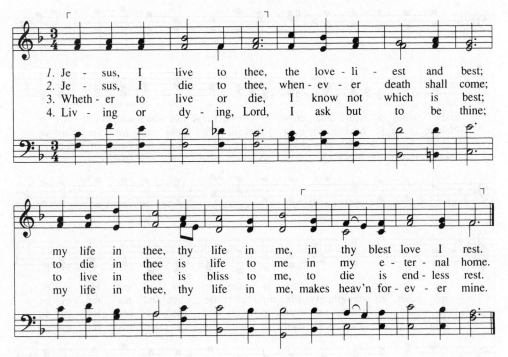

1. Je - sus, I live to thee, the love - li - est and best;
2. Je - sus, I die to thee, when - ev - er death shall come;
3. Wheth - er to live or die, I know not which is best;
4. Liv - ing or dy - ing, Lord, I ask but to be thine;

my life in thee, thy life in me, in thy blest love I rest.
to die in thee is life to me in my e - ter - nal home.
to live in thee is bliss to me, to die is end - less rest.
my life in thee, thy life in me, makes heav'n for - ev - er mine.

Henry Harbaugh, 1850

TRENTHAM S.M.
Robert Jackson. 1888

517   I've Found a Friend, O Such a Friend!

Greater love has no one than this, that he lay down his life for his friends. John 15:13

1. I've found a Friend, O   such   a Friend! He loved me ere   I   knew him;
2. I've found a Friend, O   such   a Friend! He bled, he died to   save me;
3. I've found a Friend, O   such   a Friend! All pow'r to him is   giv-en,
4. I've found a Friend, O   such   a Friend! So   kind and true and   ten-der,

he drew me with the   cords of love, and   thus he bound me   to him;
and not a-lone the   gift   of life, but   his own self he   gave me!
to guard me on my   on-ward course, and bring me safe to   heav-en:
so wise a Coun-sel - or   and guide, so   might-y   a   de - fend-er!

and   round my heart still close-ly twine those ties which naught can   sev-er,
Naught that I have mine own I'll call, I'll   hold it for the   Giv-er,
e - ter - nal glo-ry gleams a-far, to   nerve my faint en-deav-or:
From him who loves me now so   well what pow'r my soul can   sev-er?

for   I   am his, and   he   is   mine, for - ev - er and   for - ev - er.
my heart, my strength, my life, my   all are   his, and his   for - ev - er.
so   now to watch, to   work, to   war; and   then to   rest   for - ev - er.
Shall life or death, shall earth or   hell? No!   I   am his   for - ev - er.

James G. Small, 1866

CONSTANCE 8.7.8.7.D.
Arthur S. Sullivan, 1875

Christ, of All My Hopes the Ground

To me, to live is Christ and to die is gain. Phil. 1:21

518

1. Christ, of all my hopes the ground, Christ, the spring of
2. Let your love my heart in - flame; keep your fear be -
3. Foun - tain of o'er - flow - ing grace, free - ly from your
4. Firm - ly trust - ing in your blood, noth - ing shall my
5. Thus, O thus, an en - trance give to the land of

all my joy, still in you may I be found, still for
fore my sight; be your praise my high - est aim; be your
ful - ness give; till I close my earth - ly race, may I
heart con - found; safe - ly I shall pass the flood, safe - ly
cloud - less sky; hav - ing known it "Christ to live," let me

you my pow'rs em - ploy, still for you my pow'rs em - ploy.
smile my chief de - light, be your smile my chief de - light.
prove it "Christ to live," may I prove it "Christ to live."
reach Im - man - uel's ground, safe - ly reach Im - man - uel's ground.
know it "gain to die," let me know it "gain to die."

Ralph Wardlaw, 1817
Mod.

HENDON 7.7.7.7.rep.
Henri A. César Malan. 1827

519   Fountain of Never-Ceasing Grace

If anyone is thirsty, let him come to me and drink. John 7:37

1. Foun - tain of nev - er - ceas - ing grace, your saints' ex - haust- less theme,
2. In you we have a righ - teous- ness by God him - self ap - proved;
3. As all, when Ad - am sinned a - lone, in his trans- gres - sion died,

great ob - ject of im - mor - tal praise, es - sen - tial - ly su - preme,
our rock, our sure foun - da - tion this, which nev - er can be moved.
so by the righ - teous- ness of One are sin - ners jus - ti - fied;

we bless you for the glo - rious fruits your in - car - na - tion gives,
Our ran - som by your death was paid, for all your peo - ple giv'n,
we to your mer - it, gra - cious Lord, with hum - blest joy sub - mit,

the righ - teous- ness which grace im - putes, and faith a - lone re - ceives.
the law you per - fect - ly o - beyed, that they might en - ter heav'n.
a - gain to par - a - dise re - stored, in you a - lone com - plete.

Augustus M. Toplady, 1740–1778
Alt. 1961. mod.

ST. MATTHEW C.M.D.
William Croft, 1708

Jesus, Thy Blood and Righteousness

Justified freely by his grace through the redemption that came by Christ Jesus.
Rom. 3:24

520

1. Je - sus, thy blood and righ - teous - ness my beau - ty
2. Bold shall I stand in thy great day; for who aught
3. When from the dust of death I rise to claim my
4. Je - sus, be end - less praise to thee, whose bound - less
5. O let the dead now hear thy voice; now bid thy

are, my glo - rious dress; 'midst flam - ing worlds, in
to my charge shall lay? Ful - ly ab - solved through
man - sion in the skies, ev'n then this shall be
mer - cy hath for me— for me a full a -
ban - ished ones re - joice; their beau - ty this, their

these ar - rayed, with joy shall I lift up my head.
these I am from sin and fear, from guilt and shame.
all my plea, Je - sus hath lived, hath died, for me.
tone - ment made, an ev - er - last - ing ran - som paid.
glo - rious dress, Je - sus, thy blood and righ - teous - ness.

Nikolaus Ludwig von Zinzendorf, 1739
Tr. by John Wesley, 1740; alt.

GERMANY L.M.
William Gardiner's *Sacred Melodies*, 1815

521 My Hope Is Built on Nothing Less

No one can lay any foundation other than the one already laid, which is Jesus Christ.
1 Cor. 3:11

1. My hope is built on noth-ing less than Je-sus' blood and
2. When dark-ness veils his love-ly face, I rest on his un-
3. His oath, his cov-e-nant, his blood sup-port me in the
4. When he shall come with trum-pet sound, O may I then in

righ-teous-ness; I dare not trust the sweet-est frame, but
chang-ing grace; in ev-ery high and storm-y gale, my
whelm-ing flood; when all a-round my soul gives way, he
him be found; dressed in his righ-teous-ness a-lone, fault-

whol-ly lean on Je-sus' name.
an-chor holds with-in the veil.
then is all my hope and stay.
less to stand be-fore the throne.

REFRAIN

On Christ, the sol-id rock, I stand; all oth-er ground is sink-ing sand, all oth-er ground is sink-ing sand.

Edward Mote, 1834

SOLID ROCK L.M.ref.
William B. Bradbury, 1863

My Hope Is Built on Nothing Less

522

No one can lay any foundation other than the one already laid, which is Jesus Christ.
1 Cor. 3:11

1. My hope is built on noth-ing less than Je-sus' blood and righ-teous-ness; I dare not trust the sweet-est frame, but whol-ly lean on Je-sus' name.

2. When dark-ness veils his love-ly face, I rest on his un-chang-ing grace; in ev-ery high and storm-y gale, my an-chor holds with-in the veil.

3. His oath, his cov-e-nant, his blood sup-port me in the whelm-ing flood; when all a-round my soul gives way, he then is all my hope and stay.

4. When he shall come with trum-pet sound, O may I then in him be found; dressed in his righ-teous-ness a-lone, fault-less to stand be-fore the throne.

REFRAIN

On Christ, the sol-id rock, I stand; all oth-er ground is sink-ing sand.

Edward Mote, 1834

ST. PETERSBURG 8.8.8.8.8.8.
Dmitri Bortniansky, 1825

523

My Hope Is in the Lord

Christ in you, the hope of glory. Col. 1:27

1. My hope is in the Lord who gave him-self for me,
2. No mer-it of my own his an-ger to sup-press,
3. And now for me he stands be-fore the Fa-ther's throne.
4. His grace has planned it all, 'tis mine but to be-lieve,

and paid the price of all my sin at Cal-va-ry.
my on-ly hope is found in Je-sus' righ-teous-ness.
He shows his wound-ed hands, and names me as his own.
and rec-og-nize his work of love and Christ re-ceive.

REFRAIN

For me he died, for me he lives,
For me he died, for me he lives,

and ev-er-last-ing life and light he free-ly gives.

Norman J. Clayton, 1945

WAKEFIELD 6.6.6.6.ref.
Norman J. Clayton, 1945

Thy Works, Not Mine, O Christ

524

He saved us, not because of righteous things we had done, but because of his mercy.
Titus 3:5

1. Thy works, not mine, O Christ, speak glad-ness to this heart; they
tell me all is done; they bid my fear de-part.

2. Thy pains, not mine, O Christ, up - on the shame-ful tree, have
paid the law's full price and pur-chased peace for me.

3. Thy cross, not mine, O Christ, has borne the aw - ful load of
sins that none in heav'n or earth could bear but God.

4. Thy righ - teous-ness, O Christ, a - lone can cov - er me: no
righ - teous-ness a - vails save that which is of thee.

REFRAIN

To whom, save thee, who canst a - lone for sin a - tone, Lord, shall I flee?

Horatius Bonar, 1857

DARWALL 6.6.6.6.8.8.
John Darwall, 1770

525 A Child of the King

We are God's children. Now if we are children, then we are heirs—heirs of God and coheirs with Christ. Rom. 8:16, 17

1. My Fa-ther is rich in hous-es and lands, he hold-eth the
2. My Fa-ther's own Son, the Sav-ior of men, once wan-dered o'er
3. I once was an out-cast strang-er on earth, a sin-ner by
4. A tent or a cot-tage, why should I care? They're build-ing a

wealth of the world in his hands! Of ru-bies and dia-monds, of
earth as the poor-est of them; but now he is reign-ing for-
choice, and an a-lien by birth! But I've been a-dopt-ed, my
pal-ace for me o-ver there! Though ex-iled from home, yet

sil - ver and gold, his cof - fers are full, he has
ev - er on high, and will give me a home in
name's writ - ten down, an heir to a man - sion, a
still I may sing: all glo - ry to God, I'm a

REFRAIN

rich - es un - told.
heav'n by and by.
robe, and a crown. I'm a child of the King, a child of the King!
child of the King!

With Je - sus, my Sav - ior, I'm a child of the King.

Hattie E. Buell, 1877; alt. 1990

BINGHAMTON 10.11.11.11.ref.
John B. Sumner, 1877

Blessed Are the Sons of God 526

Dear friends, now we are children of God. 1 John 3:2

1. Bless - ed are the sons of God, they are bought with Christ's own blood;
2. They are jus - ti - fied by grace, they en - joy the Sav - ior's peace;
3. They are lights up - on the earth, chil - dren of a heav'n - ly birth;

they are ran - somed from the grave, life e - ter - nal they shall have:
all their sins are washed a - way, they shall stand in God's great day:
one with God, with Je - sus one, glo - ry is in them be - gun:

REFRAIN

With them num - bered may we be, here and in e - ter - ni - ty.

Joseph Humphreys, 1743; alt.

ROSEFIELD 7.7.7.7.7.7.
Henri A. César Malan, 1834

527

The Beatitudes

Blessed are the poor in spirit, for theirs is the kingdom of heaven. Matt. 5:3

1. Blest are the hum - ble souls that see their emp - ti-
2. Blest are the men of bro - ken heart, who mourn for
3. Blest are the meek, who stand a - far from rage and
4. Blest are the souls that thirst for grace, hun - ger and

ness and pov - er - ty; trea - sures of grace to
sin with in - ward smart; the blood of Christ di -
pas - sion, noise and war; God will se - cure their
long for righ - teous - ness; they shall be well sup -

them are giv'n, and crowns of joy laid up in heaven.
vine - ly flows, a heal - ing balm for all their woes.
hap - py state, and plead their cause a - gainst the great.
plied and fed, with liv - ing streams and liv - ing bread.

5. Blest are the men whose hearts do move
   and melt with sympathy and love;
   from Christ the Lord shall they obtain
   like sympathy and love again.

6. Blest are the pure, whose hearts are clean
   from the defiling pow'rs of sin;
   with endless pleasure they shall see
   a God of spotless purity.

7. Blest are the men of peaceful life,
   who quench the coals of growing strife;
   they shall be called the heirs of bliss,
   the sons of God, the God of peace.

8. Blest are the suff'rers who partake
   of pain and shame for Jesus' sake;
   their souls shall triumph in the Lord,
   glory and joy are their reward.

Isaac Watts, 1674–1748

QUEBEC L.M.
Henry Baker, 1854

My Faith Looks Up to Thee

528

Let us run with perseverance the race marked out for us. Let us fix our eyes on Jesus,
the author and perfecter of our faith. Heb. 12:1, 2

1. My faith looks up to thee, thou Lamb of Cal - va - ry,
2. May thy rich grace im- part strength to my faint - ing heart,
3. While life's dark maze I tread, and griefs a - round me spread,
4. When ends life's tran - sient dream, when death's cold, sul - len stream

Sav - ior di - vine: now hear me while I pray, take all my
my zeal in - spire; as thou hast died for me, O may my
be thou my guide; bid dark - ness turn to day, wipe sor - row's
shall o'er me roll, blest Sav - ior, then, in love, fear and dis -

guilt a - way, O let me from this day be whol - ly thine.
love to thee pure, warm, and change - less be, a liv - ing fire.
tears a - way, nor let me ev - er stray from thee a - side.
trust re- move; O bear me safe a - bove, a ran - somed soul.

Ray Palmer, 1830

OLIVET 6.6.4.6.6.6.4.
Lowell Mason. 1832

529 Love Divine, All Loves Excelling

He who loves me will be loved by my Father, and I too will love him and show myself to him. John 14:21

1. Love di - vine, all loves ex - cel - ling, Joy of heav'n, to earth come down:
2. Breathe, O breathe thy lov - ing Spir - it in - to ev - 'ry trou- bled breast;
3. Come, Al - might- y to de - liv - er, let us all thy life re - ceive;
4. Fin - ish, then, thy new cre - a - tion; pure and spot- less let us be:

fix in us thy hum - ble dwell- ing, all thy faith - ful mer - cies crown:
let us all in thee in - her - it, let us find the prom - ised rest:
sud - den - ly re - turn, and nev - er, nev - er - more thy tem - ples leave.
let us see thy great sal - va - tion per - fect - ly re - stored in thee;

Je - sus, thou art all com - pas - sion, pure, un - bound- ed love thou art;
take a - way the love of sin - ning; Al - pha and O - me - ga be;
Thee we would be al - ways bless- ing, serve thee as thy hosts a - bove,
changed from glo - ry in - to glo - ry, till in heav'n we take our place,

vis - it us with thy sal - va - tion, en - ter ev - 'ry trem- bling heart.
End of faith, as its Be - gin - ning, set our hearts at lib - er - ty.
pray, and praise thee, with - out ceas - ing, glo - ry in thy per - fect love.
till we cast our crowns be - fore thee, lost in won - der, love, and praise.

Charles Wesley, 1747

BEECHER 8.7.8.7.D.
John Zundel, 1870; alt. 1990

Lord, I Want to Be a Christian

530

Like newborn babies, crave pure spiritual milk, so that by it you may grow up in your salvation. 1 Pet. 2:2

1. Lord, I want to be a Chris-tian in my heart, in my heart.
2. Lord, I want to be more lov-ing in my heart, in my heart.
3. Lord, I want to be more ho-ly in my heart, in my heart.
4. Lord, I want to be like Je-sus in my heart, in my heart.

Lord, I want to be a Chris-tian in my heart.
Lord, I want to be more lov-ing in my heart.
Lord, I want to be more ho-ly in my heart.
Lord, I want to be like Je-sus in my heart.

In my heart, in my heart,
in my heart, in my heart,

Lord, I want to be a Chris-tian in my heart.
Lord, I want to be more lov-ing in my heart.
Lord, I want to be more ho-ly in my heart.
Lord, I want to be like Je-sus in my heart.

Spiritual

LORD, I WANT TO BE A CHRISTIAN Irreg.
Spiritual

531
Savior, Blessed Savior

Our salvation is nearer now than when we first believed. Rom. 13:11

1. Sav - ior, bless - ed Sav - ior, lis - ten while we sing;
2. Near - er, ev - er near - er, Christ, we draw to thee,
3. Great, and ev - er great - er, are thy mer - cies here;
4. High - er then, and high - er, bear the ran - somed soul—

hearts and voic - es rais - ing prais - es to our King:
deep in ad - o - ra - tion, bend - ing low the knee:
true and ev - er - last - ing are the glo - ries there,
earth - ly toils for - got - ten— Sav - ior, to its goal;

all we have we of - fer, all we hope to be,
thou for our re - demp - tion cam'st on earth to die;
where no pain nor sor - row, fear nor care, is known,
where, in joys un - thought of, saints with an - gels sing,

bod - y, soul, and spir - it, all we yield to thee.
thou, that we might fol - low, hast gone up on high.
where the an - gel le - gions cir - cle round thy throne.
nev - er wea - ry, rais - ing prais - es to their King.

Godfrey Thring, 1862, 1882
Alt. 1961

HERMAS 6.5.6.5.D.
Frances R. Havergal, 1871

Teach Me, O Lord, Thy Holy Way

Teach me your way, O LORD, and I will walk in your truth; give me an undivided heart.
Ps. 86:11

1. Teach me, O Lord, thy ho - ly way, and give me
2. Guide me, O Sav - ior, with thy hand, and so con -
3. Help me, O Sav - ior, here to trace the sa - cred
4. Guard me, O Lord, that I may ne'er for - sake the
5. Bless me in ev - 'ry task, O Lord, be - gun, con -

an o - be - dient mind; that in thy ser - vice
trol my thoughts and deeds, that I may tread the
foot - steps thou hast trod; and, meek - ly walk - ing
right, or do the wrong: a - gainst temp - ta - tion
tin - ued, done for thee: ful - fil thy per - fect

I may find my soul's de - light from day to day.
path which leads right on - ward to the bless - ed land.
with my God, to grow in good - ness, truth, and grace.
make me strong, and round me spread thy shel - t'ring care.
work in me; and thine a - bound - ing grace af - ford.

William T. Matson, 1866

PENITENCE L.M.
St. Albans Tune Book. 1875

533 I Am Thine, O Lord, I Have Heard Thy Voice

My sheep listen to my voice; I know them, and they follow me. John 10:27

1. I am thine, O Lord, I have heard thy voice, and it told thy
2. Con - se - crate me now to thy ser - vice, Lord, by the pow'r of
3. O the pure de - light of a sin - gle hour that be - fore thy
4. There are depths of love that I can - not know till I cross the

love to me; but I long to rise in the arms of faith, and be
grace di - vine; let my soul look up with a stead - fast hope, and my
throne I spend, when I kneel in prayer, and with thee, my God, I com -
nar - row sea; there are heights of joy that I may not reach till I

clos - er drawn to thee.
will be lost in thine. Draw me near - er, near - er, bless - ed
mune as friend with friend. near - er, near - er,
rest in peace with thee.

REFRAIN

Lord, to the cross where thou hast died; draw me near - er, near - er,

near - er bless - ed Lord, to thy pre - cious, bleed - ing side.

Fanny J. Crosby, 1875

I AM THINE 10.7.10.7.ref.
William H. Doane, 1875; alt. 1990

O for a Closer Walk with God 534

*What does the LORD require of you? To act justly and to love mercy and to walk
humbly with your God.* Mic. 6:8

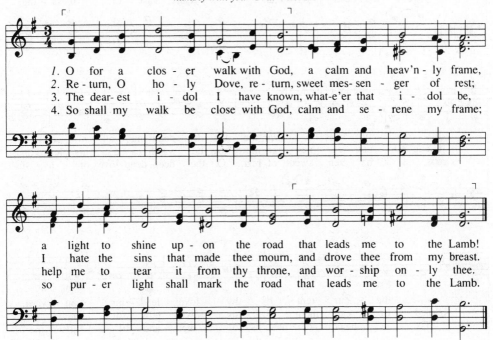

1. O for a clos - er walk with God, a calm and heav'n - ly frame,
2. Re - turn, O ho - ly Dove, re - turn, sweet mes - sen - ger of rest;
3. The dear- est i - dol I have known, what-e'er that i - dol be,
4. So shall my walk be close with God, calm and se - rene my frame;

a light to shine up - on the road that leads me to the Lamb!
I hate the sins that made thee mourn, and drove thee from my breast.
help me to tear it from thy throne, and wor - ship on - ly thee.
so pur - er light shall mark the road that leads me to the Lamb.

William Cowper, 1779

BEATITUDO C.M.
John B. Dykes, 1875

535

O the Deep, Deep Love of Jesus!

*Having loved his own who were in the world, he now showed them the full extent
of his love.* John 13:1

1. O the deep, deep love of Je - sus! Vast, un - mea- sured,
2. O the deep, deep love of Je - sus! Spread his praise from
3. O the deep, deep love of Je - sus! Love of ev - 'ry

bound - less, free; roll - ing as a might - y o - cean
shore to shore; how he lov - eth, ev - er lov - eth,
love the best: 'tis an o - cean vast of bless - ing,

in its full - ness o - ver me. Un - der- neath me, all a - round me,
chang- eth nev - er, nev - er- more; how he watch- es o'er his loved ones,
'tis a ha - ven sweet of rest. O the deep, deep love of Je - sus!

is the cur - rent of thy love; lead - ing on - ward,
died to call them all his own; how for them he
'Tis a heav'n of heav'ns to me; and it lifts me

lead - ing home- ward, to thy glo - rious rest a - bove.
in - ter - ced - eth, watch - eth o'er them from the throne.
up to glo - ry, for it lifts me up to thee.

Samuel Trevor Francis, 1834–1925

EBENEZER (or TON-Y-BOTEL) 8.7.8.7.D.
Thomas John Williams, 1890

Searcher of Hearts, from Mine Erase 536

Search me, O God, and know my heart. Ps. 139:23

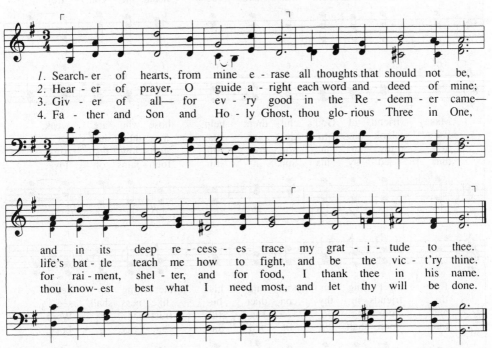

1. Search- er of hearts, from mine e - rase all thoughts that should not be,
2. Hear - er of prayer, O guide a - right each word and deed of mine;
3. Giv - er of all— for ev - 'ry good in the Re - deem- er came—
4. Fa - ther and Son and Ho - ly Ghost, thou glo- rious Three in One,

and in its deep re - cess - es trace my grat - i - tude to thee.
life's bat - tle teach me how to fight, and be the vic - t'ry thine.
for rai - ment, shel - ter, and for food, I thank thee in his name.
thou know- est best what I need most, and let thy will be done.

George P. Morris, 1838

BEATITUDO C.M.
John B. Dykes, 1875

537 Take Time to Be Holy

Just as you used to offer the parts of your body in slavery to impurity ... so now offer them in slavery to righteousness leading to holiness. Rom. 6:19

1. Take time to be ho - ly, speak oft with thy Lord;
2. Take time to be ho - ly, the world rush - es on;
3. Take time to be ho - ly, let him be thy guide,
4. Take time to be ho - ly, be calm in thy soul;

a - bide in him al - ways, and feed on his Word.
spend much time in se - cret with Je - sus a - lone.
and run not be - fore him, what - ev - er be - tide;
each thought and each mo - tive be - neath his con - trol;

Make friends of God's chil - dren; help those who are weak;
By look - ing to Je - sus, like him thou shalt be;
in joy or in sor - row, still fol - low thy Lord,
thus led by his Spir - it to foun - tains of love,

for - get - ting in noth - ing his bless - ing to seek.
thy friends in thy con - duct his like - ness shall see.
and, look - ing to Je - sus, still trust in his Word.
thou soon shalt be fit - ted for ser - vice a - bove.

William D. Longstaff, 1887

HOLINESS 6.5.6.5.D.
George C. Stebbins, 1890

More about Jesus Would I Know

538

*Like newborn babies, crave pure spiritual milk, so that by it you may grow up
in your salvation. 1 Pet. 2:2*

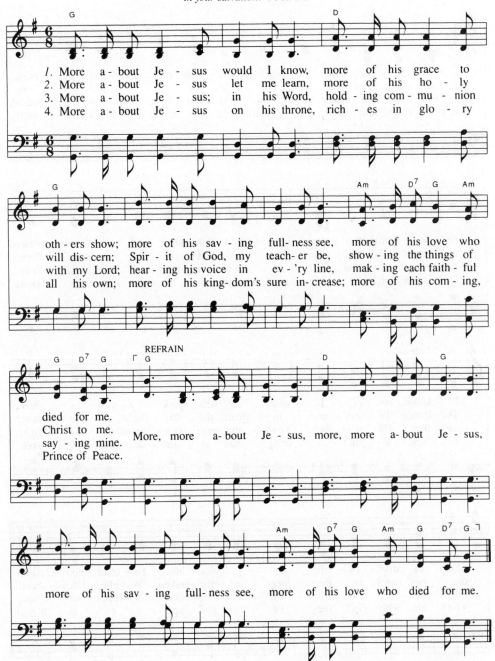

1. More a-bout Je - sus would I know, more of his grace to
2. More a-bout Je - sus let me learn, more of his ho - ly
3. More a-bout Je - sus; in his Word, hold - ing com - mu - nion
4. More a-bout Je - sus on his throne, rich - es in glo - ry

oth - ers show; more of his sav - ing full-ness see, more of his love who
will dis-cern; Spir - it of God, my teach-er be, show - ing the things of
with my Lord; hear - ing his voice in ev - 'ry line, mak - ing each faith - ful
all his own; more of his king-dom's sure in-crease; more of his com - ing,

died for me.
Christ to me.
say - ing mine.
Prince of Peace.

REFRAIN

More, more a-bout Je - sus, more, more a-bout Je - sus,

more of his sav - ing full-ness see, more of his love who died for me.

Eliza E. Hewitt, 1887

SWENEY L.M.ref.
John R. Sweney, 1887

539 Jerusalem the Golden

The city [was] of pure gold, as pure as glass. Rev. 21:18

1. Je - ru - sa - lem the gold - en, with milk and hon - ey blest,
2. They stand, those halls of Zi - on, all ju - bi - lant with song,
3. There is the throne of Da - vid; and there, from care re - leased,
4. O sweet and bless - ed coun - try, the home of God's e - lect!

be - neath your con - tem - pla - tion sink heart and voice op - pressed.
and bright with man - y an an - gel, and all the mar - tyr throng.
the song of them that tri - umph, the shout of them that feast;
O sweet and bless - ed coun - try that ea - ger hearts ex - pect!

I know not, O I know not, what joys a - wait us there;
The Prince is ev - er in them, the day - light is se - rene;
and they who with their Lead - er have con - quered in the fight,
Je - sus, in mer - cy bring us to that dear land of rest;

what ra - dian - cy of glo - ry, what bliss be - yond com - pare.
the pas - tures of the bless - ed are decked in glo - rious sheen.
for - ev - er and for - ev - er are clad in robes of white.
who are, with God the Fa - ther and Spir - it, ev - er blest.

Bernard of Cluny, 12th cent.
Tr. by John Mason Neale, 1851; alt.; mod.

EWING 7.6.7.6.D.
Alexander Ewing, 1853

A Few More Years Shall Roll

My days are like the evening shadow. Ps. 102:11

1. A few more years shall roll, a few more sea - sons come,
2. A few more storms shall beat on this wild rock - y shore,
3. A few more Sab - baths here shall cheer us on our way,
4. 'Tis but a lit - tle while, and he shall come a - gain,

and we shall be with those that rest a - sleep with - in the tomb:
and we shall be where tem - pests cease, and surg - es swell no more:
and we shall reach the end - less rest, th'e - ter - nal Sab - bath day:
who died that we might live, who lives that we with him may reign:

then, O my Lord, pre - pare my soul for that great day;
then, O my Lord, pre - pare my soul for that calm day;
then, O my Lord, pre - pare my soul for that sweet day;
then, O my Lord, pre - pare my soul for that glad day;

REFRAIN

O wash me in thy pre - cious blood, and take my sins a - way.

Horatius Bonar, 1844

LEOMINSTER S.M.D.
George William Martin, 1862
Arr. by Arthur S. Sullivan, 1874

541 When the Roll Is Called Up Yonder

The Lord himself will come down from heaven, with a loud command ... and with the trumpet call of God, and the dead in Christ will rise first. 1 Thess. 4:16

1. When the trum-pet of the Lord shall sound and time shall be no more,
2. On that bright and cloud-less morn-ing when the dead in Christ shall rise,
3. Let us la-bor for the Mas-ter from the dawn till set-ting sun,

and the morn-ing breaks, e-ter-nal, bright, and fair;
and the glo-ry of his res-ur-rec-tion share;
let us talk of all his won-drous love and care;

when the saved of earth shall gath-er o-ver on the oth-er shore,
when his cho-sen ones shall gath-er to their home be-yond the skies,
then when all of life is o-ver, and our work on earth is done,

and the roll is called up yon-der, I'll be there.
and the roll is called up yon-der, I'll be there.
and the roll is called up yon-der, I'll be there.

James M. Black, 1856–1938

ROLL CALL Irreg.
James M. Black, 1856–1938

542   Who Are These like Stars Appearing

There before me was a great multitude that no one could count ... standing before the throne and in front of the Lamb. They were wearing white robes. Rev. 7:9

1. Who are these like stars ap-pear-ing, these be-fore God's throne who stand?
2. Who are these of daz-zling bright-ness, these in God's own truth ar-rayed,
3. These are they who have con-tend-ed for their Sav-ior's hon-or long,
4. These are they whose hearts were riv-en, sore with woe and an-guish tried,
5. These, like priests, have watched and wait-ed, of-f'ring up to Christ their will;

Each a gold-en crown is wear-ing; who are all this glo-rious band?
clad in robes of pur-est white-ness, robes whose lus-ter ne'er shall fade,
• wres-tling on till life was end-ed, fol-l'wing not the sin-ful throng;
who in prayer full oft have striv-en with the God they glo-ri-fied;
soul and bod-y con-se-crat-ed, day and night to serve him still:

Al - le - lu - ia! Hark, they sing, prais-ing loud their heav'n-ly King.
ne'er be touched by time's rude hand? Whence come all this glo-rious band?
• these, who well the fight sus-tained, tri-umph through the Lamb have gained.
now, their pain-ful con-flict o'er, God has bid them weep no more.
now in God's most ho-ly place blest they stand be-fore his face.

Heinrich T. Schenk, 1719
Tr. by Frances E. Cox, 1841, 1864

ALL SAINTS OLD 8.7.8.7.7.7.
Darmstadt Gesangbuch, 1698

Around the Throne of God in Heaven

543

The promise is for you and your children. Acts 2:39

1. A - round the throne of God in heav'n thou - sands of chil - dren stand,
2. In flow - ing robes of spot - less white see ev - 'ry one ar - rayed;
3. What brought them to that world a - bove, that heav'n so bright and fair,
4. Be - cause the Sav - ior shed his blood to wash a - way their sin;
5. On earth they sought the Sav - ior's grace, on earth they loved his name;

chil - dren whose sins are all for - giv'n, a ho - ly, hap - py band,
dwell - ing in ev - er - last - ing light and joys that nev - er fade,
where all is peace, and joy, and love; how came those chil - dren there,
bathed in that pure and pre - cious flood, be - hold them white and clean,
so now they see his bless - ed face, and stand be - fore the Lamb,

REFRAIN

sing - ing, "Glo - ry, glo - ry, glo - ry be to God on high."

Anne H. Shepherd, 1836; alt.

CHILDREN'S PRAISES C.M.ref.
Henry E. Matthews, ca. 1853

544 How Bright These Glorious Spirits Shine!

These in white robes—who are they? Rev. 7:13

1. How bright these glo - rious spir - its shine! Whence all their white ar - ray?
2. Now, with tri - um - phal palms, they stand be - fore the throne on high,
3. Hun - ger and thirst are felt no more, nor suns with scorch- ing ray;
4. 'Mong pas - tures green he'll lead his flock where liv - ing streams ap - pear;

How came they to the bliss - ful seats of ev - er - last - ing day?
and serve the God they love, a- midst the glo - ries of the sky.
God is their sun, whose cheer - ing beams dif - fuse e - ter - nal day.
and God the Lord from ev - 'ry eye shall wipe off ev - 'ry tear.

Lo! these are they from suf- f'rings great who came to realms of light,
His pres - ence fills each heart with joy, tunes ev - 'ry mouth to sing;
The Lamb which dwells a - midst the throne shall o'er them still pre - side,
To him who sits up - on the throne, the God whom we a - dore,

and in the blood of Christ have washed those robes which shine so bright.
by day, by night, the sa - cred courts with glad ho - san - nas ring.
feed them with nour - ish - ment di - vine, and all their foot- steps guide.
and to the Lamb that once was slain, be glo - ry ev - er - more!

Isaac Watts, 1707
Scottish Paraphrases, 1781

BETHLEHEM (FINK) C.M.D.
Gottfried W. Fink, 1842

When This Passing World Is Done

545

Brothers, we have an obligation. Rom. 8:12

1. When this pass-ing world is done, when has sunk yon glar-ing sun,
2. When I hear the wick-ed call on the rocks and hills to fall,
3. When I stand be-fore the throne, dressed in beau-ty not my own,
4. When the praise of heav'n I hear, loud as thun-ders to the ear,
5. Cho-sen not for good in me, wak-ened up from wrath to flee,

when we stand with Christ in glo-ry, look-ing o'er life's fin-ished sto-ry,
when I see them start and shrink on the fi-ery del-uge brink,
• when I see thee as thou art, love thee with un-sin-ning heart,
loud as man-y wa-ters' noise, sweet as harp's me-lo-dious voice,
hid-den in the Sav-ior's side, by the Spir-it sanc-ti-fied,

then, Lord, shall I ful-ly know, not till then, how much I owe.
then, Lord, shall I ful-ly know, not till then, how much I owe.
• then, Lord, shall I ful-ly know, not till then, how much I owe.
then, Lord, shall I ful-ly know, not till then, how much I owe.
teach me, Lord, on earth to show, by my love, how much I owe.

Robert Murray McCheyne, 1837

MOUNT ZION 7.7.7.7.7.7.
Arthur S. Sullivan, 1867

546 The Sands of Time Are Sinking

They will see his face. Rev. 22:4

1. The sands of time are sink - ing, the dawn of heav - en breaks,
2. The King there in his beau - ty with - out a veil is seen;
3. O Christ, he is the foun - tain, the deep sweet well of love!
4. The bride eyes not her gar - ment, but her dear bride-groom's face;

the sum - mer morn I've sighed for, the fair sweet morn a - wakes;
it were a well - spent jour - ney though sev'n deaths lay be - tween:
The streams on earth I've tast - ed more deep I'll drink a - bove:
I will not gaze at glo - ry, but on my King of grace;

dark, dark hath been the mid - night, but day - spring is at hand,
the Lamb with his fair ar - my doth on Mount Zi - on stand,
there to an o - cean ful - ness his mer - cy doth ex - pand,
not at the crown he gift - eth, but on his pierc - ed hand:

and glo - ry, glo - ry dwell - eth in Em - man - uel's land.
and glo - ry, glo - ry dwell - eth in Em - man - uel's land.
and glo - ry, glo - ry dwell - eth in Em - man - uel's land.
the Lamb is all the glo - ry of Em - man - uel's land.

Anne R. Cousin, 1857
Based upon Samuel Rutherford, 1600–1661

RUTHERFORD 7.6.7.6.7.6.7.6.7.5
Chrétien Urhan, 1834
Arr. by Edward F. Rimbault, 1867

With Harps and with Viols

547

They sang a new song before the throne. Rev. 14:3

1. With harps and with vi - ols, there stand a great throng
2. All these once were sin - ners, de - filed in his sight,
3. He mak - eth the reb - el a priest and a king,
4. How help - less and hope - less we sin - ners had been,
5. A - loud in his prais - es our voic - es shall ring,

in the pres - ence of Je - sus, and sing this new song:
now ar - rayed in pure gar - ments in praise they u - nite:
he hath bought us and taught us this new song to sing:
if he nev - er had loved us till cleansed from our sin:
so that oth - ers, be - liev - ing, this new song shall sing:

REFRAIN

Un - to him who hath loved us and washed us from sin,

un - to him be the glo - ry for - ev - er. A - men.

Arthur T. Pierson, 1837–1911

HARPS AND VIOLS 6.5.7.5.ref.
Philip P. Bliss, 1838–1876

548

No Night There

There will be no more night. Rev. 22:5

1. In the land of fade-less day lies the cit-y four-square;
2. All the gates of pearl are made in the cit-y four-square;
3. And the gates shall nev-er close to the cit-y four-square;
4. There they need no sun-shine bright, in that cit-y four-square;

it shall nev-er pass a-way, and there is no night there.
all the streets with gold are laid, and there is no night there.
there life's crys-tal riv-er flows, and there is no night there.
for the Lamb is all the light, and there is no night there.

REFRAIN

God shall wipe a-way all tears; there's no
God shall wipe a-way all tears;

death, no pain, nor fears; and they count not
there's no death, no pain, nor fears; and they count not time

time by years, for there is no night there.
by years, by years, for there is no night there.

John R. Clements, 1868–1946

NO NIGHT THERE 7.6.7.6.ref.
Hart P. Danks

By the Sea of Crystal   549

Before the throne there was what looked like a sea of glass, clear as crystal. Rev. 4:6

1. By the sea of crys-tal, saints in glo-ry stand, myr-i-ads in
2. Out of trib-u-la-tion, death and Sa-tan's hand, they have been trans-
3. "Un-to God Al-might-y, sit-ting on the throne, and the Lamb, vic-

num-ber, drawn from ev-ery land. Robed in white ap-par-el, washed in
lat-ed at the Lord's com-mand. In their hands they're hold-ing palms of
to-rious, be the praise a-lone. God has wrought sal-va-tion, he did

Je-sus' blood, they now reign in heav-en with the Lamb of God.
vic-to-ry; hark! the ju-b'lant cho-rus shouts tri-um-phant-ly:
won-drous things. Who shall not ex-tol you, ho-ly King of kings!"

William Kuipers, 1933
Mod.

CRYSTAL 6.5.6.5.D.
John Vanderhoven, 1933

550 There Is a Land of Pure Delight

You are about to cross over and take possession of that good land. Deut. 4:22

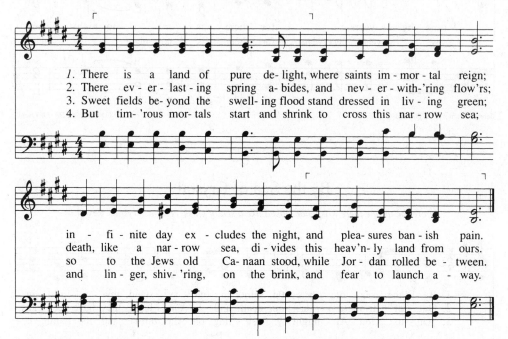

1. There is a land of pure de- light, where saints im - mor - tal reign;
2. There ev - er - last - ing spring a- bides, and nev - er - with-'ring flow'rs;
3. Sweet fields be- yond the swell- ing flood stand dressed in liv - ing green;
4. But tim- 'rous mor- tals start and shrink to cross this nar - row sea;

in - fi - nite day ex - cludes the night, and plea- sures ban - ish pain.
death, like a nar - row sea, di - vides this heav'n- ly land from ours.
so to the Jews old Ca- naan stood, while Jor - dan rolled be - tween.
and lin- ger, shiv- 'ring, on the brink, and fear to launch a - way.

5. O could we make our doubts remove,
those gloomy doubts that rise,
and see the Canaan that we love,
with unbeclouded eyes;

6. Could we but climb where Moses stood
and view the landscape o'er,
not Jordan's stream, nor death's cold flood,
should fright us from the shore.

Isaac Watts, 1707

MEDITATION C.M.
John H. Gower, 1890

551 How Blest Is He Whose Trespass

Blessed is he whose transgressions are forgiven, whose sins are covered.
Ps. 32:1

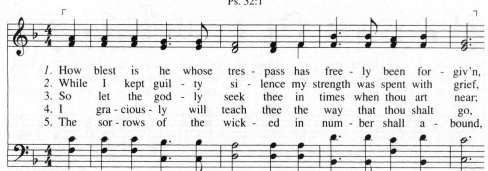

1. How blest is he whose tres - pass has free - ly been for - giv'n,
2. While I kept guil - ty si - lence my strength was spent with grief,
3. So let the god - ly seek thee in times when thou art near;
4. I gra - cious- ly will teach thee the way that thou shalt go,
5. The sor - rows of the wick - ed in num - ber shall a - bound,

whose sin is whol - ly cov - ered be - fore the sight of heav'n.
thy hand was heav - y on me, my soul found no re - lief;
• no whelm - ing floods shall reach them, nor cause their hearts to fear.
and with mine eye up - on thee my coun - sel make thee know.
but those that trust Je - ho - vah, his mer - cy shall sur - round.

Blest he to whom Je - ho - vah will not im - pute his sin,
but when I owned my tres - pass, my sin hid not from thee,
• In thee, O Lord, I hide me, thou sav - est me from ill,
But be ye not un - rul - y, or slow to un - der - stand;
Then in the Lord be joy - ful, in song lift up your voice.

who has a guile - less spir - it, whose heart is true with - in.
when I con - fessed trans - gres - sion, then thou for - gav - est me.
• and songs of thy sal - va - tion my heart with rap - ture thrill.
be not per - verse, but will - ing to heed my wise com - mand.
Be glad in God, ye righ - teous, re - joice, ye saints, re - joice.

From Psalm 32
The Psalter, 1912; alt.

RUTHERFORD 7.6.7.6.D.
Chrétien Urhan, 1834
Arr. by Edward F. Rimbault, 1867

552 From out the Depths I Cry, O Lord, to Thee

Out of the depths I cry to you, O Lord. Ps. 130:1

1. From out the depths I cry, O Lord, to thee; Lord, hear my call.
2. I wait for God, the Lord, and on his Word my hope re - lies;
3. Hope in the Lord, ye wait - ing saints, and he will well pro - vide;

I love thee, Lord, for thou dost heed my plea, for - giv - ing all.
my soul still waits and looks un - to the Lord till light a - rise.
for mer - cy and re - demp - tion full and free with him a - bide.

If thou dost mark our sins, who then shall stand?
I look for him to drive a - way my night,
From sin and e - vil, might - y though they seem,

But grace and mer - cy dwell at thy right hand.
yea, more than watch - men look for morn - ing light.
his arm al - might - y will his saints re - deem.

From Psalm 130
The Psalter, 1912; alt. 1961

SANDON 10.4.10.4.10.10
Charles H. Purday, 1860

My Sins, My Sins, My Savior!

553

For the sake of your name, O LORD, forgive my iniquity, though it is great. Ps. 25:11

1. My sins, my sins, my Sav - ior! They take such hold on me,
   I am not a - ble to look up, save on - ly, Christ, to thee;
   in thee is all for - give - ness, in thee a - bun - dant grace,
   my shad - ow and my sun - shine the bright - ness of thy face.

2. My sins, my sins, my Sav - ior! Their guilt I nev - er knew
   till with thee in the des - ert I near thy pas - sion drew;
   till with thee in the gar - den I heard thy plead - ing pray'r,
   and saw the sweat - drops blood - y that told thy sor - row there.

3. There - fore my songs, my Sav - ior, e'en in this time of woe,
   shall tell of all thy good - ness to suf - f'ring man be - low;
   thy good - ness and thy fa - vor, whose pres - ence from a - bove
   re - joice those hearts, my Sav - ior, that live in thee and love.

John S. B. Monsell, 1863

MONSELL 7.6.7.6.D.
John S. B. Monsell, 1863

554 From Depths of Woe I Raise to Thee

Out of the depths I cry to you, O Lord. Ps. 130:1

1. From depths of woe I raise to thee the voice of lam - en - ta - tion;
2. To wash a - way the crim - son stain, grace, grace a - lone a - vail - eth;
3. There - fore my trust is in the Lord, and not in mine own mer - it;
4. What though I wait the live - long night, and till the dawn ap - pear - eth,

Lord, turn a gra - cious ear to me and hear my sup - pli - ca - tion:
our works, a - las! are all in vain; in much the best life fail - eth:
on him my soul shall rest, his Word up - holds my faint - ing spir - it:
my heart still trust - eth in his might; it doubt - eth not nor fear - eth:

if thou in - iq - ui - ties dost mark, our se - cret sins
no man can glo - ry in thy sight, all must a - like
his prom - ised mer - cy is my fort, my com - fort, and
do thus, O ye of Is - rael's seed, ye of the Spir -

and mis - deeds dark, O who shall stand be - fore thee?
con - fess thy might, and live a - lone by mer - cy.
my sweet sup - port; I wait for it with pa - tience.
it born in - deed; and wait till God ap - pear - eth.

5. Though great our sins and sore our woes, his grace much more aboundeth;
his helping love no limit knows, our utmost need it soundeth.
Our Shepherd good and true is he, who will at last his Israel free
from all their sin and sorrow.

From Psalm 130
Martin Luther, 1523
Trans. composite; alt. 1961

AUS TIEFER NOT 8.7.8.7.8.8.7.
Melody by Martin Luther, 1524
Johann Walther's *Gesangbüchlein*, 1524; arr.; alt. 1990

Lord, I Was Blind: I Could Not See   555

As for you, you were dead in your transgressions and sins. Eph. 2:1

1. Lord, I was blind: I could not see in thy marred
2. Lord, I was deaf: I could not hear the thrill - ing
3. Lord, I was dumb: I could not speak the grace and
4. Lord, I was dead: I could not stir my life - less
5. Lord, thou hast made the blind to see, the deaf to

vis - age an - y grace; but now the beau - ty
mu - sic of thy voice; but now I hear thee
glo - ry of thy name; but now, as touched with
soul to come to thee; but now, since thou hast
hear, the dumb to speak, the dead to live; and

of thy face in ra - diant vi - sion dawns on me.
and re - joice, and all thine ut - tered words are dear.
liv - ing flame, my lips thine ea - ger prais - es wake.
quick- ened me, I rise from sin's dark sep - ul - cher.
lo, I break the chains of my cap - tiv - i - ty!

William T. Matson, 1833–1899

BODMIN L.M.
Alfred Scott-Gatty, 1847–1918

556 Though Your Sins Be as Scarlet

Though your sins are like scarlet, they shall be as white as snow; though they are red
as crimson, they shall be like wool. Is. 1:18

1. "Though your sins be as scar - let, they shall be as white as snow;
2. Hear the voice that en - treats you, O re - turn ye un - to God!
3. He'll for - give your trans - gres - sions, and re - mem - ber them no more;

though your sins be as scar - let, they shall be as white as snow.
Hear the voice that en - treats you, O re - turn ye un - to God!
he'll for - give your trans - gres - sions, and re - mem - ber them no more.

Though they be red like crim - son, they shall be as wool.
He is of great com - pas - sion, and of won - drous love.
"Look un - to me, ye peo - ple," saith the Lord your God.

Though your sins be as scar - let, though your sins be as scar - let,
Hear the voice that en - treats you, hear the voice that en - treats you,
He'll for - give your trans - gres - sions, he'll for - give your trans - gres - sions,

they shall be as white as snow, they shall be as white as snow."
O re - turn ye un - to God! O re - turn ye un - to God!
and re - mem - ber them no more, and re - mem - ber them no more.

Fanny J. Crosby, 1820–1915

COMPASSION 7.7.7.7.7.5.7.7.7.7.
William H. Doane, 1832–1915
Arr. by Henry J. Van Andel

Blest Are the Undefiled 557

Blessed are they whose ways are blameless, who walk according to the law
of the LORD. Ps. 119:1

1. Blest are the un - de - filed in heart, whose ways are right and clean,
2. Blest are the men who keep your word and prac - tice your com - mands;
3. Great is their peace who love your law; how firm their souls a - bide!
4. Then shall my heart have in - ward joy, and keep my face from shame,

who nev - er from the law de - part, but fly from ev - 'ry sin.
with their whole heart they seek the Lord, and serve you with their hands.
Nor can a bold temp - ta - tion draw their stead - y feet a - side.
when all your stat - utes I o - bey, and hon - or all your name.

From Psalm 119
Isaac Watts. 1719: mod.

DOWNS C.M.
Lowell Mason, 1832

558 That Man Is Blest Who, Fearing God

Blessed is the man who does not walk in the counsel of the wicked. Ps. 1:1

1. That man is blest who, fear - ing God, from sin re - strains his feet, who will not stand with wick - ed men, who shuns the scorn - ers' seat.

2. Yea, blest is he who makes God's law his por - tion and de - light, and med - i - tates up - on that law with glad - ness day and night.

3. That man is nour - ished like a tree set by the riv - ers' side; its leaf is green, its fruit is sure, and thus his works a - bide.

4. The wick - ed like the driv - en chaff are swept from off the land; they shall not gath - er with the just, nor in the judg - ment stand.

5. The Lord will guard the righ - teous well, their way to him is known; the way of sin - ners, far from God, shall sure - ly be o'er - thrown.

From Psalm 1
The Psalter, 1912; alt. 1961

IRISH C.M.
Hymns and Sacred Poems, Dublin, 1749

Father, I Know That All My Life

559

I have learned to be content whatever the circumstances. Phil. 4:11

1. Fa - ther, I know that all my life is por- tioned out for me;
2. I would not have the rest - less will that hur - ries to and fro,
3. I ask thee for the dai - ly strength, to none that ask de - nied,
4. In ser - vice which thy will ap- points there are no bonds for me;

the chang - es that are sure to come, I do not fear to see:
seek - ing for some great thing to do, or se - cret thing to know;
a mind to blend with out - ward life, while keep - ing at thy side,
my se - cret heart is taught the truth that makes thy chil - dren free;

I ask thee for a pres - ent mind, in - tent on pleas - ing thee.
I would be treat - ed as a child, and guid - ed where I go.
con - tent to fill a lit - tle space, if thou be glo - ri - fied.
a life of self - re - nounc - ing love is one of lib - er - ty.

Anna L. Waring, 1850

MORWELLHAM 8.6.8.6.8.6.
Charles Steggall, 1826–1905

560 Lord, Speak to Me That I May Speak

The things you have heard me say ... entrust to reliable men who will also be qualified to teach others. 2 Tim. 2:2

1. Lord, speak to me that I may speak in liv-ing ech-oes of your
2. O teach me, Lord, that I may teach the pre-cious things you do im-
3. O fill me with your full-ness, Lord, un-til my ver-y heart o'er-

tone; as you have sought, so let me seek your
part; and wing my words, that they may reach the
flow in kin-dling thought and glow-ing word your

err-ing chil-dren lost and lone.
hid-den depths of man-y a heart.
love to tell, your praise to show.

REFRAIN
O use me, Lord, use
e-ven me, just as you will and when and where; un-

til your bless - ed face I see, your rest, your joy, your glo - ry share.

Frances R. Havergal, 1872
Mod.
Tune © 1985, Gail Smith. Used by permission.

FORT LAUDERDALE L.M.D.
Gail Smith, 1985; alt. 1990

Lord, Speak to Me That I May Speak 561

*The things you have heard me say ... entrust to reliable men who will also be qualified
to teach others.* 2 Tim. 2:2

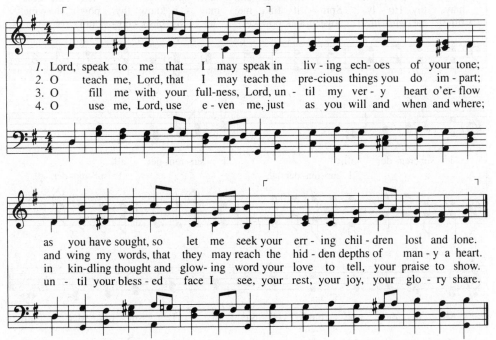

1. Lord, speak to me that I may speak in liv - ing ech - oes of your tone;
2. O teach me, Lord, that I may teach the pre - cious things you do im - part;
3. O fill me with your full-ness, Lord, un - til my ver - y heart o'er-flow
4. O use me, Lord, use e - ven me, just as you will and when and where;

as you have sought, so let me seek your err - ing chil - dren lost and lone.
and wing my words, that they may reach the hid - den depths of man - y a heart.
in kin-dling thought and glow- ing word your love to tell, your praise to show.
un - til your bless - ed face I see, your rest, your joy, your glo - ry share.

Frances R. Havergal, 1872
Mod.

CANONBURY L.M.
Robert Schumann, 1839; arr.

562 All to Jesus I Surrender

We have left everything to follow you! Mark 10:28

1. All to Je - sus I sur - ren - der, all to him I free - ly give;
2. All to Je - sus I sur - ren - der, hum - bly at his feet I bow,
3. All to Je - sus I sur - ren - der, make me, Sav - ior, whol - ly thine;
4. All to Je - sus I sur - ren - der, Lord, I give my - self to thee;

may I ev - er love and trust him, in his pres - ence dai - ly live.
world - ly plea- sures all for - sak - en, take me, Je - sus, take me now.
may thy Ho - ly Spir - it fill me, may I know thy pow'r di - vine.
fill me with thy love and pow - er, let thy bless - ing fall on me.

REFRAIN

I sur - ren- der all, I sur - ren- der all.
I sur- ren- der all, I sur- ren- der all.

All to thee, my bless - ed Sav - ior, I sur - ren - der all.

Judson W. VanDeVenter, 1896
Alt. 1990

SURRENDER 8.7.8.7.ref.
Winfield S. Weeden. 1896

What Kind of Man Can Live in the World

563

LORD, who may dwell in your sanctuary? Who may live on your holy hill? Ps. 15:1

1. What kind of man can live in the world where God lives?
2. What kind of man can speak in the world where God speaks?
3. What kind of man can rule in the world where God rules?

One who in ac - tion is right and whose con - duct is blame-less;
One who can say what is true but a - void speak-ing slan - der;
One who will swear to his hurt but a - bide by his prom-ise;

one who can speak the truth in his heart at all times;
one who will work the good of his friends and neigh - bors;
one who will use his wealth to re - lieve the need - y;

one who o - beys all that God in his love has taught us.
one who sup - ports men of God in con - tempt of e - vil.
he who ac - com - plish- es this is se - cure for - ev - er.

Based on Psalm 15
Jonathan Barnes, 1973

WHAT KIND OF MAN 12.14.12.13.
David G. Wilson, 1973

564

Blessed Is the Man

Blessed is the man who does not walk in the counsel of the wicked. Ps. 1:1

1. Bless - ed is the man, the man who does not walk in the
2. He is like a tree, a tree that flour - ish - es, be - ing
3. The un - god - ly are not so, for they are like the chaff which the

coun - sel of the un - god - ly: bless - ed is that man.
plant - ed by the wa - ter: bless - ed is that man.
wind blows clean a - way. The un - god - ly are not so. The un -

He who re - jects the way, re - jects the way of sin and who
He will bring forth fruit, his leaf will with - er not, for in
god - ly will not stand up - on the judg - ment day nor be -
Bless - ed is the man, the man who does not walk in the

turns a - way from scof - fing: bless - ed is that man. But his de -
all he does he pros - pers: bless - ed is that man. For his de -
long to God's own peo - ple: the un - god - ly will not stand. But God knows the
coun - sel of the un - god - ly: bless - ed is that man.

light, by day and night, is the law of God Al - might - y.
light, by day and night, is the law of God Al - might - y.
way of righ - teous men and un - god - ly ways will per - ish.

D.S. al Fine

Michael Baughen, 1969

BLESSED IS THE MAN 11.14.12.12.8.8.
Michael Baughen, 1969
Arr. by Jim Thornton, 1969

All for Jesus! 565

Offer your bodies as living sacrifices, holy and pleasing to God. Rom. 12:1

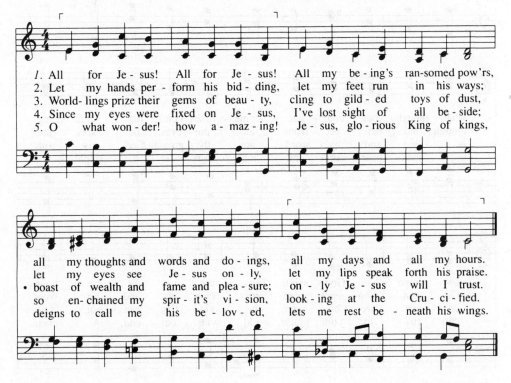

1. All for Je - sus! All for Je - sus! All my be - ing's ran-somed pow'rs,
2. Let my hands per - form his bid - ding, let my feet run in his ways;
3. World- lings prize their gems of beau - ty, cling to gild - ed toys of dust,
4. Since my eyes were fixed on Je - sus, I've lost sight of all be - side;
5. O what won - der! how a - maz - ing! Je - sus, glo - rious King of kings,

all my thoughts and words and do - ings, all my days and all my hours.
let my eyes see Je - sus on - ly, let my lips speak forth his praise.
boast of wealth and fame and plea - sure; on - ly Je - sus will I trust.
so en - chained my spir - it's vi - sion, look - ing at the Cru - ci - fied.
deigns to call me his be - lov - ed, lets me rest be - neath his wings.

Mary D. James, 1889

WYCLIFF 8.7.8.7.
John Stainer, *The Crucifixion*, 1887

566   Fear Not, O Little Flock

Do not be afraid, little flock, for your Father has been pleased to give you the kingdom.
Luke 12:32

1. Fear not, O lit-tle flock, the foe who mad-ly
2. Be of good cheer; your cause be-longs to him who
3. As true as God's own Word is true, nor earth nor
4. A-men, Lord Je-sus, grant our pray'r; great Cap-tain,

seeks your o-ver-throw; dread not his rage and pow'r:
can a-venge your wrongs; leave it to him, our Lord:
hell with all their crew a-gainst us shall pre-vail.
now your arm make bare, fight for us once a-gain;

what though your cour-age some-times faints, his seem-ing
though hid-den yet from all our eyes, he sees the
A jest and by-word are they grown; God is with
so shall your saints and mar-tyrs raise a might-y

tri-umph o'er God's saints lasts but a lit-tle hour.
Gid-eon who shall rise to save us and his Word.
us, we are his own; our vic-t'ry can-not fail.
cho-rus to your praise, world with-out end. A-men.

Attr. to Johann Michael Altenburg, 1584–1640
Tr. by Catherine Winkworth, 1855; mod.

JEHOVAH NISSI 8.8.6.D.
Edward Patrick Crawford, 1846–1912

Rise, My Soul, to Watch and Pray

Watch and pray so that you will not fall into temptation. Matt. 26:41

1. Rise, my soul, to watch and pray, from thy sleep a - wak - en; be not
2. Watch a - gainst the dev - il's snares, lest a - sleep he find thee; for in -
3. Watch! Let not the wick- ed world with its pow'r de - feat thee. Watch lest
4. Watch a - gainst thy - self, my soul, lest with grace thou tri - fle; let not
5. But while watch-ing, al - so pray to the Lord un - ceas- ing. He will

by the e - vil day un - a-wares o'er - tak - en. For the foe,
deed no pains he spares to de - ceive and blind thee. Sa - tan's prey
• with her pomp un- furled she be - tray and cheat thee. Watch and see
self thy thoughts con - trol nor God's mer - cy sti - fle. Pride and sin
free thee, be thy stay, strength and faith in - creas - ing. O Lord, bless

well we know, oft his har - vest reap - eth while the Chris - tian sleep- eth.
oft are they who se - cure are sleep - ing and no watch are keep- ing.
• lest there be faith- less friends to charm thee, who but seek to harm thee.
lurk with - in all thy hopes to scat - ter; heed not when they flat - ter.
in dis - tress and let noth- ing swerve me from the will to serve thee.

Johann B. Freystein, 1697, cento
Tr. by Catherine Winkworth, 1863; alt.

STRAF MICH NICHT 7.6.7.6.3.3.6.6.
Hundert Arien, Dresden, 1694

568
In the Hour of Trial

The Lord knows how to rescue godly men from trials. 2 Pet. 2:9

1. In the hour of tri - al, Je - sus, plead for me;
2. With its witch - ing plea - sures would this vain world charm,
3. If with sore af - flic - tion thou in love chas - tise,
4. When in dust and ash - es to the grave I sink,

lest by base de - ni - al I de - part from thee;
or its sor - did trea - sures spread to work me harm,
pour thy ben - e - dic - tion on the sac - ri - fice;
while heav'n's glo - ry flash - es o'er the shelv - ing brink,

when thou seest me wa - ver, with a look re - call,
bring to my re - mem - brance sad Geth - sem - a - ne,
then, up - on thine al - tar free - ly of - fered up,
on thy truth re - ly - ing through that mor - tal strife,

nor for fear or fa - vor suf - fer me to fall.
or, in dark - er sem - blance, cross - crowned Cal - va - ry.
though the flesh may fal - ter, faith shall drink the cup.
Lord, re - ceive me, dy - ing, to e - ter - nal life.

James Montgomery, 1834; alt.

PENITENCE (LANE) 6.5.6.5.D.
Spencer Lane, 1879

Jesus, Lord of Life and Glory

569

The LORD is my rock, my fortress and my deliverer. 2 Sam. 22:2

1. Je - sus, Lord of life and glo - ry, bend from heav'n thy gra - cious ear;
2. From the depth of na - ture's blind - ness, from the hard-'ning pow'r of sin,
3. When temp - ta - tion sore - ly press - es, in the day of Sa - tan's pow'r,
4. When the world a - round is smil - ing, in the time of wealth and ease,

while our wait - ing souls a - dore thee, Friend of help - less sin - ners, hear:
from all mal - ice and un - kind - ness, from the pride that lurks with - in,
in our times of deep dis - tress - es, in each dark and try - ing hour,
earth - ly joys our hearts be - guil - ing, in the day of health and peace,

REFRAIN

by thy mer - cy, O de - liv - er us, good Lord.

5. In our weary hours of sickness,
   in our times of grief and pain,
   when we feel our mortal weakness,
   when the creature's help is vain,
   (Refrain)

6. In the solemn hour of dying,
   in the awful Judgment Day,
   may our souls, on thee relying,
   find thee still our rock and stay:
   (Refrain)

James J. Cummins, 1839

ST. AUSTIN 8.7.8.7.4.7.
Gregorian chant
Arr. in the *Bristol Tune Book*, 1876

570   Faith of Our Fathers!

Contend for the faith that was once for all entrusted to the saints. Jude 3

1. Faith of our fa - thers! liv - ing still in spite of
2. Our fa - thers, chained in pris - ons dark, were still in
3. Faith of our fa - thers! God's great pow'r shall draw all
4. Faith of our fa - thers! we will love both friend and

dun - geon, fire, and sword; O how our hearts beat high with joy
heart and con - science free; and blest would be their chil - dren's fate
na - tions un - to thee; and through the truth that comes from God
foe in all our strife, and preach thee, too, as love knows how

REFRAIN

when - e'er we hear God's glo - rious Word:
if they, like them, should die for thee:
his peo - ple shall in - deed be free: Faith of our fa - thers,
by wit - ness true and vir - tuous life:

ho - ly faith! We will be true to thee till death.

Frederick W. Faber, 1849; alt.
Alt. 1961

ST. CATHERINE 8.8.8.8.8.8.
Henri F. Hemy, 1864
Arr. by James G. Walton, 1870

Stand Up, Stand Up for Jesus

Endure hardship with us like a good soldier of Christ Jesus. 2 Tim. 2:3

1. Stand up, stand up for Je - sus, ye sol - diers of the cross;
2. Stand up, stand up for Je - sus, the trum - pet call o - bey;
3. Stand up, stand up for Je - sus, stand in his strength a - lone;
4. Stand up, stand up for Je - sus, the strife will not be long;

lift high his roy - al ban - ner, it must not suf - fer loss:
forth to the might - y con - flict in this his glo - rious day:
the arm of flesh will fail you, ye dare not trust your own:
this day the noise of bat - tle, the next the vic - tor's song:

from vic - t'ry un - to vic - t'ry his ar - my he shall lead,
ye that are men now serve him a - gainst un - num - bered foes;
put on the gos - pel ar - mor, each piece put on with pray'r;
to him that o - ver - com - eth a crown of life shall be;

till ev - 'ry foe is van - quished, and Christ is Lord in - deed.
let cour - age rise with dan - ger, and strength to strength op - pose.
where du - ty calls, or dan - ger, be nev - er want - ing there.
he with the King of glo - ry shall reign e - ter - nal - ly.

George Duffield, 1858

WEBB 7.6.7.6.D.
George J. Webb, 1837

572

Onward, Christian Soldiers

I will build my church, and the gates of Hades will not overcome it. Matt. 16:18

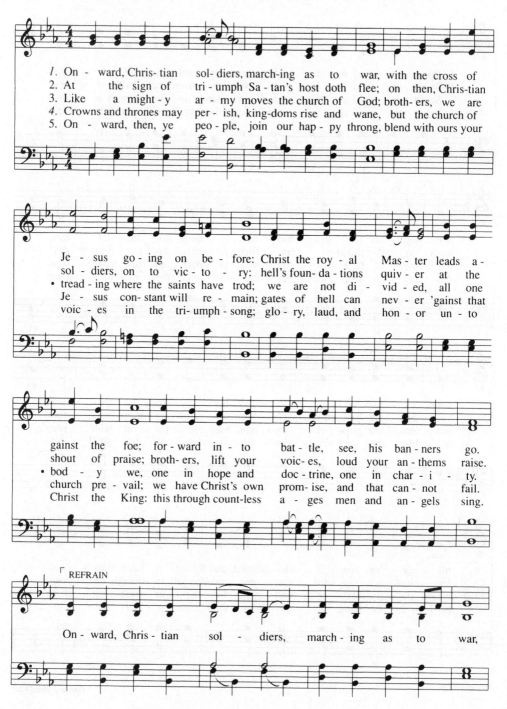

1. On - ward, Chris- tian sol- diers, march-ing as to war, with the cross of
2. At the sign of tri - umph Sa - tan's host doth flee; on then, Chris-tian
3. Like a might - y ar - my moves the church of God; broth- ers, we are
4. Crowns and thrones may per - ish, king-doms rise and wane, but the church of
5. On - ward, then, ye peo - ple, join our hap - py throng, blend with ours your

Je - sus go - ing on be - fore: Christ the roy - al Mas - ter leads a -
sol - diers, on to vic - to - ry: hell's foun- da - tions quiv - er at the
tread - ing where the saints have trod; we are not di - vid - ed, all one
Je - sus con - stant will re - main; gates of hell can nev - er 'gainst that
voic - es in the tri- umph-song; glo - ry, laud, and hon - or un - to

gainst the foe; for - ward in - to bat - tle, see, his ban - ners go.
shout of praise; broth- ers, lift your voic- es, loud your an - thems raise.
bod - y we, one in hope and doc - trine, one in char - i - ty.
church pre - vail; we have Christ's own prom- ise, and that can - not fail.
Christ the King: this through count-less a - ges men and an - gels sing.

REFRAIN

On - ward, Chris - tian sol - diers, march - ing as to war,

with the cross of Je - sus go - ing on be - fore.

Sabine Baring-Gould, 1865

ST. GERTRUDE 6.5.6.5.D.ref.
Arthur S. Sullivan, 1871

Am I a Soldier of the Cross 573

Endure hardship with us like a good soldier of Christ Jesus. 2 Tim. 2:3

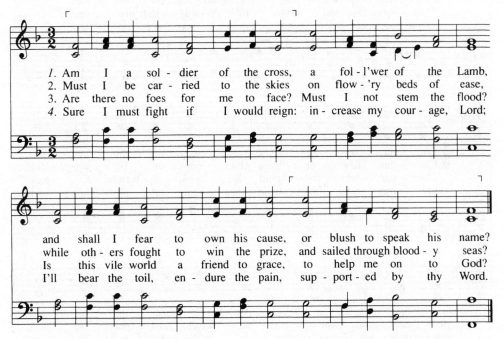

1. Am I a sol - dier of the cross, a fol - l'wer of the Lamb,
2. Must I be car - ried to the skies on flow - 'ry beds of ease,
3. Are there no foes for me to face? Must I not stem the flood?
4. Sure I must fight if I would reign: in - crease my cour - age, Lord;

and shall I fear to own his cause, or blush to speak his name?
while oth - ers fought to win the prize, and sailed through blood - y seas?
Is this vile world a friend to grace, to help me on to God?
I'll bear the toil, en - dure the pain, sup - port - ed by thy Word.

5. Thy saints, in all this glorious war,
shall conquer, though they die;
they view the triumph from afar,
and seize it with their eye.

6. When that illustrious day shall rise,
and all thine armies shine
in robes of vict'ry through the skies,
the glory shall be thine.

Isaac Watts, 1724

MARLOW C.M.
John Chetham's *Book of Psalmody*, 1718; arr.

574 Christian, Dost Thou See Them

Put on the full armor of God so that you can take your stand against the devil's schemes. Eph. 6:11

1. Chris - tian, dost thou see them on the ho - ly ground,
how the pow'rs of dark - ness rage thy steps a - round?
Chris - tian, up and smite them, count - ing gain but loss,
in the strength that com - eth by the ho - ly cross.

2. Chris - tian, dost thou feel them, how they work with - in,
striv - ing, tempt - ing, lur - ing, goad - ing in - to sin?
Chris - tian, nev - er trem - ble; nev - er be down - cast;
gird thee for the bat - tle, watch and pray and fast.

3. Chris - tian, dost thou hear them, how they speak thee fair?
"Al - ways fast and vig - il? Al - ways watch and prayer?"
Chris - tian, an - swer bold - ly, "While I breathe I pray!"
Peace shall fol - low bat - tle, night shall end in day.

4. Hear the words of Je - sus: "O my ser - vant true;
thou art ver - y wea - ry— I was wea - ry too;
but that toil shall make thee some day all mine own,
and the end of sor - row shall be near my throne."

Attr. to Andrew of Crete, ca. 660–732
Tr. by John Mason Neale, 1862; alt.

ST. ANDREW OF CRETE 6.5.6.5.D.
John B. Dykes, 1868

Soldiers of Christ, Arise

Be strong in the Lord and in his mighty power. Put on the full armor of God.
Eph. 6:10, 11

1. Sol - diers of Christ, a - rise, and put your ar - mor on,
2. Stand then in his great might, with all his strength en - dued;
3. To keep your ar - mor bright, at - tend with con - stant care;

strong in the strength which God sup - plies through his e - ter - nal Son.
but take, to arm you for the fight, the pan - o - ply of God.
still walk - ing in your Cap - tain's sight, and watch - ing un - to prayer.

Strong in the Lord of Hosts, and in his might - y pow'r,
Leave no un - guard - ed place, no weak - ness of the soul;
From strength to strength go on; wres - tle and fight and pray;

who in the strength of Je - sus trusts is more than con - quer - or.
take ev - 'ry vir - tue, ev - 'ry grace, and for - ti - fy the whole.
tread all the pow'rs of dark - ness down, and win the well- fought day.

Charles Wesley, 1749

DIADEMATA S.M.D.
George J. Elvey, 1868

576 Awake, My Soul, Stretch Every Nerve

Since we are surrounded by such a great cloud of witnesses ... let us run
with perseverance the race marked out for us. Heb. 12:1

1. A - wake, my soul, stretch ev - 'ry nerve, and press with
2. A cloud of wit - ness - es a - round hold you in
3. 'Tis God's all - an - i - mat - ing voice that calls you
4. That prize with peer - less glo - ries bright, which shall new
5. Blest Sav - ior, in - tro - duced by you, have I my

vig - or on; a heav'n - ly race de - mands your zeal,
full sur - vey: for - get the steps al - read - y trod,
from on high; 'tis his own hand pre - sents the prize
lus - ter boast, when vic - tors' wreaths and mon - archs' gems
race be - gun; and, crowned with vic - t'ry, at your feet

and an im - mor - tal crown, and an im - mor - tal crown.
and on - ward urge your way, and on - ward urge your way.
to your as - pir - ing eye, to your as - pir - ing eye:
shall blend in com - mon dust, shall blend in com - mon dust.
I'll lay my hon - ors down, I'll lay my hon - ors down.

Philip Doddridge, 1755
Mod.

CHRISTMAS C.M.rep.
From George Frederick Handel, *Siroe*, 1728
Arr. by Lowell Mason, 1821

Stand Up, My Soul; Shake Off Your Fears

Put on the full armor of God. Eph. 6:13

1. Stand up, my soul; shake off your fears, and gird the
2. Hell and your sins re - sist your course; but hell and
3. Then let my soul march bold - ly on, press for - ward
4. There shall I wear a star - ry crown, and tri - umph

gos - pel ar - mor on; march to the gates of
sin are van - quished foes: your Je - sus nailed them
to the heav'n - ly gate; there peace and joy e -
in al - might - y grace; while all the ar - mies

end - less joy, where your great Cap - tain Sav - ior's gone.
to the cross, and sang the tri - umph when he rose.
ter - nal reign, and glit - t'ring robes for con - qu'rors wait.
of the skies join in my glo - rious Lead - er's praise.

Isaac Watts, 1707
Mod.

WALTHAM L.M.
J. Baptiste Calkin, 1872

578

The Son of God Goes Forth to War

They did not love their lives so much as to shrink from death. Rev. 12:11

1. The Son of God goes forth to war, a king-ly crown to gain;
2. The mar-tyr first, whose ea-gle eye could pierce be-yond the grave,
3. A glo-rious band, the cho-sen few on whom the Spir-it came,
4. A no-ble ar-my, men and boys, the ma-tron and the maid,

his blood-red ban-ner streams a-far: who fol-lows in his train?
who saw his Mas-ter in the sky, and called on him to save:
twelve val-iant saints, their hope they knew, and mocked the cross and flame:
a-round the Sav-ior's throne re-joice, in robes of light ar-rayed:

Who best can drink his cup of woe, tri-um-phant o-ver pain,
like him, with par-don on his tongue in midst of mor-tal pain,
they met the ty-rant's bran-dished steel, the li-on's gor-y mane;
they climbed the steep as-cent of heav'n through per-il, toil, and pain:

who pa-tient bears his cross be-low, he fol-lows in his train.
he prayed for them that did the wrong: who fol-lows in his train?
they bowed their necks the death to feel: who fol-lows in their train?
O God, to us may grace be giv'n to fol-low in their train.

Reginald Heber, 1827

ALL SAINTS NEW C.M.D.
Henry S. Cutler, 1872

Dare to Be a Daniel!

579

"Daniel ... pays no attention to you, O king, or to the decree you put in writing."...
So ... they brought Daniel and threw him into the lions' den. Dan. 6:13, 16

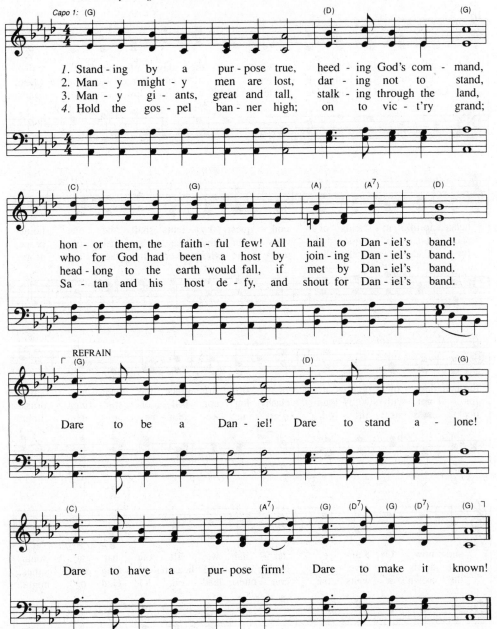

1. Stand - ing by a pur - pose true, heed - ing God's com - mand,
2. Man - y might - y men are lost, dar - ing not to stand,
3. Man - y gi - ants, great and tall, stalk - ing through the land,
4. Hold the gos - pel ban - ner high; on to vic - t'ry grand;

hon - or them, the faith - ful few! All hail to Dan - iel's band!
who for God had been a host by join - ing Dan - iel's band.
head - long to the earth would fall, if met by Dan - iel's band.
Sa - tan and his host de - fy, and shout for Dan - iel's band.

REFRAIN

Dare to be a Dan - iel! Dare to stand a - lone!

Dare to have a pur - pose firm! Dare to make it known!

Philip P. Bliss, 1873

DANIEL 7.5.7.6.ref.
Philip P. Bliss, 1873

580 Lead On, O King Eternal

I am the LORD your God ... who directs you in the way you should go. Is. 48:17

1. Lead on, O King e - ter - nal, the day of march has come;
2. Lead on, O King e - ter - nal, till sin's fierce war shall cease,
3. Lead on, O King e - ter - nal: we fol - low, not with fears;

hence - forth in fields of con - quest thy tents shall be our home:
and ho - li - ness shall whis - per the sweet a - men of peace;
for glad - ness breaks like morn - ing where - e'er thy face ap - pears;

through days of prep - a - ra - tion thy grace has made us strong,
for not with swords loud clash - ing, nor roll of stir - ring drums,
thy cross is lift - ed o'er us; we jour - ney in its light:

and now, O King e - ter - nal, we lift our bat - tle song.
but deeds of love and mer - cy, the heav'n - ly king - dom comes.
the crown a - waits the con - quest; lead on, O God of might.

Ernest W. Shurtleff, 1888

LANCASHIRE 7.6.7.6.D.
Henry Smart, 1836

Fight the Good Fight

581

Fight the good fight of the faith. 1 Tim. 6:12

1. Fight the good fight with all thy might; Christ is thy
2. Run the straight race through God's good grace, lift up thine
3. Cast care a - side; up - on thy Guide lean, and his
4. Faint not, nor fear, his arms are near; he chang - eth

strength, and Christ thy right: lay hold on life, and
eyes, and seek his face; life with its way be -
mer - cy will pro - vide; lean, and the trust - ing
not, and thou art dear; on - ly be - lieve, and

it shall be thy joy and crown e - ter - nal - ly.
fore us lies, Christ is the path, and Christ the prize.
soul shall prove, Christ is its life, and Christ its love.
thou shalt see that Christ is all in all to thee.

John S. B. Monsell, 1863

MOZART L.M.
From Wolfgang Amadeus Mozart (1756–1791), *Kyrie* in the *Twelfth Mass*
Arrangement attr. to Mozart

582

Yield Not to Temptation

But the Lord is faithful, and he will strengthen and protect you from the evil one.
2 Thess. 3:3

1. Yield not to temp-ta-tion, for yield-ing is sin;
2. Shun e-vil com-pan-ions; bad lan-guage dis-dain;
3. To him that o'er-com-eth God giv-eth a crown;

each vic-t'ry will help you some oth-er to win;
God's name hold in rev-'rence, nor take it in vain;
through faith we shall con-quer, though of-ten cast down;

fight man-ful-ly on-ward; dark pas-sions sub-due;
be thought-ful and ear-nest, kind-heart-ed and true;
he who is the Sav-ior our strength will re-new;

look ev-er to Je-sus, he will car-ry you through.
look ev-er to Je-sus, he will car-ry you through.
look ev-er to Je-sus, he will car-ry you through.

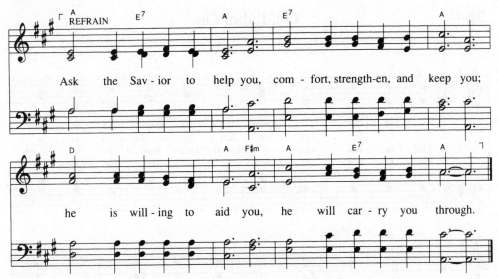

REFRAIN

Ask the Sav-ior to help you, com-fort, strength-en, and keep you;

he is will-ing to aid you, he will car-ry you through.

Horatio R. Palmer, 1868

YIELD NOT 11.11.11.12.ref.
Horatio R. Palmer, 1868

Fountain of Good, to Own Thy Love 583

Whatever you did for one of the least of these brothers of mine, you did for me.
Matt. 25:40

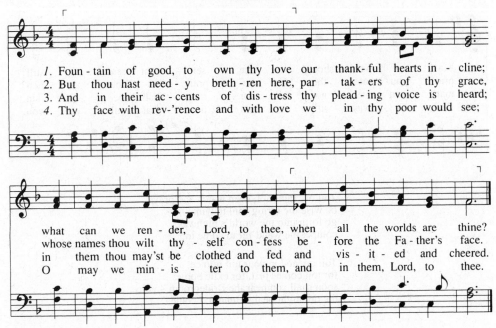

1. Foun-tain of good, to own thy love our thank-ful hearts in-cline;
2. But thou hast need-y breth-ren here, par-tak-ers of thy grace,
3. And in their ac-cents of dis-tress thy plead-ing voice is heard;
4. Thy face with rev-'rence and with love we in thy poor would see;

what can we ren-der, Lord, to thee, when all the worlds are thine?
whose names thou wilt thy-self con-fess be-fore the Fa-ther's face.
in them thou may'st be clothed and fed and vis-it-ed and cheered.
O may we min-is-ter to them, and in them, Lord, to thee.

Philip Doddridge, 1702–1751

ST. ETHELDREDA C.M.
Thomas Turton, 1780–1864

584 Go, Labor On

*Let us not become weary in doing good, for at the proper time we will reap a harvest
if we do not give up. Gal. 6:9*

1. Go, la - bor on: spend and be spent, your joy to
   do the Fa - ther's will; it is the way the
   Mas - ter went; should not the ser - vant tread it still?

2. Go, la - bor on: 'tis not for naught; your earth - ly
   loss is heav'n - ly gain; men heed you, love you,
   praise you not; the Mas - ter prais - es— what are men?

3. Go, la - bor on: e - nough while here if he should
   praise you, if he deign your will - ing heart to
   mark and cheer; no toil for him shall be in vain.

4. Go, la - bor on while it is day: the world's dark
   night is has - t'ning on. Speed, speed your work, cast
   sloth a - way; it is not thus that souls are won.

5. Toil on, faint not, keep watch and pray;
   be wise the erring soul to win;
   go forth into the world's highway,
   compel the wand'rer to come in.

6. Toil on, and in your toil rejoice;
   for toil comes rest, for exile home;
   soon shall you hear the Bridegroom's voice,
   the midnight peal, "Behold, I come."

Horatius Bonar, 1843
Mod.

PENTECOST L.M.
William Boyd, 1868

Take My Life, and Let It Be

585

*Just as you used to offer the parts of your body in slavery to impurity ... so now offer
them in slavery to righteousness.* Rom. 6:19

1. Take my life, and let it be con - se - crat - ed,
2. Take my hands, and let them move at the im - pulse
3. Take my voice, and let me sing, al - ways, on - ly,
4. Take my sil - ver and my gold; not a mite would

Lord, to thee. Take my mo - ments and my days; let them
of thy love. Take my feet, and let them be swift and
for my King. Take my lips, and let them be filled with
I with - hold. Take my in - tel - lect, and use ev - 'ry

flow in cease- less praise, let them flow in cease- less praise.
beau - ti - ful for thee, swift and beau - ti - ful for thee.
mes - sag - es from thee, filled with mes - sa - ges from thee.
pow'r as thou shalt choose, ev - 'ry pow'r as thou shalt choose.

5. Take my will, and make it thine;
   it shall be no longer mine.
   Take my heart, it is thine own;
   it shall be thy royal throne,
   it shall be thy royal throne.

6. Take my love; my Lord, I pour
   at thy feet its treasure-store.
   Take my self, and I will be
   ever, only, all for thee,
   ever, only, all for thee.

Frances R. Havergal, 1874

HENDON 7.7.7.7.rep.
Henri A. César Malan. 1827

586 Take My Life, and Let It Be

Just as you used to offer the parts of your body in slavery to impurity ... so now offer
them in slavery to righteousness. Rom. 6:19

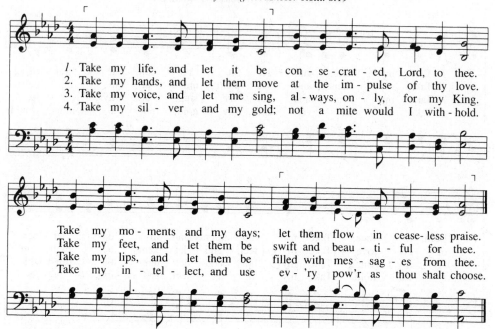

1. Take my life, and let it be con - se - crat - ed, Lord, to thee.
2. Take my hands, and let them move at the im - pulse of thy love.
3. Take my voice, and let me sing, al - ways, on - ly, for my King.
4. Take my sil - ver and my gold; not a mite would I with - hold.

Take my mo - ments and my days; let them flow in cease - less praise.
Take my feet, and let them be swift and beau - ti - ful for thee.
Take my lips, and let them be filled with mes - sag - es from thee.
Take my in - tel - lect, and use ev - 'ry pow'r as thou shalt choose.

5. Take my will, and make it thine;
   it shall be no longer mine.
   Take my heart, it is thine own;
   it shall be thy royal throne.

6. Take my love; my Lord, I pour
   at thy feet its treasure-store.
   Take my self, and I will be
   ever, only, all for thee.

Frances R. Havergal, 1874

ST. BEES 7.7.7.7.
John B. Dykes, 1862

587 Who Is on the Lord's Side?

Whoever is for the LORD, come to me. Ex. 32:26

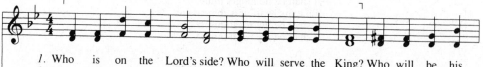

1. Who is on the Lord's side? Who will serve the King? Who will be his
2. Not for weight of glo - ry, not for crown and palm, en - ter we the
3. Je - sus, thou hast bought us, not with gold or gem, but with thine own
4. Fierce may be the con - flict, strong may be the foe, but the King's own

help - ers, oth - er lives to bring? Who will leave the world's side?
ar - my, raise the war - rior psalm; but for Love that claim - eth
life - blood, for thy di - a - dem: with thy bless - ing fill - ing
ar - my none can o - ver - throw: round his stan - dard rang - ing,

Who will face the foe? Who is on the Lord's side? Who for
lives for whom he died: he whom Je - sus nam - eth must be
each who comes to thee, thou hast made us will - ing, thou hast
vic - t'ry is se - cure; for his truth un - chang - ing makes the

him will go? By thy call of mer - cy, by thy grace di - vine,
on his side. By thy love con - strain - ing, by thy grace di - vine,
made us free. By thy grand re - demp - tion, by thy grace di - vine,
tri - umph sure. Joy - ful - ly en - list - ing by thy grace di - vine,

we are on the Lord's side, Sav - ior, we are thine.

Frances R. Havergal, 1877

ARMAGEDDON 6.5.6.5.6.5.D.
German melody
Arr. by John Goss, 1871

588 Who Is on the Lord's Side?

Whoever is for the LORD, come to me. Ex. 32:26

1. Who is on the Lord's side? Who will serve the King? Who will
2. Not for weight of glo-ry, not for crown and palm, en-ter
3. Je-sus, thou hast bought us, not with gold or gem, but with
4. Fierce may be the con-flict, strong may be the foe, but the

be his help-ers, oth-er lives to bring? Who will leave the world's side?
we the ar-my, raise the war-rior psalm; but for Love that claim-eth
thine own life-blood, for thy di-a-dem: with thy bless-ing fill-ing
King's own ar-my none can o-ver-throw: round his stan-dard rang-ing,

Who will face the foe? Who is on the Lord's side? Who for him will
lives for whom he died: he whom Je-sus nam-eth must be on his
each who comes to thee, thou hast made us will-ing, thou hast made us
vic-t'ry is se-cure; for his truth un-chang-ing makes the tri-umph

go? By thy call of mer-cy, by thy grace di-vine,
side. By thy love con-strain-ing, by thy grace di-vine,
free. By thy grand re-demp-tion, by thy grace di-vine,
sure. Joy-ful-ly en-list-ing by thy grace di-vine,

By thy call of mer-cy, by thy grace di-vine,
(Etc.)

we are on the Lord's side, Sav - ior, we are thine.

Frances R. Havergal, 1877

RACHIE 6.5.6.5.6.5.D.
Caradog Roberts, 1878–1935

Fill Thou My Life, O Lord My God   589

I will extol the LORD at all times; his praise will always be on my lips. Ps. 34:1

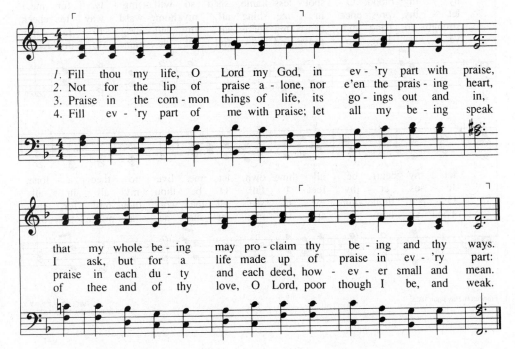

1. Fill   thou   my   life, O   Lord my God, in   ev - 'ry part with   praise,
2. Not   for   the   lip   of   praise a - lone, nor   e'en the prais - ing   heart,
3. Praise in   the com - mon   things of   life, its   go - ings out   and   in,
4. Fill   ev - 'ry   part   of   me with praise; let   all   my   be - ing   speak

that   my   whole be - ing   may pro - claim thy   be - ing   and thy   ways.
I   ask,   but   for   a   life made up   of   praise in   ev - 'ry   part:
praise in   each   du - ty   and each deed, how - ev - er small and   mean.
of   thee   and   of   thy   love, O   Lord, poor though I   be, and   weak.

5. So shalt thou, Lord, from me, e'en me,
   receive the glory due,
   and so shall I begin on earth
   the song forever new.

6. So shall no part of day or night
   from sacredness be free:
   but all my life, in ev'ry step,
   be fellowship with thee.

Horatius Bonar, 1866

ST. FLAVIAN C.M.
Day's *Psalter*, 1562

590

Jesus, Master, Whose I Am

The God whose I am and whom I serve. Acts 27:23

1. Je - sus, Mas - ter, whose I am, pur - chased thine a - lone to be
2. Je - sus, Mas - ter, I am thine: keep me faith - ful, keep me near;
3. Je - sus, Mas - ter, whom I serve, though so fee - bly and so ill,
4. Lord, thou need - est not, I know, ser - vice such as I can bring;

by thy blood, O spot - less Lamb, shed so will - ing - ly for me,
let thy pres - ence in me shine all my home - ward way to cheer.
strength-en hand and heart and nerve all thy bid - ding to ful - fil.
yet I long to prove and show full al - le - giance to my King.

let my heart be all thine own, let me live to thee a - lone.
Je - sus, at thy feet I fall, O be thou my all in all.
O - pen thou mine eyes to see all the work thou hast for me.
Thou an hon - or art to me: let me be a praise to thee.

Frances R. Havergal, 1865

WELLS 7.7.7.7.7.7.
Dmitri Bortniansky, 1752–1825; arr.

Jesus Calls Us

591

"Come, follow me," Jesus said.... At once they left their nets and followed him.
Matt. 4:19, 20

1. Je - sus calls us: o'er the tu - mult of our life's wild, rest - less sea, day by day his sweet voice sound - eth, say - ing, "Chris - tian, fol - low me":
2. As, of old, a - pos - tles heard it by the Gal - i - le - an lake, turned from home and toil and kin - dred, leav - ing all for his dear sake.
3. Je - sus calls us from the wor - ship of the vain world's gold - en store, from each i - dol that would keep us, say - ing, "Chris - tian, love me more."
4. In our joys and in our sor - rows, days of toil and hours of ease, still he calls, in cares and plea - sures, "Chris - tian, love me more than these."
5. Je - sus calls us: by thy mer - cies, Sav - ior, may we hear thy call, give our hearts to thine o - bedience, serve and love thee best of all.

Cecil Frances Alexander, 1852; alt.

GALILEE 8.7.8.7.
William H. Jude, 1887

592

Jesus Bids Us Shine

Let your light shine before men, that they may see your good deeds and praise your Father in heaven. Matt. 5:16

1. Je - sus bids us shine with a pure, clear light,
2. Je - sus bids us shine, first of all for him;
3. Je - sus bids us shine, then, for all a - round;

like a lit - tle can - dle burn - ing in the night.
well he sees and knows it, if our light grows dim.
man - y kinds of dark - ness in the world are found:

In this world of dark - ness so let us shine—
He looks down from heav - en to see us shine—
sin and want and sor - row; so we must shine—

you in your small cor - ner, and I in mine.
you in your small cor - ner, and I in mine.
you in your small cor - ner, and I in mine.

Susan Warner, 1819–1885

JESUS BIDS US SHINE 5.5.6.5.6.4.6.4.
Edwin O. Excell, 1851–1921

Take Thou Our Minds, Dear Lord

593

*Love the Lord your God with all your heart and with all your soul and with
all your mind.* Matt. 22:37

1. Take thou our minds, dear Lord, we hum-bly pray;
2. Take thou our hearts, O Christ, they are thine own;
3. Take thou our wills, Most High! Hold thou full sway;
4. Take thou our selves, O Lord, mind, heart, and will;

give us the mind of Christ each pass-ing day;
come thou with-in our souls and claim thy throne;
have in our in-most souls thy per-fect way;
through our sur-ren-dered souls thy plans ful-fill.

teach us to know the truth that sets us free;
help us to shed a-broad thy death-less love;
guard thou each sa-cred hour from self-ish ease;
We yield our-selves to thee— time, tal-ents, all;

grant us in all our thoughts to hon-or thee.
use us to make the earth like heav'n a-bove.
guide thou our or-dered lives as thou dost please.
we hear, and hence-forth heed thy sov-'reign call.

William Hiram Foulkes, 1918

SURSUM CORDA 10.10.10.10.
George Lomas, 1876

594

Hope of the World

Christ Jesus our hope. 1 Tim. 1:1

1. Hope of the world, thou Christ of great com - pas - sion, speak to our
2. Hope of the world, God's gift from high - est heav - en, bring- ing to
3. Hope of the world, a - foot on dust - y high - ways, show- ing to
4. Hope of the world, who by thy cross didst save us from death and
5. Hope of the world, O Christ o'er death vic - to - rious, who by this

fear - ful hearts by con - flict rent. Save us, thy peo - ple, from con -
hun - gry souls the bread of life, still let thy Spir - it un - to
• wan - d'ring souls the path of light; walk thou be - side us, lest the
dark de - spair, from sin and guilt; we ren - der back the love thy
sign didst con - quer grief and pain, we would be faith - ful to thy

sum - ing pas - sion, who by our own false hopes and aims are spent.
us be giv - en, to heal earth's wounds and end her bit - ter strife.
• tempt - ing by - ways, lure us a - way from thee to end - less night.
mer - cy gave us; take thou our lives, and use them as thou wilt.
gos - pel glo - rious: Thou art our Lord! Thou dost for - ev - er reign!

Georgia E. Harkness, 1954

VICAR 11.10.11.10.
V. Earle Copes, 1963

Let Your Heart Be Broken

595

He will be an instrument for noble purposes, made holy, useful to the Master and prepared to do any good work. 2 Tim. 2:21

1. Let your heart be bro-ken for a world in need: feed the mouths that hun-ger, soothe the wounds that bleed, give the cup of wat-er and the loaf of bread— be the hands of Je-sus, serv-ing in his stead.

2. Here on earth ap-ply-ing prin-ci-ples of love, vis-i-ble ex-pres-sion— God still rules a-bove— liv-ing il-lus-tra-tion of the Liv-ing Word to the minds of all who've nev-er seen or heard.

3. Blest to be a bless-ing, priv-i-leged to care, chal-lenged by the need— ap-par-ent ev-ery-where. Where man-kind is want-ing, fill the va-cant place; be the means through which the Lord re-veals his grace.

4. Let your heart be ten-der and your vi-sion clear; see man-kind as God sees, serve him far and near. Let your heart be bro-ken by a broth-er's pain; share your rich re-sourc-es, give and give a-gain.

Bryan Jeffery Leech, 1975

PENITENCE (LANE) 6.5.6.5.D.
Spencer Lane, 1879

596

You Came to Us, Dear Jesus

Whatever you did for one of the least of these brothers of mine, you did for me.
Matt. 25:40

1. You came to us, dear Jesus, in our dying,
as broken, bleeding we could make no sign.
Compassion, Lord, brought you where we were lying,
to lift us up, to pour on oil and wine.

2. You came to us, dear Jesus, in our yearning,
as faint and famished we before you stood;
compassion, Lord, our emptiness discerning,
moved you to multiply the loaves for food.

3. You came to us, dear Jesus, in our fearing:
our dread the lashing waves, the tempest shrill.
Compassion, Lord, drew you to us, and nearing,
to wind and water you said, "Peace, be still!"

4. You came to us, dear Jesus, in our sighing,
for blind and lame and paralyzed we lay.
Compassion, Lord, turned you to still our crying
and touch our darkened eyes with light of day.

5. We come to you, dear Jesus, in your brothers
in prison, needy, hungry, sick, and cold;
compassion, Lord, sees you in all these others,
in touching them our Savior's hand we hold.

6. You came to us, dear Jesus, in your dying;
your wounds poured love as blood upon the tree.
Compassion, Lord, from Calvary is crying,
"Bind up their wounds as you would do to me!"

Edmund P. Clowney, 1985

HIGHWOOD 11.10.11.10.
R. R. Terry, 1865–1938

Though I May Speak with Bravest Fire

597

If I speak in the tongues of men and of angels, but have not love, I am only a resounding gong or a clanging cymbal. 1 Cor. 13:1

1. Though I may speak with brav-est fire, and have the gift to all in-spire, and have not love, my words are vain, as sound-ing brass, and hope-less gain.
2. Though I may give all I pos-sess, and striv-ing so my love pro-fess, but not be giv'n by love with-in, the pro-fit soon turns strange-ly thin.
3. Come, Spir-it, come, our hearts con-trol, our spir-its long to be made whole. Let in-ward love guide ev-ery deed; by this we wor-ship and are freed.

Hal Hopson, 1972

GIFT OF LOVE L.M.
American folk tune
Arr. by Hal Hopson, 1972

598

Guide Me, O Thou Great Jehovah

He will be our guide even to the end. Ps. 48:14

1. Guide me, O thou great Je - ho - vah, pil - grim through this
2. O - pen now the crys - tal foun - tain, whence the heal - ing
3. When I tread the verge of Jor - dan, bid my anx - ious

bar - ren land; I am weak, but thou art might-y; hold me with thy
stream doth flow; let the fire and cloud-y pil - lar lead me all my
fears sub - side; Death of death, and hell's De-struc-tion, land me safe on

pow'r - ful hand; Bread of heav - en, Bread of heav - en,
jour - ney through; strong De - liv - 'rer, strong De - liv - 'rer,
Ca - naan's side; songs of prais - es, songs of prais - es

feed me till I want no more, feed me till I want no more.
be thou still my strength and shield, be thou still my strength and shield.
I will ev - er give to thee, I will ev - er give to thee.

William Williams, 1745
St. 1 tr. by Peter Williams, 1771
St. 2–3 tr. by William Williams, 1772

CWM RHONDDA 8.7.8.7.8.7.rep.
John Hughes, 1907

Savior, like a Shepherd Lead Us

I am the good shepherd; I know my sheep and my sheep know me. John 10:14

1. Sav - ior, like a shep-herd lead us, much we need thy ten - der care;
2. We are thine; do thou be - friend us, be the guard- ian of our way;
3. Thou hast prom- ised to re - ceive us, poor and sin - ful though we be;
4. Ear - ly let us seek thy fa - vor; ear - ly let us do thy will;

in thy pleas - ant pas - tures feed us, for our use thy folds pre - pare:
keep thy flock, from sin de - fend us, seek us when we go a - stray:
thou hast mer - cy to re - lieve us, grace to cleanse, and pow'r to free:
bless - ed Lord and on - ly Sav - ior, with thy love our bo - soms fill:

bless - ed Je - sus, bless - ed Je - sus, thou hast bought us, thine we are;
bless - ed Je - sus, bless - ed Je - sus, hear, O hear us when we pray;
bless - ed Je - sus, bless - ed Je - sus, let us ear - ly turn to thee;
bless - ed Je - sus, bless - ed Je - sus, thou hast loved us, love us still;

bless - ed Je - sus, bless - ed Je - sus, thou hast bought us, thine we are.
bless - ed Je - sus, bless - ed Je - sus, hear, O hear us when we pray.
bless - ed Je - sus, bless - ed Je - sus, let us ear - ly turn to thee.
bless - ed Je - sus, bless - ed Je - sus, thou hast loved us, love us still.

Hymns for the Young, 1836,
attr. to Dorothy Ann Thrupp; alt.

SHEPHERD 8.7.8.7.4.4.7.rep.
William B. Bradbury, 1859

600 He Leadeth Me: O Blessed Thought!

You hold me by my right hand. You guide me with your counsel. Ps. 73:23, 24

1. He lead - eth me: O bless - ed thought! O words with heav'n - ly
2. Some- times 'mid scenes of deep - est gloom, some - times where E - den's
3. Lord, I would clasp thy hand in mine, nor ev - er mur - mur
4. And when my task on earth is done, when, by thy grace, the

com - fort fraught! What - e'er I do, wher - e'er I be, still
bow - ers bloom, by wa - ters calm, o'er trou - bled sea, still
nor re - pine; con - tent, what - ev - er lot I see, since
vic - t'ry's won, e'en death's cold wave I will not flee, since

'tis God's hand that lead - eth me.
'tis his hand that lead - eth me.
'tis my God that lead - eth me.
God through Jor - dan lead - eth me.

REFRAIN

He lead - eth me, he lead - eth me;

by his own hand he lead - eth me: his faith - ful fol - l'wer

I would be, for by his hand he lead - eth me.

Joseph H. Gilmore, 1862; alt.

HE LEADETH ME L.M.D.
William B. Bradbury, 1864

Jesus, Savior, Pilot Me

601

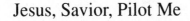

When you pass through the waters, I will be with you. Is. 43:2

1. Je - sus, Sav - ior, pi - lot me o - ver life's tem - pes - tuous sea;
2. As a moth - er stills her child, thou canst hush the o - cean wild;
3. When at last I near the shore, and the fear - ful break - ers roar

un - known waves be - fore me roll, hid - ing rock and treach - 'rous shoal;
bois - t'rous waves o - bey thy will when thou say'st to them, "Be still."
'twixt me and the peace - ful rest, then, while lean - ing on thy breast,

chart and com - pass come from thee: Je - sus, Sav - ior, pi - lot me.
Won - drous Sov - ereign of the sea, Je - sus, Sav - ior, pi - lot me.
may I hear thee say to me, "Fear not, I will pi - lot thee."

Edward Hopper, 1871

PILOT 7.7.7.7.7.7.
John E. Gould, 1871

602

O God, My Faithful God

The one who calls you is faithful and he will do it. 1 Thess. 5:24

1. O God, my faith-ful God, true foun-tain ev-er-flow-ing,
2. Give me the strength to do with read-y heart and will-ing,
3. Keep me from say-ing words that lat-er need re-call-ing;
4. When dan-gers gath-er round, oh, keep me calm and fear-less;

with-out whom noth-ing is, all per-fect gifts be-stow-ing:
what-ev-er you com-mand, my call-ing here ful-fill-ing—
guard me, lest i-dle speech may from my lips be fall-ing:
help me to bear the cross when life seems dark and cheer-less;

give me a health-y frame, and may I have with-in
to do it when I ought, with all my strength; and bless
but when, with-in my place, I must and ought to speak,
help me, as you have taught, to love both great and small,

a con-science free from blame, a soul un-stained by sin.
what-ev-er I have wrought, for you must give suc-cess.
then to my words give grace, lest I of-fend the weak.
and, by your Spir-it's might, to live at peace with all.

Johann Heermann, 1585–1647
Tr. by Catherine Winkworth, 1863; alt.

DARMSTADT (or WAS FRAG' ICH NACH DER WELT) 6.7.6.7.6.6.6.6.
Ahasuerus Fritsch, 1679
Arr. by Johann Sebastian Bach (1685–1750) in *Cantata 45*

He Who Would Valiant Be

Anyone who does not take his cross and follow me is not worthy of me. Matt. 10:38

1. He who would valiant be 'gainst all dis - as - ter,
2. Who so be - set him round with dis - mal sto - ries,
3. Since, Lord, thou dost de - fend us with thy Spir - it,

let him in con - stan - cy fol - low the Mas - ter.
do but them - selves con - found— his strength the more is.
we know we at the end shall life in - her - it.

There's no dis - cour - age - ment shall make him once re - lent
No foes shall stay his might; though he with gi - ants fight,
Then, fan - cies, flee a - way! I'll fear not what men say,

his first a - vowed in - tent to be a pil - grim.
he will make good his right to be a pil - grim.
I'll la - bor night and day to be a pil - grim.

John Bunyan, *The Pilgrim's Progress*, 1678; alt.

ST. DUNSTAN'S 6.5.6.5.6.6.6.5.
Charles Winfred Douglas, 1917; alt. 1990

604 Rejoice, Ye Pure in Heart

Who may ascend the hill of the LORD?... He who has clean hands and a pure heart.
Ps. 24:3, 4

1. Re - joice, ye pure in heart, re - joice, give thanks, and sing;
2. Bright youth and snow-crowned age, strong men and maid- ens meek,
3. With all the an - gel choirs, with all the saints on earth,
4. Yes, on through life's long path, still chant - ing as ye go,

your fes - tal ban - ner wave on high, the cross of Christ your King.
raise high your free, ex - ult - ing song; God's won-drous prais - es speak.
pour out the strains of joy and bliss, true rap - ture, no - blest mirth!
from youth to age, by night and day, in glad- ness and in woe.

REFRAIN

Re - joice, re - joice, re - joice, give thanks, and sing.
Re - joice, re - joice,

5. At last the march shall end,
   the wearied ones shall rest;
   the pilgrims find their Father's house,
   Jerusalem the blest.

6. Then on, ye pure in heart,
   rejoice, give thanks, and sing;
   your glorious banner wave on high,
   the cross of Christ your King.

Edward H. Plumptre, 1865

MARION S.M.ref.
Arthur H. Messiter, 1885

All the Way My Savior Leads Me

605

He goes on ahead of them, and his sheep follow him because they know his voice.
John 10:4

1. All the way my Sav-ior leads me; what have I to ask be-side?
2. All the way my Sav-ior leads me, cheers each wind-ing path I tread,
3. All the way my Sav-ior leads me— O the ful-ness of his love!

Can I doubt his ten-der mer-cy, who through life has been my guide?
gives me grace for ev-'ry tri-al, feeds me with the liv-ing bread.
Per-fect rest to me is prom-ised in my Fa-ther's house a-bove:

Heav'n-ly peace, di-vin-est com-fort, here by faith in him to dwell;
Though my wea-ry steps may fal-ter, and my soul a-thirst may be,
when my spir-it, clothed, im-mor-tal, wings its flight to realms of day,

for I know, what-e'er be-fall me, Je-sus do-eth all things well; well.
gush-ing from the rock be-fore me, lo, a spring of joy I see; see!
this my song through end-less a-ges: Je-sus led me all the way; way!

Fanny J. Crosby, 1875

ALL THE WAY 8.7.8.7.D.
Robert Lowry, 1875; alt. 1990

606 Teach Me Thy Way, O Lord

Teach me your way, O Lord; lead me in a straight path. Ps. 27:11

1. Teach me thy way, O Lord; teach me thy way!
2. When I am sad at heart, teach me thy way!
3. When doubts and fears a - rise, teach me thy way!
4. Long as my life shall last, teach me thy way!

Thy guid - ing grace af - ford; teach me thy way!
When earth - ly joys de - part, teach me thy way!
When storms o'er - spread the skies, teach me thy way!
Wher - e'er my lot be cast, teach me thy way!

Help me to walk a - right, more by faith, less by sight;
In hours of lone - li - ness, in times of dire dis - tress,
Shine through the cloud and rain, thro' sor - row, toil, and pain;
Un - til the race is run, un - til the jour - ney's done,

lead me with heav'n - ly light; teach me thy way!
in fail - ure or suc - cess, teach me thy way!
make thou my path - way plain; teach me thy way!
un - til the crown is won, teach me thy way!

B. Mansell Ramsey, 1919

CAMACHA 6.4.6.4.6.6.6.4
B. Mansell Ramsey, 1919

Thy Loving-kindness, Lord, Is Good and Free

607

Answer me, O LORD, out of the goodness of your love; in your great mercy turn to me.
Ps. 69:16

1. Thy lov - ing - kind - ness, Lord, is good and free:
2. Need - y and sor - row - ful, to thee I cry;
3. With joy the meek shall see my soul re - stored;
4. Let heav'n a - bove his grace and glo - ry tell;

in ten - der mer - cy turn thou un - to me;
let thy sal - va - tion set my soul on high:
your heart shall live, ye saints that seek the Lord;
let earth and sea and all that in them dwell:

hide not thy face from me in my dis - tress;
then I will sing and praise thy ho - ly name;
he helps the need - y and re - gards their cries;
sal - va - tion to his peo - ple God will give,

in mer - cy hear my pray'r, thy ser - vant bless.
my thank - ful song thy mer - cy shall pro - claim.
those in dis - tress the Lord will not de - spise.
and they that love his name with him shall live.

From Psalm 69:16, 17, 29, 30, 32–36
The Psalter, 1912

ELLERS 10.10.10.10.
Edward J. Hopkins, 1869

608

To God My Earnest Voice I Raise

I cry aloud to the LORD; I lift up my voice to the LORD for mercy. Ps. 142:1

1. To God my ear - nest voice I raise, to God my
2. When gloom and sor - row com - pass me, the path I
3. O Lord, my Sav - ior, now to thee, with - out a
4. Be thou my help when trou - bles throng, for I am

voice im - plor - ing prays; be - fore his face my
take is known to thee, and all the toils that
hope be - sides, I flee, to thee, my shel - ter
weak and foes are strong; my cap - tive soul from

grief I show and tell my trou - ble and my woe.
foes do lay to snare thy ser - vant in his way.
from the strife, my por - tion in the land of life.
pris - on bring, and thank - ful prais - es I will sing.

From Psalm 142
The Psalter, 1912

ROCKINGHAM OLD L.M.
Arr. by Edward Miller, 1790

Why Should Cross and Trial Grieve Me?

609

Yet I am always with you; you hold me by my right hand. You guide me with your
counsel, and afterward you will take me into glory. Ps. 73:23, 24

1. Why should cross and tri - al grieve me? Christ is near with his cheer;
2. God oft gives me days of glad - ness; shall I grieve if he give
3. Death can - not de - stroy for- ev - er; from our fears, cares, and tears
4. Lord, my Shep- herd, take me to thee. Thou art mine; I was thine,
5. Thou art mine; I love and own thee. Light of joy, ne'er shall I

nev - er will he leave me. Who can rob me of the heav - en
sea - sons, too, of sad- ness? God is good and tem- pers ev - er
• it will us de - liv - er. It will close life's mourn-ful sto - ry,
e - ven ere I knew thee. I am thine, for thou hast bought me;
from my heart de - throne thee. Sav - ior, let me soon be - hold thee

that God's Son for my own to my faith hath giv - en?
all my ill, and he will whol - ly leave me nev - er.
• make a way that we may en - ter heav'n - ly glo - ry.
lost I stood, but thy blood free sal - va - tion brought me.
face to face; may thy grace ev - er - more en - fold me!

Paul Gerhardt, 1653, cento
Trans. composite, based on John Kelly, 1867

WARUM SOLLT' ICH MICH DENN GRÄMEN 8.3.3.6.8.3.3.6.
Johann G. Ebeling, 1666

610 "Take Up Your Cross," the Savior Said

If anyone would come after me, he must deny himself and take up his cross
and follow me. Matt. 16:24

1. "Take up your cross," the Sav - ior said, "if you would
2. Take up your cross; let not its weight fill your weak
3. Take up your cross; nor heed the shame, and let your
4. Take up your cross, then, in his strength, and calm - ly
5. Take up your cross, and fol - low on, nor think till

my dis - ci - ple be; take up your cross with
soul with vain a - larm; his strength shall bear your
fool - ish pride be still; your Lord re - fused not
sin's wild del - uge brave; 'twill guide you to a
death to lay it down; for on - ly he who

will - ing heart, and hum - bly fol - low af - ter me."
spir - it up, and brace your heart, and nerve your arm.
bet - ter home, it points to glo - ry o'er the grave.
bears the cross may hope to wear the glo - rious crown.
e'en to die up - on a cross, on Cal - v'ry's hill.

Charles W. Everest, 1833
Mod.

QUEBEC L.M.
Henry Baker, 1854

I Want Jesus to Walk with Me

611

When you pass through the waters, I will be with you. Is. 43:2

1. I want Je - sus to walk with me; I want
2. In my tri - als, Lord, walk with me; in my
3. When I'm in trou - ble, Lord, walk with me; when I'm in

Je - sus to walk with me; all a - long my
tri - als, Lord, walk with me; when my heart is
trou - ble, Lord, walk with me; when my head is

pil - grim jour - ney, Lord, I want Je - sus to walk with me.
al - most break - ing, Lord, I want Je - sus to walk with me.
bowed in sor - row, Lord, I want Je - sus to walk with me.

Spiritual

WALK WITH ME Irreg.
Spiritual
Arr. by John F. Wilson, 1964; alt. 1990

612 O Lord, Be Gracious to Me

My soul is in anguish. How long, O LORD, how long? Ps. 6:3

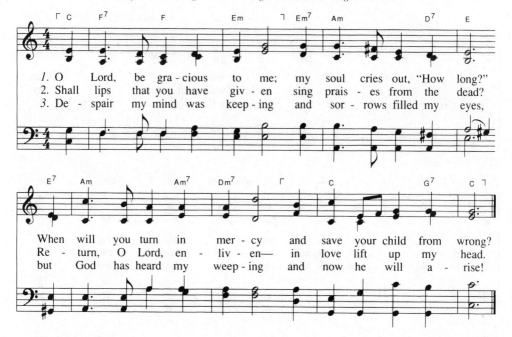

1. O Lord, be gra - cious to me; my soul cries out, "How long?"
2. Shall lips that you have giv - en sing prais - es from the dead?
3. De - spair my mind was keep - ing and sor - rows filled my eyes,

When will you turn in mer - cy and save your child from wrong?
Re - turn, O Lord, en - liv - en— in love lift up my head.
but God has heard my weep - ing and now he will a - rise!

Based on Psalm 6
Michael Perry, 1973
Text and tune © 1973, Hope Publishing Co. All rights reserved. Used by permission.

O LORD, BE GRACIOUS 7.6.7.6.
Norman L. Warren, 1973

613 Give Thanks unto the Lord, Jehovah

Give thanks to the LORD, for he is good; his love endures forever. Ps. 118:1

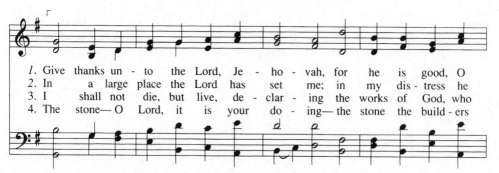

1. Give thanks un - to the Lord, Je - ho - vah, for he is good, O
2. In a large place the Lord has set me; in my dis - tress he
3. I shall not die, but live, de - clar - ing the works of God, who
4. The stone— O Lord, it is your do - ing— the stone the build - ers

praise his name! Let Is - rael say, "The Lord be prais - ed;
heard my cry. I will not fear; the Lord is with me—
tried me sore, and chas - tened me, but in his mer - cy
did de - spise, is made the head - stone of the cor - ner,

his mer - cy ev - er is the same." Let Aa - ron's house now praise Je -
what can man do, when God is nigh? The Lord is chief a - mong my
not un - to death has giv'n me o'er. The gates of righ - teous - ness set
and it is mar - v'lous in our eyes. This is the day, of days most

ho - vah; the Lord is good, O praise his name. Let all that
help - ers; and I shall see my foes o'er - thrown: far bet - ter
o - pen, the gate of God! I'll en - ter in to praise you,
glo - rious, the Lord has made; we'll joy and sing. Send now pros -

fear the Lord ex - tol him; his mer - cy ev - er is the same.
than in man or princ - es, my trust I place in God a - lone.
Lord, who pray'r have an - swered, and have saved me from all my sin.
per - i - ty, we pray, Lord; and, O our God, sal - va - tion bring!

From Psalm 118:1–9, 17–25
Anon.; alt. 1990, mod.

RENDEZ A DIEU 9.8.9.8.D.
Strasbourg Psalter, 1545
Arr. in Louis Bourgeois's *Genevan Psalter,* 1551; alt. 1990

614
Now Israel May Say, and That in Truth

If the LORD had not been on our side ... they would have swallowed us alive.
Ps. 124:2, 3

1. Now Is - ra - el may say, and that in truth, if that the
2. Yea, when their wrath a - gainst us fierce - ly rose, the swell - ing
3. Blest be the Lord who made us not their prey: as from the

Lord had not our right main - tained, if that the Lord had
tide had o'er us spread its wave, the rag - ing stream had
snare a bird es - cap - eth free, their net is rent and

not with us re - mained, when cru - el men a - gainst us
then be - come our grave, the surg - ing flood, in proud - ly
so es - caped are we: our on - ly help is in Je -

rose to strive, we sure - ly had been swal - lowed up a - live.
swell - ing roll, most sure - ly then had o - ver - whelmed our soul.
ho - vah's name, who made the earth and all the heav'n - ly frame.

From Psalm 124
The Psalter, 1912

OLD 124TH 10.10.10.10.10.
Louis Bourgeois, 1551

Come, Ye Disconsolate, Where'er Ye Languish 615

*Let us then approach the throne of grace with confidence, so that we may receive
mercy and find grace to help us in our time of need.* Heb. 4:16

1. Come, ye dis - con - so - late, wher - e'er ye lan - guish,
2. Joy of the com - fort - less, light of the stray - ing,
3. Here see the Bread of Life; see wa - ters flow - ing

come to the mer - cy seat, fer - vent - ly kneel:
hope of the pen - i - tent, fade - less and pure!
forth from the throne of God, pure from a - bove:

here bring your wound - ed hearts, here tell your an - guish;
Here speaks the Com - fort - er, in mer - cy say - ing,
come to the feast pre - pared; come, ev - er know - ing

earth has no sor - rows that heav'n can - not heal.
"Earth has no sor - rows that heav'n can - not cure."
earth has no sor - rows but heav'n can re - move.

St. 1–2, Thomas Moore, 1816; alt.
St. 3, Thomas Hastings, 1832

ALMA 11.10.11.10.
Samuel Webbe, 1792; arr.

616 Leaning on the Everlasting Arms

The eternal God is your refuge, and underneath are the everlasting arms. Deut. 33:27

1. What a fel - low - ship, what a joy di - vine,
2. Oh, how sweet to walk in this pil - grim way,
3. What have I to dread, what have I to fear,

lean - ing on the ev - er - last - ing arms;
lean - ing on the ev - er - last - ing arms;
lean - ing on the ev - er - last - ing arms?

what a bless - ed - ness, what a peace is mine,
oh, how bright the path grows from day to day,
I have bless - ed peace with my Lord so near,

lean - ing on the ev - er - last - ing arms.
lean - ing on the ev - er - last - ing arms.
lean - ing on the ev - er - last - ing arms.

CONSOLATION

REFRAIN

Lean - ing, lean - ing,
Lean - ing on Je - sus, lean - ing on Je - sus,

safe and se - cure from all a - larms;

lean - ing, lean - ing,
lean - ing on Je - sus, lean - ing on Je - sus,

lean - ing on the ev - er - last - ing arms.

Elisha A. Hoffman, 1887

SHOWALTER 10.9.10.9.ref.
Anthony J. Showalter, 1887

617

My Anchor Holds

We have this hope as an anchor for the soul, firm and secure. Heb. 6:19

1. Though the an - gry surg - es roll on my tem - pest - driv - en soul,
2. Might - y tides a - bout me sweep, per - ils lurk with - in the deep,
3. I can feel the an - chor fast as I meet each sud - den blast,
4. Trou - bles al - most 'whelm the soul; griefs like bil - lows o'er me roll;

I am peace - ful, for I know, wild - ly though the winds may blow,
an - gry clouds o'er - shade the sky, and the tem - pest ris - es high;
and the ca - ble, though un - seen, bears the heav - y strain be - tween;
tempt - ers seek to lure a - stray, storms ob - scure the light of day:

I've an an - chor safe and sure, that can ev - er - more en - dure.
still I stand the tem - pest's shock, for my an - chor grips the Rock.
through the storm I safe - ly ride, till the turn - ing of the tide.
but in Christ I can be bold, I've an an - chor that shall hold.

CONSOLATION

REFRAIN

And it holds, my an-chor holds;
And it holds, my an-chor holds;

blow your wild - est, then, O gale,
blow your wild - - est, then, O gale,

on my bark so small and frail: by his grace I shall not fail,

for my an - chor holds, my an-chor holds.
for my an-chor holds, it firm-ly holds,

W. C. Martin; alt.

ANCHOR 7.7.7.7.7.7.ref.
Daniel B. Towner, 1850–1919

618

His Eye Is on the Sparrow

Are not two sparrows sold for a penny? Yet not one of them will fall to the ground apart from the will of your Father. Matt. 10:29

Unison

1. Why should I feel dis - cour - aged, why should the shad - ows come, why should my heart be lone - ly and long for heav'n and home, when Je - sus is my por - tion?

2. "Let not your heart be trou - bled," his ten - der word I hear, and rest - ing on his good - ness, I lose my doubt and fear; tho' by the path he lead - eth,

3. When - ev - er I am tempt - ed, when - ev - er clouds a - rise, when songs give place to sigh - ing, when hope with - in me dies, I draw the clos - er to him,

CONSOLATION

My con - stant friend is he: his eye is on the spar- row,
but one step I may see: his eye is on the spar- row,
from care he sets me free; his eye is on the spar- row,

and I know he watch - es me; his eye is on the
and I know he watch - es me; his eye is on the
and I know he cares for me; his eye is on the

spar - row, and I know he watch - es me.
spar - row, and I know he watch - es me.
spar - row, and I know he cares for me.

Civilla D. Martin, 1863–1948

SPARROW 7.6.7.6.7.6.7.7.7.7.
Charles H. Gabriel. 1856–1932: alt. 1990

619 A Shelter in the Time of Storm

The shadow of a great rock in a thirsty land. Is. 32:2

1. The Lord's our rock, in him we hide, a shel-ter in the time of storm,
2. A shade by day, de-fense by night, a shel-ter in the time of storm;
3. The rag-ing storms may round us beat, a shel-ter in the time of storm;
4. O Rock di-vine, O Ref-uge dear, a shel-ter in the time of storm;

se-cure what-ev-er ill be-tide, a shel-ter in the time of storm.
no fears a-larm, no foes af-fright, a shel-ter in the time of storm.
we'll nev-er leave our safe re-treat, a shel-ter in the time of storm.
be thou our help-er ev-er near, a shel-ter in the time of storm.

REFRAIN

Oh, Je-sus is a rock in a wea-ry land, a wea-ry land, a wea-ry land;

oh, Je-sus is a rock in a wea-ry land, a shel-ter in the time of storm.

Vernon J. Charlesworth, ca. 1880
Alt. by Ira D. Sankey, 1885

SHELTER L.M.ref.
Ira D. Sankey, 1885

O Lord, I Love You, My Shield, My Tower

I love you, O Lord, my strength. Ps. 18:1

1. O Lord, I love you, my shield, my tow'r, my strong-hold, my rock, my sav-ing pow'r. I wor-ship you! Bless your ho-ly name! What un-ceas-ing praise your mer-cies claim!

2. Cords of death had bound my heart with fear; tid-al waves of Sa-tan crest-ed near. "God, my God," I cried, "hear from your throne; save me from these depths, make mer-cy known!"

3. Sav-ing might brought an-swer, Lord Most High. Dark your path; your storm clouds swept the sky; light-ning flashed, deep thun-der spoke your word. Wa-ters part-ed; death your sum-mons heard.

4. You came down, al-might-y Lord, my stay, drew me up and drove my foes a-way. Your right hand put Sa-tan's host to flight, then clasped me, em-braced in your de-light.

5. Now among all nations I would sing,
   praising our anointed Lord, our King.
   Hear his cry of triumph from the grave,
   see him leap the wall of death to save.

6. His the righteousness that claims reward,
   his the saving coming of the Lord.
   Hail him, Victor in that deadly strife:
   Jesus is our rock, our Prince of life.

From Psalm 18
Edmund P. Clowney, 1989

SAINT-SAËNS 9.9.9.9.
From Camille Saint-Saëns, *Symphony No. 3 in C Minor*, 1886
Arr. by Lawrence C. Roff, 1990

621 Sometimes a Light Surprises

For you who revere my name, the sun of righteousness will rise with healing
in its wings. Mal. 4:2

1. Some - times a light sur - pris - es the Chris - tian while he sings;
2. In ho - ly con - tem - pla - tion we sweet - ly then pur - sue
3. It can bring with it noth - ing but he will bear us through;
4. Though vine nor fig tree nei - ther their wont - ed fruit shall bear,

it is the Lord, who ris - es with heal - ing in his wings:
the theme of God's sal - va - tion, and find it ev - er new;
who gives the lil - ies cloth - ing will clothe his peo - ple too;
though all the field should with - er, nor flocks nor herds be there;

when com - forts are de - clin - ing, he grants the soul a - gain
set free from pres - ent sor - row, we cheer - ful - ly can say,
be - neath the spread - ing heav - ens no crea - ture but is fed;
yet God the same a - bid - eth, his praise shall tune my voice,

a sea - son of clear shin - ing, to cheer it af - ter rain.
"Let the un - known to - mor - row bring with it what it may."
and he who feeds the ra - vens will give his chil - dren bread.
for, while in him con - fid - ing, I can - not but re - joice.

William Cowper, 1779

BENTLEY 7.6.7.6.D.
John Hullah, 1867

I Waited for the Lord Most High

I proclaim righteousness in the great assembly. Ps. 40:9

1. I wait-ed for the Lord Most High, and he in-clined to hear my
2. A new and joy-ful song of praise he taught my thank-ful heart to
3. O Lord my God, how man-i-fold your won-drous works which I be-
4. Be-fore your peo-ple I con-fess the won-ders of your righ-teous-

cry; he took me from de-struc-tion's pit and from the mir-y clay;
raise; and man-y, see-ing me re-stored, shall fear the Lord and trust;
hold, and all your lov-ing, gra-cious thought you have be-stowed on man;
ness; you know, O Lord, that I have made your great sal-va-tion known,

up-on a rock he set my feet, and stead-fast made my way.
and blest are they that trust the Lord, the hum-ble and the just.
to count your mer-cies I have sought, but bound-less is their span.
your truth and faith-ful-ness dis-played, your lov-ing-kind-ness shown.

5. Withhold not now your grace from me,
O Lord, your mercy let me see,
to me your loving-kindness show,
your truth be still my stay;
let them preserve me where I go,
and keep me ev'ry day.

6. Let all who seek to see your face
be glad and joyful in your grace;
let those who your salvation love
forevermore proclaim:
O praise the Lord who dwells above,
and magnify his name.

Psalm 40:1–5, 9–11, 16
The Psalter. 1912: alt. 1990. mod.

DUNSTAN 8.8.8.6.8.6.
Joseph Barnby, 1883

623 Moment by Moment

Our Lord Jesus Christ ... died for us so that, whether we are awake or asleep, we may live together with him. 1 Thess. 5:9, 10

1. Dy - ing with Je - sus, by death reck - oned mine; liv - ing with
2. Nev - er a tri - al that he is not there, nev - er a
3. Nev - er a weak - ness that he doth not feel, nev - er a

Je - sus, a new life di - vine; look - ing to Je - sus till
bur - den that he doth not bear, nev - er a sor - row that
sick - ness that he can - not heal; mo - ment by mo - ment, in

glo - ry doth shine, mo - ment by mo - ment, O Lord, I am thine.
he doth not share, mo - ment by mo - ment, I'm un - der his care;
woe or in weal, Je - sus, my Sav - ior, a - bides with me still.

REFRAIN

Mo - ment by mo - ment I'm kept in his love; mo - ment by

mo - ment I've life from a - bove; Look - ing to Je - sus till

glo - ry doth shine; mo - ment by mo - ment, O Lord, I am thine.

Daniel W. Whittle, 1893

WHITTLE 10.10.10.10.ref.
May Whittle Moody, 1893

Through All the Changing Scenes of Life   624

I will extol the LORD at all times; his praise will always be on my lips. Ps. 34:1

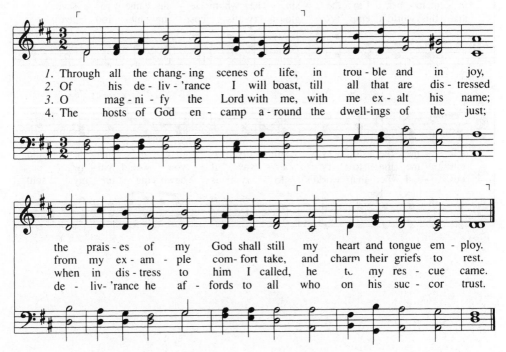

1. Through all the chang-ing scenes of life, in trou - ble and in joy,
2. Of his de - liv - 'rance I will boast, till all that are dis - tressed
3. O mag - ni - fy the Lord with me, with me ex - alt his name;
4. The hosts of God en - camp a - round the dwell-ings of the just;

the prais - es of my God shall still my heart and tongue em - ploy.
from my ex - am - ple com - fort take, and charm their griefs to rest.
when in dis - tress to him I called, he to my res - cue came.
de - liv - 'rance he af - fords to all who on his suc - cor trust.

5. O make but trial of his love;
experience will decide
how blest they are, and only they,
who in his truth confide.

6. Fear him, ye saints, and you will then
have nothing else to fear:
make you his service your delight;
he'll make your wants his care.

From Psalm 34:1–4, 7–9
Tate and Brady's *New Version,* 1696, 1698

DOWNS C.M.
Lowell Mason, 1832

625 Tell Me the Old, Old Story

The message of the cross ... to us who are being saved ... is the power of God.
1 Cor. 1:18

1. Tell me the old, old story of un-seen things a-bove,
2. Tell me the sto-ry soft-ly, with ear-nest tones and grave;
3. Tell me the same old sto-ry, when you have cause to fear

of Je-sus and his glo-ry, of Je-sus and his love:
re-mem-ber, I'm the sin-ner whom Je-sus came to save:
that this world's emp-ty glo-ry is cost-ing me too dear:

tell me the sto-ry sim-ply, as to a lit-tle child,
tell me the sto-ry al-ways, if you would real-ly be,
yes, and when that world's glo-ry is dawn-ing on my soul,

for I am weak and wea - ry, and help - less and de - filed.
in an - y time of trou - ble, a com - fort - er to me.
tell me the old, old sto - ry, "Christ Je - sus makes thee whole."

REFRAIN

Tell me the old, old sto - ry, tell me the old, old sto - ry,

tell me the old, old sto - ry of Je - sus and his love.

Katherine Hankey, 1866; alt.

EVANGEL 7.6.7.6.D.ref.
William H. Doane. 1869

626 O Lord, by Grace Delivered

I will exalt you, O LORD, for you lifted me out of the depths. Ps. 30:1

1. O Lord, by grace de - liv - ered, I now with songs ex - tol;
2. His ho - ly name re - mem - ber; you saints, Je - ho - vah praise;
3. In pros - p'rous days I boast - ed: un - moved I shall re - main;
4. What prof - it if I per - ish, if life you do not spare?
5. My grief is turned to glad - ness, to you my thanks I raise,

my foes you have not suf - fered to glo - ry o'er my fall.
his an - ger lasts a mo - ment, his fa - vor all our days;
• for, Lord, by your good fa - vor my cause you did main - tain;
Shall dust re - peat your prais - es, shall it your truth de - clare?
who have re - moved my sor - row and gird - ed me with praise;

O Lord, my God, I sought you, and you did heal and save;
for sor - row, like a pil - grim, may tar - ry for a night,
• I soon was sore - ly trou - bled, for you did hide your face;
O Lord, on me have mer - cy, and my pe - ti - tion hear;
and now, no lon - ger si - lent, my heart your praise will sing;

you, Lord, from death did ran - som and keep me from the grave.
but joy the heart will glad - den when dawns the morn - ing light.
• I cried to you, Je - ho - vah, I sought Je - ho - vah's grace.
that you may be my help - er, in mer - cy, Lord, ap - pear.
O Lord, my God, for - ev - er my thanks to you I bring.

From Psalm 30
The Psalter, 1912; alt. 1990, mod.

NOEL C.M.D.
Traditional English melody
Arr. by Arthur S. Sullivan, 1874

Behold the Throne of Grace! 627

*Let us then approach the throne of grace with confidence, so that we may receive
mercy and find grace to help us in our time of need.* Heb. 4:16

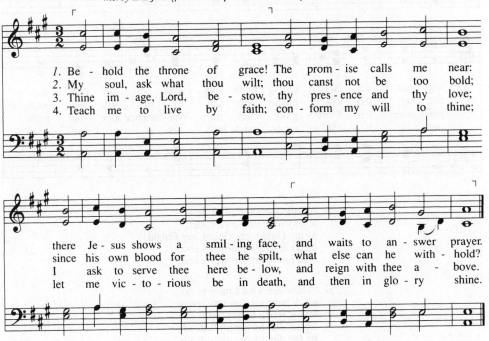

1. Be - hold the throne of grace! The prom - ise calls me near:
2. My soul, ask what thou wilt; thou canst not be too bold;
3. Thine im - age, Lord, be - stow, thy pres - ence and thy love;
4. Teach me to live by faith; con - form my will to thine;

there Je - sus shows a smil - ing face, and waits to an - swer prayer.
since his own blood for thee he spilt, what else can he with - hold?
I ask to serve thee here be - low, and reign with thee a - bove.
let me vic - to - rious be in death, and then in glo - ry shine.

John Newton, 1779

STATE STREET S.M.
Jonathan C. Woodman. 1844

628

Come, My Soul, Thy Suit Prepare

Ask and it will be given to you. Matt. 7:7

1. Come, my soul, thy suit prepare: Jesus loves to an-swer prayer; he himself has bid thee pray, therefore will not say thee nay; therefore will not say thee nay.

2. Thou art coming to a King, large petitions with thee bring; for his grace and pow'r are such, none can ever ask too much; none can ever ask too much.

3. With my burden I begin: "Lord, remove this load of sin; let thy blood, for sinners spilt, set my conscience free from guilt; set my conscience free from guilt.

4. "Lord, I come to thee for rest, take possession of my breast; there thy blood-bought right maintain, and without a rival reign; and without a rival reign.

5. "While I am a pilgrim here,
let thy love my spirit cheer;
as my Guide, my Guard, my Friend,
lead me to my journey's end;
lead me to my journey's end.

6. "Show me what I have to do,
ev'ry hour my strength renew:
let me live a life of faith,
let me die thy people's death;
let me die thy people's death."

John Newton, 1779

HENDON 7.7.7.7.rep.
Henri A. César Malan, 1827

What a Friend We Have in Jesus

629

Do not be anxious about anything, but in everything, by prayer and petition,
with thanksgiving, present your requests to God. Phil. 4:6

1. What a Friend we have in Je - sus, all our sins and griefs to bear!
2. Have we tri - als and temp - ta - tions? Is there trou - ble an - y - where?
3. Are we weak and heav - y - lad - en, cum - bered with a load of care?

What a priv - i - lege to car - ry ev - 'ry - thing to God in prayer!
We should nev - er be dis - cour - aged: take it to the Lord in prayer!
Pre - cious Sav - ior, still our ref - uge— take it to the Lord in prayer!

O what peace we of - ten for - feit, O what need - less pain we bear,
Can we find a friend so faith - ful, who will all our sor - rows share?
Do thy friends de - spise, for - sake thee? Take it to the Lord in prayer!

all be - cause we do not car - ry ev - 'ry - thing to God in prayer.
Je - sus knows our ev - 'ry weak - ness— take it to the Lord in prayer!
In his arms he'll take and shield thee; thou wilt find a so - lace there.

Joseph Scriven, ca. 1855

WHAT A FRIEND 8.7.8.7.D.
Charles C. Converse. 1868

630 Eternal Father, Strong to Save

You rule over the surging sea; when its waves mount up, you still them. Ps. 89:9

1. E - ter - nal Fa - ther, strong to save, whose arm doth bind the
2. O Sav - ior, whose al - might - y word the winds and waves sub -
3. O sa - cred Spir - it, who didst brood up - on the cha - os
4. O Trin - i - ty of love and pow'r, our breth - ren shield in

rest - less wave, who bidd'st the might - y o - cean deep its
mis - sive heard, who walk - edst on the foam - ing deep and
dark and rude, who badd'st its an - gry tu - mult cease, and
dan - ger's hour; from rock and tem - pest, fire and foe, pro -

own ap - point - ed lim - its keep: O hear us when we
calm a - mid its rage didst sleep: O hear us when we
gav - est light and life and peace: O hear us when we
tect them where - so - e'er they go; and ev - er let there

cry to thee for those in per - il on the sea.
cry to thee for those in per - il on the sea.
cry to thee for those in per - il on the sea.
rise to thee glad hymns of praise from land and sea.

William Whiting, 1860, 1869

MELITA 8.8.8.8.8.8.
John B. Dykes, 1861

From Every Stormy Wind That Blows

631

There, above the cover between the two cherubim that are over the ark of the Testimony, I will meet with you. Ex. 25:22

1. From ev - 'ry storm - y wind that blows, from ev - 'ry
2. There is a place where Je - sus sheds the oil of
3. There is a spot where spir - its blend, where friend holds
4. Ah, whith - er could we flee for aid, when tempt - ed,

swell - ing tide of woes, there is a calm, a
glad - ness on our heads, a place than all be -
fel - low - ship with friend, tho' sun - dered far; by
des - o - late, dis - mayed, or how the hosts of

sure re - treat; 'tis found be - neath the mer - cy seat.
sides more sweet; it is the blood- stained mer - cy seat.
faith they meet a - round the com - mon mer - cy seat.
hell de - feat, had suf - f'ring saints no mer - cy seat?

5. There, there on eagle wings we soar,
and time and sense seem all no more,
and heav'n comes down our souls to greet,
and glory crowns the mercy seat.

6. O may my hand forget her skill,
my tongue be silent, cold, and still,
this bounding heart forget to beat,
if I forget the mercy seat.

Hugh Stowell, 1828, 1831

RETREAT L.M.
Thomas Hastings, 1842
Arr. by Rhys Thomas, 1916

632

When the Weary, Seeking Rest

Hear from heaven, your dwelling place, and when you hear, forgive. 1 Kings 8:30

1. When the wea - ry, seek - ing rest, to thy good - ness flee;
2. When the strang - er asks a home, all his toils to end;
3. When the world - ling, sick at heart, lifts his soul a - bove;

when the heav - y - lad - en cast all their load on thee;
when the hun - gry crav - eth food, and the poor a friend;
when the prod - i - gal looks back to his Fa - ther's love;

when the trou - bled, seek- ing peace, on thy name shall call; when the sin - ner,
when the wid - ow weeps to thee, sad and lone and low; when the or - phan
when the proud man, in his pride, stoops to seek thy face; when the bur - dened

REFRAIN

seek - ing life, at thy feet shall fall:
brings to thee all his or - phan woe: hear then in love, O
brings his guilt to thy throne of grace:

Lord, the cry in heav'n, thy dwell - ing place on high.

Horatius Bonar, 1866

INTERCESSION NEW 7.5.7.5.7.5.7.5.8.8.
William H. Callcott, 1867
Refrain adapted from Mendelssohn, 1846

Father, We Thank You for the Night 633

"Love the Lord your God with all your heart." ... "Love your neighbor as yourself."
Matt. 22:37, 39

1. Fa - ther, we thank you for the night, and for the
2. Help us to do the things we should, to be to
3. Lord, keep our lips from sin to - day; help us to

love - ly morn - ing light; for rest and food and
oth - ers kind and good; in all we do, in
trust and to o - bey. Lord, keep our feet from

lov - ing care, and all that makes the day so fair.
work or play, to grow more lov - ing ev - 'ry day.
e - vil ways; and fill our hearts with joy and praise.

Sts. 1–2, Rebecca J. Weston, 1885
St. 3, Helen K. Noordewier, 1949
Alt. 1990, mod.

ONSLOW L.M.
Daniel Batchellor, 1885
Arr. by E.R.B., 1904; alt. 1990

634   Sweet Hour of Prayer

One day Peter and John were going up to the temple at the time of prayer. Acts. 3:1

1. Sweet hour of prayer, sweet hour of prayer, that calls me from a world of care,
2. Sweet hour of prayer, sweet hour of prayer, the joys I feel, the bliss I share
3. Sweet hour of prayer, sweet hour of prayer, thy wings shall my pe - ti - tion bear

and bids me at my Fa-ther's throne, make all my wants and wish - es known!
of those whose anx- ious spir - its burn with strong de - sires for thy re - turn!
to him, whose truth and faith - ful - ness en - gage the wait - ing soul to bless:

In sea - sons of dis - tress and grief, my soul has of - ten found re - lief,
With such I has - ten to the place where God, my Sav - ior, shows his face,
and since he bids me seek his face, be - lieve his Word, and trust his grace,

and oft es- caped the tempt - er's snare, by thy re - turn, sweet hour of prayer.
and glad - ly take my sta - tion there, and wait for thee, sweet hour of prayer.
I'll cast on him my ev - 'ry care, and wait for thee, sweet hour of prayer.

William W. Walford, ca. 1842

SWEET HOUR L.M.D.
William B. Bradbury, 1859

How Good It Is to Thank the Lord

635

It is good to praise the Lord and make music to your name, O Most High. Ps. 92:1

1. How good it is to thank the Lord, and praise to you, Most
2. O Lord, with joy my heart ex-pands be-fore the won-ders
3. When as the grass the wick-ed grow, when sin-ners flour-ish
4. The righ-teous man shall flour-ish well, and in the house of

High, ac-cord, to show your love with morn-ing light, and
of your hands; great works, Je-ho-vah, you have wrought, ex-
here be-low, then is there end-less ru-in nigh, but
God shall dwell; he shall be like a good-ly tree, and

tell your faith-ful-ness each night; yea, good it is your
ceed-ing deep your ev-'ry thought; a fool-ish man knows
you, O Lord, are throned on high; your foes shall fall be-
all his life shall fruit-ful be; for righ-teous is the

praise to sing, and all our sweet-est mu-sic bring.
not their worth, nor he whose mind is of the earth.
fore your might, the wick-ed shall be put to flight.
Lord and just, he is my rock, in him I trust.

From Psalm 92:1–9, 12–15
The Psalter, 1912; mod.

ST. PETERSBURG 8.8.8.8.8.8.
Dmitri Bortniansky, 1825

636 **Can a Little Child like Me**

Always giving thanks to God the Father for everything. Eph. 5:20

Fa - ther in heav - en, we thank thee!

Attr. to Mary Mapes Dodge, 1831–1905

THANKSGIVING (BASSWOOD) 7.7.7.7.7.7.ref.
W. K. Basswood

What Shall I Render to My God

637

How can I repay the LORD for all his goodness to me? Ps. 116:12

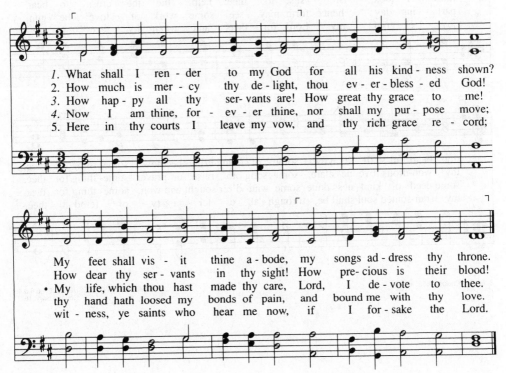

1. What shall I ren - der to my God for all his kind - ness shown?
2. How much is mer - cy thy de - light, thou ev - er - bless - ed God!
3. How hap - py all thy ser - vants are! How great thy grace to me!
4. Now I am thine, for - ev - er thine, nor shall my pur - pose move;
5. Here in thy courts I leave my vow, and thy rich grace re - cord;

My feet shall vis - it thine a - bode, my songs ad - dress thy throne.
How dear thy ser - vants in thy sight! How pre - cious is their blood!
My life, which thou hast made thy care, Lord, I de - vote to thee.
thy hand hath loosed my bonds of pain, and bound me with thy love.
wit - ness, ye saints who hear me now, if I for - sake the Lord.

From Psalm 116:12–19
Isaac Watts. 1719

DOWNS C.M.
Lowell Mason, 1832

638 Savior, Thy Dying Love Thou Gavest Me

In view of God's mercy ... offer your bodies as living sacrifices, holy and pleasing
to God—this is your spiritual act of worship. Rom. 12:1

1. Sav - ior, thy dy - ing love thou gav - est me, nor should I
2. O'er the blest mer - cy seat, plead - ing for me, up - ward in
3. Give me a faith - ful heart, guid - ed by thee, that each de -
4. All that I am and have— thy gifts so free— ev - er in

aught with- hold, dear Lord, from thee: in love my soul would bow,
faith I look, Je - sus, to thee: help me the cross to bear,
part - ing day hence- forth may see some work of love be - gun,
joy or grief, my Lord, for thee; and when thy face I see,

my heart ful - fil its vow, some of- f'ring bring thee now, some- thing for thee.
thy won-drous love de- clare, some song to raise, or prayer, some- thing for thee.
some deed of kind- ness done, some wan- d'rer sought and won, some- thing for thee.
my ran-somed soul shall be, through all e - ter - ni - ty, of - fered to thee.

S. Dryden Phelps, 1862; alt.

SOMETHING FOR JESUS 6.4.6.4.6.6.6.4.
Robert Lowry, 1871

Thy Life Was Given for Me

639

Christ's love compels us ... that those who live should no longer live for themselves
but for him who died for them and was raised again. 2 Cor. 5:14, 15

1. Thy life was giv'n for me, thy blood, O Lord, was shed,
2. Long years were spent for me in wea - ri - ness and woe,
3. Thou, Lord, hast borne for me more than my tongue can tell
4. And thou hast brought to me down from thy home a - bove
5. O let my life be giv'n, my years for thee be spent;

that I might ran - somed be, and quick - ened from the dead:
that through e - ter - ni - ty thy glo - ry I might know:
• of bit - t'rest ag - o - ny, to res - cue me from hell;
sal - va - tion full and free, thy par - don and thy love:
world - fet - ters all be riv'n and joy with suf - f'ring blent:

thy life was giv'n for me; what have I giv'n for thee?
long years were spent for me; have I spent one for thee?
• thou suf - feredst all for me; what have I borne for thee?
great gifts thou brought - est me; what have I brought to thee?
thou gav'st thy - self for me, I give my - self to thee.

Frances R. Havergal, 1858
Recast in *Church Hymns*, 1871

DEVOTION 6.6.6.D.
John H. Gower, 1895

640

My Tribute

Not to us, O LORD, not to us but to your name be the glory, because of your love and faithfulness. Ps. 115:1

How can I say thanks for the things you have done for me?

Things so un-de-served, yet you gave to prove your love for me; the

voic-es of a mil-lion an-gels could not ex-press my grat-i-tude.

All that I am, and ev-er hope to be, I owe it all to thee.

To God be the glo-ry, to God be the glo-ry,

THANKFULNESS

to God be the glo - ry for the things he has done.

With his blood he has saved me; with his pow'r he has raised me;

to God be the glo - ry for the things he has done.

Just let me live my life— let it be pleas - ing, Lord, to thee;

and if I gain an - y praise, let it go to Cal - va - ry. With his

Andraé Crouch, 1971

MY TRIBUTE Irreg.
Andraé Crouch, 1971

641 How Long Wilt Thou Forget Me

How long, O LORD? Will you forget me forever? Ps. 13:1

1. How long wilt thou for - get me, O Lord, thou God of grace?
2. O Lord my God, be - hold me, and hear my ear - nest cries;
3. But I with ex - pec - ta - tion have on thy grace re - lied;

How long shall fears be - set me, while dark - ness hides thy face?
lest sleep of death en - fold me, en - light - en thou mine eyes;
my heart in thy sal - va - tion shall still with joy con - fide;

How long shall griefs dis - tress me and turn my day to night?
lest now my foe in - sult - ing should boast of his suc - cess,
and I with voice of sing - ing will praise the Lord a - bove,

How long shall foes op - press me and tri - umph in their might?
and en - e - mies ex - ult - ing re - joice in my dis - tress.
who, rich - est boun - ties bring - ing, has dealt with me in love.

From Psalm 13
The Psalter, 1912

ANGEL'S STORY 7.6.7.6.D.
Arthur H. Mann, 1883

Be Thou My Vision

Whatever was to my profit I now consider loss for the sake of Christ. Phil. 3:7

1. Be thou my vi - sion, O Lord of my heart; naught be all else to me, save that thou art— thou my best thought by day or by night, wak - ing or sleep- ing, thy pres - ence my light.

2. Be thou my wis - dom, and thou my true word; I ev - er with thee and thou with me, Lord; thou my great Fa - ther, I thy true son; thou in me dwell- ing, and I with thee one.

3. Be thou my bat - tle shield, sword for my fight; be thou my dig - ni - ty, thou my de - light, thou my soul's shel - ter, thou my high tow'r: raise thou me heav'n-ward, O Pow'r of my pow'r.

4. Rich - es I heed not, nor man's emp- ty praise, thou mine in - her - i - tance, now and al - ways: thou and thou on - ly, first in my heart, High King of heav - en, my trea - sure thou art.

5. High King of heav - en, my vic - to - ry won, may I reach heav - en's joys, O bright heav'n's Sun! Heart of my own heart, what - ev - er be - fall, still be my vi - sion, O Rul - er of all.

Ancient Irish poem, ca. 8th cent.
Tr. by Mary E. Byrne, 1905
Versified by Eleanor H. Hull, 1912

SLANE 10.10.10.10.
Traditional Irish melody
Arr. by David Evans, 1927

643   Judge Me, God of My Salvation

Vindicate me, O God, and plead my cause. Ps. 43:1

1. Judge me, God of my sal - va - tion, plead my cause, for
2. For my strength, my God, thou art:...... why am I cast
3. At thy sa - cred al - tar bend - ing, God, my God, my

thee I trust: hear my ear - nest sup - pli - ca - tion,
off by thee in the sor - row of my heart,......
bound - less joy, harp and voice, in wor - ship blend - ing,

save me from my foes un - just. O my soul, why
while the foe op - press - es me? Light and truth, my
for thy praise will I em - ploy. O my soul, why

art thou griev- ing? What dis - qui - ets and dis - mays? Hope in
way at - tend - ing, send thou forth to be my guide, till, thy
art thou griev- ing? What dis - qui - ets and dis - mays? Hope in

God; his help re - ceiv - ing, I shall yet my Sav - ior praise.
ho - ly mount as - cend - ing, I with - in thy house a - bide.
God; his help re - ceiv - ing, I shall yet my Sav - ior praise.

From Psalm 43
The Psalter, 1912; alt. 1961

BLAENHAFREN 8.7.8.7.D.
Traditional Welsh melody

May the Mind of Christ My Savior 644

Your attitude should be the same as that of Christ Jesus. Phil. 2:5

1. May the mind of Christ my Sav - ior live in me from day to day,
2. May the Word of God dwell rich - ly in my heart from hour to hour,
3. May the peace of God my Fa - ther rule my life in ev - ery- thing,
4. May the love of Je - sus fill me as the wa - ters fill the sea;
5. May his beau - ty rest up - on me as I seek the lost to win,

by his love and pow'r con - trol - ling all I do and say.
so that all may see I tri - umph on - ly through his pow'r.
that I may be calm to com - fort sick and sor - row - ing.
him ex - alt - ing, self a - bas - ing, this is vic - to - ry.
and may they for - get the chan - nel, see - ing on - ly him.

Kate B. Wilkinson, 1925

ST. LEONARDS 8.7.8.5.
A. Cyril Barham-Gould, 1925; alt. 1990

645   Jesus, the Very Thought of Thee

The love of Christ ... that surpasses knowledge. Eph. 3:18, 19

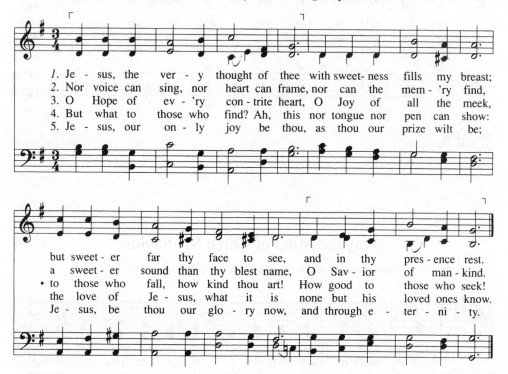

1. Je - sus, the ver - y thought of thee with sweet-ness fills my breast;
2. Nor voice can sing, nor heart can frame, nor can the mem - 'ry find,
3. O Hope of ev - 'ry con - trite heart, O Joy of all the meek,
4. But what to those who find? Ah, this nor tongue nor pen can show:
5. Je - sus, our on - ly joy be thou, as thou our prize wilt be;

but sweet - er far thy face to see, and in thy pres - ence rest.
a sweet - er sound than thy blest name, O Sav - ior of man - kind.
• to those who fall, how kind thou art! How good to those who seek!
the love of Je - sus, what it is none but his loved ones know.
Je - sus, be thou our glo - ry now, and through e - ter - ni - ty.

Latin, 11th cent.
Tr. by Edward Caswall, 1849

ST. AGNES C.M.
John B. Dykes, 1866

646   Jesus, Thou Joy of Loving Hearts

I have told you this so that my joy may be in you and that your joy may be complete.
John 15:11

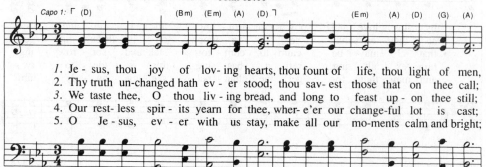

Capo 1: (D)   (Bm) (Em) (A) (D)   (Em) (A) (D) (G) (A)

1. Je - sus, thou joy of lov - ing hearts, thou fount of life, thou light of men,
2. Thy truth un-changed hath ev - er stood; thou sav - est those that on thee call;
3. We taste thee, O thou liv - ing bread, and long to feast up - on thee still;
4. Our rest-less spir - its yearn for thee, wher - e'er our change-ful lot is cast;
5. O Je - sus, ev - er with us stay, make all our mo-ments calm and bright;

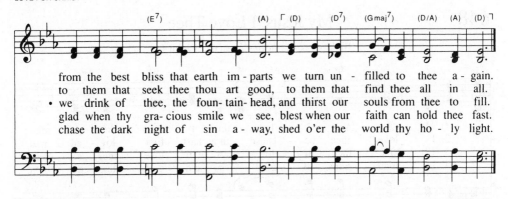

from the best bliss that earth im - parts we turn un - filled to thee a - gain.
to them that seek thee thou art good, to them that find thee all in all.
• we drink of thee, the foun - tain- head, and thirst our souls from thee to fill.
glad when thy gra- cious smile we see, blest when our faith can hold thee fast.
chase the dark night of sin a - way, shed o'er the world thy ho - ly light.

Attr. to Bernard of Clairvaux, ca. 1150
Arr. and tr. by Ray Palmer, 1858

QUEBEC L.M.
Henry Baker, 1854

How Sweet the Name of Jesus Sounds 647

Your name is like perfume poured out. Song of Sol. 1:3

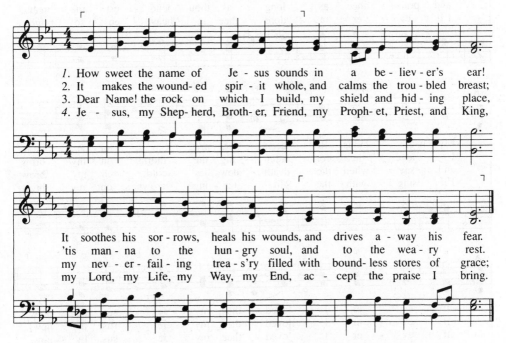

1. How sweet the name of Je - sus sounds in a be - liev - er's ear!
2. It makes the wound- ed spir - it whole, and calms the trou - bled breast;
3. Dear Name! the rock on which I build, my shield and hid - ing place,
4. Je - sus, my Shep- herd, Broth- er, Friend, my Proph- et, Priest, and King,

It soothes his sor - rows, heals his wounds, and drives a - way his fear.
'tis man - na to the hun - gry soul, and to the wea - ry rest.
my nev - er - fail - ing trea - s'ry filled with bound- less stores of grace;
my Lord, my Life, my Way, my End, ac - cept the praise I bring.

5. Weak is the effort of my heart,
and cold my warmest thought;
but when I see thee as thou art,
I'll praise thee as I ought.

6. Till then I would thy love proclaim
with every fleeting breath;
and may the music of thy name
refresh my soul in death.

John Newton, 1779; alt.

ST. PETER C.M.
Alexander R. Reinagle, 1836

648

My Jesus, I Love Thee

We love because he first loved us. 1 John 4:19

1. My Je - sus, I love thee, I know thou art mine;
2. I love thee be - cause thou hast first lov - ed me,
3. I'll love thee in life, I will love thee in death;
4. In man - sions of glo - ry and end - less de - light,

for thee all the fol - lies of sin I re - sign.
and pur - chased my par - don on Cal - va - ry's tree.
and praise thee as long as thou lend - est me breath;
I'll ev - er a - dore thee in heav - en so bright;

My gra - cious Re - deem - er, my Sav - ior art thou;
I love thee for wear - ing the thorns on thy brow;
and say, when the death - dew lies cold on my brow:
I'll sing with the glit - ter - ing crown on my brow:

if ev - er I loved thee, my Je - sus, 'tis now.
if ev - er I loved thee, my Je - sus, 'tis now.
if ev - er I loved thee, my Je - sus, 'tis now.
if ev - er I loved thee, my Je - sus, 'tis now.

William R. Featherstone, 1864

CARITAS 11.11.11.11.
Adoniram J. Gordon. 1894

More Love to Thee, O Christ

649

Lord, you know all things; you know that I love you. John 21:17

1. More love to thee, O Christ, more love to thee!
2. Once earth-ly joy I craved, sought peace and rest;
3. Let sor-row do its work, send grief and pain;
4. Then shall my lat-est breath whis-per thy praise;

Hear thou the prayer I make on bend-ed knee;
now thee a-lone I seek; give what is best:
sweet are thy mes-sen-gers, sweet their re-frain,
this be the part-ing cry my heart shall raise,

REFRAIN

this is my ear-nest plea,
this all my prayer shall be,
when they can sing with me,   more love, O Christ, to thee,
this still its prayer shall be,

more love to thee, more love to thee!

Elizabeth Payson Prentiss, 1869

MORE LOVE TO THEE 6.4.6.4.6.6.4.4.
William H. Doane. 1868

650

I Will Sing of My Redeemer

Jesus Christ, who gave himself for us to redeem us. Titus 2:13, 14

1. I will sing of my Re - deem - er, and his
2. I will tell the won - drous sto - ry, how my
3. I will praise my dear Re - deem - er, his tri -
4. I will sing of my Re - deem - er and his

won - drous love to me: on the cru - el cross he
lost es - tate to save, in his bound - less love and
um - phant pow'r I'll tell, how the vic - to - ry he
heav'n - ly love to me; he from death to life has

suf - fered, from the curse to set me free.
mer - cy, he the ran - som free - ly gave.
giv - eth o - ver sin and death and hell.
brought me, Son of God, with him to be.

REFRAIN

Sing, O sing of my Re-deem-er!
Sing, O sing of my Re-deem-er! Sing, O sing of my Re-deem-er!

He pur-chased me,
With his blood he pur-chased me;
With his blood he pur-chased me, he pur-chased me;
He pur-chased me, with his blood he pur-chased me;

on the cross he sealed my par-don,
on the cross he sealed my par-don, on the cross he sealed my par-don,

paid the debt and made me free.
paid the debt and made me free, and made me free, and made me free.

Philip P. Bliss, 1876

MY REDEEMER 8.7.8.7.ref.
James McGranahan. 1840–1907

651   He Lifted Me

He lifted me ... out of the mud and mire; he set my feet on a rock. Ps. 40:2

1. In lov - ing - kind - ness Je - sus came my soul in mer - cy
2. He called me long be - fore I heard, be - fore my sin - ful
3. His brow was pierced with man - y a thorn, his hands by cru - el
4. Now on a high - er plane I dwell, and with my soul I

to re - claim, and from the depths of sin and shame
heart was stirred, but when I took him at his word,
nails were torn, when from my guilt and grief, for - lorn,
know 'tis well; yet how or why, I can - not tell,

thro' grace he lift - ed me.
for - giv'n he lift - ed me.
in love he lift - ed me.
he should have lift - ed me.

REFRAIN

From sink- ing sand he

He lift - ed me.

lift - ed me, with ten - der hand he lift - ed me, from shades of night

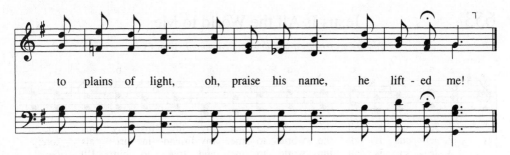

to plains of light, oh, praise his name, he lift-ed me!

Charles H. Gabriel, 1905

HE LIFTED ME 8.8.8.6.ref.
Charles H. Gabriel, 1905

Savior, Teach Me, Day by Day 652

We love because he first loved us. 1 John 4:19

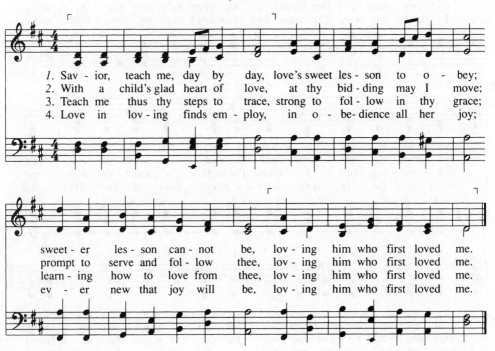

1. Sav - ior, teach me, day by day, love's sweet les - son to o - bey;
2. With a child's glad heart of love, at thy bid - ding may I move;
3. Teach me thus thy steps to trace, strong to fol - low in thy grace;
4. Love in lov - ing finds em - ploy, in o - be - dience all her joy;

sweet - er les - son can - not be, lov - ing him who first loved me.
prompt to serve and fol - low thee, lov - ing him who first loved me.
learn - ing how to love from thee, lov - ing him who first loved me.
ev - er new that joy will be, lov - ing him who first loved me.

Jane E. Leeson, 1842

POSEN 7.7.7.7.
Georg C. Strattner, 1691
Arr. by J. A. Freylinghausen, 1705

653

Jesus Is All the World to Me

You are my friends if you do what I command. John 15:14

1. Je - sus is all the world to me, my life, my joy, my all;
2. Je - sus is all the world to me, my Friend in tri - als sore;
3. Je - sus is all the world to me, and true to him I'll be;
4. Je - sus is all the world to me, I want no bet - ter friend;

he is my strength from day to day, with - out him I would fall.
I go to him for bless - ings, and he gives them o'er and o'er.
oh, how could I this Friend de - ny, when he's so true to me?
I trust him now, I'll trust him when life's fleet - ing days shall end.

When I am sad, to him I go, no oth - er one can
He sends the sun - shine and the rain, he sends the har - vest's
Fol - low - ing him I know I'm right, he watch - es o'er me
Beau - ti - ful life with such a Friend; beau - ti - ful life that

cheer me so; when I am sad he makes me glad, he's my Friend.
gold - en grain; sun - shine and rain, har - vest of grain, he's my Friend.
day and night; fol - low - ing him, by day and night, he's my Friend.
has no end; e - ter - nal life, e - ter - nal joy, he's my Friend.

Will L. Thompson, 1904

ELIZABETH Irreg.
Will L. Thompson, 1904

O Jesus, I Have Promised

654

Whoever serves me must follow me; and where I am, my servant also will be.
John 12:26

1. O Je - sus, I have prom - ised to serve thee to the end;
2. O let me feel thee near me, the world is ev - er near;
3. O Je - sus, thou hast prom - ised to all who fol - low thee,

be thou for - ev - er near me, my Mas - ter and my Friend:
I see the sights that daz - zle, the tempt - ing sounds I hear:
that where thou art in glo - ry there shall thy ser - vant be;

I shall not fear the bat - tle if thou art by my side,
my foes are ev - er near me, a - round me and with - in;
and, Je - sus, I have prom - ised to serve thee to the end;

nor wan - der from the path - way if thou wilt be my guide.
but, Je - sus, draw thou near - er, and shield my soul from sin.
O give me grace to fol - low, my Mas - ter and my Friend.

John E. Bode, 1868

ANGEL'S STORY 7.6.7.6.D.
Arthur H. Mann, 1883

655 O Safe to the Rock That Is Higher Than I

The LORD has become my fortress, and my God the rock in whom I take refuge.
Ps. 94:22

1. O safe to the Rock that is high - er than I
2. In the calm of the noon - tide, in sor - row's lone hour,
3. How oft in the con - flict, when pressed by the foe,

my soul in its con - flicts and sor - rows would fly;
in times when temp - ta - tion casts o'er me its pow'r,
I have fled to my ref - uge and breathed out my woe!

so sin - ful, so wea - ry, thine, thine would I be;
in the tem - pests of life, on its wide, heav - ing sea,
How of - ten when tri - als like sea bil - lows roll,

thou blest Rock of A - ges, I'm hid - ing in thee.
thou blest Rock of A - ges, I'm hid - ing in thee.
have I hid - den in thee, O thou Rock of my soul!

REFRAIN

Hid - ing in thee, hid - ing in thee— thou

blest Rock of A - ges, I'm hid - ing in thee.

William O. Cushing, 1876

HIDING IN THEE 11.11.11.11.ref.
Ira D. Sankey, 1877

656

Jesus, Priceless Treasure

To you who believe ... [he] is precious. 1 Pet. 2:7

1. Je - sus, price - less trea - sure, source of pur - est plea - sure,
2. In thine arms I rest me; foes who would mo - lest me
3. Sa - tan, I de - fy thee; death, I now de - cry thee;
4. Hence with earth - ly trea - sure! Thou art all my plea - sure,
5. Hence, all fear and sad - ness! For the Lord of glad - ness,

tru - est Friend to me: ah, how long in an - guish shall my spir - it
can - not reach me here. Though the earth be shak - ing, ev - 'ry heart be
• fear, I bid thee cease. World, thou shalt not harm me nor thy threats a -
Je - sus, all my choice. Hence, thou emp - ty glo - ry! Naught to me thy
Je - sus, en - ters in. Those who love the Fa - ther, though the storms may

lan - guish, yearn - ing, Lord, for thee? Thine I am, O spot - less Lamb!
quak - ing, Je - sus calms my fear. Light - nings flash and thun - ders crash;
• larm me while I sing of peace. God's great pow'r guards ev - 'ry hour;
sto - ry, told with tempt - ing voice. Pain or loss or shame or cross
gath - er, still have peace with - in. Yea, what - e'er I here must bear,

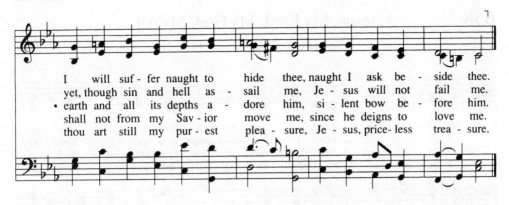

I will suf - fer naught to hide thee, naught I ask be - side thee.
yet, though sin and hell as - sail me, Je - sus will not fail me.
• earth and all its depths a - dore him, si - lent bow be - fore him.
shall not from my Sav - ior move me, since he deigns to love me.
thou art still my pur - est plea - sure, Je - sus, price-less trea - sure.

Johann Franck, 1655
Tr. by Catherine Winkworth, 1863

JESU, MEINE FREUDE 6.6.5.6.6.5.7.8.6.
Johann Crüger, 1649

In Sweet Communion, Lord, with Thee 657

I am always with you; you hold me by my right hand. Ps. 73:23

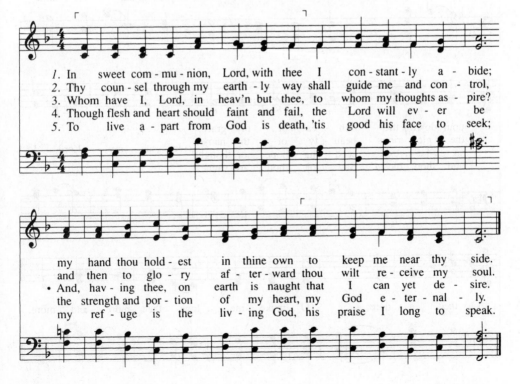

1. In sweet com - mu - nion, Lord, with thee I con - stant - ly a - bide;
2. Thy coun - sel through my earth - ly way shall guide me and con - trol,
3. Whom have I, Lord, in heav'n but thee, to whom my thoughts as - pire?
4. Though flesh and heart should faint and fail, the Lord will ev - er be
5. To live a - part from God is death, 'tis good his face to seek;

my hand thou hold - est in thine own to keep me near thy side.
and then to glo - ry af - ter - ward thou wilt re - ceive my soul.
• And, hav - ing thee, on earth is naught that I can yet de - sire.
the strength and por - tion of my heart, my God e - ter - nal - ly.
my ref - uge is the liv - ing God, his praise I long to speak.

From Psalm 73:23–28
The Psalter, 1912

ST. FLAVIAN C.M.
Day's *Psalter*, 1562

658 Jesus, My Lord, My God, My All

Whom have I in heaven but you? Ps. 73:25

1. Je - sus, my Lord, my God, my all, hear me, blest Sav - ior, when I call; hear me, and from thy dwell - ing place
2. Je - sus, too late I thee have sought; how can I love thee as I ought? And how ex - tol thy match - less fame,
3. Je - sus, what didst thou find in me that thou hast dealt so lov - ing - ly? How great the joy that thou hast brought,
4. Je - sus, of thee shall be my song; to thee my heart and soul be - long; all that I have or am is thine,

pour down the rich - es of thy grace:
the glo - rious beau - ty of thy name?
so far ex - ceed - ing hope or thought!
and thou, blest Sav - ior, thou art mine:

REFRAIN

Je - sus, my Lord, I thee a - dore; O make me love thee more and more.

Henry Collins, 1854

SARAH 8.8.8.8.8.8.
Hughes M. Huffman, 1976

Tune © 1976, Hughes M. Huffman, assigned to InterVarsity Christian Fellowship. Used by permission.

Let Us Praise God Together

Glorify the LORD with me; let us exalt his name together. Ps. 34:3

1. Let us praise God to-geth-er, let us praise;
2. Let us seek God to-geth-er, let us pray;
3. Let us serve God to-geth-er, him o-bey;

let us praise God to-geth-er all our days.
let us seek his for-give-ness as we pray.
let our lives show his good-ness through each day.

He is faith-ful in all his ways, he is wor-thy of
He will cleanse us from all our sin, he will help us the
Christ the Lord is the world's true light, let us serve him with

all our praise, his name be ex-alt-ed on high.
fight to win, his name be ex-alt-ed on high.
all our might, his name be ex-alt-ed on high.

James E. Seddon, 1982

LET US BREAK BREAD Irreg.
Spiritual

660

O God beyond All Praising

I will praise you, O LORD, with all my heart. Ps. 138:1

1. O God be-yond all prais-ing, we wor-ship you to-day
2. Then hear, O gra-cious Sav-ior, ac-cept the love we bring,

and sing the love a-maz-ing that songs can-not re-pay;
that we who know your fa-vor may serve you as our King;

for we can on-ly won-der at ev-ery gift you send,
and wheth-er our to-mor-rows be filled with good or ill,

at bless-ings with-out num-ber and mer-cies with-out end:
we'll tri-umph through our sor-rows and rise to bless you still:

we lift our hearts be - fore you and wait up - on your word,
to mar - vel at your beau - ty and glo - ry in your ways,

we hon - or and a - dore you, our great and might - y Lord.
and make a joy - ful du - ty our sac - ri - fice of praise.

Michael Perry, 1982

THAXTED 13.13.13.13.13.13.
From Gustav Holst, *The Planets*, 1918

Text © 1982, Hope Publishing Co. All rights reserved. Used by permission.

As Pants the Hart for Cooling Streams 661

As the deer pants for streams of water, so my soul pants for you, O God. Ps. 42:1

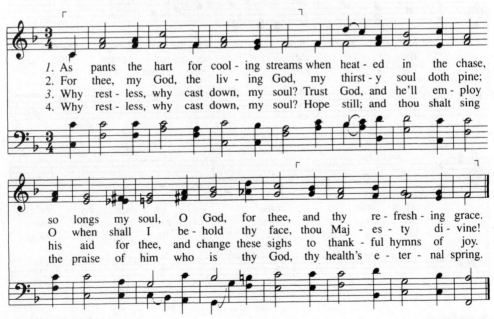

1. As pants the hart for cool - ing streams when heat - ed in the chase,
2. For thee, my God, the liv - ing God, my thirst - y soul doth pine;
3. Why rest - less, why cast down, my soul? Trust God, and he'll em - ploy
4. Why rest - less, why cast down, my soul? Hope still; and thou shalt sing

so longs my soul, O God, for thee, and thy re - fresh - ing grace.
O when shall I be - hold thy face, thou Maj - es - ty di - vine!
his aid for thee, and change these sighs to thank - ful hymns of joy.
the praise of him who is thy God, thy health's e - ter - nal spring.

From Psalm 42
Tate and Brady's *New Version*, 1696, 1698

SPOHR C.M.
Louis Spohr, 1835; arr.

662 As the Hart Longs for Flowing Streams

As the deer pants for streams of water, so my soul pants for you, O God. Ps. 42:1

1. As the hart longs for flow-ing streams,
so longs my soul for thee, O God.
My soul does thirst for the liv-ing God;
when shall I come to see thy face?

2. My tears have fed me day and night,
while men have said, "Where is your God?"
But I re-call as my soul pours dry,
the days of praise with-in thy house.

3. Why do I mourn and toil with-in,
when it is mine to hope in God?
I shall a-gain sing praise to him;
he is my help, he is my God.

Based on Psalm 42
Danna Harkins, 1975

AS THE HART LONGS L.M.
Appalachian folk melody
Arr. by Danna Harkins, 1975

O God Eternal, You Are My God!

663

O God, you are my God, earnestly I seek you. Ps. 63:1

Unison

1. O God e-ter-nal, you are my God! For
2. On ho-ly ground your glo-ry I saw; your
3. You feed my soul as if with a feast— I
4. For you have been the help of my life; you

you I long in bod-y and soul; as in a dry and
stead-fast love is bet-ter than life; I'll bless your name as
sing your praise with ju-bi-lant lips; up-on my bed I
take and keep me un-der your wing; I cling to you, and

wa-ter-less land I search, I thirst, I faint for you.
long as I live and lift my hands to you in prayer.
call you to mind and med-i-tate on you at night.
find your sup-port; O God my joy, you are my God!

From Psalm 63
Christopher M. Idle, 1973

O GOD ETERNAL 9.9.9.8.
Traditional melody
Arr. by Norman L. Warren, 1973

664

Call Jehovah Your Salvation

He ... will rest in the shadow of the Almighty. Ps. 91:1

1. Call Je - ho - vah your sal - va - tion, rest be - neath th'Al -
2. From the sword at noon - day wast - ing, from the noi - some
3. Since, with pure and firm af - fec - tion you on God have

might - y's shade; in his se - cret hab - i - ta - tion
pes - ti - lence, in the depth of mid - night blast - ing,
set your love, with the wings of his pro - tec - tion

dwell, and nev - er be dis - mayed: there no tu - mult shall a -
God shall be your sure de - fense: he shall charge his an - gel
he will shield you from a - bove: you shall call on him in

larm you, you shall dread no hid - den snare: guile nor
le - gions watch and ward o'er you to keep; though you
trou - ble, he will hear - ken, he will save; here for

vi - o - lence can harm you, in e - ter - nal safe-guard there.
walk through hos - tile re - gions, though in des - ert wilds you sleep.
grief re - ward you dou - ble, crown with life be - yond the grave.

From Psalm 91
James Montgomery, 1822; mod.
Tune © 1977, Hope Publishing Co. All rights reserved. Used by permission.

CHRIST CHURCH (or SYDNOR) 8.7.8.7.D.
Richard Dirksen, 1977

What Time I Am Afraid 665

When I am afraid, I will trust in you. Ps. 56:3

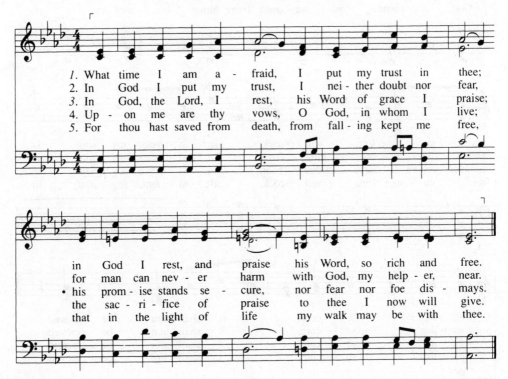

1. What time I am a - fraid, I put my trust in thee;
2. In God I put my trust, I nei - ther doubt nor fear,
3. In God, the Lord, I rest, his Word of grace I praise;
4. Up - on me are thy vows, O God, in whom I live;
5. For thou hast saved from death, from fall - ing kept me free,

in God I rest, and praise his Word, so rich and free.
for man can nev - er harm with God, my help - er, near.
• his prom - ise stands se - cure, nor fear nor foe dis - mays.
the sac - ri - fice of praise to thee I now will give.
that in the light of life my walk may be with thee.

From Psalm 56:3, 4, 11–13
The Psalter, 1912

HOLY GUIDE 6.6.6.6.
Uzziah C. Burnap, 1895

666   In Silence My Soul Is Waiting

My soul finds rest in God alone; my salvation comes from him. Ps. 62:1

Unison

1. In si - lence my soul is wait - ing, is wait - ing for
2. You set on a man and you beat him, the pack of you
3. You plot for his un - der - min - ing, you slan - der him
4. Be si - lent, my soul, in wait - ing, in wait - ing for

God a - lone; de - liv - 'rance from him is com - ing, my
knock him down; as a tot - ter - ing wall he stag - gers, sub -
with your lies; you love, with faint praise, to damn him; sweet -
God a - lone; as - sur - ance from him is com - ing, my

res - cu - er, fort, and rock. In si - lence my soul is
sides like a sag - ging fence. In si - lence my soul is
tongued, you've a curse - filled heart. In si - lence my soul is
res - cu - er, fort, and rock. Be si - lent, my soul, in

wait - ing; se - cure, I shall not be moved.
wait - ing; se - cure, I shall not be moved.
wait - ing; se - cure, I shall not be moved.
wait - ing; se - cure, I shall not be moved.

5. There's safety in God, and honor,
   my refuge, my rock, my strength,
   so hide in our God, you people,
   and pour out your hearts to him.
   Be silent, my soul, in waiting;
   secure, I shall not be moved.

6. Just puffs of the wind, the people,
   great men are illusions, all;
   as breath in the air, they're measured,
   then weightless they fade away.
   Be silent, my soul, in waiting;
   secure, I shall not be moved.

7. Don't trust, then, in cruel extortion,
   don't plunder, defraud, and steal;
   don't set your heart on possessions,
   especially if they increase.
   Be silent, my soul, in waiting;
   secure, I shall not be moved.

8. Uniquely, our God has spoken,
   of two things I've heard him speak:
   he's the source of pow'r and mercy;
   to men he repays their deeds.
   Be silent, my soul, in waiting;
   secure, I shall not be moved.

From Psalm 62
Michael Saward, 1973

SILENCE 8.7.8.7.8.7.
Christian Strover, 1973

God Is My Strong Salvation 667

The LORD is my light and my salvation—whom shall I fear? Ps. 27:1

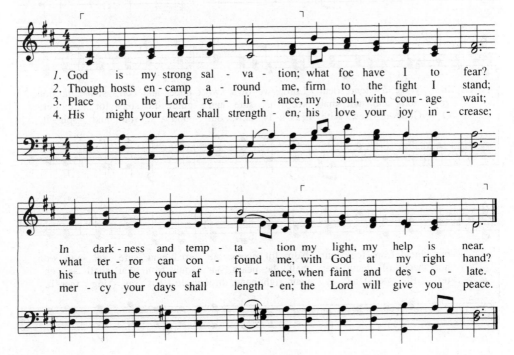

1. God is my strong sal - va - tion; what foe have I to fear?
2. Though hosts en - camp a - round me, firm to the fight I stand;
3. Place on the Lord re - li - ance, my soul, with cour - age wait;
4. His might your heart shall strength - en, his love your joy in - crease;

In dark - ness and temp - ta - tion my light, my help is near.
what ter - ror can con - found me, with God at my right hand?
his truth be your af - fi - ance, when faint and des - o - late.
mer - cy your days shall length - en; the Lord will give you peace.

From Psalm 27
James Montgomery, 1822; mod.

MEIN LEBEN 7.6.7.6.
Melchior Vulpius, 1609; arr.

668 Who Trusts in God, a Strong Abode

He is my stronghold, my refuge and my savior. 2 Sam. 22:3

1. Who trusts in God, a strong a-bode in heav'n and earth pos-sess-es;
2. Though Sa-tan's wrath be-set our path, and world-ly scorn as-sail us,
3. In all the strife of mor-tal life our feet shall stand se-cure-ly;

who looks in love to Christ a-bove, no fear his heart op-press-es.
while you are near we will not fear, your strength shall nev-er fail us:
temp-ta-tion's hour shall lose its pow'r, for you shall guard us sure-ly.

In you a-lone, dear Lord, we own sweet hope and con-so-la-tion:
your rod and staff shall keep us safe, and guide our steps for-ev-er;
O God, re-new, with heav'n-ly dew, our bod-y, soul, and spir-it,

our shield from foes, our balm for woes, our great and sure sal-va-tion.
nor shades of death, nor hell be-neath, our souls from you shall sev-er.
un-til we stand at your right hand, through Je-sus' sav-ing mer-it.

St. 1, Joachim Magdeburg, 1572; st. 2–3, anon., 1597
Tr. by Benjamin H. Kennedy, 1863
Alt. by W. Walsham How, 1864; mod.

CONSTANCE 8.7.8.7.D.
Arthur S. Sullivan, 1875

Commit Now All Your Griefs

669

Commit your way to the LORD; trust in him and he will do this. Psalm 37:5

1. Com - mit now all your griefs and ways in - to his hands;
2. Give to the winds your fears; hope, and be un - dis - mayed;
3. Still heav - y is your heart? Still sink your spir - its down?
4. Far, far a - bove your thought his coun - sel shall ap - pear,

to his sure truth and ten - der care, who earth and heav'n com - mands.
God hears your sighs and counts your tears, God shall lift up your head.
Cast off the weight, let fear de - part, and ev - ery care be gone.
when ful - ly he the work has wrought that caused your need - less fear.

Who points the clouds their course, whom winds and seas o - bey,
Through waves and clouds and storms he gent - ly clears your way;
He ev - ery - where has sway, and all things serve his might;
Leave to his sov - ereign will to choose and to com - mand;

he shall di - rect your wan - d'ring feet, he shall pre - pare your way.
wait for his time, so shall the night soon end in joy - ous day.
his ev - ery act pure bless - ing is, his path un - sul - lied light.
with won - der filled, you then shall own how wise, how strong his hand.

Paul Gerhardt, 1653
John Wesley, 1737; alt.; mod.

DIADEMATA S.M.D.
George J. Elvey, 1868

670   If Thou But Suffer God to Guide Thee

*Cast your cares on the LORD and he will sustain you; he will never let
the righteous fall.* Ps. 55:22

1. If thou but suf - fer God to guide thee, and hope in
2. What can these anx - ious cares a - vail thee, these nev - er -
3. On - ly be still, and wait his lei - sure in cheer - ful
4. All are a - like be - fore the High - est; 'tis eas - y
5. Sing, pray, and keep his ways un - swerv - ing, so do thine

him through all thy ways, he'll give thee strength, what - e'er be - tide thee,
ceas - ing moans and sighs? What can it help, if thou be - wail thee
hope, with heart con - tent to take what - e'er thy Fa - ther's plea - sure
to our God, we know, to raise thee up though low thou li - est,
own part faith - ful - ly, and trust his Word— though un - de - serv - ing,

and bear thee through the e - vil days: Who trusts in God's un -
o'er each dark mo - ment as it flies? Our cross and tri - als
and all - dis - cern - ing love hath sent; nor doubt our in - most
to make the rich man poor and low; true won - ders still by
thou yet shalt find it true for thee; God nev - er yet for -

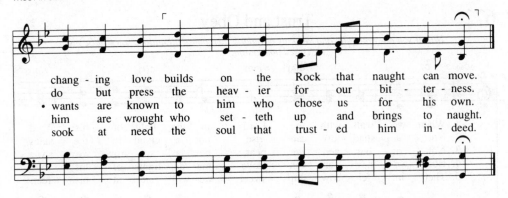

chang - ing	love builds	on	the	Rock	that	naught	can move.
do	but press	the	heav - ier	for	our	bit -	ter - ness.
• wants	are known	to	him who	chose	us	for	his own.
him	are wrought who	set - teth	up	and	brings	to	naught.
sook	at need	the	soul	that	trust - ed	him	in - deed.

Georg Neumark, 1641
Tr. by Catherine Winkworth, 1855, 1863

NEUMARK 9.8.9.8.8.8.
Georg Neumark, 1657

Forever Trusting in the Lord

671

Trust in the LORD and do good. Ps. 37:3

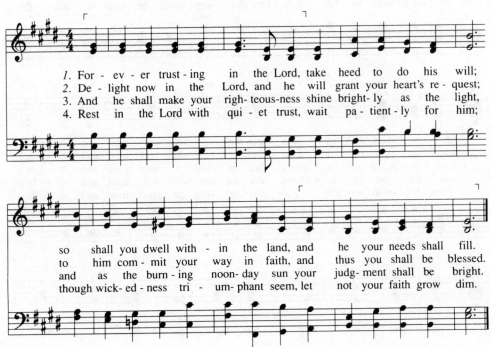

1. For - ev - er trust - ing	in	the Lord, take	heed	to	do	his	will;
2. De - light now in the	Lord, and	he will	grant	your heart's re -	quest;
3. And he shall make your	righ - teous-ness shine	bright - ly	as	the	light,
4. Rest in the Lord with	qui - et trust, wait	pa - tient - ly	for	him;

so	shall you dwell with - in	the land, and	he your needs shall	fill.
to	him com - mit your	way in faith, and	thus you shall be	blessed.
and	as the burn - ing	noon- day sun your	judg- ment shall be	bright.
though	wick- ed - ness tri - um- phant seem, let	not your faith grow	dim.

From Psalm 37:3–7
The Psalter, 1912: alt. 1990. mod.

MEDITATION C.M.
John H. Gower, 1890

672 Trust and Obey

Now if you obey me fully and keep my covenant, then out of all nations you will be my treasured possession. Ex. 19:5

1. When we walk with the Lord in the light of his Word,
2. Not a shad-ow can rise, not a cloud in the skies,
3. Not a bur-den we bear, not a sor-row we share,
4. But we nev-er can prove the de-lights of his love
5. Then in fel-low-ship sweet we will sit at his feet,

what a glo-ry he sheds on our way! While we do his good will,
but his smile quick-ly drives it a - way; not a doubt or a fear,
but our toil he doth rich-ly re-pay; not a grief nor a loss,
un-til all on the al-tar we lay; for the fa-vor he shows,
or we'll walk by his side in the way; what he says we will do,

he a-bides with us still, and with all who will trust and o-bey.
not a sigh nor a tear, can a-bide while we trust and o-bey.
not a frown or a cross, but is blest if we trust and o-bey.
and the joy he be-stows, are for them who will trust and o-bey.
where he sends we will go, nev-er fear, on-ly trust and o-bey.

REFRAIN

Trust and o - bey, for there's no oth - er way

C⁷(A⁷) F(D) F/C(D/A) C⁷(A⁷) F(D)

to be hap-py in Je-sus, but to trust and o-bey.

John H. Sammis, 1887

TRUST AND OBEY 6.6.9.D.ref.
Daniel B. Towner, 1887

Cast Your Burden on the Lord 673

Cast your cares on the LORD and he will sustain you. Ps. 55:22

1. Cast your bur-den on the Lord, on-ly lean up-on his word;
2. He sus-tains you by his hand, he en-a-bles you to stand;
3. Hu-man coun-sels come to naught; that shall stand which God has wrought;
4. Heav'n and earth may pass a-way, God's free grace shall not de-cay;
5. Je-sus, guard-ian of your flock, be your-self our con-stant rock;

you will soon have cause to bless his e-ter-nal faith-ful-ness.
those whom Je-sus once has loved from his grace are nev-er moved.
his com-pas-sion, love, and pow'r are the same for-ev-er-more.
he has prom-ised to ful-fil all the plea-sure of his will.
make us, by your pow'r-ful hand, strong as Zi-on's moun-tain stand.

Based on Psalm 55
Rowland Hill's *Psalms and Hymns*, 1783; mod.

MERCY 7.7.7.7.
Louis M. Gottschalk, 1867; arr.

674 I Need Thee Every Hour

Hear, O LORD, and answer me, for I am poor and needy. Ps. 86:1

1. I need thee ev - 'ry hour, most gra - cious Lord;
2. I need thee ev - 'ry hour; stay thou near - by;
3. I need thee ev - 'ry hour, in joy or pain;
4. I need thee ev - 'ry hour; teach me thy will,
5. I need thee ev - 'ry hour, Most Ho - ly One;

no ten - der voice like thine can peace af - ford.
temp - ta - tions lose their pow'r when thou art nigh.
come quick - ly, and a - bide, or life is vain.
and thy rich prom - is - es in me ful - fil.
O make me thine in - deed, thou bless - ed Son.

REFRAIN

I need thee, O I need thee, ev - 'ry hour I need thee;

O bless me now, my Sav - ior, I come to thee.

Annie S. Hawks, 1872
Refrain added by Robert Lowry, 1872

NEED 6.4.6.4.ref.
Robert Lowry, 1872

Only Trust Him

675

He is able to save completely those who come to God through him. Heb. 7:25

1. Come, ev-'ry soul by sin op-pressed, there's mer-cy with the Lord,
2. For Je-sus shed his pre-cious blood rich bless-ings to be-stow;
3. Yes, Je-sus is the truth, the way, that leads you in-to rest;
4. Come then, and join this ho-ly band, and on to glo-ry go,

and he will sure-ly give you rest, by trust-ing in his Word.
plunge now in-to the crim-son flood that wash-es white as snow.
be-lieve in him with-out de-lay, and you are ful-ly blessed.
to dwell in that ce-les-tial land, where joys im-mor-tal flow.

REFRAIN

On-ly trust him, on-ly trust him, on-ly trust him now;

he will save you, he will save you, he will save you now.

John H. Stockton, 1874

MINERVA C.M.ref.
John H. Stockton, 1874

676 Day by Day and with Each Passing Moment

Your strength will equal your days. Deut. 33:25

1. Day by day and with each pass-ing mo-ment, strength I find to
2. Ev-ery day the Lord him-self is near me with a spe-cial
3. Help me then in ev-ery trib-u-la-tion so to trust your

meet my tri-als here; trust-ing in my Fa-ther's wise be-stow-ment,
mer-cy for each hour; all my cares he fain would bear, and cheer me,
prom-is-es, O Lord, that I lose not faith's sweet con-so-la-tion

I've no cause for wor-ry or for fear. He whose heart is kind be-
he whose name is Coun-sel-or and Pow'r. The pro-tec-tion of his
of-fered me with-in your ho-ly Word. Help me, Lord, when toil and

yond all mea-sure gives un-to each day what he deems best— lov-ing-
child and trea-sure is a charge that on him-self he laid; "As your
trou-ble meet-ing, e'er to take, as from a fa-ther's hand, one by

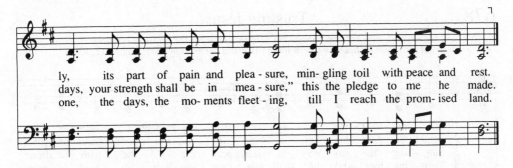

ly, its part of pain and plea - sure, min- gling toil with peace and rest.
days, your strength shall be in mea - sure," this the pledge to me he made.
one, the days, the mo- ments fleet - ing, till I reach the prom- ised land.

Carolina Sandell Berg, 1865
Tr. by A. L. Skoog, 1931; mod.

BLOTT EN DAG Irreg.
Oscar Ahnfelt, 1872; alt. 1990

Praise the Savior, Ye Who Know Him!   677

Jesus Christ is the same yesterday and today and forever.   Heb. 13:8

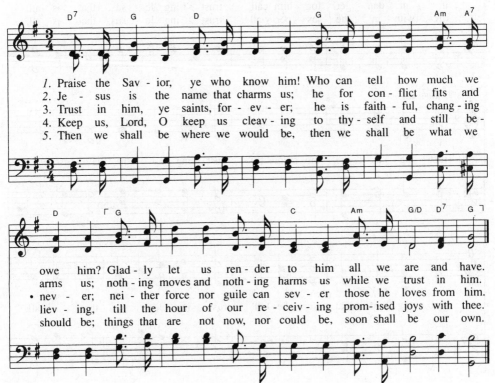

1. Praise the Sav - ior, ye who know him! Who can tell how much we
2. Je - sus is the name that charms us; he for con - flict fits and
3. Trust in him, ye saints, for - ev - er; he is faith - ful, chang - ing
4. Keep us, Lord, O keep us cleav - ing to thy - self and still be -
5. Then we shall be where we would be, then we shall be what we

owe him? Glad - ly let us ren - der to him all we are and have.
arms us; noth - ing moves and noth - ing harms us while we trust in him.
nev - er; nei - ther force nor guile can sev - er those he loves from him.
liev - ing, till the hour of our re - ceiv - ing prom- ised joys with thee.
should be; things that are not now, nor could be, soon shall be our own.

Thomas Kelly, 1806

ACCLAIM 8.8.8.5.
Traditional German melody

678

Trusting Jesus

*That we, who were the first to hope in Christ, might be for the praise of his glory. And
you also were included in Christ when you heard the word of truth.* Eph. 1:12, 13

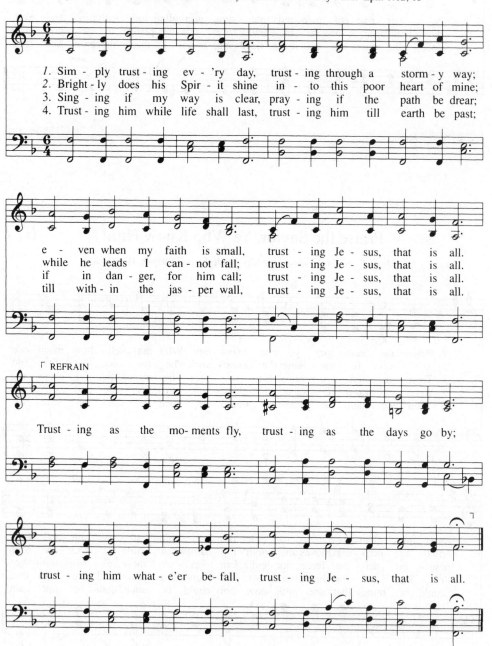

1. Sim - ply trust - ing ev - 'ry day, trust - ing through a storm - y way;
2. Bright - ly does his Spir - it shine in - to this poor heart of mine;
3. Sing - ing if my way is clear, pray - ing if the path be drear;
4. Trust - ing him while life shall last, trust - ing him till earth be past;

e - ven when my faith is small, trust - ing Je - sus, that is all.
while he leads I can - not fall; trust - ing Je - sus, that is all.
if in dan - ger, for him call; trust - ing Je - sus, that is all.
till with - in the jas - per wall, trust - ing Je - sus, that is all.

REFRAIN

Trust - ing as the mo - ments fly, trust - ing as the days go by;

trust - ing him what - e'er be - fall, trust - ing Je - sus, that is all.

Edgar Page Stites, 1876

TRUSTING JESUS 7.7.7.7.ref.
Ira D. Sankey, 1876

'Tis So Sweet to Trust in Jesus

679

The life I live in the body, I live by faith in the Son of God, who loved me and gave himself for me. Gal. 2:20

1. 'Tis so sweet to trust in Je-sus, just to take him at his word;
2. O how sweet to trust in Je-sus, just to trust his cleans-ing blood;
3. Yes, 'tis sweet to trust in Je-sus, just from sin and self to cease;
4. I'm so glad I learned to trust thee, pre-cious Je-sus, Sav-ior, Friend;

just to rest up-on his prom-ise; just to know, "Thus saith the Lord."
just in sim-ple faith to plunge me 'neath the heal-ing, cleans-ing flood!
just from Je-sus sim-ply tak-ing life and rest, and joy and peace.
and I know that thou art with me, wilt be with me to the end.

REFRAIN

Je-sus, Je-sus, how I trust him! How I've proved him o'er and o'er!

Je-sus, Je-sus, pre-cious Je-sus! O for grace to trust him more!

Louisa M. R. Stead, 1882

TRUST IN JESUS 8.7.8.7.ref.
William J. Kirkpatrick, 1882

680

Consider the Lilies

Do not store up for yourselves treasures on earth. Matt. 6:19

1. Don't store up trea-sures on earth where thieves can de-stroy and break
2. God will pro-vide for your life, the things that you need day to
3. Take no con-cern for your clothes, con-sid-er the lil-ies that
4. God will sup-ply for each day, al-read-y he knows what you

through; store up your wealth where it can-not be lost and
day. See how he cares for the birds in the air, and
grow. Sol-o-mon's robes nev-er once e-qualed theirs; what
need; pray and be-lieve in the prom-ise he made and

REFRAIN

there will your heart be, too.
you are worth more than they.
splen-dor God can be-stow. Give God first place in your life;
then see Christ in-ter-cede.

give him your joy, give him your sor-row. Give him your tal-ents, your

trust, and time, and God will take care of to-mor-row.

Grace Hawthorne, 1977
Alt. 1990

CONSIDER THE LILIES 7.8.10.7.ref.
Tom Fettke, 1977

How Gentle God's Commands

681

My yoke is easy and my burden is light. Matt. 11:30

1. How gen - tle God's com- mands, how kind his pre - cepts are!
2. While Prov - i - dence sup - ports, let saints se - cure - ly dwell;
3. Why should this anx - ious load press down your wea - ry mind?
4. His good - ness stands ap- proved, down to the pres - ent day;

Come, cast your bur - dens on the Lord, and trust his con - stant care.
that hand, which bears all na - ture up, shall guide his chil - dren well.
Haste to your heav'n-ly Fa - ther's throne, and sweet re - fresh-ment find.
I'll drop my bur - den at his feet, and bear a song a - way.

Philip Doddridge, 1755

DENNIS S.M.
Hans G. Nägeli, 1773–1836
Arr. by Lowell Mason, 1845

682

In Thee, O Lord, I Put My Trust

In you, O LORD, I have taken refuge. Ps. 31:1

1. In thee, O Lord, I put my trust, I call up-on thy name;
2. Bow down thine ear to my re-quest, and swift de-liv-'rance send;
3. Since thou my rock and for-tress art, my lead-er be, and guide;
4. Oh, Lord, in thee is all my trust; "Thou art my God," I cried.

O save me in thy righ-teous-ness, nor let me suf-fer shame.
be thou to me a rock of strength, a for-tress to de-fend.
from all temp-ta-tion res-cue me, thou dost my strength a-bide.
"My life, my times are in thy hand, I in thy strength con-fide."

From Psalm 31:1–4, 14, 15
Anon., 1977

IN THEE, O LORD C.M.
Attr. to J. C. Lowry, 1818
Arr. by Tom Fettke, 1977

683

Not Haughty Is My Heart

My heart is not proud, O LORD, my eyes are not haughty. Ps. 131:1

1. Not haugh-ty is my heart, not loft-y is my pride;
2. With child-like trust, O Lord, in you I calm-ly rest,
3. Ye peo-ple of the Lord, in him a-lone con-fide;

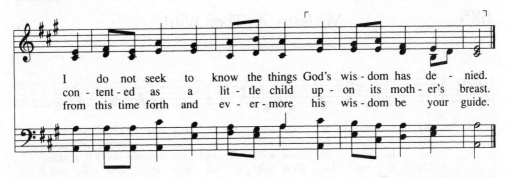

I do not seek to know the things God's wis - dom has de - nied.
con - tent - ed as a lit - tle child up - on its moth - er's breast.
from this time forth and ev - er - more his wis - dom be your guide.

From Psalm 131
The Psalter, 1912
Mod.

OLMUTZ S.M.
Gregorian chant
Arr. by Lowell Mason, 1824; alt. 1990

My Times Are in Thy Hand

684

My times are in your hands. Ps. 31:15

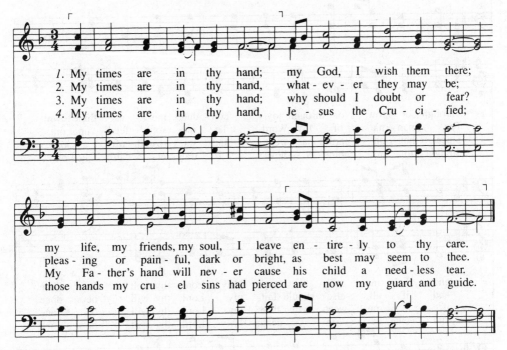

1. My times are in thy hand; my God, I wish them there;
2. My times are in thy hand, what - ev - er they may be;
3. My times are in thy hand; why should I doubt or fear?
4. My times are in thy hand, Je - sus the Cru - ci - fied;

my life, my friends, my soul, I leave en - tire - ly to thy care.
pleas - ing or pain - ful, dark or bright, as best may seem to thee.
My Fa - ther's hand will nev - er cause his child a need - less tear.
those hands my cru - el sins had pierced are now my guard and guide.

Based on Psalm 31
William F. Lloyd, 1824

VIGIL S.M.
St. Albans Tune Book, 1875; arr.

685

My Jesus, As Thou Wilt!

Not as I will, but as you will. Matt. 26:39

1. My Je - sus, as thou wilt! O may thy will be mine;
2. My Je - sus, as thou wilt! If need - y here and poor,
3. My Je - sus, as thou wilt! Though seen through man - y a tear,
4. My Je - sus, as thou wilt! All shall be well for me;

in - to thy hand of love I would my all re - sign.
give me thy peo - ple's bread, their por - tion rich and sure.
let not my star of hope grow dim or dis - ap - pear.
each chang - ing fu - ture scene I glad - ly trust with thee.

Through sor - row, or through joy, con - duct me as thine own;
The man - na of thy Word let my soul feed up - on;
Since thou on earth hast wept, and sor - rowed oft a - lone,
Straight to my home a - bove I trav - el calm - ly on,

and help me still to say, "My Lord, thy will be done."
and if all else should fail, my Lord, thy will be done.
if I must weep with thee, my Lord, thy will be done.
and sing, in life or death, "My Lord, thy will be done."

Benjamin Schmolck, ca. 1704
Tr. by Jane Borthwick, 1854

JEWETT 6.6.6.6.D.
Carl Maria von Weber, 1820
Arr. by Joseph P. Holbrook, 1862

Thy Way, Not Mine, O Lord

Offer yourselves to God. Rom. 6:13

1. Thy way, not mine, O Lord, how - ev - er dark it be!
2. The king - dom that I seek is thine; so let the way
3. Take thou my cup, and it with joy or sor - row fill

Lead me by thine own hand, choose out the path for me;
that leads to it be thine, else I must sure - ly stray.
as best to thee may seem; choose thou my good and ill.

smooth let it be or rough, it will be still the best;
I dare not choose my lot; I would not if I might:
Not mine, not mine the choice in things or great or small;

wind - ing or straight, it leads right on - ward to thy rest.
choose thou for me, my God, so shall I walk a - right.
be thou my guide, my strength, my wis - dom, and my all.

Horatius Bonar, 1857

INVITATION 6.6.6.6.D.
Frederick C. Maker, 1881

687 Make Me a Captive, Lord

Whoever loses his life for my sake will find it. Matt. 10:39

1. Make me a cap-tive, Lord, and then I shall be free;
2. My heart is weak and poor un-til it mas-ter find;
3. My pow'r is faint and low till I have learned to serve;
4. My will is not my own till thou hast made it thine;

force me to ren-der up my sword, and I shall con-qu'ror be;
it has no spring of ac-tion sure— it var-ies with the wind;
it wants the need-ed fire to glow, it wants the breeze to nerve;
if it would reach the mon-arch's throne, it must its crown re-sign:

I sink in life's a-larms when by my-self I stand;
it can-not free-ly move till thou hast wrought its chain;
it can-not drive the world un-til it-self be driv'n;
it on-ly stands un-bent, a-mid the clash-ing strife,

im-pris-on me with-in thine arms, and strong shall be my hand.
en-slave it with thy match-less love, and death-less it shall reign.
its flag can on-ly be un-furled when thou shalt breathe from heav'n.
when on thy bo-som it has leaned, and found in thee its life.

George Matheson, 1890

PARADOXY S.M.D.
Donald P. Hustad, 1953

Have Thine Own Way, Lord!

688

*Does not the potter have the right to make out of ... clay some pottery
for noble purposes?* Rom. 9:21

1. Have thine own way, Lord! Have thine own way!
2. Have thine own way, Lord! Have thine own way!
3. Have thine own way, Lord! Have thine own way!
4. Have thine own way, Lord! Have thine own way!

Thou art the pot - ter; I am the clay.
Search me and try me, Mas - ter, to - day!
Wound - ed and wea - ry, help me, I pray!
Hold o'er my be - ing ab - so - lute sway!

Mold me and make me af - ter thy will,
Whit - er than snow, Lord, wash me just now,
Pow - er, all pow - er, sure - ly is thine!
Fill with thy Spir - it till all shall see

while I am wait - ing, yield - ed and still.
as in thy pres - ence hum - bly I bow.
Touch me and heal me, Sav - ior di - vine!
Christ on - ly, al - ways, liv - ing in me!

Adelaide A. Pollard, 1902

HOLY DESIRE 9.9.9.9.
George C. Stebbins, 1907

689

Be Still, My Soul

Be patient, then, brothers, until the Lord's coming. Jas. 5:7

1. Be still, my soul: the Lord is on your side;
   bear pa - tient - ly the cross of grief or pain; leave to your
   God to or - der and pro - vide; in ev - 'ry change he
   faith - ful will re - main. Be still, my soul: your best, your heav'n - ly

2. Be still, my soul: your God will un - der - take
   to guide the fu - ture as he has the past. Your hope, your
   con - fi - dence let noth - ing shake; all now mys - te - rious
   shall be bright at last. Be still, my soul: the waves and winds still

3. Be still, my soul: when dear - est friends de - part,
   and all is dark - ened in the vale of tears, then shall you
   bet - ter know his love, his heart, who comes to soothe your
   sor - row and your fears. Be still, my soul: your Je - sus can re -

4. Be still, my soul: the hour is has - t'ning on
   when we shall be for - ev - er with the Lord, when dis - ap -
   point - ment, grief, and fear are gone, sor - row for - got, love's
   pur - est joys re - stored. Be still, my soul: when change and tears are

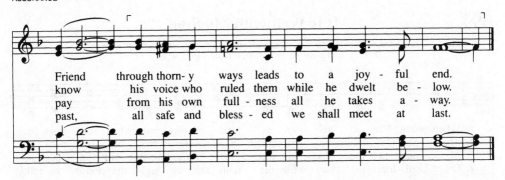

Friend | through thorn-y | ways leads | to | a | joy - ful | end.
know | his voice who | ruled them | while | he | dwelt | be - low.
pay | from his own | full - ness | all | he | takes | a - way.
past, | all safe and | bless - ed | we | shall | meet | at | last.

Katharina von Schlegel, 1752
Tr. by Jane Borthwick, 1855; alt. 1990, mod.
Tune © Breitkopf & Härtel, Wiesbaden. Used by permission.

FINLANDIA 10.10.10.10.10.10.
Jean Sibelius, 1899; arr.

I Know That My Redeemer Lives

690

I know that my Redeemer lives. Job 19:25

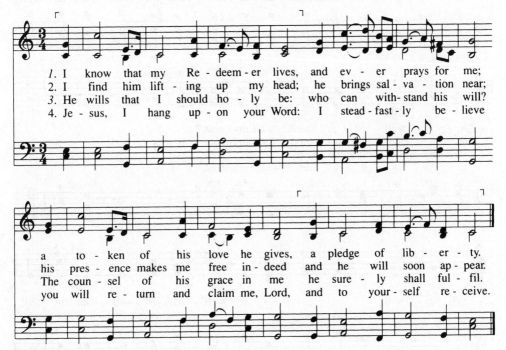

1. I know that my Re - deem - er lives, and ev - er prays for me;
2. I find him lift - ing up my head; he brings sal - va - tion near;
3. He wills that I should ho - ly be: who can with- stand his will?
4. Je - sus, I hang up - on your Word: I stead - fast - ly be - lieve

a to - ken of his love he gives, a pledge of lib - er - ty.
his pres - ence makes me free in - deed and he will soon ap - pear.
The coun - sel of his grace in me he sure - ly shall ful - fil.
you will re - turn and claim me, Lord, and to your - self re - ceive.

Charles Wesley, 1742
Mod.

BRADFORD C.M.
George Frederick Handel, 1741; arr.

691 It Is Well with My Soul

*The peace of God, which transcends all understanding, will guard your hearts
and your minds in Christ Jesus. Phil. 4:7*

1. When peace, like a riv - er, at - tend - eth my way, when sor - rows like
2. Though Sa - tan should buf - fet, though tri - als should come, let this blest as -
3. My sin— O the bliss of this glo - ri - ous thought!—my sin, not in
4. O Lord, haste the day when the faith shall be sight, the clouds be rolled

sea bil - lows roll; what - ev - er my lot, thou hast taught me to say,
sur - ance con - trol, that Christ has re - gard - ed my help - less es - tate,
part, but the whole, is nailed to the cross and I bear it no more;
back as a scroll, the trump shall re - sound and the Lord shall de - scend,

REFRAIN

"It is well, it is well with my soul."
and has shed his own blood for my soul. It is well
praise the Lord, praise the Lord, O my soul! It is well
"E - ven so"— it is well with my soul.

with my soul; it is well, it is well with my soul.
with my soul;

Horatio G. Spafford, 1873

VILLE DU HAVRE 11.8.11.9.ref.
Philip P. Bliss, 1876

To You, O Lord, I Fly

Keep me safe, O God, for in you I take refuge. Ps. 16:1

692

1. To you, O Lord, I fly and on your help de - pend;
2. The lot to me that fell is beau - ti - ful and fair;
3. I keep be - fore me still the Lord whom I have proved;

you are my Lord and King Most High; great God, my soul de - fend.
the her - i - tage in which I dwell is good be - yond com - pare.
at my right hand he guards from ill, and I shall not be moved.

A her - i - tage for me Je - ho - vah will re - main;
I praise the Lord a - bove whose coun - sel guides a - right;
Life's path - way you will show, to your right hand will guide,

my por - tion rich and full is he, my right he will main - tain.
my heart in - structs me in his love in sea - sons of the night.
where streams of plea - sure ev - er flow, and bound - less joys a - bide.

From Psalm 16:1, 2, 5–8, 11
The Psalter, 1912
Alt. 1990, mod.

LEOMINSTER S.M.D.
George William Martin, 1862
Arr. by Arthur S. Sullivan, 1874

693 Blessed Assurance

I will sing praise to my God as long as I live. Ps. 146:2

1. Bless-ed as - sur - ance, Je - sus is mine! O what a fore - taste of
2. Per - fect sub - mis - sion, per - fect de - light, vi-sions of rap - ture now
3. Per - fect sub - mis - sion, all is at rest, I in my Sav - ior am

glo - ry di - vine! Heir of sal - va - tion, pur - chase of God,
burst on my sight; an - gels de - scend - ing, bring from a - bove
hap - py and blest; watch-ing and wait - ing, look-ing a - bove,

born of his Spir - it, washed in his blood.
ech - oes of mer - cy, whis - pers of love. This is my sto - ry,
filled with his good - ness, lost in his love.

REFRAIN

this is my song, prais-ing my Sav - ior all the day long; this is my

ASSURANCE

sto - ry, this is my song, prais-ing my Sav - ior all the day long.

Fanny J. Crosby, 1873

ASSURANCE 9.10.9.9.ref.
Phoebe P. Knapp, 1873

Lord, I Lift My Soul to Thee   694

To you, O LORD, I lift up my soul. Ps. 25:1

1. Lord, I lift my soul to thee, O my God, I trust thy might;
2. Yea, may none be put to shame, none who wait for thee to bless;
3. Lord, to me thy ways make known, guide in truth and teach thou me;
4. Lord, re-mem-ber in thy love all thy mer-cies man-i-fold,

let not foes ex-ult o'er me, shame me not be-fore their sight.
but dis-hon-ored be their name who with-out a cause trans-gress.
thou my Sav-ior art a-lone, all the day I wait for thee.
ten-der mer-cies from a-bove, change-less from the days of old.

5. Sins of youth remember not,
   nor my trespasses record;
   let not mercy be forgot,
   for thy goodness' sake, O Lord.

6. Grace and truth shall mark the way
   where the Lord his own will lead,
   if his Word they still obey
   and his testimonies heed.

Psalm 25:1–7, 10
The Psalter, 1912

SEYMOUR 7.7.7.7.
Carl Maria von Weber, 1826; arr.

695 By Grace I Am an Heir of Heaven

That, having been justified by his grace, we might become heirs having the hope of eternal life. Titus 3:7

1. By grace I am an heir of heav - en: why doubt this,
2. By grace a - lone shall I in - her - it that bliss - ful
3. By grace! These pre - cious words re - mem - ber when sore - ly
4. By grace! Be this in death my com - fort; de - spite my

O my trem - bling heart? If what the Scrip - tures prom - ise clear - ly
home be - yond the skies. Works count for naught, the Lord in - car - nate
by your sins op - pressed, when Sa - tan comes to vex your spir - it,
fears, 'tis well with me. I know my sin in all its great - ness,

is true and firm in ev - 'ry part, this al - so must be
has won for me the heav'n - ly prize. Sal - va - tion by his
when trou - bled con - science sighs for rest; what rea - son can - not
but al - so him who sets me free. My heart to naught but

truth di - vine: by grace a crown of life is mine.
death he wrought, his grace a - lone my par - don bought.
com - pre - hend, God does to you by grace ex - tend.
joy gives place since I am saved by grace, by grace.

Christian L. Scheidt, 1742, cento
Tr. by H. Breuckner

NEUMARK 9.8.9.8.8.8.
Georg Neumark, 1657

I've Found the Pearl of Greatest Price!

696

A merchant [was] looking for fine pearls. When he found one of great value,
he ... sold everything he had and bought it. Matt. 13:45, 46

1. I've found the pearl of great-est price! My heart doth sing for joy;
2. Christ is my Proph-et, Priest, and King; my Proph-et full of light,
3. For he in-deed is Lord of lords, and he the King of kings;
4. Christ is my peace; he died for me, for me he shed his blood;
5. Christ Je-sus is my all in all, my com-fort and my love;

and sing I must, for Christ is mine! Christ shall my song em - ploy.
my great High Priest be - fore the throne, my King of heav'n - ly might.
he is the Sun of Righ-teous-ness, with heal - ing in his wings.
and as my won-drous sac - ri - fice, of - fered him-self to God.
my life be-low, and he shall be my joy and crown a - bove.

REFRAIN

I've found the pearl of great - est price! My heart doth sing for joy;

and sing I must, for Christ is mine! Christ shall my song em - ploy.

John Mason, 1683; alt.

JERUSALEM C.M.D.
Charles H. Purday, 1799–1885

697 Wonderful Words of Life

Lord, to whom shall we go? You have the words of eternal life. John 6:68

1. Sing them o - ver a - gain to me, won - der - ful words of life;
2. Christ, the bless - ed One, gives to all, won - der - ful words of life;
3. Sweet - ly ech - o the gos - pel call, won - der - ful words of life;

let me more of their beau - ty see, won - der - ful words of life.
sin - ner, list to the lov - ing call, won - der - ful words of life.
of - fer par - don and peace to all, won - der - ful words of life.

Words of life and beau - ty, teach me faith and du - ty:
All so free - ly giv - en, woo - ing us to heav - en:
Je - sus, on - ly Sav - ior, sanc - ti - fy for - ev - er:

REFRAIN

beau - ti - ful words, won - der - ful words, won - der - ful words of life; life.

Philip P. Bliss, 1874

WORDS OF LIFE 8.6.8.6.6.6.ref.
Philip P. Bliss, 1874

O Happy Day, That Fixed My Choice

698

*My soul rejoices in my God. For he has clothed me with garments of salvation
and arrayed me in a robe of righteousness.* Is. 61:10

1. O hap - py day, that fixed my choice on you, my
2. O hap - py bond, that seals my vows to him who
3. 'Tis done! the great trans - ac - tion's done! I am my
4. Now rest, my long - di - vid - ed heart; fixed on this
5. High heav'n, that heard the sol - emn vow, that vow re -

Sav - ior and my God! Well may this glow - ing
mer - its all my love! Let cheer - ful an - thems
Lord's, and he is mine; he drew me, and I
bliss - ful cen - ter, rest; with ash - es who would
newed shall dai - ly hear, till in life's lat - est

heart re - joice, and tell its rap - tures all a - broad.
fill his house, while to that sa - cred shrine I move.
fol - lowed on, charmed to con - fess the voice di - vine.
grudge to part, when called on an - gels' bread to feast?
hour I bow, and bless in death a bond so dear.

Philip Doddridge, 1702–1751
Mod.

BROOKFIELD L.M.
Thomas B. Southgate, 1855

699   Like a River Glorious

I will extend peace to her like a river. Is. 66:12

1. Like a riv-er glo-rious is God's per-fect peace, o-ver
2. Hid-den in the hol-low of his bless-ed hand, nev-er
3. Ev-'ry joy or tri-al fall-eth from a-bove, traced up-

all vic-to-rious in its bright in-crease; per-fect, yet it
foe can fol-low, nev-er trai-tor stand; not a surge of
on our di-al by the Sun of Love. We may trust him

flow-eth full-er ev-'ry day, per-fect, yet it grow-eth deep-er
wor-ry, not a shade of care, not a blast of hur-ry, touch the
ful-ly all for us to do; they who trust him whol-ly find him

REFRAIN

all the way.
spir-it there. Stayed up-on Je-ho-vah, hearts are ful-ly blest,
whol-ly true.

find - ing, as he prom - ised, per - fect peace and rest.

Frances R. Havergal, 1874

WYE VALLEY 6.5.6.5.D.ref.
James Mountain, 1876

Come, We That Love the Lord 700

Let the people of Zion be glad in their King. Ps. 149:2

1. Come, we that love the Lord, and let our joys be known;
2. Let those re - fuse to sing that nev - er knew our God;
3. The men of grace have found glo - ry be - gun be - low;
4. The hill of Zi - on yields a thou - sand sa - cred sweets,
5. Then let our songs a - bound, and ev - 'ry tear be dry;

join in a song with sweet ac - cord, and thus sur - round the throne.
but chil - dren of the heav'n - ly King may speak their joys a - broad.
ce - les - tial fruits on earth - ly ground from faith and hope may grow.
be - fore we reach the heav'n - ly fields or walk the gold - en streets.
we're march - ing through Im - man - uel's ground to fair - er worlds on high.

Isaac Watts, 1707; alt.

ST. THOMAS S.M.
Aaron Williams, 1763

701

Redeemed, How I Love to Proclaim It!

In him we have redemption through his blood. Eph. 1:7

1. Re-deemed, how I love to pro-claim it! Re-deemed by the
2. Re-deemed and so hap-py in Je-sus, no lan-guage my
3. I think of my bless-ed Re-deem-er, I think of him

blood of the Lamb; re-deemed thro' his in-fi-nite mer-cy, his
rap-ture can tell; I know that the light of his pres-ence with
all the day long; I sing, for I can-not be si-lent; his

REFRAIN

child, and for-ev-er, I am. Re-deemed, re-deemed,
me doth con-tin-ual-ly dwell.
love is the theme of my song.

re-deemed by the blood of the Lamb; re-deemed thro' his

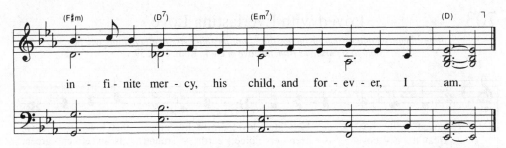

in - fi - nite mer - cy, his child, and for - ev - er, I am.

Fanny J. Crosby, 1882

ADA 9.8.9.8.ref.
A. L. Butler, 1967

Peace, Perfect Peace   702

You will keep in perfect peace him whose mind is steadfast, because he trusts in you.
Is. 26:3

1. Peace, per - fect peace, in this dark world of sin?
2. Peace, per - fect peace, by throng - ing du - ties pressed?
3. Peace, per - fect peace, with sor - rows surg - ing round?
4. Peace, per - fect peace, with loved ones far a - way?

The blood of Je - sus whis - pers peace with - in.
To do the will of Je - sus, this is rest.
On Je - sus' bos - om naught but calm is found.
In Je - sus' keep - ing we are safe and they.

5. Peace, perfect peace, our future all unknown?
Jesus we know, and he is on the throne.

6. Peace, perfect peace, death shad'wing us and ours?
Jesus has vanquished death and all its pow'rs.

7. It is enough: earth's struggles soon shall cease,
and Jesus call us to heav'n's perfect peace.

Edward H. Bickersteth, 1875

PAX TECUM 10.10.
George T. Caldbeck, 1877
Arr. by Charles J. Vincent, 1877

703 Loved with Everlasting Love

I am convinced that neither death nor life ... nor anything else in all creation, will be able to separate us from the love of God. Rom. 8:38, 39

1. Loved with ev - er - last - ing love, drawn by grace that love to know,
2. Heav'n a - bove is deep - er blue, earth a - round is sweet - er green,
3. Taste the good - ness of the Lord: wel-comed home to his em - brace,
4. His for - ev - er, on - ly his— who the Lord and me shall part?

Spir - it sent from Christ a - bove, thou dost wit - ness it is so.
that which glows in ev - ery hue Christ-less eyes have nev - er seen.
all his love as blood out - poured seals the par - don of his grace.
Ah, with what a rest of bliss Christ can fill the lov - ing heart.

O this full and pre - cious peace from his pres - ence all di - vine;
Birds in song his glo - ries show, flow'rs with rich - er beau - ties shine
Can I doubt his love for me, when I trace that love's de - sign?
Heav'n and earth may fade and flee, first-born light in gloom de - cline,

in a love that can - not cease, I am his and he is mine; mine.
since I know, as now I know, I am his and he is mine; mine.
By the cross of Cal - va - ry I am his and he is mine. mine.
but while God and I shall be, I am his and he is mine; mine.

George W. Robinson, 1890
Rev. by Edmund P. Clowney, 1986

EVERLASTING LOVE 7.7.7.7.D.
James Mountain, ca. 1890

Thou Wilt Keep Him in Perfect Peace

704

You will keep in perfect peace him whose mind is steadfast, because he trusts in you.
Is. 26:3

Unison

1. Thou wilt keep him in per - fect peace, thou wilt keep him in per - fect peace, thou wilt keep him in per - fect peace, whose mind is stayed on thee.
2. Mar - vel not that I say un - to you, mar - vel not that I say un - to you, mar - vel not that I say un - to you, "You must be born a - gain."
3. Tho' your sins as scar - let be, tho' your sins as scar - let be, tho' your sins as scar - let be, they shall be white as snow.
4. If the Son shall make you free, if the Son shall make you free, if the Son shall make you free, you shall be free in - deed.
5. They that wait up - on the Lord, they that wait up - on the Lord, they that wait up - on the Lord, they shall re - new their strength.

Anon.

FÜRCHTE DICH NICHT 8.8.8.6.
Robert Witty
Arr. by Paul Beckwith, 1976

705 I Know Whom I Have Believed

I know whom I have believed, and am convinced that he is able to guard what I have entrusted to him for that day. 2 Tim. 1:12

1. I know not why God's won-drous grace to me he has made known,
2. I know not how this sav-ing faith to me he did im - part,
3. I know not how the Spir - it moves, con - vinc - ing men of sin,
4. I know not what of good or ill may be re-served for me,
5. I know not when my Lord may come, at night or noon-day fair,

nor why, un-wor - thy, Christ in love re - deemed me for his own.
nor how be - liev-ing in his Word wrought peace with-in my heart.
re - veal - ing Je - sus through the Word, cre - at - ing faith in him.
of wea - ry ways or gold - en days, be - fore his face I see.
nor if I'll walk the vale with him, or "meet him in the air."

REFRAIN

But "I know whom I have be - liev - ed, and am per - suad - ed that he is a - ble to keep that which I've com - mit - ted un - to him a- gainst that day."

Daniel W. Whittle, 1883

EL NATHAN C.M.ref.
James McGranahan. 1883

Jesus Lives, and So Shall I

706

Where, O death, is your sting? 1 Cor. 15:55

1. Je - sus lives, and so shall I. Death! thy sting is gone for - ev - er!
2. Je - sus lives and reigns su - preme; and, his king - dom still re - main - ing,
3. Je - sus lives, and by his grace, vic - t'ry o'er my pas- sions giv - ing,
4. Je - sus lives! I know full well naught from him my heart can sev - er,
5. Je - sus lives and death is now but my en - trance in - to glo - ry.

He who deigned for me to die, lives, the bands of death to sev - er.
I shall al - so be with him, ev - er liv - ing, ev - er reign - ing.
• I will cleanse my heart and ways, ev - er to his glo - ry liv - ing.
life nor death nor pow'rs of hell, joy nor grief, hence- forth for - ev - er.
Cour - age, then, my soul, for thou hast a crown of life be - fore thee;

He shall raise me from the dust: Je - sus is my hope and trust.
God has prom- ised; be it must: Je - sus is my hope and trust.
• Me he rais - es from the dust: Je - sus is my hope and trust.
None of all his saints is lost: Je - sus is my hope and trust.
thou shalt find thy hopes were just: Je - sus is the Chris- tian's trust.

Christian F. Gellert, 1757
Tr. by J. D. Lang, 1826

JESUS, MEINE ZUVERSICHT 7.8.7.8.7.7.
Johann Crüger, 1653; arr.

707

Jesus, I My Cross Have Taken

If anyone would come after me, he must deny himself and take up his cross and follow me. Mark 8:34

1. Je - sus, I my cross have tak - en, all to leave and fol - low thee;
2. Let the world de - spise and leave me, they have left my Sav - ior too;
3. Man may trou - ble and dis - tress me, 'twill but drive me to thy breast;
4. Take, my soul, thy full sal - va - tion, rise o'er sin and fear and care;

des - ti - tute, de - spised, for - sak - en, thou from hence my all shall be.
hu - man hearts and looks de - ceive me; thou art not, like man, un - true;
life with tri - als hard may press me, heav'n will bring me sweet - er rest.
joy to find in ev - 'ry sta - tion some - thing still to do or bear;

Per - ish ev - 'ry fond am - bi - tion, all I've sought or hoped or known;
and, while thou shalt smile up - on me, God of wis - dom, love, and might,
O 'tis not in grief to harm me while thy love is left to me;
think what Spir - it dwells with - in thee, what a Fa - ther's smile is thine,

yet how rich is my con - di - tion, God and heav'n are still my own.
foes may hate and friends may shun me; show thy face, and all is bright.
O 'twere not in joy to charm me, were that joy un - mixed with thee.
what a Sav - ior died to win thee: child of heav'n, shouldst thou re - pine?

5. Hasten on from grace to glory, armed by faith and winged by prayer;
heav'n's eternal day's before thee, God's own hand shall guide thee there.
Soon shall close thy earthly mission, swift shall pass thy pilgrim days;
hope shall change to glad fruition, faith to sight, and prayer to praise.

Henry F. Lyte, 1824, 1833
Alt. 1990

ELLESDIE 8.7.8.7.D.
Attr. to Wolfgang Amadeus Mozart, 1756–1791
Arr. in Joshua Leavitt's *The Christian Lyre*, 1831; rev.

O Love That Wilt Not Let Me Go 708

I have loved you with an everlasting love; I have drawn you with loving-kindness.
Jer. 31:3

1. O Love that wilt not let me go,
I rest my weary soul in thee;
I give thee back the life I owe,
that in thine ocean depths its flow may richer, fuller be.

2. O Light that follow'st all my way,
I yield my flickering torch to thee;
my heart restores its borrowed ray,
that in thy sunshine's blaze its day may brighter, fairer be.

3. O Joy that seek-est me through pain,
I cannot close my heart to thee;
I trace the rainbow through the rain,
and feel the promise is not vain that morn shall tearless be.

4. O Cross that lift-est up my head,
I dare not ask to fly from thee;
I lay in dust life's glory dead,
and from the ground there blossoms red life that shall endless be.

George Matheson, 1882

ST. MARGARET 8.8.8.8.6.
Albert L. Peace, 1885

709

Now I Belong to Jesus

Whether we live or die, we belong to the Lord. Rom. 14:8

1. Je - sus, my Lord, will love me for - ev - er, from him no pow'r of
2. Once I was lost in sin's deg - ra - da - tion; Je - sus came down to
3. Joy floods my soul for Je - sus has saved me, freed me from sin that

e - vil can sev - er; he gave his life to ran - som my soul,
bring me sal - va - tion, lift - ed me up from sor - row and shame,
long had en - slaved me; his pre - cious blood he gave to re - deem,

REFRAIN

now I be - long to him.
now I be - long to him. Now I be - long to Je - sus, Je - sus be -
now I be - long to him.

longs to me, not for the years of time a - lone, but for e - ter - ni - ty.

Norman J. Clayton, 1943

ELLSWORTH 10.10.9.6.ref.
Norman J. Clayton, 1943

God of Our Fathers

710

The LORD Almighty is with us; the God of Jacob is our fortress. Ps. 46:7

Organ or trumpets
before each stanza

1. God of our fa-thers, whose al-might-y
2. Thy love di-vine hath led us in the
3. From war's a-larms, from dead-ly pes-ti-
4. Re-fresh thy peo-ple on their toil-some

hand | leads forth in beau-ty all the star-ry
past; | in this free land by thee our lot is
lence, | be thy strong arm our ev-er-sure de-
way, | lead us from night to nev-er-end-ing

band | of shin-ing worlds in splen-dor through the
cast; | be thou our rul-er, guard-ian, guide, and
fense; | thy true re-li-gion in our hearts in-
day; | fill all our lives with love and grace di-

skies, | our grate-ful songs be-fore thy throne a-rise.
stay; | thy Word our law, thy paths our cho-sen way.
crease, | thy boun-teous good-ness nour-ish us in peace.
vine, | and glo-ry, laud, and praise be ev-er thine.

Daniel C. Roberts, 1876

NATIONAL HYMN 10.10.10.10.
George William Warren, 1892

711 God the All-Terrible!

Come and see the works of the LORD.... He makes wars cease to the ends of the earth.
Ps. 46:8, 9

1. God the all-ter-ri-ble! King, who or-dain-est great winds thy clar-i-ons, light-nings thy sword, show forth thy pit-y on high where thou reign-est; give to us peace in our time, O Lord.

2. God the om-nip-o-tent! might-y a-veng-er, watch-ing in-vis-i-ble, judg-ing un-heard, save us in mer-cy, O save us from dan-ger; give to us peace in our time, O Lord.

3. God the all-mer-ci-ful! earth hath for-sak-en thy ways of bless-ed-ness, slight-ed thy Word; bid not thy wrath in its ter-rors a-wak-en; give to us peace in our time, O Lord.

4. God the all-righ-teous One! man hath de-fied thee; yet to e-ter-ni-ty stand-eth thy Word; false-hood and wrong shall not tar-ry be-side thee; give to us peace in our time, O Lord.

5. God the all-wise! by the fire of thy chas-t'ning, earth shall to free-dom and truth be re-stored; through the thick dark-ness thy king-dom is has-t'ning; thou wilt give peace in thy time, O Lord.

St. 1–3, Henry F. Chorley, 1842
St. 4–5, John Ellerton, 1870

RUSSIAN HYMN 11.10.11.9.
Alexis Lwoff. 1833

O God of Love, O King of Peace

He makes wars cease to the ends of the earth. Ps. 46:9

1. O God of love, O King of peace, make wars throughout the world to cease; the wrath of sin - ful
man re - strain; give peace, O God, give peace a - gain.

2. Re - mem - ber, Lord, your works of old, the won - ders
that our fa - thers told; re - mem - ber not our
sin's dark stain; give peace, O God, give peace a - gain.

3. Whom shall we trust but you, O Lord? Where rest but
on your faith - ful Word? None ev - er called on
you in vain; give peace, O God, give peace a - gain.

4. Where saints and an - gels dwell a - bove all hearts are
knit in ho - ly love; O bind us in that
heav'n - ly chain; give peace, O God, give peace a - gain.

Henry W. Baker, 1861
Mod.

QUEBEC L.M.
Henry Baker, 1854

713   Great King of Nations, Hear Our Prayer

His mercy extends to those who fear him, from generation to generation. Luke 1:50

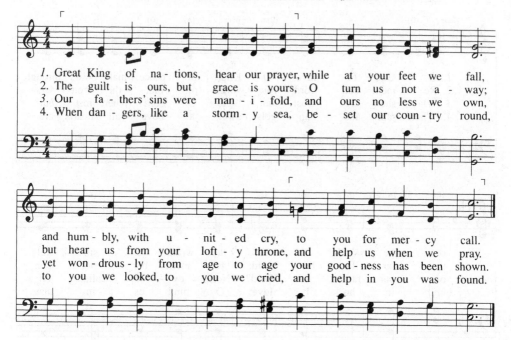

1. Great King of na-tions, hear our prayer, while at your feet we fall,
2. The guilt is ours, but grace is yours, O turn us not a-way;
3. Our fa-thers' sins were man-i-fold, and ours no less we own,
4. When dan-gers, like a storm-y sea, be-set our coun-try round,

and hum-bly, with u-nit-ed cry, to you for mer-cy call.
but hear us from your loft-y throne, and help us when we pray.
yet won-drous-ly from age to age your good-ness has been shown.
to you we looked, to you we cried, and help in you was found.

5. With one consent we meekly bow
beneath your chast'ning hand,
and, pouring forth confession meet,
mourn with our mourning land.

6. With pitying eye behold our need,
as thus we lift our prayer;
correct us with your judgments, Lord,
then let your mercy spare.

John H. Gurney, 1838
Mod.

ST. ANNE C.M.
Attr. to William Croft, 1678–1727
Tate and Brady's *Supplement to the New Version,* 1708

714   We Plow the Fields

He has shown kindness by giving you rain from heaven and crops in their seasons;
he provides you with plenty of food and fills your hearts with joy. Acts 14:17

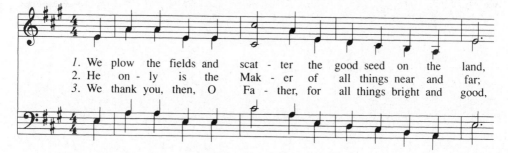

1. We plow the fields and scat-ter the good seed on the land,
2. He on-ly is the Mak-er of all things near and far;
3. We thank you, then, O Fa-ther, for all things bright and good,

but it is fed and wa - tered by God's al - might - y hand;
he paints the way - side flow - er, he lights the eve - ning star;
the seed - time and the har - vest, our life, our health, our food;

he sends the snow in win - ter, the warmth to swell the grain,
the winds and waves o - bey him, by him the birds are fed;
no gifts have we to of - fer for all your love im - parts,

the breez - es and the sun - shine, and soft re - fresh - ing rain.
much more to us, his chil - dren, he gives our dai - ly bread.
but that which you de - sire now: our hum - ble, thank- ful hearts.

REFRAIN

All good gifts a - round us are sent from heav'n a - bove;

then thank the Lord, O thank the Lord for all his love.

Matthias Claudius, 1782
Tr. by Jane M. Campbell, 1861; alt. 1990, mod.

WIR PFLÜGEN 7.6.7.6.D.ref.
Johann A. P. Schulz, 1800

715   Come, Ye Thankful People, Come

The harvest is the end of the age, and the harvesters are angels. Matt. 13:39

1. Come, ye thank-ful peo-ple, come, raise the song of har-vest home:
2. All the world is God's own field, fruit un-to his praise to yield;
3. For the Lord our God shall come, and shall take his har-vest home;
4. E-ven so, Lord, quick-ly come to thy fi-nal har-vest home;

all is safe-ly gath-ered in, ere the win-ter storms be-gin;
wheat and tares to-geth-er sown, un-to joy or sor-row grown:
from his field shall in that day all of-fens-es purge a-way;
gath-er thou thy peo-ple in, free from sor-row, free from sin;

God, our Mak-er, doth pro-vide for our wants to be sup-plied:
first the blade, and then the ear, then the full corn shall ap-pear:
give his an-gels charge at last in the fire the tares to cast,
there for-ev-er pu-ri-fied, in thy pres-ence to a-bide:

come to God's own tem-ple, come, raise the song of har-vest home.
Lord of har-vest, grant that we whole-some grain and pure may be.
but the fruit-ful ears to store in his gar-ner ev-er-more.
come, with all thine an-gels, come, raise the glo-rious har-vest home.

Henry Alford, 1844, 1867

ST. GEORGE'S, WINDSOR 7.7.7.7.D.
George J. Elvey, 1859

Sing to the Lord of Harvest

All the people went away to eat and drink, to send portions of food and to celebrate with great joy. Neh. 8:12

1. Sing to the Lord of har - vest, sing songs of love and praise;
2. By him the clouds drop fat - ness, the des - erts bloom and spring,
3. Heap on his sa - cred al - tar the gifts his good - ness gave,
4. To God the gra - cious Fa - ther, who made us "ver - y good,"

with joy - ful hearts and voic - es your al - le - lu - ias raise!
the hills leap up in glad - ness, the val - leys laugh and sing.
the gold - en sheaves of har - vest, the souls he died to save.
to Christ, who, when we wan - dered, re - stored us with his blood,

By him the roll - ing sea - sons in fruit - ful or - der move;
He fill - eth with his full - ness all things with large in - crease;
Your hearts lay down be - fore him when at his feet you fall,
and to the Ho - ly Spir - it, who doth up - on us pour

sing to the Lord of har - vest a song of hap - py love.
he crowns the year with good - ness, with plen - ty, and with peace.
and with your lives a - dore him who gave his life for all.
his bless - ed dews and sun - shine, be praise for - ev - er - more.

John S. B. Monsell, 1866

WIE LIEBLICH IST DER MAIEN 7.6.7.6.D.
Johann Steurlein, 1575
Arr. by Healey Willan, 1959

717 Blest the Man That Fears Jehovah

Blessed are all who fear the LORD, who walk in his ways. Ps. 128:1

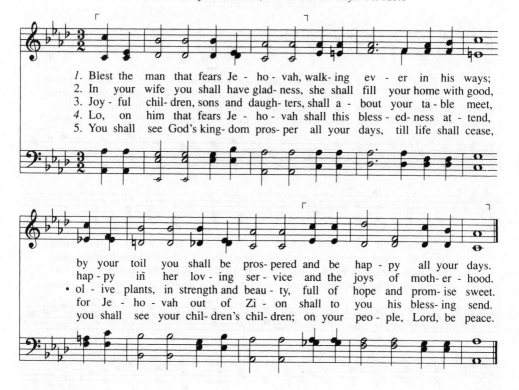

1. Blest the man that fears Je - ho - vah, walk- ing ev - er in his ways;
2. In your wife you shall have glad- ness, she shall fill your home with good,
3. Joy - ful chil- dren, sons and daugh- ters, shall a - bout your ta - ble meet,
4. Lo, on him that fears Je - ho - vah shall this bless - ed- ness at - tend,
5. You shall see God's king- dom pros- per all your days, till life shall cease,

by your toil you shall be pros- pered and be hap - py all your days.
hap - py in her lov - ing ser - vice and the joys of moth- er - hood.
• ol - ive plants, in strength and beau - ty, full of hope and prom- ise sweet.
for Je - ho - vah out of Zi - on shall to you his bless- ing send.
you shall see your chil- dren's chil- dren; on your peo - ple, Lord, be peace.

From Psalm 128
The Psalter, 1912; mod.

GALILEE 8.7.8.7.
William H. Jude. 1887

O Happy Home, Where Thou Art Loved

718

As for me and my household, we will serve the LORD. Josh. 24:15

1. O hap - py home, where thou art loved the dear- est, thou lov - ing
Friend and Sav - ior of our race, and where a - mong the guests there
nev - er com - eth one who can hold such high and hon - ored place!

2. O hap - py home, where two in heart u - nit - ed in ho - ly
faith and bless - ed hope are one, whom death a lit - tle while a -
lone di - vid - eth, and can - not end the u - nion here be - gun!

3. O hap - py home, whose lit - tle ones are giv - en ear - ly to
thee in hum - ble faith and prayer, to thee, their Friend, who from the
heights of heav - en guides them, and guards with more than moth - er's care!

4. O hap - py home, where each one serves thee, low- ly, what - ev - er
his ap - point - ed work may be, till ev - 'ry com - mon task seems
great and ho - ly, when it is done, O Lord, as un - to thee!

5. O happy home, where thou art not forgotten
when joy is overflowing, full and free,
O happy home, where ev'ry wounded spirit
is brought, Physician, Comforter, to thee—

6. Until at last, when earth's day's work is ended,
all meet thee in the blessed home above,
from whence thou camest, where thou hast ascended,
thine everlasting home of peace and love.

Carl J. P. Spitta, 1833
Tr. by Sarah B. Findlater, 1858; alt.

COMMUNION 11.10.11.10.
Felix Mendelssohn–Bartholdy, 1835; arr.

719

A Christian Home

As for me and my household, we will serve the LORD. Josh. 24:15

1. O give us homes built firm up - on the Sav- ior,
2. O give us homes with god - ly fa - thers, moth- ers,
3. O Lord, our God, our homes are thine for - ev - er!

where Christ is Head and Coun - sel - or and guide; where ev - ery
who al - ways place their hope and trust in him; whose ten - der
We trust to thee their prob - lems, toil, and care; their bonds of

child is taught his love and fa - vor and gives his heart to
pa - tience tur - moil nev - er both- ers, whose calm and cour - age
love no en - e - my can sev - er, if thou art al - ways

Christ, the cru - ci - fied: how sweet to know that though his foot - steps
trou - ble can - not dim: a home where each finds joy in serv - ing
Lord and Mas - ter there: be thou the cen - ter of our least en -

wa - ver,   his faith - ful   Lord   is   walk - ing   by   his   side!
oth - ers,   and love still   shines,   tho' days   be   dark   and   grim.
deav - or—   be thou our   guest,   our hearts and homes   to   share.

Barbara B. Hart, 1965

FINLANDIA 11.10.11.10.11.10.
Jean Sibelius, 1899; arr.

Text © 1965, Singspiration Music/ASCAP. All rights reserved. Used by permission of The Benson Co., Inc. Tune © Breitkopf & Härtel, Wiesbaden. Used by permission.

Happy the Home When God Is There   720

He will direct his children and his household after him to keep the way of the LORD.
Gen. 18:19

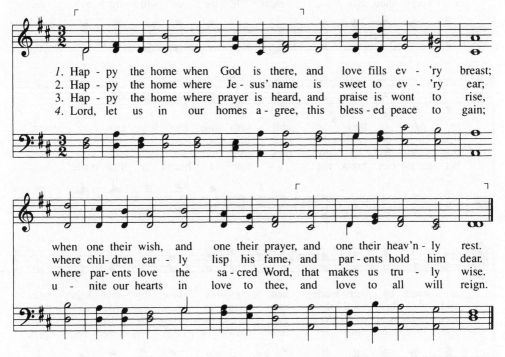

1. Hap - py   the home when   God   is there, and   love fills ev - 'ry   breast;
2. Hap - py   the home where   Je - sus' name   is   sweet to ev - 'ry   ear;
3. Hap - py   the home where prayer is   heard, and   praise is wont   to   rise,
4. Lord, let   us in   our homes a - gree,   this   bless - ed peace   to   gain;

when one their wish,   and   one their prayer, and   one their heav'n - ly   rest.
where chil - dren ear - ly   lisp his fame, and   par - ents hold   him   dear.
where par - ents love   the   sa - cred Word, that makes us tru - ly   wise.
u - nite our hearts   in   love to thee, and   love to all   will   reign.

Henry Ware, Jr., 1794–1843; alt.

DOWNS C.M.
Lowell Mason. 1832

721 O Father, All-Creating

Unless the LORD builds the house, its builders labor in vain. Ps. 127:1

1. O Father, all-creating, whose wisdom, love, and pow'r
first bound two lives together in Eden's primal hour,
today to these thy children thine earliest gifts renew,
a home by thee made happy, a love by thee kept true.

2. O Savior, guest most bounteous of old in Galilee,
vouchsafe today thy presence with these who call on thee;
their store of earthly gladness transform to heav'nly wine,
and teach them in the tasting to know the gift is thine.

3. O Spirit of the Father, breathe on them from above,
so mighty in thy pureness, so tender in thy love,
that, guarded by thy presence, from sin and strife kept free,
their lives may own thy guidance, their hearts be ruled by thee.

4. Except thou build it, Father, the house is built in vain;
except thou, Savior, bless it, the joy will turn to pain;
but naught can break the union of hearts in thee made one;
and love thy Spirit hallows is endless love begun.

John Ellerton, 1876

SAVOY CHAPEL 7.6.7.6.D.
John Baptiste Calkin, 1887; alt. 1990

O Perfect Love

722

Husbands, love your wives, just as Christ loved the church and gave himself up for her.
Eph. 5:25

1. O per - fect Love, all hu - man thought tran - scend - ing,
2. O per - fect Life, be thou their full as - sur - ance
3. Grant them the joy which bright - ens earth - ly sor - row;
4. Hear us, O Fa - ther, gra - cious and for - giv - ing,

low - ly we kneel in prayer be - fore thy throne,
of ten - der char - i - ty and stead - fast faith,
grant them the peace which calms all earth - ly strife,
through Je - sus Christ thy co - e - ter - nal Word,

that theirs may be the love which knows no end - ing,
of pa - tient hope, and qui - et, brave en - dur - ance,
and to life's day the glo - rious un - known mor - row
who, with the Ho - ly Ghost, by all things liv - ing

whom thou for - ev - er - more dost join in one.
with child - like trust that fears nor pain nor death.
that dawns up - on e - ter - nal love and life.
now and to end - less a - ges art a - dored.

St. 1–3, Dorothy F. Gurney, 1883
St. 4, John Ellerton, 1875

PERFECT LOVE 11.10.11.10.
Joseph Barnby, 1889

723 Come Away to the Skies

Arise, come, my darling; my beautiful one, come with me. Song of Sol. 2:13

1. Come a - way to the skies, my be - lov - ed, a - rise and re-
2. Now with sing - ing and praise, let us spend all the days, by our
3. For the glo - ry we were first cre - at - ed to share, both the
4. We with thanks do ap - prove the de - sign of that love which hath
5. Hal - le - lu - jah we sing to our Fa - ther and King, and his

joice in the day thou wast born; on this fes - ti - val day,
heav - en - ly Fa - ther be - stowed, while his grace we re - ceive
na - ture and king - dom di - vine! Now cre - at - ed a - gain
joined us to Je - sus' dear name; so u - nit - ed in heart,
rap - tur - ous prais - es re - peat: to the Lamb that was slain,

come ex - ult - ing a - way, and with sing - ing to Zi - on re - turn.
from his boun - ty, and live to the hon - or and glo - ry of God.
that our lives may re - main, through-out time and e - ter - ni - ty thine.
let us nev - er - more part, till we meet at the feast of the Lamb.
hal - le - lu - jah a - gain; sing, all heav - en, and fall at his feet.

The Southern Harmony, 1835; alt.

MIDDLEBURY 6.6.9.6.6.9.
The Southern Harmony, 1835
Arr. by Jack W. Burnam, b. 1946

Tune arr. © Jack W. Burnam.

The Ten Commandments

I am the LORD your God, who brought you out of Egypt, out of the land of slavery. Ex. 20:2

1. My soul, re - call with rev - 'rent won - der how
2. "I am the Lord, your God and Sov - ereign, who
3. "You shall not bow to grav - en i - dols, for
4. "The Lord is God; his name is ho - ly. Do
5. "Re - mem - ber, keep the Sab - bath ho - ly, the

God a - mid the fire and smoke pro - claimed his ho - ly
out of bond - age set you free, who saved you from the
• I, a jeal - ous God, your Lord, shall pun - ish sin in
not his ho - li - ness pro - fane. God sure - ly will not
day God sanc - ti - fied and blessed. Six days you shall do

law with thun - der from Si - nai's moun - tain when he spoke:
land of E - gypt. Then serve no oth - er gods but me.
• those who hate me, but love all those who keep my Word.
hold them guilt - less who take his ho - ly name in vain.
all your la - bor, but on the sev - enth you shall rest.

6. "Honor your father and your mother;
obey the Lord your God's command,
that you may dwell secure and prosper
with length of days upon the land.

7. "You shall not hate or kill your neighbor.
Do not commit adultery.
You shall not steal from one another
nor testify untruthfully.

8. "You shall not covet the possessions
your neighbors value as their own;
home, wife or husband, all their treasures
you shall respect as theirs alone."

9. Teach us, Lord God, to love your precepts,
the good commandments of your law.
Give us the grace to keep your statutes
with thankfulness and proper awe.

The Ten Commandments
Versified by Dewey Westra, 1899–1979
Alt. in *Psalter Hymnal*, 1987

LES COMMANDEMENTS DE DIEU 9.8.9.8.
Genevan Psalter, 1547
Arr. by Claude Goudimel, 1564; rev.

725

The Lord's Prayer

This, then, is how you should pray: "Our Father in heaven, hallowed be your name."
Matt. 6:9

1. Our Fa - ther, Lord of heav'n and earth, let praise and hon - or
2. For - give us, Lord, our sins and debts as we to debt - ors

clothe your name. Your king - dom come, your will be done; through -
show your grace. Re - move us from all tempt - ing paths and

out the world com - plete your reign. Teach us, O Lord, to
guard us from the dev - il's ways; for glo - ry, strength, and

trust in you for bread and breath each day a - new.
heav - en's throne be - long to you, and you a - lone.

The Lord's Prayer
Versified by Henry J. de Jong, 1982
Text vers. ©1987, CRC Publications. All rights reserved. Used by permission.

MELITA 8.8.8.8.8.8.
John B. Dykes, 1861

Spirit of the Living God

That you may be filled to the measure of all the fullness of God. Eph. 3:19

726

Spir - it of the liv - ing God, fall fresh on me.

Spir - it of the liv - ing God, fall fresh on me.

Break me! Melt me! Mold me! Fill me!

Spir - it of the liv - ing God, fall fresh on me.

Daniel Iverson, 1926

IVERSON Irreg.
Daniel Iverson, 1926

727 Lead Me, Lord, Lead Me in Thy Righteousness

Lead me, O LORD, in your righteousness. Ps. 5:8

1. Lead me, Lord, lead me in thy right-teous-ness, make thy way
2. Teach me, Lord, teach me tru-ly how to live, that I may

plain be - fore my face. For it is thou, Lord, thou, Lord,
come to know...... thee, and in thy pres - ence serve thee with

on - ly, that mak - est me dwell in safe - ty.
glad - ness, and sing songs of praise to thy glo - ry.

St. 1, Samuel S. Wesley, 1810–1876
St. 2, George F. Strickling
Tune © E. C. Schirmer, Inc. Used by permission.

LEAD ME, LORD 10.8.
Samuel S. Wesley, 1810–1876

728 Hear Our Prayer, O Lord

The LORD ... hears the prayer of the righteous. Prov. 15:29

Hear our prayer, O Lord, hear our prayer, O Lord;

in - cline thine ear to us, and grant us thy peace. A - men.

Anon.

WHELPTON 5.5.6.5.
George Whelpton, 1897

All Things Are Thine

729

*Everything comes from you, and we have given you only what comes from
your hand.* 1 Chron. 29:14

All things are thine; no gift have we, Lord

of all gifts, to of - fer thee; and hence with grate - ful

hearts to - day, thine own be - fore thy feet we lay.

John G. Whittier, 1872

HERR JESU CHRIST L.M.
Pensum Sacrum, Görlitz, 1648
Arr. by Johann Sebastian Bach, 1685–1750

730 Benediction

*May the grace of the Lord Jesus Christ, and the love of God, and the fellowship
of the Holy Spirit be with you all. 2 Cor. 13:14*

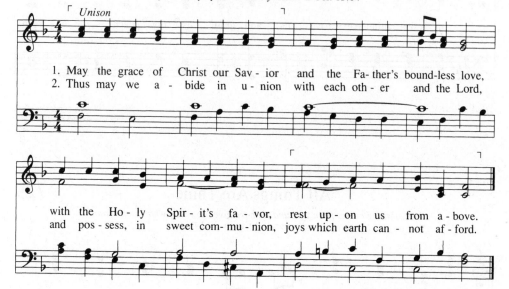

Unison

1. May the grace of Christ our Sav - ior and the Fa- ther's bound-less love,
2. Thus may we a - bide in u - nion with each oth - er and the Lord,

with the Ho - ly Spir - it's fa - vor, rest up - on us from a - bove.
and pos - sess, in sweet com- mu - nion, joys which earth can - not af - ford.

John Newton, 1779

EVENING PRAYER (STAINER) 8.7.8.7.
John Stainer, 1898

731 Doxology

Let everything that has breath praise the LORD. Ps. 150:6

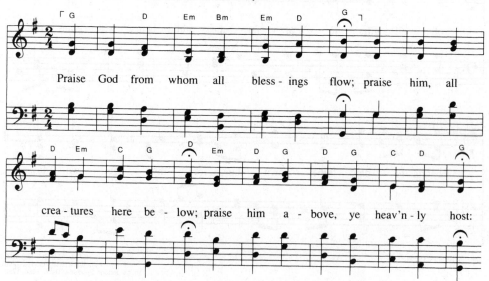

Praise God from whom all bless - ings flow; praise him, all

crea - tures here be - low; praise him a - bove, ye heav'n - ly host:

praise Fa - ther, Son, and Ho - ly Ghost. A - men.

Thomas Ken, 1709

OLD HUNDREDTH L.M.
Louis Bourgeois's *Genevan Psalter*, 1551

Doxology

732

Let everything that has breath praise the LORD. Ps. 150:6

Praise God from whom all bless - ings flow; praise him, all crea - tures here be - low; praise him a - bove, ye heav'n - ly host: praise Fa - ther, Son, and Ho - ly Ghost.

Thomas Ken, 1709

TALLIS' CANON L.M.
Thomas Tallis, ca. 1567

733

Doxology

Let everything that has breath praise the LORD. Ps. 150:6

Praise God from whom all bless-ings flow; praise him, all crea-tures here be-low: al-le-lu-ia, al-le-lu-ia! Praise him a-bove, ye heav'n-ly host, praise Fa-ther, Son, and Ho-ly Ghost: al-le-lu-ia, al-le-lu-ia, al-le-lu-ia, al-le-lu-ia, al-le-lu-ia!

Thomas Ken, 1709; alt.

LASST UNS ERFREUEN L.M.al.
Geistliche Kirchengesänge, Cologne, 1623

Gloria Patri

*Ascribe to the LORD the glory due his name; worship the LORD in the splendor
of his holiness. Ps. 29:2*

2nd cent.; tr.

GLORIA PATRI (MEINEKE) Irreg.
Charles Meineke. 1844

735

Gloria Patri

Ascribe to the LORD the glory due his name; worship the LORD in the splendor of his holiness. Ps. 29:2

Glo - ry be to the Fa - ther, and to the

Son, and to the Ho - ly Ghost; as it was in

the be - gin - ning, is now, and ev - er

shall be, world with - out end. A - men, a - men.

2nd cent.; tr.

GLORIA PATRI (GREATOREX)
Henry W. Greatorex, 1851

Gloria Patri

Ascribe to the LORD the glory due his name; worship the LORD in the splendor of his holiness. Ps. 29:2

Unison

Glo - ry be to God the Fa - ther, and to Christ his on - ly Son;

praise we too the Ho - ly Spir - it, bind - ing all the

church as one: as it was in the be - gin - ning, is for now and

ev - er - more! A - - men, a - men!

A - - men, a - men!

Gloria Patri, 2nd cent.
Adapted by Carlton Young, 1973; alt. 1990

GLORIA PATRI (YOUNG)
Carlton Young, 1973

737 Christ, We Do All Adore Thee

You are worthy, our Lord and God, to receive glory and honor and power.
Rev. 4:11

Christ, we do all a - dore thee, and we do praise thee for - ev - er;

Christ, we do all a - dore thee, and we do praise thee for - ev - er;

for on the ho - ly cross hast thou the world from sin re - deem - ed.

Christ, we do all a - dore thee, and we do praise thee for - ev - er.

rit.

(instrument)

Christ, we do all a - dore thee.

Latin hymn
Tr. and adapted by Theodore Baker, 1899

ADORE THEE
Théodore Dubois, *The Seven Last Words of Christ*, 1867

Twofold Amen

738

Let all the people say, "Amen!" Ps. 106:48

A - men, a - men.

DRESDEN
Anon.

Twofold Amen

739

Praise be to the LORD forever! Amen and Amen. Ps. 89:52

A - men, a - men.

Greek liturgy

Threefold Amen

740

Pray ... sing ... say "Amen." 1 Cor. 14:15, 16

A - men, a - men, a - men.

DANISH
Anon.

741

The Apostles' Creed

It is with your mouth that you confess and are saved. Rom. 10:10

1. In God the Fa-ther I be-lieve, Al-might-y Lord of all, who
2. Who suf-fered when he stood con-demned by Pon-tius Pi-late's code, was
3. As-cend-ing in-to heav'n a-bove, he sits at God's right hand; from
4. I do be-lieve that all the saints must now com-mune in love, and

made the heav-ens and the earth: his name be praised in awe. And
cru-ci-fied, was dead, as he him-self had long fore-told; our
there he shall re-turn to judge the liv-ing and the dead. In
that, re-deemed by Je-sus' blood, our sins are par-doned us; and

I be-lieve in Je-sus Christ, the Fa-ther's on-ly Son, con-
Lord was bur-ied in a tomb, de-scend-ed in-to hell, but
God the Spir-it I be-lieve, who guides a ho-ly church, the
at life's end my bod-y frail, up-raised from earth-ly strife, is

ceiv-ed by the Ho-ly Ghost, of vir-gin Mar-y born;
on the third day he a-rose a-gain on earth to dwell.
u-ni-ver-sal bod-y that vic-to-rious shall e-merge.
res-ur-rect-ed and re-newed in ev-er-last-ing life.

Suggested accompaniment through measure 7, at least for stanzas 2 and 4:

The Apostles' Creed, ca. 2nd cent., 6th cent.
Versified by Frank De Vries, 1975

CREDO (MILADIN) C.M.D.
George C. Miladin, 1982

742 The Apostles' Creed

It is with your mouth that you confess and are saved. Rom. 10:10

1. I be-lieve in God the Fa-ther, Mak-er of all heav'n and earth;
2. Suf-fered un-der Pon-tius Pi-late, cru-ci-fied, for me he died;
3. At God's right hand he is seat-ed till his com-ing, as he said;
4. I be-lieve the church of Je-sus, u-ni-ver-sal, e'er re-mains;

and in Je-sus Christ, our Sav-ior, God's own Son, of match-less worth;
laid with-in the grave so si-lent, gates of hell he o-pened wide;
fi-nal judg-ment will be met-ed to the liv-ing and the dead;
we are one through all the a-ges, in com-mu-nion of the saints.

by the Spir-it was con-ceiv-ed, of the vir-gin Mar-y born,
for the stone-sealed tomb was emp-ty; on the third day he a-rose;
I con-fess the Ho-ly Spir-it who was sent through Christ the Son
I be-lieve sins are for-giv-en, that our bod-ies will be raised

he in whom I have be-liev-ed: God Al-might-y, Three in One.
in-to heav-en made his en-try, might-y con-qu'ror of his foes.
to ap-ply sal-va-tion's mer-it— God, the Spir-it, Three in One.
to e-ter-nal life in heav-en: ev-er let his name be praised.

The Apostles' Creed, ca. 2nd cent., 6th cent.
Versified anon.

MEAD HOUSE 8.7.8.7.D.
Cyril V. Taylor, 1951

PSALTER READINGS

PSALTER
READINGS

PSALM 1

Blessed is the man who does not walk in the counsel of the wicked or stand in the way of sinners or sit in the seat of mockers.

But his delight is in the law of the LORD, and on his law he meditates day and night.

He is like a tree planted by streams of water, which yields its fruit in season and whose leaf does not wither. Whatever he does prospers.

Not so the wicked! They are like chaff that the wind blows away.

Therefore the wicked will not stand in the judgment, nor sinners in the assembly of the righteous.

For the LORD watches over the way of the righteous, but the way of the wicked will perish.

PSALM 2

Why do the nations conspire and the peoples plot in vain?

The kings of the earth take their stand and the rulers gather together against the LORD and against his Anointed One.

"Let us break their chains," they say, "and throw off their fetters."

The One enthroned in heaven laughs; the Lord scoffs at them.

Then he rebukes them in his anger and terrifies them in his wrath, saying, "I have installed my King on Zion, my holy hill."

I will proclaim the decree of the LORD: He said to me, "You are my Son; today I have become your Father.

"Ask of me, and I will make the nations your inheritance, the ends of the earth your possession.

"You will rule them with an iron scepter; you will dash them to pieces like pottery."

Therefore, you kings, be wise; be warned, you rulers of the earth.

Serve the LORD with fear and rejoice with trembling.

Kiss the Son, lest he be angry and you be destroyed in your way, for his wrath can flare up in a moment.

Blessed are all who take refuge in him.

PSALM 4

Answer me when I call to you, O my righteous God.

Give me relief from my distress; be merciful to me and hear my prayer.

How long, O men, will you turn my glory into shame? How long will you love delusions and seek false gods?

Know that the LORD has set apart the godly for himself; the LORD will hear when I call to him.

In your anger do not sin; when you are on your beds, search your hearts and be silent.

Offer right sacrifices and trust in the LORD.

Many are asking, "Who can show us any good?"

Let the light of your face shine upon us, O LORD.

You have filled my heart with greater joy than when their grain and new wine abound.

I will lie down and sleep in peace, for you alone, O LORD, make me dwell in safety.

PSALM 5

Give ear to my words, O LORD, consider my sighing.

Listen to my cry for help, my King and my God, for to you I pray.

In the morning, O LORD, you hear my voice; in the morning I lay my requests before you and wait in expectation.

You are not a God who takes pleasure in evil; with you the wicked cannot dwell.

The arrogant cannot stand in your presence; you hate all who do wrong.

You destroy those who tell lies; bloodthirsty and deceitful men the LORD abhors.

But I, by your great mercy, will come into your house; in reverence will I bow down toward your holy temple.

Lead me, O LORD, in your righteousness because of my enemies—make straight your way before me.

Not a word from their mouth can be trusted; their heart is filled with destruction.

Their throat is an open grave; with their tongue they speak deceit.

Declare them guilty, O God! Let their intrigues be their downfall.

Banish them for their many sins, for they have rebelled against you.

But let all who take refuge in you be glad; let them ever sing for joy.

Spread your protection over them, that those who love your name may rejoice in you.

For surely, O LORD, you bless the righteous;

you surround them with your favor as with a shield.

PSALM 8

O LORD, our Lord, how majestic is your name in all the earth!

You have set your glory above the

heavens.

From the lips of children and infants you have ordained praise,

because of your enemies, to silence the foe and the avenger.

When I consider your heavens, the work of your fingers, the moon and the stars, which you have set in place,

what is man that you are mindful of him, the son of man that you care for him?

You made him a little lower than the heavenly beings and crowned him with glory and honor.

You made him ruler over the works of your hands; you put everything under his feet:

all flocks and herds, and the beasts of the field, the birds of the air, and the fish of the sea, all that swim the paths of the seas.

O LORD, our Lord, how majestic is your name in all the earth!

PSALM 9:7–11

The LORD reigns forever; he has established his throne for judgment.

He will judge the world in righteousness; he will govern the peoples with justice.

The LORD is a refuge for the oppressed, a stronghold in times of trouble.

Those who know your name will trust in you, for you, LORD, have never forsaken those who seek you.

Sing praises to the LORD, enthroned in Zion;

proclaim among the nations what he has done.

PSALM 11

In the LORD I take refuge.

How then can you say to me: "Flee like a bird to your mountain.

"For look, the wicked bend their bows; they set their arrows against the strings to shoot from the shadows at the upright in heart.

"When the foundations are being destroyed, what can the righteous do?"

The LORD is in his holy temple; the LORD is on his heavenly throne.

He observes the sons of men; his eyes examine them.

The LORD examines the righteous, but the wicked and those who love violence his soul hates.

On the wicked he will rain fiery coals and burning sulfur; a scorching wind will be their lot.

For the LORD is righteous, he loves justice;

upright men will see his face.

PSALM 13

How long, O LORD? Will you forget me forever? How long will you hide your face from me?

How long must I wrestle with my thoughts and every day have sorrow in my heart? How long will my enemy triumph over me?

Look on me and answer, O LORD my God. Give light to my eyes, or I will sleep in death;

my enemy will say, "I have overcome him," and my foes will rejoice when I fall.

But I trust in your unfailing love; my heart rejoices in your salvation.

I will sing to the LORD, for he has been good to me.

PSALM 15

LORD, who may dwell in your sanctuary?

Who may live on your holy hill?

He whose walk is blameless and who does what is righteous,

who speaks the truth from his heart and has no slander on his tongue,

who does his neighbor no wrong and casts no slur on his fellowman,

who despises a vile man but honors those who fear the LORD,

who keeps his oath even when it hurts,

who lends his money without usury,

and does not accept a bribe against the innocent.

He who does these things will never be shaken.

PSALM 16

Keep me safe, O God,

for in you I take refuge.

I said to the LORD, "You are my Lord; apart from you I have no good thing."

As for the saints who are in the land, they are the glorious ones in whom is all my delight.

The sorrows of those will increase who run after other gods.

I will not pour out their libations of blood or take up their names on my lips.

LORD, you have assigned me my portion and my cup; you have made my lot secure.

The boundary lines have fallen for me in pleasant places; surely I have a delightful inheritance.

I will praise the LORD, who counsels me; even at night my heart instructs me.

I have set the LORD always before me. Because he is at my right hand, I will not be shaken.

Therefore my heart is glad and my tongue rejoices; my body also will rest secure,

because you will not abandon me to the grave, nor will you let your Holy One see decay.

You have made known to me the path of life;

you will fill me with joy in your presence, with eternal pleasures at your right hand.

PSALM 17

Hear, O LORD, my righteous plea; listen to my cry.

Give ear to my prayer—it does not rise from deceitful lips.

May my vindication come from you; may your eyes see what is right.

Though you probe my heart and examine me at night, though you test me, you will find nothing; I have resolved that my mouth will not sin.

As for the deeds of men—by the word of your lips I have kept myself from the ways of the violent.

My steps have held to your paths; my feet have not slipped.

I call on you, O God, for you will answer me; give ear to me and hear my prayer.

Show the wonder of your great love, you who save by your right hand those who take refuge in you from their foes.

Keep me as the apple of your eye; hide me in the shadow of your wings from the wicked who assail me, from my mortal enemies who surround me.

They close up their callous hearts, and their mouths speak with arrogance.

They have tracked me down, they now surround me, with eyes alert, to throw me to the ground.

They are like a lion hungry for prey, like a great lion crouching in cover.

Rise up, O LORD, confront them, bring them down; rescue me from the wicked by your sword.

O LORD, by your hand save me from such men, from men of this world whose

reward is in this life.

You still the hunger of those you cherish; their sons have plenty, and they store up wealth for their children.

And I—in righteousness I will see your face; when I awake, I will be satisfied with seeing your likeness.

PSALM 18:1–19

I love you, O LORD, my strength.

The LORD is my rock, my fortress and my deliverer; my God is my rock, in whom I take refuge.

He is my shield and the horn of my salvation, my stronghold.

I call to the LORD, who is worthy of praise, and I am saved from my enemies.

The cords of death entangled me; the torrents of destruction overwhelmed me.

The cords of the grave coiled around me; the snares of death confronted me.

In my distress I called to the LORD; I cried to my God for help.

From his temple he heard my voice; my cry came before him, into his ears.

The earth trembled and quaked, and the foundations of the mountains shook; they trembled because he was angry.

Smoke rose from his nostrils; consuming fire came from his mouth, burning coals blazed out of it.

He parted the heavens and came down; dark clouds were under his feet.

He mounted the cherubim and flew; he soared on the wings of the wind.

He made darkness his covering, his canopy around him—the dark rain clouds of the sky.

Out of the brightness of his presence clouds advanced, with hailstones and bolts of lightning.

The LORD thundered from heaven; the voice of the Most High resounded.

He shot his arrows and scattered the enemies, great bolts of lightning and routed them.

The valleys of the sea were exposed and the foundations of the earth laid bare—

at your rebuke, O LORD, at the blast of breath from your nostrils.

He reached down from on high and took hold of me; he drew me out of deep waters.

He rescued me from my powerful enemy, from my foes, who were too strong for me.

They confronted me in the day of my disaster, but the LORD was my support.

He brought me out into a spacious place; he rescued me because he delighted in me.

PSALM 18:25–36

To the faithful you show yourself faithful, to the blameless you show yourself blameless,

to the pure you show yourself pure, but to the crooked you show yourself shrewd.

You save the humble

but bring low those whose eyes are haughty.

You, O LORD, keep my lamp burning; my God turns my darkness into light.

With your help I can advance against a troop; with my God I can scale a wall.

As for God, his way is perfect; the word of the LORD is flawless.

He is a shield for all who take refuge in him.

For who is God besides the LORD? And who is the Rock except our God?

It is God who arms me with strength and makes my way perfect.

He makes my feet like the feet of a deer; he enables me to stand on the heights.

He trains my hands for battle; my

arms can bend a bow of bronze.

You give me your shield of victory, and your right hand sustains me; you stoop down to make me great.

You broaden the path beneath me, so that my ankles do not turn.

PSALM 19

The heavens declare the glory of God; the skies proclaim the work of his hands.

Day after day they pour forth speech; night after night they display knowledge.

There is no speech or language where their voice is not heard.

Their voice goes out into all the earth, their words to the ends of the world.

In the heavens he has pitched a tent for the sun, which is like a bridegroom coming forth from his pavilion, like a champion rejoicing to run his course.

It rises at one end of the heavens and makes its circuit to the other; nothing is hidden from its heat.

The law of the LORD is perfect, reviving the soul.

The statutes of the LORD are trustworthy, making wise the simple.

The precepts of the LORD are right, giving joy to the heart.

The commands of the LORD are radiant, giving light to the eyes.

The fear of the LORD is pure, enduring forever.

The ordinances of the LORD are sure and altogether righteous.

They are more precious than gold, than much pure gold;

they are sweeter than honey, than honey from the comb.

By them is your servant warned; in keeping them there is great reward.

Who can discern his errors? Forgive my hidden faults.

Keep your servant also from willful sins; may they not rule over me.

Then will I be blameless, innocent of great transgression.

May the words of my mouth and the meditation of my heart be pleasing in your sight, O LORD, my Rock and my Redeemer.

PSALM 20

May the LORD answer you when you are in distress; may the name of the God of Jacob protect you.

May he send you help from the sanctuary and grant you support from Zion.

May he remember all your sacrifices and accept your burnt offerings.

May he give you the desire of your heart and make all your plans succeed.

We will shout for joy when you are victorious and will lift up our banners in the name of our God.

May the LORD grant all your requests

Now I know that the LORD saves his anointed; he answers him from his holy heaven with the saving power of his right hand.

Some trust in chariots and some in horses, but we trust in the name of the LORD our God.

They are brought to their knees and fall, but we rise up and stand firm.

O LORD, save the king! Answer us when we call!

PSALM 22:1–22

My God, my God, why have you forsaken me?

Why are you so far from saving me, so far from the words of my groaning?

O my God, I cry out by day, but you do not answer, by night, and am not silent.

Yet you are enthroned as the Holy

One; you are the praise of Israel.

In you our fathers put their trust; they trusted and you delivered them.

They cried to you and were saved; in you they trusted and were not disappointed.

But I am a worm and not a man, scorned by men and despised by the people.

All who see me mock me; they hurl insults, shaking their heads:

"He trusts in the LORD; let the LORD rescue him.

"Let him deliver him, since he delights in him."

Yet you brought me out of the womb; you made me trust in you even at my mother's breast.

From birth I was cast upon you; from my mother's womb you have been my God.

Do not be far from me, for trouble is near and there is no one to help.

Many bulls surround me; strong bulls of Bashan encircle me.

Roaring lions tearing their prey open their mouths wide against me.

I am poured out like water, and all my bones are out of joint.

My heart has turned to wax; it has melted away within me.

My strength is dried up like a potsherd, and my tongue sticks to the roof of my mouth; you lay me in the dust of death.

Dogs have surrounded me;

a band of evil men has encircled me, they have pierced my hands and my feet.

I can count all my bones; people stare and gloat over me.

They divide my garments among them and cast lots for my clothing.

But you, O LORD, be not far off; O my Strength, come quickly to help me.

Deliver my life from the sword, my precious life from the power of the dogs.

Rescue me from the mouth of the lions; save me from the horns of the wild oxen.

I will declare your name to my brothers; in the congregation I will praise you.

PSALM 23

The LORD is my shepherd, I shall not be in want.

He makes me lie down in green pastures, he leads me beside quiet waters, he restores my soul.

He guides me in paths of righteousness for his name's sake.

Even though I walk through the valley of the shadow of death, I will fear no evil, for you are with me; your rod and your staff, they comfort me.

You prepare a table before me in the presence of my enemies.

You anoint my head with oil; my cup overflows.

Surely goodness and love will follow me all the days of my life,

and I will dwell in the house of the LORD forever.

PSALM 24

The earth is the LORD's, and everything in it, the world, and all who live in it;

for he founded it upon the seas and established it upon the waters.

Who may ascend the hill of the LORD? Who may stand in his holy place?

He who has clean hands and a pure heart, who does not lift up his soul to an idol or swear by what is false.

He will receive blessing from the LORD and vindication from God his Savior.

Such is the generation of those who seek him, who seek your face, O God of Jacob.

Lift up your heads, O you gates; be lifted up, you ancient doors, that the King of glory may come in.

Who is this King of glory? The LORD strong and mighty, the LORD mighty in battle.

Lift up your heads, O you gates; lift them up, you ancient doors, that the King of glory may come in.

Who is he, this King of glory? The LORD Almighty—he is the King of glory.

PSALM 25

To you, O LORD, I lift up my soul; in you I trust, O my God.

Do not let me be put to shame, nor let my enemies triumph over me.

No one whose hope is in you will ever be put to shame,

but they will be put to shame who are treacherous without excuse.

Show me your ways, O LORD, teach me your paths;

guide me in your truth and teach me, for you are God my Savior, and my hope is in you all day long.

Remember, O LORD, your great mercy and love, for they are from of old.

Remember not the sins of my youth and my rebellious ways; according to your love remember me, for you are good, O LORD.

Good and upright is the LORD; therefore he instructs sinners in his ways.

He guides the humble in what is right and teaches them his way.

All the ways of the LORD are loving and faithful for those who keep the demands of his covenant.

For the sake of your name, O LORD, forgive my iniquity, though it is great.

Who, then, is the man that fears the

LORD? He will instruct him in the way chosen for him.

He will spend his days in prosperity, and his descendants will inherit the land.

The LORD confides in those who fear him; he makes his covenant known to them.

My eyes are ever on the LORD, for only he will release my feet from the snare.

Turn to me and be gracious to me, for I am lonely and afflicted.

The troubles of my heart have multiplied; free me from my anguish.

Look upon my affliction and my distress and take away all my sins.

See how my enemies have increased and how fiercely they hate me!

Guard my life and rescue me; let me not be put to shame, for I take refuge in you.

May integrity and uprightness protect me, because my hope is in you.

Redeem Israel, O God, from all their troubles!

PSALM 26

Vindicate me, O LORD, for I have led a blameless life;

I have trusted in the LORD without wavering.

Test me, O LORD, and try me, examine my heart and my mind;

for your love is ever before me, and I walk continually in your truth.

I do not sit with deceitful men, nor do I consort with hypocrites;

I abhor the assembly of evildoers and refuse to sit with the wicked.

I wash my hands in innocence, and go about your altar, O LORD, proclaiming aloud your praise and telling of all your wonderful deeds.

I love the house where you live, O LORD, the place where your glory dwells.

Do not take away my soul along with sinners, my life with bloodthirsty men,

in whose hands are wicked schemes, whose right hands are full of bribes.

But I lead a blameless life; redeem me and be merciful to me.

My feet stand on level ground; in the great assembly I will praise the LORD.

PSALM 27

The LORD is my light and my salvation—whom shall I fear?

The LORD is the stronghold of my life—of whom shall I be afraid?

When evil men advance against me to devour my flesh, when my enemies and my foes attack me, they will stumble and fall.

Though an army besiege me, my heart will not fear; though war break out against me, even then will I be confident.

One thing I ask of the LORD, this is what I seek:

that I may dwell in the house of the LORD all the days of my life, to gaze upon the beauty of the LORD and to seek him in his temple.

For in the day of trouble he will keep me safe in his dwelling;

he will hide me in the shelter of his tabernacle and set me high upon a rock.

Then my head will be exalted above the enemies who surround me;

at his tabernacle will I sacrifice with shouts of joy; I will sing and make music to the LORD.

Hear my voice when I call, O LORD; be merciful to me and answer me.

My heart says of you, "Seek his face!" Your face, LORD, I will seek.

Do not hide your face from me, do not turn your servant away in anger; you have been my helper.

Do not reject me or forsake me, O God my Savior.

Though my father and mother forsake me, the LORD will receive me.

Teach me your way, O LORD; lead me in a straight path because of my oppressors.

Do not turn me over to the desire of my foes, for false witnesses rise up against me, breathing out violence.

I am still confident of this: I will see the goodness of the LORD in the land of the living.

Wait for the LORD; be strong and take heart and wait for the LORD.

PSALM 28

To you I call, O LORD my Rock; do not turn a deaf ear to me.

For if you remain silent, I will be like those who have gone down to the pit.

Hear my cry for mercy as I call to you for help,

as I lift up my hands toward your Most Holy Place.

Do not drag me away with the wicked, with those who do evil,

who speak cordially with their neighbors but harbor malice in their hearts.

Repay them for their deeds and for their evil work;

repay them for what their hands have done and bring back upon them what they deserve.

Since they show no regard for the works of the LORD and what his hands have done,

he will tear them down and never build them up again.

Praise be to the LORD, for he has heard my cry for mercy.

The LORD is my strength and my shield;

my heart trusts in him, and I am helped.

My heart leaps for joy and I will give thanks to him in song.

The LORD is the strength of his people, a fortress of salvation for his anointed one.

Save your people and bless your inheritance; be their shepherd and carry them forever.

PSALM 29

Ascribe to the LORD, O mighty ones, ascribe to the LORD glory and strength.

Ascribe to the LORD the glory due his name; worship the LORD in the splendor of his holiness.

The voice of the LORD is over the waters; the God of glory thunders, the LORD thunders over the mighty waters.

The voice of the LORD is powerful; the voice of the LORD is majestic.

The voice of the LORD breaks the cedars; the LORD breaks in pieces the cedars of Lebanon.

He makes Lebanon skip like a calf, Sirion like a young wild ox.

The voice of the LORD strikes with flashes of lightning.

The voice of the LORD shakes the desert; the LORD shakes the Desert of Kadesh.

The voice of the LORD twists the oaks and strips the forests bare.

And in his temple all cry, "Glory!"

The LORD sits enthroned over the flood; the LORD is enthroned as King forever.

The LORD gives strength to his people; the LORD blesses his people with peace.

PSALM 30

I will exalt you, O LORD, for you lifted me out of the depths and did not let my enemies gloat over me.

O LORD my God, I called to you for help and you healed me.

O LORD, you brought me up from the grave; you spared me from going down into the pit.

Sing to the LORD, you saints of his; praise his holy name.

For his anger lasts only a moment, but his favor lasts a lifetime;

weeping may remain for a night, but rejoicing comes in the morning.

When I felt secure, I said, "I will never be shaken."

O LORD, when you favored me, you made my mountain stand firm; but when you hid your face, I was dismayed.

To you, O LORD, I called; to the Lord I cried for mercy:

"What gain is there in my destruction, in my going down into the pit?

"Will the dust praise you? Will it proclaim your faithfulness?

"Hear, O LORD, and be merciful to me; O LORD, be my help."

You turned my wailing into dancing; you removed my sackcloth and clothed me with joy, that my heart may sing to you and not be silent.

O LORD my God, I will give you thanks forever.

PSALM 31:1–14

In you, O LORD, I have taken refuge; let me never be put to shame; deliver me in your righteousness.

Turn your ear to me, come quickly to my rescue;

be my rock of refuge, a strong fortress

to save me.

Since you are my rock and my fortress, for the sake of your name lead and guide me.

Free me from the trap that is set for me, for you are my refuge.

Into your hands I commit my spirit; redeem me, O LORD, the God of truth.

I hate those who cling to worthless idols; I trust in the LORD.

I will be glad and rejoice in your love,

for you saw my affliction and knew the anguish of my soul.

You have not handed me over to the enemy but have set my feet in a spacious place.

Be merciful to me, O LORD, for I am in distress;

my eyes grow weak with sorrow, my soul and my body with grief.

My life is consumed by anguish and my years by groaning;

my strength fails because of my affliction, and my bones grow weak.

Because of all my enemies, I am the utter contempt of my neighbors;

I am a dread to my friends—those who see me on the street flee from me.

I am forgotten by them as though I were dead; I have become like broken pottery.

For I hear the slander of many; there is terror on every side;

they conspire against me and plot to take my life.

But I trust in you, O LORD; I say, "You are my God."

PSALM 31:15–24

My times are in your hands; deliver me from my enemies and from those who pursue me.

Let your face shine on your servant;

save me in your unfailing love.

Let me not be put to shame, O LORD, for I have cried out to you; but let the wicked be put to shame and lie silent in the grave.

Let their lying lips be silenced, for with pride and contempt they speak arrogantly against the righteous.

How great is your goodness, which you have stored up for those who fear you,

which you bestow in the sight of men on those who take refuge in you.

In the shelter of your presence you hide them from the intrigues of men;

in your dwelling you keep them safe from accusing tongues.

Praise be to the LORD, for he showed his wonderful love to me when I was in a besieged city.

In my alarm I said, "I am cut off from your sight!"

Yet you heard my cry for mercy when I called to you for help.

Love the LORD, all his saints!

The LORD preserves the faithful, but the proud he pays back in full.

Be strong and take heart, all you who hope in the LORD.

PSALM 32

Blessed is he whose transgressions are forgiven, whose sins are covered.

Blessed is the man whose sin the LORD does not count against him and in whose spirit is no deceit.

When I kept silent, my bones wasted away through my groaning all day long.

For day and night your hand was heavy upon me; my strength was sapped as in the heat of summer.

Then I acknowledged my sin to you and did not cover up my iniquity.

I said, "I will confess my transgres-

sions to the LORD"—and you forgave the guilt of my sin.

Therefore let everyone who is godly pray to you while you may be found;

surely when the mighty waters rise, they will not reach him.

You are my hiding place;

you will protect me from trouble and surround me with songs of deliverance.

I will instruct you and teach you in the way you should go; I will counsel you and watch over you.

Do not be like the horse or the mule, which have no understanding but must be controlled by bit and bridle or they will not come to you.

Many are the woes of the wicked, but the LORD's unfailing love surrounds the man who trusts in him.

Rejoice in the LORD and be glad, you righteous; sing, all you who are upright in heart!

PSALM 33

Sing joyfully to the LORD, you righteous; it is fitting for the upright to praise him.

Praise the LORD with the harp; make music to him on the ten-stringed lyre.

Sing to him a new song; play skillfully, and shout for joy.

For the word of the LORD is right and true; he is faithful in all he does.

The LORD loves righteousness and justice;

the earth is full of his unfailing love.

By the word of the LORD were the heavens made, their starry host by the breath of his mouth.

He gathers the waters of the sea into jars; he puts the deep into storehouses.

Let all the earth fear the LORD; let all the people of the world revere him.

For he spoke, and it came to be; he commanded, and it stood firm.

The LORD foils the plans of the nations; he thwarts the purposes of the peoples.

But the plans of the LORD stand firm forever, the purposes of his heart through all generations.

Blessed is the nation whose God is the LORD, the people he chose for his inheritance.

From heaven the LORD looks down and sees all mankind;

from his dwelling place he watches all who live on earth—

he who forms the hearts of all, who considers everything they do.

No king is saved by the size of his army; no warrior escapes by his great strength.

A horse is a vain hope for deliverance; despite all its great strength it cannot save.

But the eyes of the LORD are on those who fear him, on those whose hope is in his unfailing love,

to deliver them from death and keep them alive in famine.

We wait in hope for the LORD;

he is our help and our shield.

In him our hearts rejoice, for we trust in his holy name.

May your unfailing love rest upon us, O LORD, even as we put our hope in you.

PSALM 34

I will extol the LORD at all times; his praise will always be on my lips.

My soul will boast in the LORD; let the afflicted hear and rejoice.

Glorify the LORD with me; let us exalt his name together.

I sought the LORD, and he answered me; he delivered me from all my fears.

Those who look to him are radiant; their faces are never covered with shame.

This poor man called, and the LORD heard him; he saved him out of all his troubles.

The angel of the LORD encamps around those who fear him, and he delivers them.

Taste and see that the LORD is good; blessed is the man who takes refuge in him.

Fear the LORD, you his saints, for those who fear him lack nothing.

The lions may grow weak and hungry, but those who seek the LORD lack no good thing.

Come, my children, listen to me; I will teach you the fear of the LORD.

Whoever of you loves life and desires to see many good days,

keep your tongue from evil and your lips from speaking lies.

Turn from evil and do good; seek peace and pursue it.

The eyes of the LORD are on the righteous and his ears are attentive to their cry;

the face of the LORD is against those who do evil, to cut off the memory of them from the earth.

The righteous cry out, and the LORD hears them; he delivers them from all their troubles.

The LORD is close to the brokenhearted and saves those who are crushed in spirit.

A righteous man may have many troubles, but the LORD delivers him from them all;

he protects all his bones, not one of them will be broken.

Evil will slay the wicked; the foes of the righteous will be condemned.

The LORD redeems his servants; no one will be condemned who takes refuge in him.

PSALM 36

An oracle is within my heart concerning the sinfulness of the wicked: There is no fear of God before his eyes.

For in his own eyes he flatters himself too much to detect or hate his sin.

The words of his mouth are wicked and deceitful; he has ceased to be wise and to do good.

Even on his bed he plots evil; he commits himself to a sinful course and does not reject what is wrong.

Your love, O LORD, reaches to the heavens, your faithfulness to the skies.

Your righteousness is like the mighty mountains, your justice like the great deep.

O LORD, you preserve both man and beast.

How priceless is your unfailing love!

Both high and low among men find refuge in the shadow of your wings.

They feast on the abundance of your house; you give them drink from your river of delights.

For with you is the fountain of life; in your light we see light.

Continue your love to those who know you, your righteousness to the upright in heart.

May the foot of the proud not come against me, nor the hand of the wicked drive me away.

See how the evildoers lie fallen— thrown down, not able to rise!

PSALM 37:1–9

Do not fret because of evil men or be envious of those who do wrong;

for like the grass they will soon wither, like green plants they will soon die away.

Trust in the LORD and do good; dwell in the land and enjoy safe pasture.

Delight yourself in the LORD and he will give you the desires of your heart.

Commit your way to the LORD; trust in him and he will do this:

He will make your righteousness shine like the dawn, the justice of your cause like the noonday sun.

Be still before the LORD and wait patiently for him;

do not fret when men succeed in their ways, when they carry out their wicked schemes.

Refrain from anger and turn from wrath; do not fret—it leads only to evil.

For evil men will be cut off, but those who hope in the LORD will inherit the land.

PSALM 37:23–40

If the LORD delights in a man's way, he makes his steps firm;

though he stumble, he will not fall, for the LORD upholds him with his hand.

I was young and now I am old, yet I have never seen the righteous forsaken or their children begging bread.

They are always generous and lend freely; their children will be blessed.

Turn from evil and do good; then you will dwell in the land forever.

For the LORD loves the just and will not forsake his faithful ones.

They will be protected forever, but the offspring of the wicked will be cut off;

the righteous will inherit the land and dwell in it forever.

The mouth of the righteous man utters wisdom, and his tongue speaks what is just.

The law of his God is in his heart; his feet do not slip.

The wicked lie in wait for the righteous, seeking their very lives;

but the LORD will not leave them in their power or let them be condemned when brought to trial.

Wait for the LORD and keep his way.

He will exalt you to inherit the land; when the wicked are cut off, you will see it.

I have seen a wicked and ruthless man flourishing like a green tree in its native soil,

but he soon passed away and was no more; though I looked for him, he could not be found.

Consider the blameless, observe the upright; there is a future for the man of peace.

But all sinners will be destroyed; the future of the wicked will be cut off.

The salvation of the righteous comes from the LORD; he is their stronghold in time of trouble.

The LORD helps them and delivers them; he delivers them from the wicked and saves them, because they take refuge in him.

PSALM 39

I said, "I will watch my ways and keep my tongue from sin;

"I will put a muzzle on my mouth as long as the wicked are in my presence."

But when I was silent and still, not even saying anything good, my anguish increased.

My heart grew hot within me, and as I meditated, the fire burned; then I spoke with my tongue:

"Show me, O LORD, my life's end and the number of my days; let me know how fleeting is my life.

"You have made my days a mere handbreadth; the span of my years is as

nothing before you. **Each man's life is but a breath.**

"Man is a mere phantom as he goes to and fro: He bustles about, but only in vain; he heaps up wealth, not knowing who will get it.

"But now, Lord, what do I look for? My hope is in you.

"Save me from all my transgressions; do not make me the scorn of fools.

"I was silent; I would not open my mouth, for you are the one who has done this.

"Remove your scourge from me; I am overcome by the blow of your hand.

"You rebuke and discipline men for their sin; you consume their wealth like a moth—each man is but a breath.

"Hear my prayer, O LORD, listen to my cry for help;

"be not deaf to my weeping.

"For I dwell with you as an alien, a stranger, as all my fathers were.

"Look away from me, that I may rejoice again before I depart and am no more."

PSALM 40:1–11

I waited patiently for the LORD; he turned to me and heard my cry.

He lifted me out of the slimy pit, out of the mud and mire; he set my feet on a rock and gave me a firm place to stand.

He put a new song in my mouth, a hymn of praise to our God.

Many will see and fear and put their trust in the LORD.

Blessed is the man who makes the LORD his trust, who does not look to the proud, to those who turn aside to false gods.

Many, O LORD my God, are the wonders you have done.

The things you planned for us no one can recount to you;

were I to speak and tell of them, they would be too many to declare.

Sacrifice and offering you did not desire, but my ears you have pierced;

burnt offerings and sin offerings you did not require.

Then I said, "Here I am, I have come— it is written about me in the scroll.

"I desire to do your will, O my God; your law is within my heart."

I proclaim righteousness in the great assembly; I do not seal my lips, as you know, O LORD.

I do not hide your righteousness in my heart; I speak of your faithfulness and salvation.

I do not conceal your love and your truth from the great assembly.

Do not withhold your mercy from me, O LORD; may your love and your truth always protect me.

PSALM 40:11–17

Do not withhold your mercy from me, O LORD; may your love and your truth always protect me.

For troubles without number surround me; my sins have overtaken me, and I cannot see.

They are more than the hairs of my head, and my heart fails within me.

Be pleased, O LORD, to save me; O LORD, come quickly to help me.

May all who seek to take my life be put to shame and confusion; may all who desire my ruin be turned back in disgrace.

May those who say to me, "Aha! Aha!" be appalled at their own shame.

But may all who seek you rejoice and be glad in you;

may those who love your salvation always say, "The LORD be exalted!"

Yet I am poor and needy; may the Lord think of me.

You are my help and my deliverer; O my God, do not delay.

PSALM 41

Blessed is he who has regard for the weak; the LORD delivers him in times of trouble.

The LORD will protect him and preserve his life;

he will bless him in the land and not surrender him to the desire of his foes.

The LORD will sustain him on his sick-bed and restore him from his bed of illness.

I said, "O LORD, have mercy on me; heal me, for I have sinned against you."

My enemies say of me in malice, "When will he die and his name perish?"

Whenever one comes to see me, he speaks falsely, while his heart gathers slander;

then he goes out and spreads it abroad.

All my enemies whisper together against me; they imagine the worst for me, saying,

"A vile disease has beset him; he will never get up from the place where he lies."

Even my close friend, whom I trusted, he who shared my bread, has lifted up his heel against me.

But you, O LORD, have mercy on me; raise me up, that I may repay them.

I know that you are pleased with me, for my enemy does not triumph over me.

In my integrity you uphold me and set me in your presence forever.

Praise be to the LORD, the God of Israel,

from everlasting to everlasting.

Amen and Amen.

PSALM 42

As the deer pants for streams of water, so my soul pants for you, O God.

My soul thirsts for God, for the living God. When can I go and meet with God?

My tears have been my food day and night,

while men say to me all day long, "Where is your God?"

These things I remember as I pour out my soul:

how I used to go with the multitude, leading the procession to the house of God, with shouts of joy and thanksgiving among the festive throng.

Why are you downcast, O my soul? Why so disturbed within me?

Put your hope in God, for I will yet praise him, my Savior and my God.

My soul is downcast within me; therefore I will remember you from the land of the Jordan, the heights of Hermon—from Mount Mizar.

Deep calls to deep in the roar of your waterfalls; all your waves and breakers have swept over me.

By day the LORD directs his love, at night his song is with me—a prayer to the God of my life.

I say to God my Rock, "Why have you forgotten me?

"Why must I go about mourning, oppressed by the enemy?"

My bones suffer mortal agony as my foes taunt me, saying to me all day long, "Where is your God?"

Why are you downcast, O my soul? Why so disturbed within me?

Put your hope in God, for I will yet praise him, my Savior and my God.

PSALM 43

Vindicate me, O God, and plead my cause against an ungodly nation;

rescue me from deceitful and wicked men.

You are God my stronghold. Why have you rejected me?

Why must I go about mourning, oppressed by the enemy?

Send forth your light and your truth, let them guide me;

let them bring me to your holy mountain, to the place where you dwell.

Then will I go to the altar of God, to God, my joy and my delight.

I will praise you with the harp, O God, my God.

Why are you downcast, O my soul? Why so disturbed within me?

Put your hope in God, for I will yet praise him, my Savior and my God.

PSALM 44

We have heard with our ears, O God; our fathers have told us what you did in their days, in days long ago.

With your hand you drove out the nations and planted our fathers;

you crushed the peoples and made our fathers flourish.

It was not by their sword that they won the land, nor did their arm bring them victory;

it was your right hand, your arm, and the light of your face, for you loved them.

You are my King and my God, who decrees victories for Jacob.

Through you we push back our enemies; through your name we trample our foes.

I do not trust in my bow, my sword does not bring me victory;

but you give us victory over our enemies, you put our adversaries to shame.

In God we make our boast all day long, and we will praise your name forever.

But now you have rejected and humbled us; you no longer go out with our armies.

You made us retreat before the enemy, and our adversaries have plundered us.

You gave us up to be devoured like sheep and have scattered us among the nations.

You sold your people for a pittance, gaining nothing from their sale.

You have made us a reproach to our neighbors, the scorn and derision of those around us.

You have made us a byword among the nations; the peoples shake their heads at us.

My disgrace is before me all day long, and my face is covered with shame—

at the taunts of those who reproach and revile me, because of the enemy, who is bent on revenge.

All this happened to us, though we had not forgotten you or been false to your covenant.

Our hearts had not turned back; our feet had not strayed from your path.

But you crushed us and made us a haunt for jackals and covered us over with deep darkness.

If we had forgotten the name of our God or spread out our hands to a foreign god,

would not God have discovered it, since he knows the secrets of the heart?

Yet for your sake we face death all day long; we are considered as sheep to be slaughtered.

Awake, O Lord! Why do you sleep? Rouse yourself! Do not reject us forever.

Why do you hide your face and forget our misery and oppression?

We are brought down to the dust; our bodies cling to the ground.

Rise up and help us; redeem us because of your unfailing love.

PSALM 45

My heart is stirred by a noble theme as I recite my verses for the king;

my tongue is the pen of a skillful writer.

You are the most excellent of men and your lips have been anointed with grace, since God has blessed you forever.

Gird your sword upon your side, O mighty one; clothe yourself with splendor and majesty.

In your majesty ride forth victoriously in behalf of truth, humility and righteousness; let your right hand display awesome deeds.

Let your sharp arrows pierce the hearts of the king's enemies; let the nations fall beneath your feet.

Your throne, O God, will last for ever and ever; a scepter of justice will be the scepter of your kingdom.

You love righteousness and hate wickedness; therefore God, your God, has set you above your companions by anointing you with the oil of joy.

All your robes are fragrant with myrrh and aloes and cassia; from palaces adorned with ivory the music of the strings makes you glad.

Daughters of kings are among your honored women; at your right hand is the royal bride in gold of Ophir.

Listen, O daughter, consider and give ear: Forget your people and your father's house.

The king is enthralled by your

beauty; honor him, for he is your lord.

The Daughter of Tyre will come with a gift, men of wealth will seek your favor.

All glorious is the princess within her chamber; her gown is interwoven with gold.

In embroidered garments she is led to the king; her virgin companions follow her and are brought to you.

They are led in with joy and gladness; they enter the palace of the king.

Your sons will take the place of your fathers; you will make them princes throughout the land.

I will perpetuate your memory through all generations; therefore the nations will praise you for ever and ever.

PSALM 46

God is our refuge and strength, an ever-present help in trouble.

Therefore we will not fear, though the earth give way and the mountains fall into the heart of the sea,

though its waters roar and foam and the mountains quake with their surging.

There is a river whose streams make glad the city of God, the holy place where the Most High dwells.

God is within her, she will not fall; God will help her at break of day.

Nations are in uproar, kingdoms fall; he lifts his voice, the earth melts.

The LORD Almighty is with us;

the God of Jacob is our fortress.

Come and see the works of the LORD, the desolations he has brought on the earth.

He makes wars cease to the ends of the earth; he breaks the bow and shatters the spear, he burns the shields with fire.

"Be still, and know that I am God;

I will be exalted among the nations, I will be exalted in the earth."

The LORD Almighty is with us;

the God of Jacob is our fortress.

PSALM 47

Clap your hands, all you nations; shout to God with cries of joy.

How awesome is the LORD Most High, the great King over all the earth!

He subdued nations under us, peoples under our feet.

He chose our inheritance for us, the pride of Jacob, whom he loved.

God has ascended amid shouts of joy, the LORD amid the sounding of trumpets.

Sing praises to God, sing praises; sing praises to our King, sing praises.

For God is the King of all the earth; sing to him a psalm of praise.

God reigns over the nations; God is seated on his holy throne.

The nobles of the nations assemble as the people of the God of Abraham,

for the kings of the earth belong to God; he is greatly exalted.

PSALM 48

Great is the LORD, and most worthy of praise, in the city of our God, his holy mountain.

It is beautiful in its loftiness, the joy of the whole earth.

Like the utmost heights of Zaphon is Mount Zion, the city of the Great King.

God is in her citadels; he has shown himself to be her fortress.

When the kings joined forces, when they advanced together,

they saw her and were astounded; they fled in terror.

Trembling seized them there, pain like that of a woman in labor.

You destroyed them like ships of Tarshish shattered by an east wind.

As we have heard, so have we seen in the city of the LORD Almighty, in the city of our God:

God makes her secure forever.

Within your temple, O God, we meditate on your unfailing love.

Like your name, O God, your praise reaches to the ends of the earth;

your right hand is filled with righteousness.

Mount Zion rejoices, the villages of Judah are glad because of your judgments.

Walk about Zion, go around her, count her towers,

consider well her ramparts, view her citadels, that you may tell of them to the next generation.

For this God is our God for ever and ever;

he will be our guide even to the end.

PSALM 50:1–15

The Mighty One, God, the LORD, speaks and summons the earth from the rising of the sun to the place where it sets.

From Zion, perfect in beauty, God shines forth.

Our God comes and will not be silent; a fire devours before him, and around him a tempest rages.

He summons the heavens above, and the earth, that he may judge his people:

"Gather to me my consecrated ones, who made a covenant with me by sacrifice."

And the heavens proclaim his righteousness, for God himself is judge.

"Hear, O my people, and I will speak, O

Israel, and I will testify against you: I am God, your God.

"I do not rebuke you for your sacrifices or your burnt offerings, which are ever before me.

"I have no need of a bull from your stall or of goats from your pens,

"for every animal of the forest is mine, and the cattle on a thousand hills.

"I know every bird in the mountains, and the creatures of the field are mine.

"If I were hungry I would not tell you, for the world is mine, and all that is in it.

"Do I eat the flesh of bulls or drink the blood of goats?

"Sacrifice thank offerings to God, fulfill your vows to the Most High,

"and call upon me in the day of trouble;

"I will deliver you, and you will honor me."

PSALM 51

Have mercy on me, O God, according to your unfailing love;

according to your great compassion blot out my transgressions.

Wash away all my iniquity and cleanse me from my sin.

For I know my transgressions, and my sin is always before me.

Against you, you only, have I sinned and done what is evil in your sight,

so that you are proved right when you speak and justified when you judge.

Surely I was sinful at birth, sinful from the time my mother conceived me.

Surely you desire truth in the inner parts; you teach me wisdom in the inmost place.

Cleanse me with hyssop, and I will be clean;

wash me, and I will be whiter than snow.

Let me hear joy and gladness; let the bones you have crushed rejoice.

Hide your face from my sins and blot out all my iniquity.

Create in me a pure heart, O God, and renew a steadfast spirit within me.

Do not cast me from your presence or take your Holy Spirit from me.

Restore to me the joy of your salvation and grant me a willing spirit, to sustain me.

Then I will teach transgressors your ways, and sinners will turn back to you.

Save me from bloodguilt, O God, the God who saves me, and my tongue will sing of your righteousness.

O Lord, open my lips, and my mouth will declare your praise.

You do not delight in sacrifice, or I would bring it; you do not take pleasure in burnt offerings.

The sacrifices of God are a broken spirit; a broken and contrite heart, O God, you will not despise.

In your good pleasure make Zion prosper; build up the walls of Jerusalem.

Then there will be righteous sacrifices, whole burnt offerings to delight you; then bulls will be offered on your altar.

PSALM 52

Why do you boast of evil, you mighty man? Why do you boast all day long, you who are a disgrace in the eyes of God?

Your tongue plots destruction; it is like a sharpened razor, you who practice deceit.

You love evil rather than good, falsehood rather than speaking the truth.

You love every harmful word, O you deceitful tongue!

Surely God will bring you down to ever-lasting ruin:

he will snatch you up and tear you from your tent; he will uproot you from the land of the living.

The righteous will see and fear; they will laugh at him, saying,

"Here now is the man who did not make God his stronghold but trusted in his great wealth and grew strong by destroying others!"

But I am like an olive tree flourishing in the house of God;

I trust in God's unfailing love for ever and ever.

I will praise you forever for what you have done; in your name I will hope, for your name is good.

I will praise you in the presence of your saints.

PSALM 53

The fool says in his heart, "There is no God."

They are corrupt, and their ways are vile; there is no one who does good.

God looks down from heaven on the sons of men to see if there are any who understand, any who seek God.

Everyone has turned away, they have together become corrupt; there is no one who does good, not even one.

Will the evildoers never learn—those who devour my people as men eat bread and who do not call on God?

There they were, overwhelmed with dread, where there was nothing to dread.

God scattered the bones of those who attacked you;

you put them to shame, for God de-spised them.

Oh, that salvation for Israel would come out of Zion!

When God restores the fortunes of his people, let Jacob rejoice and Israel be glad!

PSALM 56

Be merciful to me, O God, for men hotly pursue me; all day long they press their attack.

My slanderers pursue me all day long; many are attacking me in their pride.

When I am afraid, I will trust in you.

In God, whose word I praise, in God I trust; I will not be afraid. What can mortal man do to me?

All day long they twist my words; they are always plotting to harm me.

They conspire, they lurk, they watch my steps, eager to take my life.

On no account let them escape; in your anger, O God, bring down the nations.

Record my lament; list my tears on your scroll—are they not in your record?

Then my enemies will turn back when I call for help. By this I will know that God is for me.

In God, whose word I praise, in the LORD, whose word I praise—in God I trust; I will not be afraid. What can man do to me?

I am under vows to you, O God; I will present my thank offerings to you.

For you have delivered me from death and my feet from stumbling, that I may walk before God in the light of life.

PSALM 57

Have mercy on me, O God, have mercy on me, for in you my soul takes refuge.

I will take refuge in the shadow of your wings until the disaster has passed.

I cry out to God Most High, to God, who fulfills his purpose for me.

He sends from heaven and saves me, rebuking those who hotly pursue me; God sends his love and his faithfulness.

I am in the midst of lions; I lie among ravenous beasts—men whose teeth are spears and arrows, whose tongues are sharp swords.

Be exalted, O God, above the heavens; let your glory be over all the earth.

They spread a net for my feet—I was bowed down in distress.

They dug a pit in my path—but they have fallen into it themselves.

My heart is steadfast, O God, my heart is steadfast; I will sing and make music.

Awake, my soul! Awake, harp and lyre! I will awaken the dawn.

I will praise you, O Lord, among the nations; I will sing of you among the peoples.

For great is your love, reaching to the heavens; your faithfulness reaches to the skies.

Be exalted, O God, above the heavens;

let your glory be over all the earth.

PSALM 61

Hear my cry, O God; listen to my prayer.

From the ends of the earth I call to you, I call as my heart grows faint;

lead me to the rock that is higher than I.

For you have been my refuge, a strong tower against the foe.

I long to dwell in your tent forever and take refuge in the shelter of your wings.

For you have heard my vows, O God; you have given me the heritage of those who fear your name.

Increase the days of the king's life, his

years for many generations.

May he be enthroned in God's presence forever;

appoint your love and faithfulness to protect him.

Then will I ever sing praise to your name and fulfill my vows day after day.

PSALM 62

My soul finds rest in God alone; my salvation comes from him.

He alone is my rock and my salvation; he is my fortress, I will never be shaken.

How long will you assault a man?

Would all of you throw him down— this leaning wall, this tottering fence?

They fully intend to topple him from his lofty place; they take delight in lies.

With their mouths they bless, but in their hearts they curse.

Find rest, O my soul, in God alone; my hope comes from him.

He alone is my rock and my salvation; he is my fortress, I will not be shaken.

My salvation and my honor depend on God; he is my mighty rock, my refuge.

Trust in him at all times, O people; pour out your hearts to him, for God is our refuge.

Lowborn men are but a breath, the highborn are but a lie;

if weighed on a balance, they are nothing; together they are only a breath.

Do not trust in extortion or take pride in stolen goods;

though your riches increase, do not set your heart on them.

One thing God has spoken, two things have I heard: that you, O God, are strong, and that you, O Lord, are loving.

Surely you will reward each person according to what he has done.

PSALM 63

O God, you are my God, earnestly I seek you;

my soul thirsts for you, my body longs for you, in a dry and weary land where there is no water.

I have seen you in the sanctuary and beheld your power and your glory.

Because your love is better than life, my lips will glorify you.

I will praise you as long as I live, and in your name I will lift up my hands.

My soul will be satisfied as with the richest of foods; with singing lips my mouth will praise you.

On my bed I remember you; I think of you through the watches of the night.

Because you are my help, I sing in the shadow of your wings.

My soul clings to you;

your right hand upholds me.

They who seek my life will be destroyed; they will go down to the depths of the earth.

They will be given over to the sword and become food for jackals.

But the king will rejoice in God;

all who swear by God's name will praise him, while the mouths of liars will be silenced.

PSALM 65

Praise awaits you, O God, in Zion;

to you our vows will be fulfilled.

O you who hear prayer, to you all men will come.

When we were overwhelmed by sins, you forgave our transgressions.

Blessed are those you choose and bring near to live in your courts!

We are filled with the good things of

your house, of your holy temple.

You answer us with awesome deeds of righteousness, O God our Savior, the hope of all the ends of the earth and of the farthest seas,

who formed the mountains by your power, having armed yourself with strength,

who stilled the roaring of the seas, the roaring of their waves, and the turmoil of the nations.

Those living far away fear your wonders; where morning dawns and evening fades you call forth songs of joy.

You care for the land and water it; you enrich it abundantly.

The streams of God are filled with water to provide the people with grain, for so you have ordained it.

You drench its furrows and level its ridges; you soften it with showers and bless its crops.

You crown the year with your bounty, and your carts overflow with abundance.

The grasslands of the desert overflow; the hills are clothed with gladness.

The meadows are covered with flocks and the valleys are mantled with grain; they shout for joy and sing.

PSALM 66

Shout with joy to God, all the earth!

Sing the glory of his name; make his praise glorious!

Say to God, "How awesome are your deeds!

"So great is your power that your enemies cringe before you.

"All the earth bows down to you; they sing praise to you, they sing praise to your name."

Come and see what God has done,

how awesome his works in man's behalf!

He turned the sea into dry land, they passed through the waters on foot—come, let us rejoice in him.

He rules forever by his power, his eyes watch the nations—let not the rebellious rise up against him.

Praise our God, O peoples, let the sound of his praise be heard;

he has preserved our lives and kept our feet from slipping.

For you, O God, tested us; you refined us like silver.

You brought us into prison and laid burdens on our backs.

You let men ride over our heads;

we went through fire and water, but you brought us to a place of abundance.

I will come to your temple with burnt offerings and fulfill my vows to you— vows my lips promised and my mouth spoke when I was in trouble.

I will sacrifice fat animals to you and an offering of rams; I will offer bulls and goats.

Come and listen, all you who fear God; let me tell you what he has done for me.

I cried out to him with my mouth; his praise was on my tongue.

If I had cherished sin in my heart, the Lord would not have listened; but God has surely listened and heard my voice in prayer.

Praise be to God, who has not rejected my prayer or withheld his love from me!

PSALM 67

May God be gracious to us and bless us and make his face shine upon us,

that your ways may be known on earth, your salvation among all nations.

May the peoples praise you, O God; may all the peoples praise you.

May the nations be glad and sing for joy,

for you rule the peoples justly and guide the nations of the earth.

May the peoples praise you, O God; may all the peoples praise you.

Then the land will yield its harvest, and God, our God, will bless us.

God will bless us, and all the ends of the earth will fear him.

PSALM 68:1–20

May God arise, may his enemies be scattered; may his foes flee before him.

As smoke is blown away by the wind, may you blow them away;

as wax melts before the fire, may the wicked perish before God.

But may the righteous be glad and rejoice before God; may they be happy and joyful.

Sing to God, sing praise to his name, extol him who rides on the clouds—

his name is the LORD—and rejoice before him.

A father to the fatherless, a defender of widows, is God in his holy dwelling.

God sets the lonely in families, he leads forth the prisoners with singing; but the rebellious live in a sun-scorched land.

When you went out before your people, O God, when you marched through the wasteland,

the earth shook, the heavens poured down rain, before God, the One of Sinai, before God, the God of Israel.

You gave abundant showers, O God; you refreshed your weary inheritance.

Your people settled in it, and from your bounty, O God, you provided for the poor.

The Lord announced the word, and great was the company of those who proclaimed it:

"Kings and armies flee in haste; in the camps men divide the plunder.

"Even while you sleep among the campfires, the wings of my dove are sheathed with silver, its feathers with shining gold."

When the Almighty scattered the kings in the land, it was like snow fallen on Zalmon.

The mountains of Bashan are majestic mountains; rugged are the mountains of Bashan.

Why gaze in envy, O rugged mountains, at the mountain where God chooses to reign, where the LORD himself will dwell forever?

The chariots of God are tens of thousands and thousands of thousands; the Lord has come from Sinai into his sanctuary.

When you ascended on high, you led captives in your train; you received gifts from men, even from the rebellious— that you, O LORD God, might dwell there.

Praise be to the Lord, to God our Savior, who daily bears our burdens.

Our God is a God who saves; from the Sovereign LORD comes escape from death.

PSALM 69:1–18

Save me, O God, for the waters have come up to my neck.

I sink in the miry depths, where there is no foothold.

I have come into the deep waters; the floods engulf me.

I am worn out calling for help; my throat is parched.

My eyes fail, looking for my God.

Those who hate me without reason outnumber the hairs of my head;

many are my enemies without cause, those who seek to destroy me.

I am forced to restore what I did not steal.

You know my folly, O God; my guilt is not hidden from you.

May those who hope in you not be disgraced because of me, O Lord, the LORD Almighty;

may those who seek you not be put to shame because of me, O God of Israel.

For I endure scorn for your sake, and shame covers my face.

I am a stranger to my brothers, an alien to my own mother's sons;

for zeal for your house consumes me, and the insults of those who insult you fall on me.

When I weep and fast, I must endure scorn; when I put on sackcloth, people make sport of me.

Those who sit at the gate mock me, and I am the song of the drunkards.

But I pray to you, O LORD, in the time of your favor;

in your great love, O God, answer me with your sure salvation.

Rescue me from the mire, do not let me sink;

deliver me from those who hate me, from the deep waters.

Do not let the floodwaters engulf me or the depths swallow me up or the pit close its mouth over me.

Answer me, O LORD, out of the goodness of your love; in your great mercy turn to me.

Do not hide your face from your servant; answer me quickly, for I am in trouble.

Come near and rescue me; redeem me because of my foes.

PSALM 69:19–36

You know how I am scorned, disgraced and shamed; all my enemies are before you.

Scorn has broken my heart and has left me helpless;

I looked for sympathy, but there was none, for comforters, but I found none.

They put gall in my food and gave me vinegar for my thirst.

May the table set before them become a snare; may it become retribution and a trap.

May their eyes be darkened so they cannot see, and their backs be bent forever.

Pour out your wrath on them; let your fierce anger overtake them.

May their place be deserted; let there be no one to dwell in their tents.

For they persecute those you wound and talk about the pain of those you hurt.

Charge them with crime upon crime; do not let them share in your salvation.

May they be blotted out of the book of life and not be listed with the righteous.

I am in pain and distress; may your salvation, O God, protect me.

I will praise God's name in song and glorify him with thanksgiving.

This will please the LORD more than an ox, more than a bull with its horns and hoofs.

The poor will see and be glad—you who seek God, may your hearts live!

The LORD hears the needy and does not despise his captive people.

Let heaven and earth praise him, the seas and all that move in them, for God will save Zion and rebuild the cities of Judah.

Then people will settle there and possess it; the children of his servants will inherit it, and those who love his name will dwell there.

PSALM 70

Hasten, O God, to save me; O LORD, come quickly to help me.

May those who seek my life be put to shame and confusion;

may all who desire my ruin be turned back in disgrace.

May those who say to me, "Aha! Aha!" turn back because of their shame.

But may all who seek you rejoice and be glad in you;

may those who love your salvation always say, "Let God be exalted!"

Yet I am poor and needy; come quickly to me, O God.

You are my help and my deliverer; O LORD, do not delay.

PSALM 72:1–19

Endow the king with your justice, O God, the royal son with your righteousness.

He will judge your people in righteousness, your afflicted ones with justice.

The mountains will bring prosperity to the people, the hills the fruit of righteousness.

He will defend the afflicted among the people and save the children of the needy; he will crush the oppressor.

He will endure as long as the sun, as long as the moon, through all generations.

He will be like rain falling on a mown field, like showers watering the earth.

In his days the righteous will flourish, prosperity will abound till the moon is no more.

He will rule from sea to sea and from the River to the ends of the earth.

The desert tribes will bow before him and his enemies will lick the dust.

The kings of Tarshish and of distant

shores will bring tribute to him;

the kings of Sheba and Seba will present him gifts.

All kings will bow down to him and all nations will serve him.

For he will deliver the needy who cry out, the afflicted who have no one to help.

He will take pity on the weak and the needy and save the needy from death.

He will rescue them from oppression and violence, for precious is their blood in his sight.

Long may he live! May gold from Sheba be given him.

May people ever pray for him and bless him all day long.

Let grain abound throughout the land; on the tops of the hills may it sway.

Let its fruit flourish like Lebanon; let it thrive like the grass of the field.

May his name endure forever; may it continue as long as the sun.

All nations will be blessed through him, and they will call him blessed.

Praise be to the LORD God, the God of Israel, who alone does marvelous deeds.

Praise be to his glorious name forever; may the whole earth be filled with his glory.

Amen and Amen.

PSALM 73

Surely God is good to Israel, to those who are pure in heart.

But as for me, my feet had almost slipped; I had nearly lost my foothold.

For I envied the arrogant when I saw the prosperity of the wicked.

They have no struggles; their bodies are healthy and strong.

They are free from the burdens common to man; they are not plagued by human ills.

Therefore pride is their necklace; they clothe themselves with violence.

From their callous hearts comes iniquity; the evil conceits of their minds know no limits.

They scoff, and speak with malice; in their arrogance they threaten oppression.

Their mouths lay claim to heaven, and their tongues take possession of the earth.

Therefore their people turn to them and drink up waters in abundance.

They say, "How can God know? Does the Most High have knowledge?"

This is what the wicked are like—always carefree, they increase in wealth.

Surely in vain have I kept my heart pure; in vain have I washed my hands in innocence.

All day long I have been plagued; I have been punished every morning.

If I had said, "I will speak thus," I would have betrayed your children.

When I tried to understand all this, it was oppressive to me,

till I entered the sanctuary of God; then I understood their final destiny.

Surely you place them on slippery ground; you cast them down to ruin.

How suddenly are they destroyed, completely swept away by terrors!

As a dream when one awakes, so when you arise, O Lord, you will despise them as fantasies.

When my heart was grieved and my spirit embittered,

I was senseless and ignorant; I was a brute beast before you.

Yet I am always with you; you hold me by my right hand.

You guide me with your counsel, and afterward you will take me into glory.

Whom have I in heaven but you? And

earth has nothing I desire besides you.

My flesh and my heart may fail, but God is the strength of my heart and my portion forever.

Those who are far from you will perish; you destroy all who are unfaithful to you.

But as for me, it is good to be near God. I have made the Sovereign LORD my refuge; I will tell of all your deeds.

PSALM 74

Why have you rejected us forever, O God?

Why does your anger smolder against the sheep of your pasture?

Remember the people you purchased of old, the tribe of your inheritance, whom you redeemed—Mount Zion, where you dwelt.

Turn your steps toward these everlasting ruins, all this destruction the enemy has brought on the sanctuary.

Your foes roared in the place where you met with us; they set up their standards as signs.

They behaved like men wielding axes to cut through a thicket of trees.

They smashed all the carved paneling with their axes and hatchets.

They burned your sanctuary to the ground; they defiled the dwelling place of your Name.

They said in their hearts, "We will crush them completely!" They burned every place where God was worshiped in the land.

We are given no miraculous signs; no prophets are left, and none of us knows how long this will be.

How long will the enemy mock you, O God? Will the foe revile your name forever?

Why do you hold back your hand,

your right hand? Take it from the folds of your garment and destroy them!

But you, O God, are my king from of old; you bring salvation upon the earth.

It was you who split open the sea by your power; you broke the heads of the monster in the waters.

It was you who crushed the heads of Leviathan and gave him as food to the creatures of the desert.

It was you who opened up springs and streams; you dried up the ever flowing rivers.

The day is yours, and yours also the night; you established the sun and moon.

It was you who set all the boundaries of the earth; you made both summer and winter.

Remember how the enemy has mocked you, O LORD, how foolish people have reviled your name.

Do not hand over the life of your dove to wild beasts; do not forget the lives of your afflicted people forever.

Have regard for your covenant, because haunts of violence fill the dark places of the land.

Do not let the oppressed retreat in disgrace; may the poor and needy praise your name.

Rise up, O God, and defend your cause; remember how fools mock you all day long.

Do not ignore the clamor of your adversaries, the uproar of your enemies, which rises continually.

PSALM 77

I cried out to God for help; I cried out to God to hear me.

When I was in distress, I sought the Lord; at night I stretched out untiring hands and my soul refused to be comforted.

I remembered you, O God, and I groaned; I mused, and my spirit grew faint.

You kept my eyes from closing; I was too troubled to speak.

I thought about the former days, the years of long ago;

I remembered my songs in the night. My heart mused and my spirit inquired:

"Will the Lord reject forever? Will he never show his favor again?

"Has his unfailing love vanished forever? Has his promise failed for all time?

"Has God forgotten to be merciful? Has he in anger withheld his compassion?"

Then I thought, "To this I will appeal: the years of the right hand of the Most High."

I will remember the deeds of the LORD; yes, I will remember your miracles of long ago.

I will meditate on all your works and consider all your mighty deeds.

Your ways, O God, are holy. What god is so great as our God?

You are the God who performs miracles; you display your power among the peoples.

With your mighty arm you redeemed your people, the descendants of Jacob and Joseph.

The waters saw you, O God, the waters saw you and writhed; the very depths were convulsed.

The clouds poured down water, the skies resounded with thunder; your arrows flashed back and forth.

Your thunder was heard in the whirlwind, your lightning lit up the world; the earth trembled and quaked.

Your path led through the sea, your way through the mighty waters, though your footprints were not seen.

You led your people like a flock by the hand of Moses and Aaron.

PSALM 80

Hear us, O Shepherd of Israel, you who lead Joseph like a flock;

you who sit enthroned between the cherubim, shine forth before Ephraim, Benjamin and Manasseh.

Awaken your might; come and save us.

Restore us, O God; make your face shine upon us, that we may be saved.

O LORD God Almighty, how long will your anger smolder against the prayers of your people?

You have fed them with the bread of tears; you have made them drink tears by the bowlful.

You have made us a source of contention to our neighbors, and our enemies mock us.

Restore us, O God Almighty; make your face shine upon us, that we may be saved.

You brought a vine out of Egypt; you drove out the nations and planted it.

You cleared the ground for it, and it took root and filled the land.

The mountains were covered with its shade, the mighty cedars with its branches.

It sent out its boughs to the Sea, its shoots as far as the River.

Why have you broken down its walls so that all who pass by pick its grapes?

Boars from the forest ravage it and the creatures of the field feed on it.

Return to us, O God Almighty! Look down from heaven and see!

Watch over this vine, the root your right hand has planted, the son you have raised up for yourself.

Your vine is cut down, it is burned with fire; at your rebuke your people perish.

Let your hand rest on the man at your right hand, the son of man you have raised up for yourself.

Then we will not turn away from you; revive us, and we will call on your name.

Restore us, O LORD God Almighty; make your face shine upon us, that we may be saved.

PSALM 84

How lovely is your dwelling place, O LORD Almighty!

My soul yearns, even faints, for the courts of the LORD; my heart and my flesh cry out for the living God.

Even the sparrow has found a home, and the swallow a nest for herself, where she may have her young—

a place near your altar, O LORD Almighty, my King and my God.

Blessed are those who dwell in your house; they are ever praising you.

Blessed are those whose strength is in you, who have set their hearts on pilgrimage.

As they pass through the Valley of Baca, they make it a place of springs; the autumn rains also cover it with pools.

They go from strength to strength, till each appears before God in Zion.

Hear my prayer, O LORD God Almighty; listen to me, O God of Jacob.

Look upon our shield, O God; look with favor on your anointed one.

Better is one day in your courts than a thousand elsewhere;

I would rather be a doorkeeper in the house of my God than dwell in the tents of the wicked.

For the LORD God is a sun and shield; the LORD bestows favor and honor;

no good thing does he withhold from those whose walk is blameless.

O LORD Almighty, blessed is the man who trusts in you.

PSALM 85

You showed favor to your land, O LORD;

you restored the fortunes of Jacob.

You forgave the iniquity of your people and covered all their sins.

You set aside all your wrath and turned from your fierce anger.

Restore us again, O God our Savior, and put away your displeasure toward us.

Will you be angry with us forever? Will you prolong your anger through all generations?

Will you not revive us again, that your people may rejoice in you?

Show us your unfailing love, O LORD, and grant us your salvation.

I will listen to what God the LORD will say; he promises peace to his people, his saints—but let them not return to folly.

Surely his salvation is near those who fear him, that his glory may dwell in our land.

Love and faithfulness meet together; righteousness and peace kiss each other.

Faithfulness springs forth from the earth, and righteousness looks down from heaven.

The LORD will indeed give what is good, and our land will yield its harvest.

Righteousness goes before him and prepares the way for his steps.

PSALM 86

Hear, O LORD, and answer me, for I am poor and needy.

Guard my life, for I am devoted to you.

You are my God; save your servant who trusts in you.

Have mercy on me, O Lord, for I call to you all day long.

Bring joy to your servant, for to you, O Lord, I lift up my soul.

You are forgiving and good, O Lord, abounding in love to all who call to you.

Hear my prayer, O LORD; listen to my cry for mercy.

In the day of my trouble I will call to you, for you will answer me.

Among the gods there is none like you, O Lord; no deeds can compare with yours.

All the nations you have made will come and worship before you, O Lord; they will bring glory to your name.

For you are great and do marvelous deeds;

you alone are God.

Teach me your way, O LORD, and I will walk in your truth;

give me an undivided heart, that I may fear your name.

I will praise you, O Lord my God, with all my heart; I will glorify your name forever.

For great is your love toward me; you have delivered me from the depths of the grave.

The arrogant are attacking me, O God; a band of ruthless men seeks my life—men without regard for you.

But you, O Lord, are a compassionate and gracious God, slow to anger, abounding in love and faithfulness.

Turn to me and have mercy on me; grant your strength to your servant and save the son of your maidservant.

Give me a sign of your goodness, that my enemies may see it and be put to shame, for you, O LORD, have helped me and comforted me.

PSALM 87

He has set his foundation on the holy mountain; the LORD loves the gates of Zion more than all the dwellings of Jacob.

Glorious things are said of you, O city of God:

"I will record Rahab and Babylon among those who acknowledge me—

Philistia too, and Tyre, along with Cush—and will say, 'This one was born in Zion.' "

Indeed, of Zion it will be said, "This one and that one were born in her,

and the Most High himself will establish her."

The LORD will write in the register of the peoples: "This one was born in Zion."

As they make music they will sing, "All my fountains are in you."

PSALM 89:1–37

I will sing of the LORD's great love forever; with my mouth I will make your faithfulness known through all generations.

I will declare that your love stands firm forever, that you established your faithfulness in heaven itself.

You said, "I have made a covenant with my chosen one, I have sworn to David my servant,

" 'I will establish your line forever and make your throne firm through all generations.' "

The heavens praise your wonders, O LORD, your faithfulness too, in the assembly of the holy ones.

For who in the skies above can compare with the LORD? Who is like the LORD among the heavenly beings?

In the council of the holy ones God is greatly feared; he is more awesome than all who surround him.

O LORD God Almighty, who is like you? You are mighty, O LORD, and your faithfulness surrounds you.

You rule over the surging sea; when its

waves mount up, you still them.

You crushed Rahab like one of the slain; with your strong arm you scattered your enemies.

The heavens are yours, and yours also the earth; you founded the world and all that is in it.

You created the north and the south; Tabor and Hermon sing for joy at your name.

Your arm is endued with power; your hand is strong, your right hand exalted.

Righteousness and justice are the foundation of your throne; love and faithfulness go before you.

Blessed are those who have learned to acclaim you, who walk in the light of your presence, O LORD.

They rejoice in your name all day long; they exult in your righteousness.

For you are their glory and strength, and by your favor you exalt our horn.

Indeed, our shield belongs to the LORD, our king to the Holy One of Israel.

Once you spoke in a vision, to your faithful people you said:

"I have bestowed strength on a warrior; I have exalted a young man from among the people.

"I have found David my servant; with my sacred oil I have anointed him.

"My hand will sustain him; surely my arm will strengthen him.

"No enemy will subject him to tribute; no wicked man will oppress him.

"I will crush his foes before him and strike down his adversaries.

"My faithful love will be with him, and through my name his horn will be exalted.

"I will set his hand over the sea, his right hand over the rivers.

"He will call out to me, 'You are my Father, my God, the Rock my Savior.'

"I will also appoint him my firstborn, the most exalted of the kings of the earth.

"I will maintain my love to him forever, and my covenant with him will never fail.

"I will establish his line forever, his throne as long as the heavens endure.

"If his sons forsake my law and do not follow my statutes,

"if they violate my decrees and fail to keep my commands,

"I will punish their sin with the rod, their iniquity with flogging;

"but I will not take my love from him, nor will I ever betray my faithfulness.

"I will not violate my covenant or alter what my lips have uttered.

"Once for all, I have sworn by my holiness—and I will not lie to David—

"that his line will continue forever and his throne endure before me like the sun;

"it will be established forever like the moon, the faithful witness in the sky."

PSALM 90

Lord, you have been our dwelling place throughout all generations.

Before the mountains were born or you brought forth the earth and the world, from everlasting to everlasting you are God.

You turn men back to dust, saying, "Return to dust, O sons of men."

For a thousand years in your sight are like a day that has just gone by, or like a watch in the night.

You sweep men away in the sleep of death; they are like the new grass of the morning—

though in the morning it springs up new, by evening it is dry and withered.

We are consumed by your anger and terrified by your indignation.

You have set our iniquities before you, our secret sins in the light of your presence.

All our days pass away under your wrath;

we finish our years with a moan.

The length of our days is seventy years—or eighty, if we have the strength;

yet their span is but trouble and sorrow, for they quickly pass, and we fly away.

Who knows the power of your anger? For your wrath is as great as the fear that is due you.

Teach us to number our days aright, that we may gain a heart of wisdom.

Relent, O LORD! How long will it be? Have compassion on your servants.

Satisfy us in the morning with your unfailing love, that we may sing for joy and be glad all our days.

Make us glad for as many days as you have afflicted us, for as many years as we have seen trouble.

May your deeds be shown to your servants, your splendor to their children.

May the favor of the Lord our God rest upon us; establish the work of our hands for us—

yes, establish the work of our hands.

PSALM 91

He who dwells in the shelter of the Most High will rest in the shadow of the Almighty.

I will say of the LORD, "He is my refuge and my fortress, my God, in whom I trust."

Surely he will save you from the fowler's snare and from the deadly pestilence.

He will cover you with his feathers,

and under his wings you will find refuge; his faithfulness will be your shield and rampart.

You will not fear the terror of night, nor the arrow that flies by day,

nor the pestilence that stalks in the darkness, nor the plague that destroys at midday.

A thousand may fall at your side, ten thousand at your right hand, but it will not come near you.

You will only observe with your eyes and see the punishment of the wicked.

If you make the Most High your dwelling—even the LORD, who is my refuge—

then no harm will befall you, no disaster will come near your tent.

For he will command his angels concerning you to guard you in all your ways;

they will lift you up in their hands, so that you will not strike your foot against a stone.

You will tread upon the lion and the cobra;

you will trample the great lion and the serpent.

"Because he loves me," says the LORD, "I will rescue him;

"I will protect him, for he acknowledges my name.

"He will call upon me, and I will answer him; I will be with him in trouble, I will deliver him and honor him.

"With long life will I satisfy him and show him my salvation."

PSALM 92

It is good to praise the LORD and make music to your name, O Most High,

to proclaim your love in the morning and your faithfulness at night, to the music of the ten-stringed lyre and the

melody of the harp.

For you make me glad by your deeds, O LORD; I sing for joy at the works of your hands.

How great are your works, O LORD, how profound your thoughts!

The senseless man does not know, fools do not understand,

that though the wicked spring up like grass and all evildoers flourish, they will be forever destroyed.

But you, O LORD, are exalted forever.

For surely your enemies, O LORD, surely your enemies will perish; all evildoers will be scattered.

You have exalted my horn like that of a wild ox; fine oils have been poured upon me.

My eyes have seen the defeat of my adversaries; my ears have heard the rout of my wicked foes.

The righteous will flourish like a palm tree, they will grow like a cedar of Lebanon;

planted in the house of the LORD, they will flourish in the courts of our God.

They will still bear fruit in old age, they will stay fresh and green,

proclaiming, "The LORD is upright; he is my Rock, and there is no wickedness in him."

PSALM 93

The LORD reigns, he is robed in majesty;

the LORD is robed in majesty and is armed with strength.

The world is firmly established; it cannot be moved.

Your throne was established long ago; you are from all eternity.

The seas have lifted up, O LORD, the

seas have lifted up their voice; the seas have lifted up their pounding waves.

Mightier than the thunder of the great waters, mightier than the breakers of the sea—the LORD on high is mighty.

Your statutes stand firm;

holiness adorns your house for endless days, O LORD.

PSALM 94

O LORD, the God who avenges, O God who avenges, shine forth.

Rise up, O Judge of the earth; pay back to the proud what they deserve.

How long will the wicked, O LORD, how long will the wicked be jubilant?

They pour out arrogant words; all the evildoers are full of boasting.

They crush your people, O LORD; they oppress your inheritance.

They slay the widow and the alien; they murder the fatherless.

They say, "The LORD does not see;

"the God of Jacob pays no heed."

Take heed, you senseless ones among the people; you fools, when will you become wise?

Does he who implanted the ear not hear? Does he who formed the eye not see?

Does he who disciplines nations not punish? Does he who teaches man lack knowledge?

The LORD knows the thoughts of man; he knows that they are futile.

Blessed is the man you discipline, O LORD, the man you teach from your law;

you grant him relief from days of trouble, till a pit is dug for the wicked.

For the LORD will not reject his people; he will never forsake his inheritance.

Judgment will again be founded on righteousness, and all the upright in heart will follow it.

Who will rise up for me against the wicked? Who will take a stand for me against evildoers?

Unless the LORD had given me help, I would soon have dwelt in the silence of death.

When I said, "My foot is slipping," your love, O LORD, supported me.

When anxiety was great within me, your consolation brought joy to my soul.

Can a corrupt throne be allied with you—one that brings on misery by its decrees?

They band together against the righteous and condemn the innocent to death.

But the LORD has become my fortress, and my God the rock in whom I take refuge.

He will repay them for their sins and destroy them for their wickedness; the LORD our God will destroy them.

PSALM 95

Come, let us sing for joy to the LORD;

let us shout aloud to the Rock of our salvation.

Let us come before him with thanksgiving and extol him with music and song.

For the LORD is the great God, the great King above all gods.

In his hand are the depths of the earth, and the mountain peaks belong to him.

The sea is his, for he made it, and his hands formed the dry land.

Come, let us bow down in worship, let us kneel before the LORD our Maker;

for he is our God and we are the people of his pasture, the flock under his care.

Today, if you hear his voice, do not harden your hearts as you did at Meribah, as you did that day at Massah in the desert,

where your fathers tested and tried me, though they had seen what I did.

For forty years I was angry with that generation; I said, "They are a people whose hearts go astray, and they have not known my ways."

So I declared on oath in my anger, "They shall never enter my rest."

PSALM 96

Sing to the LORD a new song; sing to the LORD, all the earth.

Sing to the LORD, praise his name; proclaim his salvation day after day.

Declare his glory among the nations, his marvelous deeds among all peoples.

For great is the LORD and most worthy of praise; he is to be feared above all gods.

For all the gods of the nations are idols, but the LORD made the heavens.

Splendor and majesty are before him; strength and glory are in his sanctuary.

Ascribe to the LORD, O families of nations, ascribe to the LORD glory and strength.

Ascribe to the LORD the glory due his name; bring an offering and come into his courts.

Worship the LORD in the splendor of his holiness;

tremble before him, all the earth.

Say among the nations, "The LORD reigns."

The world is firmly established, it cannot be moved; he will judge the peoples with equity.

Let the heavens rejoice, let the earth be glad;

let the sea resound, and all that is in it; let the fields be jubilant, and everything in them.

Then all the trees of the forest will sing for joy; they will sing before the LORD, for he comes, he comes to judge the earth.

He will judge the world in righteousness and the peoples in his truth.

PSALM 97

The LORD reigns, let the earth be glad;

let the distant shores rejoice.

Clouds and thick darkness surround him; righteousness and justice are the foundation of his throne.

Fire goes before him and consumes his foes on every side.

His lightning lights up the world; the earth sees and trembles.

The mountains melt like wax before the LORD, before the Lord of all the earth.

The heavens proclaim his righteousness, and all the peoples see his glory.

All who worship images are put to shame, those who boast in idols— worship him, all you gods!

Zion hears and rejoices and the villages of Judah are glad because of your judgments, O LORD.

For you, O LORD, are the Most High over all the earth; you are exalted far above all gods.

Let those who love the LORD hate evil,

for he guards the lives of his faithful ones and delivers them from the hand of the wicked.

Light is shed upon the righteous and joy on the upright in heart.

Rejoice in the LORD, you who are righteous, and praise his holy name.

PSALM 98

Sing to the LORD a new song, for he has done marvelous things;

his right hand and his holy arm have worked salvation for him.

The LORD has made his salvation known,

and revealed his righteousness to the nations.

He has remembered his love and his faithfulness to the house of Israel;

all the ends of the earth have seen the salvation of our God.

Shout for joy to the LORD, all the earth,

burst into jubilant song with music;

make music to the LORD with the harp, with the harp and the sound of singing,

with trumpets and the blast of the ram's horn—shout for joy before the LORD, the King.

Let the sea resound, and everything in it the world, and all who live in it.

Let the rivers clap their hands, let the mountains sing together for joy;

let them sing before the LORD, for he comes to judge the earth.

He will judge the world in righteousness and the peoples with equity.

PSALM 99

The LORD reigns, let the nations tremble

he sits enthroned between the cherubim, let the earth shake.

Great is the LORD in Zion; he is exalted over all the nations.

Let them praise your great and awesome name—he is holy.

The King is mighty, he loves justice—

you have established equity;

in Jacob you have done what is just and right.

Exalt the LORD our God and worship at his footstool; he is holy.

Moses and Aaron were among his priests, Samuel was among those who called on his name;

they called on the LORD and he answered them.

He spoke to them from the pillar of cloud;

they kept his statutes and the decrees he gave them.

O LORD our God, you answered them; you were to Israel a forgiving God, though you punished their misdeeds.

Exalt the LORD our God and worship at his holy mountain, for the LORD our God is holy.

PSALM 100

Shout for joy to the LORD, all the earth.

Worship the LORD with gladness; come before him with joyful songs.

Know that the LORD is God.

It is he who made us, and we are his; we are his people, the sheep of his pasture.

Enter his gates with thanksgiving and his courts with praise;

give thanks to him and praise his name.

For the LORD is good and his love endures forever;

his faithfulness continues through all generations.

PSALM 101

I will sing of your love and justice; to you, O LORD, I will sing praise.

I will be careful to lead a blameless life—when will you come to me?

I will walk in my house with blameless heart.

I will set before my eyes no vile thing.

The deeds of faithless men I hate; they will not cling to me.

Men of perverse heart shall be far from me; I will have nothing to do with evil.

Whoever slanders his neighbor in secret him will I put to silence;

whoever has haughty eyes and a proud heart, him will I not endure.

My eyes will be on the faithful in the land, that they may dwell with me;

he whose walk is blameless will minister to me.

No one who practices deceit will dwell in my house;

no one who speaks falsely will stand in my presence.

Every morning I will put to silence all the wicked in the land;

I will cut off every evildoer from the city of the LORD.

PSALM 103

Praise the LORD, O my soul; all my inmost being, praise his holy name.

Praise the LORD, O my soul, and forget not all his benefits—

who forgives all your sins and heals all your diseases,

who redeems your life from the pit and crowns you with love and compassion,

who satisfies your desires with good things so that your youth is renewed like the eagle's.

The LORD works righteousness and justice for all the oppressed.

He made known his ways to Moses, his deeds to the people of Israel:

The LORD is compassionate and gracious, slow to anger, abounding in love.

He will not always accuse, nor will he harbor his anger forever;

he does not treat us as our sins deserve or repay us according to our iniquities.

For as high as the heavens are above the earth, so great is his love for those who fear him;

as far as the east is from the west, so far has he removed our transgressions from us.

As a father has compassion on his children, so the LORD has compassion on those who fear him;

for he knows how we are formed, he remembers that we are dust.

As for man, his days are like grass, he flourishes like a flower of the field;

the wind blows over it and it is gone, and its place remembers it no more.

But from everlasting to everlasting the LORD's love is with those who fear him, and his righteousness with their children's children—

with those who keep his covenant and remember to obey his precepts.

The LORD has established his throne in heaven,

and his kingdom rules over all.

Praise the LORD, you his angels, you mighty ones who do his bidding, who obey his word.

Praise the LORD, all his heavenly hosts, you his servants who do his will.

Praise the LORD, all his works everywhere in his dominion.

Praise the LORD, O my soul.

PSALM 104

Praise the LORD, O my soul.

O LORD my God, you are very great; you are clothed with splendor and majesty.

He wraps himself in light as with a garment;

he stretches out the heavens like a tent and lays the beams of his upper chambers on their waters.

He makes the clouds his chariot and rides on the wings of the wind.

He makes winds his messengers, flames of fire his servants.

He set the earth on its foundations;

it can never be moved.

You covered it with the deep as with a garment; the waters stood above the mountains.

But at your rebuke the waters fled, at the sound of your thunder they took to flight;

they flowed over the mountains, they went down into the valleys, to the place you assigned for them.

You set a boundary they cannot cross; never again will they cover the earth.

He makes springs pour water into the ravines; it flows between the mountains.

They give water to all the beasts of the field; the wild donkeys quench their thirst.

The birds of the air nest by the waters; they sing among the branches.

He waters the mountains from his upper chambers; the earth is satisfied by the fruit of his work.

He makes grass grow for the cattle, and plants for man to cultivate—bringing forth food from the earth:

wine that gladdens the heart of man, oil to make his face shine, and bread that sustains his heart.

The trees of the LORD are well watered, the cedars of Lebanon that he planted.

There the birds make their nests; the stork has its home in the pine trees.

The high mountains belong to the wild goats; the crags are a refuge for the coneys.

The moon marks off the seasons, and the sun knows when to go down.

You bring darkness, it becomes night, and all the beasts of the forest prowl.

The lions roar for their prey and seek their food from God.

The sun rises, and they steal away; they return and lie down in their dens.

Then man goes out to his work, to his labor until evening.

How many are your works, O LORD!

In wisdom you made them all; the earth is full of your creatures.

There is the sea, vast and spacious, teeming with creatures beyond number—living things both large and small.

There the ships go to and fro and the leviathan, which you formed to frolic there.

These all look to you to give them their food at the proper time.

When you give it to them, they gather it up;

when you open your hand, they are satisfied with good things.

When you hide your face, they are terrified;

when you take away their breath, they die and return to the dust.

When you send your Spirit, they are created, and you renew the face of the earth.

May the glory of the LORD endure forever; may the LORD rejoice in his works—

he who looks at the earth, and it trembles, who touches the mountains, and they smoke.

I will sing to the LORD all my life;

I will sing praise to my God as long as I live.

May my meditation be pleasing to him, as I rejoice in the LORD.

But may sinners vanish from the earth and the wicked be no more.

Praise the LORD, O my soul.

Praise the LORD.

PSALM 106:1–23, 47, 48

Praise the LORD.

Give thanks to the LORD, for he is good; his love endures forever.

Who can proclaim the mighty acts of the LORD or fully declare his praise?

Blessed are they who maintain justice, who constantly do what is right.

Remember me, O LORD, when you show favor to your people, come to my aid when you save them,

that I may enjoy the prosperity of your chosen ones, that I may share in the joy of your nation and join your inheritance in giving praise.

We have sinned, even as our fathers did;

we have done wrong and acted wickedly.

When our fathers were in Egypt, they gave no thought to your miracles;

they did not remember your many kindnesses, and they rebelled by the sea, the Red Sea.

Yet he saved them for his name's sake, to make his mighty power known.

He rebuked the Red Sea, and it dried up; he led them through the depths as through a desert.

He saved them from the hand of the foe; from the hand of the enemy he redeemed them.

The waters covered their adversaries; not one of them survived.

Then they believed his promises and sang his praise.

But they soon forgot what he had done and did not wait for his counsel.

In the desert they gave in to their craving;

in the wasteland they put God to the test.

So he gave them what they asked for, but sent a wasting disease upon them.

In the camp they grew envious of Moses and of Aaron, who was consecrated to the LORD.

The earth opened up and swallowed Dathan; it buried the company of Abiram.

Fire blazed among their followers; a flame consumed the wicked.

At Horeb they made a calf and worshiped an idol cast from metal.

They exchanged their Glory for an image of a bull, which eats grass.

They forgot the God who saved them, who had done great things in Egypt,

miracles in the land of Ham and awesome deeds by the Red Sea.

So he said he would destroy them—

had not Moses, his chosen one, stood in the breach before him to keep his wrath from destroying them.

Save us, O LORD our God, and gather us from the nations,

that we may give thanks to your holy name and glory in your praise.

Praise be to the LORD, the God of Israel, from everlasting to everlasting.

Let all the people say, "Amen!" Praise the LORD.

PSALM 107:1–22

Give thanks to the LORD, for he is good;
his love endures forever.

Let the redeemed of the LORD say this— those he redeemed from the hand of the foe,

those he gathered from the lands, from east and west, from north and south.

Some wandered in desert wastelands, finding no way to a city where they could settle.

They were hungry and thirsty, and their lives ebbed away.

Then they cried out to the LORD in their trouble, and he delivered them from their distress.

He led them by a straight way to a city where they could settle.

Let them give thanks to the LORD for his unfailing love and his wonderful deeds for men,

for he satisfies the thirsty and fills the hungry with good things.

Some sat in darkness and the deepest gloom, prisoners suffering in iron chains,

for they had rebelled against the words of God and despised the counsel of the Most High.

So he subjected them to bitter labor;

they stumbled, and there was no one to help.

Then they cried to the LORD in their trouble, and he saved them from their distress.

He brought them out of darkness and the deepest gloom and broke away their chains.

Let them give thanks to the LORD for his unfailing love and his wonderful deeds for men,

for he breaks down gates of bronze and cuts through bars of iron.

Some became fools through their rebellious ways and suffered affliction because of their iniquities.

They loathed all food and drew near

the gates of death.

Then they cried to the LORD in their trouble, and he saved them from their distress.

He sent forth his word and healed them; he rescued them from the grave.

Let them give thanks to the LORD for his unfailing love and his wonderful deeds for men.

Let them sacrifice thank offerings and tell of his works with songs of joy.

PSALM 107:23–43

[Men] went out on the sea in ships; they were merchants on the mighty waters.

They saw the works of the LORD, his wonderful deeds in the deep.

For he spoke and stirred up a tempest that lifted high the waves.

They mounted up to the heavens and went down to the depths; in their peril their courage melted away.

They reeled and staggered like drunken men; they were at their wits' end.

Then they cried out to the LORD in their trouble, and he brought them out of their distress.

He stilled the storm to a whisper; the waves of the sea were hushed.

They were glad when it grew calm, and he guided them to their desired haven.

Let them give thanks to the LORD for his unfailing love and his wonderful deeds for men.

Let them exalt him in the assembly of the people and praise him in the council of the elders.

He turned rivers into a desert, flowing springs into thirsty ground,

and fruitful land into a salt waste, because of the wickedness of those who lived there.

He turned the desert into pools of water and the parched ground into flowing springs;

there he brought the hungry to live, and they founded a city where they could settle.

They sowed fields and planted vineyards that yielded a fruitful harvest;

he blessed them, and their numbers greatly increased, and he did not let their herds diminish.

Then their numbers decreased, and they were humbled by oppression, calamity and sorrow;

he who pours contempt on nobles made them wander in a trackless waste.

But he lifted the needy out of their affliction and increased their families like flocks.

The upright see and rejoice, but all the wicked shut their mouths.

Whoever is wise, let him heed these things and consider the great love of the LORD.

PSALM 110

The LORD says to my Lord: "Sit at my right hand until I make your enemies a footstool for your feet."

The LORD will extend your mighty scepter from Zion; you will rule in the midst of your enemies.

Your troops will be willing on your day of battle.

Arrayed in holy majesty, from the womb of the dawn you will receive the dew of your youth.

The LORD has sworn and will not change his mind: "You are a priest forever, in the order of Melchizedek."

The Lord is at your right hand; he will crush kings on the day of his wrath.

He will judge the nations, heaping up the dead and crushing the rulers of the whole earth.

He will drink from a brook beside the way; therefore he will lift up his head.

PSALM 111

Praise the LORD.

I will extol the LORD with all my heart in the council of the upright and in the assembly.

Great are the works of the LORD; they are pondered by all who delight in them.

Glorious and majestic are his deeds, and his righteousness endures forever.

He has caused his wonders to be remembered; the LORD is gracious and compassionate.

He provides food for those who fear him; he remembers his covenant forever.

He has shown his people the power of his works, giving them the lands of other nations.

The works of his hands are faithful and just; all his precepts are trustworthy.

They are steadfast for ever and ever, done in faithfulness and uprightness.

He provided redemption for his people; he ordained his covenant forever—holy and awesome is his name.

The fear of the LORD is the beginning of wisdom; all who follow his precepts have good understanding.

To him belongs eternal praise.

PSALM 112

Praise the LORD.

Blessed is the man who fears the LORD, who finds great delight in his commands.

His children will be mighty in the land; the generation of the upright will be blessed.

Wealth and riches are in his house, and his righteousness endures forever.

Even in darkness light dawns for the upright, for the gracious and compassionate and righteous man.

Good will come to him who is generous and lends freely, who conducts his affairs with justice.

Surely he will never be shaken; a righteous man will be remembered forever.

He will have no fear of bad news; his heart is steadfast, trusting in the LORD.

His heart is secure, he will have no fear; in the end he will look in triumph on his foes.

He has scattered abroad his gifts to the poor, his righteousness endures forever; his horn will be lifted high in honor.

The wicked man will see and be vexed, he will gnash his teeth and waste away;

the longings of the wicked will come to nothing.

PSALM 113

Praise the LORD.

Praise, O servants of the LORD, praise the name of the LORD.

Let the name of the LORD be praised, both now and forevermore.

From the rising of the sun to the place where it sets, the name of the LORD is to be praised.

The LORD is exalted over all the nations, his glory above the heavens.

Who is like the LORD our God, the One who sits enthroned on high, who stoops down to look on the heavens and the earth?

He raises the poor from the dust and lifts the needy from the ash heap;

he seats them with princes, with the princes of their people.

He settles the barren woman in her home as a happy mother of children.

Praise the LORD.

PSALM 114

When Israel came out of Egypt, the house of Jacob from a people of foreign tongue,

Judah became God's sanctuary, Israel his dominion.

The sea looked and fled, the Jordan turned back;

the mountains skipped like rams, the hills like lambs.

Why was it, O sea, that you fled, O Jordan, that you turned back,

you mountains, that you skipped like rams, you hills, like lambs?

Tremble, O earth, at the presence of the Lord, at the presence of the God of Jacob,

who turned the rock into a pool, the hard rock into springs of water.

PSALM 115

Not to us, O LORD, not to us but to your name be the glory,

because of your love and faithfulness.

Why do the nations say, "Where is their God?"

Our God is in heaven; he does whatever pleases him.

But their idols are silver and gold, made by the hands of men.

They have mouths, but cannot speak, eyes, but they cannot see;

they have ears, but cannot hear, noses, but they cannot smell;

they have hands, but cannot feel, feet, but they cannot walk; nor can they utter a sound with their throats.

Those who make them will be like them,

and so will all who trust in them.

O house of Israel, trust in the LORD—he is their help and shield.

O house of Aaron, trust in the LORD— he is their help and shield.

You who fear him, trust in the LORD— he is their help and shield.

The LORD remembers us and will bless us:

He will bless the house of Israel, he will bless the house of Aaron,

he will bless those who fear the LORD—small and great alike.

May the LORD make you increase, both you and your children.

May you be blessed by the LORD, the Maker of heaven and earth.

The highest heavens belong to the LORD, but the earth he has given to man.

It is not the dead who praise the LORD, those who go down to silence;

it is we who extol the LORD, both now and forevermore.

Praise the LORD.

PSALM 116

I love the LORD, for he heard my voice; he heard my cry for mercy.

Because he turned his ear to me, I will call on him as long as I live.

The cords of death entangled me, the anguish of the grave came upon me; I was overcome by trouble and sorrow.

Then I called on the name of the LORD: "O LORD, save me!"

The LORD is gracious and righteous; our God is full of compassion.

The LORD protects the simplehearted; when I was in great need, he saved me.

Be at rest once more, O my soul,

for the LORD has been good to you.

For you, O LORD, have delivered my

soul from death, my eyes from tears, my feet from stumbling,

that I may walk before the LORD in the land of the living.

I believed; therefore I said, "I am greatly afflicted."

And in my dismay I said, "All men are liars."

How can I repay the LORD for all his goodness to me?

I will lift up the cup of salvation and call on the name of the LORD.

I will fulfill my vows to the LORD in the presence of all his people.

Precious in the sight of the LORD is the death of his saints.

O LORD, truly I am your servant; I am your servant, the son of your maidservant;

you have freed me from my chains.

I will sacrifice a thank offering to you and call on the name of the LORD.

I will fulfill my vows to the LORD in the presence of all his people,

in the courts of the house of the LORD— in your midst, O Jerusalem.

Praise the LORD.

PSALM 117

Praise the LORD, all you nations;

extol him, all you peoples.

For great is his love toward us, and the faithfulness of the LORD endures forever.

Praise the LORD.

PSALM 118

Give thanks to the LORD, for he is good; his love endures forever.

Let Israel say: "His love endures forever."

Let the house of Aaron say: "His love endures forever."

Let those who fear the LORD say: "His love endures forever."

In my anguish I cried to the LORD, and he answered by setting me free.

The LORD is with me; I will not be afraid. What can man do to me?

The LORD is with me; he is my helper.

I will look in triumph on my enemies.

It is better to take refuge in the LORD than to trust in man.

It is better to take refuge in the LORD than to trust in princes.

All the nations surrounded me, but in the name of the LORD I cut them off.

They surrounded me on every side, but in the name of the LORD I cut them off.

They swarmed around me like bees, but they died out as quickly as burning thorns;

in the name of the LORD I cut them off.

I was pushed back and about to fall, but the LORD helped me.

The LORD is my strength and my song; he has become my salvation.

Shouts of joy and victory resound in the tents of the righteous:

"The LORD's right hand has done mighty things!

"The LORD's right hand is lifted high;

"the LORD's right hand has done mighty things!"

I will not die but live, and will proclaim what the LORD has done.

The LORD has chastened me severely, but he has not given me over to death.

Open for me the gates of righteousness;

I will enter and give thanks to the LORD.

This is the gate of the LORD through which the righteous may enter.

I will give you thanks, for you an-

swered me; you have become my
salvation.

The stone the builders rejected has become the capstone;

**the LORD has done this, and it is mar-
velous in our eyes.**

This is the day the LORD has made;

let us rejoice and be glad in it.

O LORD, save us; O LORD, grant us
success.

**Blessed is he who comes in the name
of the LORD. From the house of the LORD
we bless you.**

The LORD is God, and he has made his
light shine upon us.

**With boughs in hand, join in the festal
procession up to the horns of the altar.**

You are my God, and I will give you
thanks; you are my God, and I will exalt
you.

**Give thanks to the LORD, for he is
good; his love endures forever.**

PSALM 119:1–24

Blessed are they whose ways are blameless, who walk according to the law of the
LORD.

**Blessed are they who keep his statutes
and seek him with all their heart.**

They do nothing wrong; they walk in his
ways.

**You have laid down precepts that are
to be fully obeyed.**

Oh, that my ways were steadfast in
obeying your decrees!

**Then I would not be put to shame
when I consider all your commands.**

I will praise you with an upright heart as
I learn your righteous laws.

**I will obey your decrees; do not
utterly forsake me.**

How can a young man keep his way

pure? By living according to your word.

**I seek you with all my heart; do not
let me stray from your commands.**

I have hidden your word in my heart
that I might not sin against you.

**Praise be to you, O LORD; teach me
your decrees.**

With my lips I recount all the laws that
come from your mouth.

**I rejoice in following your statutes as
one rejoices in great riches.**

I meditate on your precepts and consider
your ways.

**I delight in your decrees; I will not
neglect your word.**

Do good to your servant, and I will live;
I will obey your word.

**Open my eyes that I may see wonder-
ful things in your law.**

I am a stranger on earth; do not hide
your commands from me.

**My soul is consumed with longing for
your laws at all times.**

You rebuke the arrogant, who are cursed
and who stray from your commands.

**Remove from me scorn and contempt,
for I keep your statutes.**

Though rulers sit together and slander
me, your servant will meditate on your
decrees.

**Your statutes are my delight; they are
my counselors.**

PSALM 119:33–56

Teach me, O LORD, to follow your
decrees; then I will keep them to the end.

**Give me understanding, and I will
keep your law and obey it with all my
heart.**

Direct me in the path of your commands, for there I find delight.

Turn my heart toward your statutes and not toward selfish gain.

Turn my eyes away from worthless things; preserve my life according to your word.

Fulfill your promise to your servant, so that you may be feared.

Take away the disgrace I dread, for your laws are good.

How I long for your precepts! Preserve my life in your righteousness.

May your unfailing love come to me, O LORD, your salvation according to your promise;

then I will answer the one who taunts me, for I trust in your word.

Do not snatch the word of truth from my mouth, for I have put my hope in your laws.

I will always obey your law, for ever and ever.

I will walk about in freedom, for I have sought out your precepts.

I will speak of your statutes before kings and will not be put to shame,

for I delight in your commands because I love them.

I lift up my hands to your commands, which I love, and I meditate on your decrees.

Remember your word to your servant, for you have given me hope.

My comfort in my suffering is this: Your promise preserves my life.

The arrogant mock me without restraint, but I do not turn from your law.

I remember your ancient laws, O LORD, and I find comfort in them.

Indignation grips me because of the wicked, who have forsaken your law.

Your decrees are the theme of my song wherever I lodge.

In the night I remember your name, O LORD, and I will keep your law.

This has been my practice: I obey your precepts.

PSALM 119:89–112

Your word, O LORD, is eternal; it stands firm in the heavens.

Your faithfulness continues through all generations; you established the earth, and it endures.

Your laws endure to this day, for all things serve you.

If your law had not been my delight, I would have perished in my affliction.

I will never forget your precepts, for by them you have preserved my life.

Save me, for I am yours; I have sought out your precepts.

The wicked are waiting to destroy me, but I will ponder your statutes.

To all perfection I see a limit; but your commands are boundless.

Oh, how I love your law! I meditate on it all day long.

Your commands make me wiser than my enemies, for they are ever with me.

I have more insight than all my teachers for I meditate on your statutes.

I have more understanding than the elders, for I obey your precepts.

I have kept my feet from every evil path so that I might obey your word.

I have not departed from your laws, for you yourself have taught me.

How sweet are your words to my taste, sweeter than honey to my mouth!

I gain understanding from your precepts; therefore I hate every wrong path.

Your word is a lamp to my feet and a light for my path.

I have taken an oath and confirmed it, that I will follow your righteous laws.

I have suffered much; preserve my life, O LORD, according to your word.

Accept, O LORD, the willing praise of my mouth, and teach me your laws.

Though I constantly take my life in my hands, I will not forget your law.

The wicked have set a snare for me, but I have not strayed from your precepts.

Your statutes are my heritage forever; they are the joy of my heart.

My heart is set on keeping your decrees to the very end.

PSALM 121

I lift up my eyes to the hills—where does my help come from?

My help comes from the LORD, the Maker of heaven and earth.

He will not let your foot slip—he who watches over you will not slumber;

indeed, he who watches over Israel will neither slumber nor sleep.

The LORD watches over you—the LORD is your shade at your right hand;

the sun will not harm you by day, nor the moon by night.

The LORD will keep you from all harm— he will watch over your life;

the LORD will watch over your coming and going both now and forevermore.

PSALM 122

I rejoiced with those who said to me, "Let us go to the house of the LORD."

Our feet are standing in your gates, O Jerusalem.

Jerusalem is built like a city that is

closely compacted together.

That is where the tribes go up, the tribes of the LORD,

to praise the name of the LORD according to the statute given to Israel.

There the thrones for judgment stand, the thrones of the house of David.

Pray for the peace of Jerusalem: "May those who love you be secure.

"May there be peace within your walls and security within your citadels."

For the sake of my brothers and friends, I will say, "Peace be within you."

For the sake of the house of the LORD our God, I will seek your prosperity.

PSALM 123

I lift up my eyes to you, to you whose throne is in heaven.

As the eyes of slaves look to the hand of their master,

as the eyes of a maid look to the hand of her mistress,

so our eyes look to the LORD our God, till he shows us his mercy.

Have mercy on us, O LORD, have mercy on us, for we have endured much contempt.

We have endured much ridicule from the proud, much contempt from the arrogant.

PSALM 124

If the LORD had not been on our side— let Israel say—

if the LORD had not been on our side when men attacked us,

when their anger flared against us, they would have swallowed us alive;

the flood would have engulfed us, the torrent would have swept over us, the

raging waters would have swept us away.

Praise be to the LORD, who has not let us be torn by their teeth.

We have escaped like a bird out of the fowler's snare;

the snare has been broken, and we have escaped.

Our help is in the name of the LORD, the Maker of heaven and earth.

PSALM 125

Those who trust in the LORD are like Mount Zion, which cannot be shaken but endures forever.

As the mountains surround Jerusalem, so the LORD surrounds his people both now and forevermore.

The scepter of the wicked will not remain over the land allotted to the righteous,

for then the righteous might use their hands to do evil.

Do good, O LORD, to those who are good, to those who are upright in heart.

But those who turn to crooked ways the LORD will banish with the evildoers.

Peace be upon Israel.

PSALM 126

When the LORD brought back the captives to Zion, we were like men who dreamed.

Our mouths were filled with laughter, our tongues with songs of joy.

Then it was said among the nations, "The LORD has done great things for them."

The LORD has done great things for us, and we are filled with joy.

Restore our fortunes, O LORD, like

streams in the Negev.

Those who sow in tears will reap with songs of joy.

He who goes out weeping, carrying seed to sow,

will return with songs of joy, carrying sheaves with him.

PSALM 127

Unless the LORD builds the house, its builders labor in vain.

Unless the LORD watches over the city, the watchmen stand guard in vain.

In vain you rise early and stay up late, toiling for food to eat—

for he grants sleep to those he loves.

Sons are a heritage from the LORD, children a reward from him.

Like arrows in the hands of a warrior are sons born in one's youth.

Blessed is the man whose quiver is full of them.

They will not be put to shame when they contend with their enemies in the gate.

PSALM 128

Blessed are all who fear the LORD, who walk in his ways.

You will eat the fruit of your labor; blessings and prosperity will be yours.

Your wife will be like a fruitful vine within your house; your sons will be like olive shoots around your table.

Thus is the man blessed who fears the LORD.

May the LORD bless you from Zion all the days of your life;

may you see the prosperity of Jerusalem, and may you live to see your chil-

dren's children.

Peace be upon Israel.

PSALM 129

They have greatly oppressed me from my youth—let Israel say—

they have greatly oppressed me from my youth, but they have not gained the victory over me.

Plowmen have plowed my back and made their furrows long.

But the LORD is righteous; he has cut me free from the cords of the wicked.

May all who hate Zion be turned back in shame.

May they be like grass on the roof, which withers before it can grow;

with it the reaper cannot fill his hands, nor the one who gathers fill his arms.

May those who pass by not say, "The blessing of the LORD be upon you; we bless you in the name of the LORD."

PSALM 130

Out of the depths I cry to you, O LORD; O Lord, hear my voice.

Let your ears be attentive to my cry for mercy.

If you, O LORD, kept a record of sins, O Lord, who could stand?

But with you there is forgiveness; therefore you are feared.

I wait for the LORD, my soul waits, and in his word I put my hope.

My soul waits for the Lord more than watchmen wait for the morning, more than watchmen wait for the morning.

O Israel, put your hope in the LORD, for with the LORD is unfailing love and with him is full redemption.

He himself will redeem Israel from all their sins.

PSALM 131

My heart is not proud, O LORD, my eyes are not haughty;

I do not concern myself with great matters or things too wonderful for me.

But I have stilled and quieted my soul;

like a weaned child with its mother, like a weaned child is my soul within me.

O Israel, put your hope in the LORD both now and forevermore.

PSALM 132

O LORD, remember David and all the hardships he endured.

He swore an oath to the LORD and made a vow to the Mighty One of Jacob:

"I will not enter my house or go to my bed—I will allow no sleep to my eyes, no slumber to my eyelids,

"till I find a place for the LORD, a dwelling for the Mighty One of Jacob."

We heard it in Ephrathah, we came upon it in the fields of Jaar:

"Let us go to his dwelling place; let us worship at his footstool—

"arise, O LORD, and come to your resting place, you and the ark of your might.

"May your priests be clothed with righteousness; may your saints sing for joy."

For the sake of David your servant, do not reject your anointed one.

The LORD swore an oath to David, a sure oath that he will not revoke:

"One of your own descendants I will place on your throne—

"if your sons keep my covenant and the statutes I teach them, then their sons will sit on your throne for ever and ever.'

For the LORD has chosen Zion, he has desired it for his dwelling:

"This is my resting place for ever and ever; here I will sit enthroned, for I have desired it—

"I will bless her with abundant provisions; her poor will I satisfy with food.

"I will clothe her priests with salvation, and her saints will ever sing for joy.

"Here I will make a horn grow for David and set up a lamp for my anointed one.

"I will clothe his enemies with shame, but the crown on his head will be resplendent."

PSALM 133

How good and pleasant it is when brothers live together in unity!

It is like precious oil poured on the head, running down on the beard, running down on Aaron's beard, down upon the collar of his robes.

It is as if the dew of Hermon were falling on Mount Zion.

For there the LORD bestows his blessing, even life forevermore.

PSALM 134

Praise the LORD, all you servants of the LORD,

who minister by night in the house of the LORD.

Lift up your hands in the sanctuary and praise the LORD.

May the LORD, the Maker of heaven and earth, bless you from Zion.

PSALM 135

Praise the LORD.

Praise the name of the LORD;

praise him, you servants of the LORD,

you who minister in the house of the

LORD, in the courts of the house of our God.

Praise the LORD, for the LORD is good; sing praise to his name, for that is pleasant.

For the LORD has chosen Jacob to be his own, Israel to be his treasured possession.

I know that the LORD is great, that our Lord is greater than all gods.

The LORD does whatever pleases him, in the heavens and on the earth, in the seas and all their depths.

He makes clouds rise from the ends of the earth;

he sends lightning with the rain and brings out the wind from his storehouses.

He struck down the firstborn of Egypt, the firstborn of men and animals.

He sent his signs and wonders into your midst, O Egypt, against Pharaoh and all his servants.

He struck down many nations and killed mighty kings—Sihon king of the Amorites, Og king of Bashan and all the kings of Canaan—

and he gave their land as an inheritance, an inheritance to his people Israel.

Your name, O LORD, endures forever, your renown, O LORD, through all generations.

For the LORD will vindicate his people and have compassion on his servants.

The idols of the nations are silver and gold, made by the hands of men.

They have mouths, but cannot speak, eyes, but they cannot see;

they have ears, but cannot hear, nor is there breath in their mouths.

Those who make them will be like them, and so will all who trust in them.

O house of Israel, praise the LORD; O house of Aaron, praise the LORD;

O house of Levi, praise the LORD; you who fear him, praise the LORD.

Praise be to the LORD from Zion, to him who dwells in Jerusalem.

Praise the LORD.

PSALM 136

Give thanks to the LORD, for he is good.
His love endures forever.

Give thanks to the God of gods.
His love endures forever.

Give thanks to the Lord of lords:
His love endures forever.

to him who alone does great wonders,
His love endures forever.

who by his understanding made the heavens,
His love endures forever.

who spread out the earth upon the waters,
His love endures forever.

who made the great lights—
His love endures forever.

the sun to govern the day,
His love endures forever.

the moon and stars to govern the night;
His love endures forever.

to him who struck down the firstborn of Egypt
His love endures forever.

and brought Israel out from among them
His love endures forever.

with a mighty hand and outstretched arm;
His love endures forever.

to him who divided the Red Sea asunder
His love endures forever.

and brought Israel through the midst of it,
His love endures forever.

but swept Pharaoh and his army into the Red Sea;
His love endures forever

to him who led his people through the desert,
His love endures forever.

who struck down great kings,
His love endures forever

and killed mighty kings—
His love endures forever.

Sihon king of the Amorites
His love endures forever

and Og king of Bashan—
His love endures forever.

and gave their land as an inheritance,
His love endures forever

an inheritance to his servant Israel;
His love endures forever.

to the One who remembered us in our low estate
His love endures forever

and freed us from our enemies,
His love endures forever.

and who gives food to every creature.
His love endures forever

Give thanks to the God of heaven.
His love endures forever.

PSALM 138

I will praise you, O LORD, with all my heart;

before the "gods" I will sing your praise.

I will bow down toward your holy temple and will praise your name for your love and your faithfulness,

for you have exalted above all things your name and your word.

When I called, you answered me;

you made me bold and stouthearted.

May all the kings of the earth praise you, O LORD, when they hear the words of your mouth.

May they sing of the ways of the LORD, for the glory of the LORD is great.

Though the LORD is on high, he looks upon the lowly,

but the proud he knows from afar.

Though I walk in the midst of trouble, you preserve my life;

you stretch out your hand against the anger of my foes, with your right hand you save me.

The LORD will fulfill his purpose for me;

your love, O LORD, endures forever— do not abandon the works of your hands.

PSALM 139

O LORD, you have searched me and you know me.

You know when I sit and when I rise; you perceive my thoughts from afar.

You discern my going out and my lying down; you are familiar with all my ways.

Before a word is on my tongue you know it completely, O LORD.

You hem me in—behind and before; you have laid your hand upon me.

Such knowledge is too wonderful for me, too lofty for me to attain.

Where can I go from your Spirit?

Where can I flee from your presence?

If I go up to the heavens, you are there;

if I make my bed in the depths, you are there.

If I rise on the wings of the dawn, if I settle on the far side of the sea,

even there your hand will guide me, your right hand will hold me fast.

If I say, "Surely the darkness will hide me and the light become night around me,"

even the darkness will not be dark to you; the night will shine like the day, for darkness is as light to you.

For you created my inmost being; you knit me together in my mother's womb.

I praise you because I am fearfully and wonderfully made;

your works are wonderful, I know that full well.

My frame was not hidden from you when I was made in the secret place.

When I was woven together in the depths of the earth, your eyes saw my unformed body.

All the days ordained for me were written in your book before one of them came to be.

How precious to me are your thoughts, O God!

How vast is the sum of them!

Were I to count them, they would out-number the grains of sand.

When I awake, I am still with you.

If only you would slay the wicked, O God! Away from me, you bloodthirsty men!

They speak of you with evil intent; your adversaries misuse your name.

Do I not hate those who hate you, O LORD, and abhor those who rise up against you?

I have nothing but hatred for them; I count them my enemies.

Search me, O God, and know my heart; test me and know my anxious thoughts.

See if there is any offensive way in me, and lead me in the way everlasting.

PSALM 141

O LORD, I call to you; come quickly to me. Hear my voice when I call to you.

May my prayer be set before you like

incense; may the lifting up of my hands be like the evening sacrifice.

Set a guard over my mouth, O LORD; keep watch over the door of my lips.

Let not my heart be drawn to what is evil, to take part in wicked deeds with men who are evildoers; let me not eat of their delicacies.

Let a righteous man strike me—it is a kindness; let him rebuke me—it is oil on my head.

My head will not refuse it.

Yet my prayer is ever against the deeds of evildoers;

their rulers will be thrown down from the cliffs, and the wicked will learn that my words were well spoken.

They will say, "As one plows and breaks up the earth, so our bones have been scattered at the mouth of the grave."

But my eyes are fixed on you, O Sovereign LORD; in you I take refuge—do not give me over to death.

Keep me from the snares they have laid for me, from the traps set by evildoers.

Let the wicked fall into their own nets, while I pass by in safety.

PSALM 142

I cry aloud to the LORD; I lift up my voice to the LORD for mercy.

I pour out my complaint before him; before him I tell my trouble.

When my spirit grows faint within me, it is you who know my way.

In the path where I walk men have hidden a snare for me.

Look to my right and see; no one is concerned for me.

I have no refuge; no one cares for my life.

I cry to you, O LORD; I say, "You are my refuge, my portion in the land of the living."

Listen to my cry, for I am in desperate need; rescue me from those who pursue me, for they are too strong for me.

Set me free from my prison, that I may praise your name.

Then the righteous will gather about me because of your goodness to me.

PSALM 143

O LORD, hear my prayer, listen to my cry for mercy;

in your faithfulness and righteousness come to my relief.

Do not bring your servant into judgment, for no one living is righteous before you.

The enemy pursues me, he crushes me to the ground;

he makes me dwell in darkness like those long dead.

So my spirit grows faint within me; my heart within me is dismayed.

I remember the days of long ago; I meditate on all your works and consider what your hands have done.

I spread out my hands to you; my soul thirsts for you like a parched land.

Answer me quickly, O LORD; my spirit fails.

Do not hide your face from me or I will be like those who go down to the pit.

Let the morning bring me word of your unfailing love, for I have put my trust in you.

Show me the way I should go, for to you I lift up my soul.

Rescue me from my enemies, O LORD, for I hide myself in you.

Teach me to do your will, for you are my God; may your good Spirit lead me on level ground.

For your name's sake, O LORD, preserve my life; in your righteousness, bring me out of trouble.

In your unfailing love, silence my enemies; destroy all my foes, for I am your servant.

PSALM 144

Praise be to the LORD my Rock,

who trains my hands for war, my fingers for battle.

He is my loving God and my fortress, my stronghold and my deliverer,

my shield, in whom I take refuge, who subdues peoples under me.

O LORD, what is man that you care for him, the son of man that you think of him?

Man is like a breath; his days are like a fleeting shadow.

Part your heavens, O LORD, and come down; touch the mountains, so that they smoke.

Send forth lightning and scatter the enemies; shoot your arrows and rout them.

Reach down your hand from on high; deliver me and rescue me from the mighty waters,

from the hands of foreigners whose mouths are full of lies, whose right hands are deceitful.

I will sing a new song to you, O God; on the ten-stringed lyre I will make music to you,

to the One who gives victory to kings, who delivers his servant David from the deadly sword.

Deliver me and rescue me from the hands of foreigners,

whose mouths are full of lies, whose right hands are deceitful.

Then our sons in their youth will be like well-nurtured plants,

and our daughters will be like pillars carved to adorn a palace.

Our barns will be filled with every kind of provision.

Our sheep will increase by thousands, by tens of thousands in our fields; our oxen will draw heavy loads.

There will be no breaching of walls, no going into captivity, no cry of distress in our streets.

Blessed are the people of whom this is true; blessed are the people whose God is the LORD.

PSALM 145

I will exalt you, my God the King; I will praise your name for ever and ever.

Every day I will praise you and extol your name for ever and ever.

Great is the LORD and most worthy of praise;

his greatness no one can fathom.

One generation will commend your works to another; they will tell of your mighty acts.

They will speak of the glorious splendor of your majesty, and I will meditate on your wonderful works.

They will tell of the power of your awesome works, and I will proclaim your great deeds.

They will celebrate your abundant goodness and joyfully sing of your righteousness.

The LORD is gracious and compassionate, slow to anger and rich in love.

The LORD is good to all; he has compassion on all he has made.

All you have made will praise you, O LORD; your saints will extol you.

They will tell of the glory of your kingdom and speak of your might,

so that all men may know of your mighty acts and the glorious splendor of your kingdom.

Your kingdom is an everlasting kingdom, and your dominion endures through all generations.

The LORD is faithful to all his promises and loving toward all he has made.

The LORD upholds all those who fall and lifts up all who are bowed down.

The eyes of all look to you, and you give them their food at the proper time.

You open your hand and satisfy the desires of every living thing.

The LORD is righteous in all his ways and loving toward all he has made.

The LORD is near to all who call on him, to all who call on him in truth.

He fulfills the desires of those who fear him; he hears their cry and saves them.

The LORD watches over all who love him, but all the wicked he will destroy.

My mouth will speak in praise of the LORD.

Let every creature praise his holy name for ever and ever.

PSALM 146

Praise the LORD.

Praise the LORD, O my soul.

I will praise the LORD all my life;

I will sing praise to my God as long as I live.

Do not put your trust in princes, in mortal men, who cannot save.

When their spirit departs, they return to the ground; on that very day their

plans come to nothing.

Blessed is he whose help is the God of Jacob, whose hope is in the LORD his God,

the Maker of heaven and earth, the sea, and everything in them—the LORD, who remains faithful forever.

He upholds the cause of the oppressed and gives food to the hungry.

The LORD sets prisoners free, the LORD gives sight to the blind,

the LORD lifts up those who are bowed down, the LORD loves the righteous.

The LORD watches over the alien and sustains the fatherless and the widow, but he frustrates the ways of the wicked.

The LORD reigns forever, your God, O Zion, for all generations.

Praise the LORD.

PSALM 147

Praise the LORD.

How good it is to sing praises to our God, how pleasant and fitting to praise him!

The LORD builds up Jerusalem; he gathers the exiles of Israel.

He heals the brokenhearted and binds up their wounds.

He determines the number of the stars and calls them each by name.

Great is our Lord and mighty in power; his understanding has no limit.

The LORD sustains the humble but casts the wicked to the ground.

Sing to the LORD with thanksgiving; make music to our God on the harp.

He covers the sky with clouds; he supplies the earth with rain and makes grass grow on the hills.

He provides food for the cattle and for the young ravens when they call.

His pleasure is not in the strength of the

horse, nor his delight in the legs of a man;

the LORD delights in those who fear him, who put their hope in his unfailing love.

Extol the LORD, O Jerusalem; praise your God, O Zion,

for he strengthens the bars of your gates and blesses your people within you.

He grants peace to your borders and satisfies you with the finest of wheat.

He sends his command to the earth; his word runs swiftly.

He spreads the snow like wool and scatters the frost like ashes.

He hurls down his hail like pebbles. Who can withstand his icy blast?

He sends his word and melts them; he stirs up his breezes, and the waters flow.

He has revealed his word to Jacob, his laws and decrees to Israel.

He has done this for no other nation; they do not know his laws.

Praise the LORD.

PSALM 148

Praise the LORD.

Praise the LORD from the heavens, praise him in the heights above.

Praise him, all his angels, praise him, all his heavenly hosts.

Praise him, sun and moon, praise him, all you shining stars.

Praise him, you highest heavens and you waters above the skies.

Let them praise the name of the LORD, for he commanded and they were created.

He set them in place for ever and ever;

he gave a decree that will never pass away.

Praise the LORD from the earth, you

great sea creatures and all ocean depths,

lightning and hail, snow and clouds, stormy winds that do his bidding,

you mountains and all hills, fruit trees and all cedars,

wild animals and all cattle, small creatures and flying birds,

kings of the earth and all nations, you princes and all rulers on earth,

young men and maidens, old men and children.

Let them praise the name of the LORD, for his name alone is exalted;

his splendor is above the earth and the heavens.

He has raised up for his people a horn, the praise of all his saints, of Israel, the people close to his heart.

Praise the LORD.

PSALM 149

Praise the LORD.

Sing to the LORD a new song, his praise in the assembly of the saints.

Let Israel rejoice in their Maker; let the people of Zion be glad in their King.

Let them praise his name with dancing and make music to him with tambourine and harp.

For the LORD takes delight in his people; he crowns the humble with salvation.

Let the saints rejoice in this honor and sing for joy on their beds.

May the praise of God be in their mouths and a double-edged sword in their hands,

to inflict vengeance on the nations and punishment on the peoples,

to bind their kings with fetters, their nobles with shackles of iron,

to carry out the sentence written against them.

This is the glory of all his saints.

Praise the LORD.

PSALM 150

Praise the LORD.

Praise God in his sanctuary; praise him in his mighty heavens.

Praise him for his acts of power; praise him for his surpassing greatness.

Praise him with the sounding of the trumpet, praise him with the harp and lyre,

praise him with tambourine and dancing, praise him with the strings and flute,

praise him with the clash of cymbals, praise him with resounding cymbals.

Let everything that has breath praise the LORD.

Praise the LORD.

CREEDS

THE
APOSTLES' CREED

I believe in God the Father Almighty,
    Maker of heaven and earth.

I believe in Jesus Christ, his only Son, our Lord,
    who was conceived by the Holy Spirit,
    and born of the virgin Mary.
    He suffered under Pontius Pilate,
    was crucified, died, and was buried;
    he descended into hell.
    The third day he rose again from the dead.
    He ascended into heaven
    and is seated at the right hand of God the Father Almighty.
    From there he will come to judge the living and the dead.

I believe in the Holy Spirit,
    the holy catholic church,
    the communion of saints,
    the forgiveness of sins,
    the resurrection of the body,
    and the life everlasting. Amen.

Although not written by the apostles, the Apostles' Creed is a concise summary of their teachings.
It originated as a baptismal confession, probably in the second century, and developed
into its present form by the sixth or seventh century.

THE NICENE CREED

We believe in one God, the Father Almighty,
    Maker of heaven and earth,
    of all things visible and invisible.

And in one Lord Jesus Christ, the only-begotten Son of God,
    begotten of his Father before all worlds,
    God of God, Light of Light,
    very God of very God,
    begotten, not made, being of one substance with the Father;
    by whom all things were made;
    who for us and for our salvation
    came down from heaven,
    and was incarnate by the Holy Spirit of the virgin Mary,
    and was made man;
    and was crucified also for us under Pontius Pilate;
    he suffered and was buried;
    and the third day he rose again according to the Scriptures,
    and ascended into heaven, and is seated at the right hand of the Father;
    and he shall come again, with glory, to judge both the living and the dead;
    whose kingdom shall have no end.

And we believe in the Holy Spirit, the Lord and giver of life,
    who proceeds from the Father and the Son;
    who with the Father and the Son together is worshiped and glorified;
    who spoke by the prophets;
    and we believe in one holy catholic and apostolic church;
    we acknowledge one baptism for the remission of sins;
    and we look for the resurrection of the dead,
    and the life of the world to come. Amen.

The Nicene Creed originated at the Council of Nicea (325), and an expanded form was adopted by the
Council of Chalcedon (451). It was formulated to answer heresies that denied the
biblical doctrine of the Trinity and of the person of Christ.

THE WESTMINSTER CONFESSION OF FAITH

CHAPTER I
Of the Holy Scripture

I. Although the light of nature, and the works of creation and providence do so far manifest the goodness, wisdom, and power of God, as to leave men unexcusable; yet are they not sufficient to give that knowledge of God, and of his will, which is necessary unto salvation. Therefore it pleased the Lord, at sundry times, and in divers manners, to reveal himself, and to declare that his will unto his church; and afterwards, for the better preserving and propagating of the truth, and for the more sure establishment and comfort of the church against the corruption of the flesh, and the malice of Satan and of the world, to commit the same wholly unto writing: which maketh the Holy Scripture to be most necessary; those former ways of God's revealing his will unto his people being now ceased.

The Westminster Assembly of Divines, convened by the English Parliament in 1643, completed the Confession of Faith, the Shorter Catechism and the Larger Catechism in 1647. These documents have served as the doctrinal standards, subordinate to the Word of God, for Presbyterian and other churches around the world.

II. Under the name of Holy Scripture, or the Word of God written, are now contained all the books of the Old and New Testaments, which are these:

Of the Old Testament:

Genesis	I Kings	Ecclesiastes	Obadiah
Exodus	II Kings	The Song of Songs	Jonah
Leviticus	I Chronicles	Isaiah	Micah
Numbers	II Chronicles	Jeremiah	Nahum
Deuteronomy	Ezra	Lamentations	Habakkuk
Joshua	Nehemiah	Ezekiel	Zephaniah
Judges	Esther	Daniel	Haggai
Ruth	Job	Hosea	Zechariah
I Samuel	Psalms	Joel	Malachi
II Samuel	Proverbs	Amos	

Of the New Testament:

The Gospels according to	Paul's Epistles to the Romans	the Thessalonians II	The first and second Epistles
Matthew	the Corinthians I	Timothy I	of Peter
Mark	the Corinthians II	Timothy II	The first, second,
Luke	the Galatians	Titus	and third Epistles
John	the Ephesians	Philemon	of John
The Acts of the	the Philippians	The Epistle to	The Epistle
Apostles	the Colossians	the Hebrews	of Jude
	the Thessalonians I	The Epistle of James	The Revelation of John

All which are given by inspiration of God to be the rule of faith and life.

III. The books commonly called Apocrypha, not being of divine inspiration, are no part of the canon of the Scripture, and therefore are of no authority in the church of God, nor to be any otherwise approved, or made use of, than other human writings.

IV. The authority of the Holy Scripture, for which it ought to be believed, and obeyed, dependeth not upon the testimony of any man, or church; but wholly upon God (who is truth itself) the author thereof: and therefore it is to be received, because it is the Word of God.

V. We may be moved and induced by the testimony of the church to an high and reverent esteem of the Holy Scripture. And the heavenliness of the matter, the efficacy of the doctrine, the majesty of the style, the consent of all the parts, the scope of the whole (which is, to give all glory to God), the full discovery it makes of the only way of man's salvation, the many other incomparable excellencies, and the entire perfection thereof, are arguments whereby it doth abundantly evidence itself to be the Word of God: yet notwithstanding, our full persuasion and assurance of the infallible truth and divine authority thereof, is from the inward work of the Holy Spirit bearing witness by and with the Word in our hearts.

VI. The whole counsel of God concerning all things necessary for his own glory, man's salvation, faith and life, is either expressly set down in Scripture, or by good and necessary consequence may be deduced from Scripture: unto which nothing at any time is to be added, whether by new revelations of the Spirit, or traditions of men. Nevertheless, we acknowledge the inward illumination of the Spirit of God to be necessary for the saving understanding of such things as are revealed in the Word: and that there are some circumstances concerning the worship of God, and government of the church, common to human actions and societies, which are to be ordered by the light of nature, and Christian prudence, according to the general rules of the Word, which are always to be observed.

VII. All things in Scripture are not alike plain in themselves, nor alike clear unto all: yet those things which are necessary to be known, believed, and observed for salvation, are so clearly propounded, and opened in some place of Scripture or other, that not only the learned, but the unlearned, in a due use of the ordinary means, may attain unto a sufficient understanding of them.

VIII. The Old Testament in Hebrew (which was the native language of the people of God of old), and the New Testament in Greek (which, at the time of the writing of it, was most generally known to the nations), being immediately inspired by God, and, by his singular care and providence, kept pure in all ages, are therefore authentical; so as, in all controversies of religion, the church is finally to appeal unto them. But, because these original tongues are not known to all the people of God, who have right unto, and interest in the Scriptures, and are commanded, in the fear of God, to read and search them, therefore they are to be translated into the vulgar language of every nation unto which they come, that, the Word of God dwelling plentifully in all, they may worship him in an acceptable manner; and, through patience and comfort of the Scriptures, may have hope.

IX. The infallible rule of interpretation of Scripture is the Scripture itself: and therefore, when there is a question about the true and full sense of any Scripture (which is not manifold, but one), it must be searched and known by other places that speak more clearly.

X. The supreme judge by which all controversies of religion are to be determined, and all decrees of councils, opinions of ancient writers, doctrines of men, and private spirits, are to be examined, and in whose sentence we are to rest, can be no other but the Holy Spirit speaking in the Scripture.

CHAPTER II
Of God, and of the Holy Trinity

I. There is but one only, living, and true God, who is infinite in being and perfection, a most pure spirit, invisible, without body, parts, or passions; immutable, immense, eternal, incomprehensible, almighty, most wise, most holy, most free, most absolute; working all things according to the counsel of his own immutable and most righteous will, for his own glory; most loving, gracious, merciful, long-suffering, abundant in goodness and truth, forgiving iniquity, transgression, and sin; the rewarder of them that diligently seek him; and withal, most just, and terrible in his judgments, hating all sin, and who will by no means clear the guilty.

II. God hath all life, glory, goodness, blessedness, in and of himself; and is alone in and unto himself all-sufficient, not standing in need of any creatures which he hath made, nor deriving any glory from them, but only manifesting his own glory in, by, unto, and upon them. He is the alone fountain of all being, of whom, through whom, and to whom are all things; and hath most sovereign dominion over them, to do by them, for them, or upon them whatsoever himself pleaseth. In his sight all things are open and manifest, his knowledge is infinite, infallible, and independent upon the creature, so as nothing is to him contingent, or uncertain. He is most holy in all his counsels, in all his works, and in all his commands. To him is due from angels and men, and every other creature, whatsoever worship, service, or obedience he is pleased to require of them.

III. In the unity of the Godhead there be three persons, of one substance, power, and eternity: God the Father, God the Son, and God the Holy Ghost: the Father is of none, neither begotten, nor proceeding; the Son is eternally begotten of the Father; the Holy Ghost eternally proceeding from the Father and the Son.

CHAPTER III
Of God's Eternal Decree

I. God, from all eternity, did, by the most wise and holy counsel of his own will, freely, and unchangeably ordain whatsoever comes to pass: yet so, as thereby neither is God the author of sin, nor is violence offered to the will of the creatures; nor is the liberty or contingency of second causes taken away, but rather established.

II. Although God knows whatsoever may or can come to pass upon all supposed conditions, yet hath he not decreed anything because he foresaw it as future, or as that which would come to pass upon such conditions.

III. By the decree of God, for the manifestation of his glory, some men and angels are predestinated unto everlasting life; and others foreordained to everlasting death.

IV. These angels and men, thus predestinated, and foreordained, are particularly and unchangeably designed, and their number so certain and definite, that it cannot be either increased or diminished.

V. Those of mankind that are predestinated unto life, God, before the foundation of the world was laid, according to his eternal and immutable purpose, and the secret counsel and good pleasure of his will, hath chosen, in Christ, unto everlasting glory, out of his mere free grace and love, without any foresight of faith, or good works, or perseverance in either of them, or any other thing in the creature, as conditions, or causes moving him thereunto; and all to the praise of his glorious grace.

VI. As God hath appointed the elect unto glory, so hath he, by the eternal and most free purpose of his will, foreordained all the means thereunto. Wherefore, they who are elected, being fallen in Adam, are redeemed by Christ, are effectually called unto faith in Christ by his Spirit working in due season, are justified, adopted, sanctified, and kept by his power, through faith, unto salvation. Neither are any other redeemed by Christ, effectually called, justified, adopted, sanctified, and saved, but the elect only.

VII. The rest of mankind God was pleased, according to the unsearchable counsel of his own will, whereby he extendeth or withholdeth mercy, as he pleaseth, for the glory of his sovereign power over his creatures, to pass by; and to ordain them to dishonor and wrath for their sin, to the praise of his glorious justice.

VIII. The doctrine of this high mystery of predestination is to be handled with special prudence and care, that men, attending the will of God revealed in his Word, and yielding obedience thereunto, may, from the certainty of their effectual vocation, be assured of their eternal election. So shall this doctrine afford matter of praise, reverence, and admiration of God; and of humility, diligence, and abundant consolation to all that sincerely obey the gospel.

CHAPTER IV
Of Creation

I. It pleased God the Father, Son, and Holy Ghost, for the manifestation of the glory of his eternal power, wisdom, and goodness, in the beginning, to create, or make of nothing, the world, and all things therein whether visible or invisible, in the space of six days; and all very good.

II. After God had made all other creatures, he created man, male and female, with reasonable and immortal souls, endued with knowledge, righteousness, and true holiness, after his own image; having the law of God written in their hearts, and power to fulfill it: and yet under a possibility of transgressing, being left to the liberty of their own will, which was subject unto change. Beside this law written in their hearts, they received a command, not to eat of the tree of the knowledge of good and evil; which while they kept, they were happy in their communion with God, and had dominion over the creatures.

CHAPTER V
Of Providence

I. God the great Creator of all things doth uphold, direct, dispose, and govern all creatures, actions, and things, from the greatest even to the least, by his most wise and holy providence, according to his infallible foreknowledge, and the free and immutable counsel of his own will, to the praise of the glory of his wisdom, power, justice, goodness, and mercy.

II. Although, in relation to the foreknowledge and decree of God, the first Cause, all things come to pass immutably, and infallibly; yet, by the same providence, he ordereth them to fall out, according to the nature of second causes, either necessarily, freely, or contingently.

III. God, in his ordinary providence, maketh use of means, yet is free to work without, above, and against them, at his pleasure.

IV. The almighty power, unsearchable wisdom, and infinite goodness of God so far manifest themselves in his providence, that it extendeth itself even to the first fall, and all other sins of angels and men; and that not by a bare permission, but such as hath joined with it a most wise and powerful bounding, and otherwise ordering, and governing of them, in a manifold dispensation, to his own holy ends; yet so, as the sinfulness thereof proceedeth only from the creature, and not from God, who, being most holy and righteous, neither is nor can be the author or approver of sin.

V. The most wise, righteous, and gracious God doth oftentimes leave, for a season, his own children to manifold temptations, and the corruption of their own hearts, to chastise them for their former sins, or to discover unto them the hidden strength of corruption and deceitfulness of their hearts, that they may be humbled; and, to raise them to a more close and constant dependence for their support upon himself, and to make them more watchful against all future occasions of sin, and for sundry other just and holy ends.

VI. As for those wicked and ungodly men whom God, as a righteous Judge, for former sins, doth blind and harden, from them he not only withholdeth his grace whereby they might have been enlightened in their understandings, and wrought upon in their hearts; but sometimes also withdraweth the gifts which they had, and exposeth them to such objects as their corruption makes occasions of sin; and, withal, gives them over to their own lusts, the temptations of the world, and the power of Satan, whereby it comes to pass that they harden themselves, even under those means which God useth for the softening of others.

VII. As the providence of God doth, in general, reach to all creatures; so, after a most special manner, it taketh care of his church, and disposeth all things to the good thereof.

CHAPTER VI

Of the Fall of Man, of Sin, and of the Punishment Thereof

I. Our first parents, being seduced by the subtlety and temptation of Satan, sinned, in eating the forbidden fruit. This their sin, God was pleased, according to his wise and holy counsel, to permit, having purposed to order it to his own glory.

II. By this sin they fell from their original righteousness and communion with God, and so became dead in sin, and wholly defiled in all the parts and faculties of soul and body.

III. They being the root of all mankind, the guilt of this sin was imputed; and the same death in sin, and corrupted nature, conveyed to all their posterity descending from them by ordinary generation.

IV. From this original corruption, whereby we are utterly indisposed, disabled, and made opposite to all good, and wholly inclined to all evil, do proceed all actual transgressions.

V. This corruption of nature, during this life, doth remain in those that are regenerated; and although it be, through Christ, pardoned, and mortified; yet both itself, and all the motions thereof, are truly and properly sin.

VI. Every sin, both original and actual, being a transgression of the righteous law of God, and contrary thereunto, doth, in its own nature, bring guilt upon the sinner, whereby he is bound over to the wrath of God, and curse of the law, and so made subject to death, with all miseries spiritual, temporal, and eternal.

CHAPTER VII

Of God's Covenant with Man

I. The distance between God and the creature is so great, that although reasonable creatures do owe obedience unto him as their Creator, yet they could never have any fruition of him as their blessedness and reward, but by some voluntary condescension on God's part, which he hath been pleased to express by way of covenant.

II. The first covenant made with man was a covenant of works, wherein life was promised to Adam; and in him to his posterity, upon condition of perfect and personal obedience.

III. Man, by his fall, having made himself incapable of life by that covenant, the Lord was pleased to make a second, commonly called the covenant of grace; wherein he freely offereth unto sinners life and salvation by Jesus Christ; requiring of them faith in him, that they may be saved, and promising to give unto all those that are ordained unto eternal life his Holy Spirit, to make them willing, and able to believe.

IV. This covenant of grace is frequently set forth in Scripture by the name of a testament, in reference to the death of Jesus Christ the Testator, and to the everlasting inheritance, with all things belonging to it, therein bequeathed.

V. This covenant was differently administered in the time of the law, and in the time of the gospel: under the law, it was administered by promises, prophecies, sacrifices, circumcision, the paschal lamb, and other types and ordinances delivered to the people of the Jews, all foresignifying Christ to come; which were, for that time, sufficient and efficacious, through the operation of the Spirit, to instruct and build up the elect in faith in the promised Messiah, by whom they had full remission of sins, and eternal salvation; and is called the old testament.

VI. Under the gospel, when Christ, the substance, was exhibited, the ordinances in which this covenant is dispensed are the preaching of the Word, and the administration of the sacraments of baptism and the Lord's Supper: which, though fewer in number, and administered with more simplicity, and less outward glory, yet, in them, it is held forth in more fullness, evidence and spiritual efficacy, to all nations, both Jews and Gentiles; and is called the new testament. There are not therefore two covenants of grace, differing in substance, but one and the same, under various dispensations.

CHAPTER VIII
Of Christ the Mediator

I. It pleased God, in his eternal purpose, to choose and ordain the Lord Jesus, his only begotten Son, to be the Mediator between God and man, the Prophet, Priest, and King, the Head and Savior of his church, the Heir of all things, and Judge of the world: unto whom he did from all eternity give a people, to be his seed, and to be by him in time redeemed, called, justified, sanctified, and glorified.

II. The Son of God, the second person in the Trinity, being very and eternal God, of one substance and equal with the Father, did, when the fullness of time was come, take upon him man's nature, with all the essential properties, and common infirmities thereof, yet without sin; being conceived by the power of the Holy Ghost, in the womb of the virgin Mary, of her substance. So that two whole, perfect, and distinct natures, the Godhead and the manhood, were inseparably joined together in one person, without conversion, composition, or confusion. Which person is very God, and very man, yet one Christ, the only Mediator between God and man.

III. The Lord Jesus, in his human nature thus united to the divine, was sanctified, and anointed with the Holy Spirit, above measure, having in him all the treasures of wisdom and knowledge; in whom it pleased the Father that all fullness should dwell; to the end that, being holy, harmless, undefiled, and full of grace and truth, he might be thoroughly furnished to execute the office of a mediator, and surety. Which office he took not unto himself, but was thereunto called by his Father, who put all power and judgment into his hand, and gave him commandment to execute the same.

IV. This office the Lord Jesus did most willingly undertake; which that he might discharge, he was made under the law, and did perfectly fulfill it; endured most grievous torments immediately in his soul, and most painful sufferings in his body; was crucified, and died, was buried, and remained under the power of death, yet saw no corruption. On the third day he arose from the dead, with the same body in which he suffered, with which also he ascended into heaven, and there sitteth at the right hand of his Father, making intercession, and shall return, to judge men and angels, at the end of the world.

V. The Lord Jesus, by his perfect obedience, and sacrifice of himself, which he, through the eternal Spirit, once offered up unto God, hath fully satisfied the justice of his Father; and purchased, not only reconciliation, but an everlasting inheritance in the kingdom of heaven, for all those whom the Father hath given unto him.

VI. Although the work of redemption was not actually wrought by Christ till after his incarnation, yet the virtue, efficacy, and benefits thereof were communicated unto the elect, in all ages successively from the beginning of the world, in and by those promises, types, and sacrifices, wherein he was revealed, and signified to be the seed of the woman which should bruise the serpent's head; and the Lamb slain from the beginning of the world; being yesterday and today the same, and forever.

VII. Christ, in the work of mediation, acts according to both natures, by each nature doing that which is proper to itself; yet, by reason of the unity of the person, that which is proper to one nature is sometimes in Scripture attributed to the person denominated by the other nature.

VIII. To all those for whom Christ hath purchased redemption, he doth certainly and effectually apply and communicate the same; making intercession for them, and revealing unto them, in and by the Word, the mysteries of salvation; effectually persuading them by his Spirit to believe and obey, and governing their hearts by his Word and Spirit; overcoming all their enemies by his almighty power and wisdom, in such manner, and ways, as are most consonant to his wonderful and unsearchable dispensation.

CHAPTER IX
Of Free Will

I. God hath endued the will of man with that natural liberty, that it is neither forced, nor, by any absolute necessity of nature, determined to good, or evil.

II. Man, in his state of innocency, had freedom, and power to will and to do that which was good and well pleasing to God; but yet, mutably, so that he might fall from it.

III. Man, by his fall into a state of sin, hath wholly lost all ability of will to any spiritual good accompanying salvation: so as, a natural man, being altogether averse from that good, and dead in sin, is not able, by his own strength, to convert himself, or to prepare himself thereunto.

IV. When God converts a sinner, and translates him into the state of grace, he freeth him from his natural bondage under sin; and, by his grace alone, enables him freely to will and to do that which is spiritually good; yet so, as that by reason of his remaining corruption, he doth not perfectly, nor only, will that which is good, but doth also will that which is evil.

V. The will of man is made perfectly and immutably free to good alone, in the state of glory only.

CHAPTER X
Of Effectual Calling

I. All those whom God hath predestinated unto life, and those only, he is pleased, in his appointed and accepted time, effectually to call, by his Word and Spirit, out of that state of sin and death, in which they are by nature, to grace and salvation, by Jesus Christ; enlightening their minds spiritually and savingly to understand the things of God, taking away their heart of stone, and giving unto them a heart of flesh; renewing their wills, and, by his almighty power, determining them to that which is good, and effectually drawing them to Jesus Christ: yet so, as they come most freely, being made willing by his grace.

II. This effectual call is of God's free and special grace alone, not from anything at all foreseen in man, who is altogether passive therein, until, being quickened and renewed by the Holy Spirit, he is thereby enabled to answer this call, and to embrace the grace offered and conveyed in it.

III. Elect infants, dying in infancy, are regenerated, and saved by Christ, through the Spirit, who worketh when, and where, and how he pleaseth: so also are all other elect persons who are incapable of being outwardly called by the ministry of the Word.

IV. Others, not elected, although they may be called by the ministry of the Word, and may have some common operations of the Spirit, yet they never truly come unto Christ, and therefore cannot be saved: much less can men, not professing the Christian religion, be saved in any other way whatsoever, be they never so diligent to frame their lives according to the light of nature, and the laws of that religion they do profess. And, to assert and maintain that they may, is very pernicious, and to be detested.

CHAPTER XI
Of Justification

I. Those whom God effectually calleth, he also freely justifieth: not by infusing righteousness into them, but by pardoning their sins, and by accounting and accepting their persons as righteous; not for anything wrought in them, or done by them, but for Christ's sake alone; nor by imputing faith itself, the act of believing, or any other evangelical obedience to them, as their righteousness; but by imputing the obedience and satisfaction of Christ unto them, they receiving and resting on him and his righteousness, by faith; which faith they have not of themselves, it is the gift of God.

II. Faith, thus receiving and resting on Christ and his righteousness, is the alone instrument of justification: yet is it not alone in the person justified, but is ever accompanied with all other saving graces, and is no dead faith, but worketh by love.

III. Christ, by his obedience and death, did fully discharge the debt of all those that are thus justified, and did make a proper, real, and full satisfaction to his Father's justice in their behalf. Yet, inasmuch as he was given by the Father for them; and his obedience and satisfaction accepted in their stead; and both, freely, not for anything in them; their justification is only of free grace; that both the exact justice and rich grace of God might be glorified in the justification of sinners.

IV. God did, from all eternity, decree to justify all the elect, and Christ did, in the fullness of time, die for their sins, and rise again for their justification: nevertheless, they are not justified, until the Holy Spirit doth, in due time, actually apply Christ unto them.

V. God doth continue to forgive the sins of those that are justified; and, although they can never fall from the state of justification, yet they may, by their sins, fall under God's fatherly displeasure, and not have the light of his countenance restored unto them, until they humble themselves, confess their sins, beg pardon, and renew their faith and repentance.

VI. The justification of believers under the old testament was, in all these respects, one and the same with the justification of believers under the new testament.

CHAPTER XII
Of Adoption

I. All those that are justified, God vouchsafeth, in and for his only Son Jesus Christ, to make partakers of the grace of adoption, by which they are taken into the number, and enjoy the liberties and privileges of the children of God, have his name put upon them, receive the Spirit of adoption, have access to the throne of grace with boldness, are enabled to cry, Abba, Father, are pitied, protected, provided for, and chastened by him, as by a father: yet never cast off, but sealed to the day of redemption; and inherit the promises, as heirs of everlasting salvation.

CHAPTER XIII
Of Sanctification

I. They, who are once effectually called, and regenerated, having a new heart, and a new spirit created in them, are further sanctified, really and personally, through the virtue of Christ's death and resurrection, by his Word and Spirit dwelling in them: the dominion of the whole body of sin is destroyed, and the several lusts thereof are more and more weakened and mortified; and they more and more quickened and strengthened in all saving graces, to the practice of true holiness, without which no man shall see the Lord.

II. This sanctification is throughout, in the whole man; yet imperfect in this life, there abiding still some remnants of corruption in every part; whence ariseth a continual and irreconcilable war, the flesh lusting against the Spirit, and the Spirit against the flesh.

III. In which war, although the remaining corruption, for a time, may much prevail; yet, through the continual supply of strength from the sanctifying Spirit of Christ, the regenerate part doth overcome; and so, the saints grow in grace, perfecting holiness in the fear of God.

CHAPTER XIV
Of Saving Faith

I. The grace of faith, whereby the elect are enabled to believe to the saving of their souls, is the work of the Spirit of Christ in their hearts, and is ordinarily wrought by the ministry of the Word, by which also, and by the administration of the sacraments, and prayer, it is increased and strengthened.

II. By this faith, a Christian believeth to be true whatsoever is revealed in the Word, for the authority of God himself speaking therein; and acteth differently upon that which each particular passage thereof containeth; yielding obedience to the commands, trembling at the threatenings, and embracing the promises of God for this life, and that which is to come. But the principal acts of saving faith are accepting, receiving, and resting upon Christ alone for justification, sanctification, and eternal life, by virtue of the covenant of grace.

III. This faith is different in degrees, weak or strong; may be often and many ways assailed, and weakened, but gets the victory: growing up in many to the attainment of a full assurance, through Christ, who is both the author and finisher of our faith.

CHAPTER XV
Of Repentance unto Life

I. Repentance unto life is an evangelical grace, the doctrine whereof is to be preached by every minister of the gospel, as well as that of faith in Christ.

II. By it, a sinner, out of the sight and sense not only of the danger, but also of the filthiness and odiousness of his sins, as contrary to the holy nature, and righteous law of God; and upon the apprehension of his mercy in Christ to such as are penitent, so grieves for, and hates his sins, as to turn from them all unto God, purposing and endeavoring to walk with him in all the ways of his commandments.

III. Although repentance be not to be rested in, as any satisfaction for sin, or any cause of the pardon thereof, which is the act of God's free grace in Christ; yet it is of such necessity to all sinners, that none may expect pardon without it.

IV. As there is no sin so small, but it de-serves damnation; so there is no sin so great, that it can bring damnation upon those who truly repent.

V. Men ought not to content themselves with a general repentance, but it is every man's duty to endeavor to repent of his particular sins, particularly.

VI. As every man is bound to make pri-vate confession of his sins to God, praying for the pardon thereof; upon which, and the forsaking of them, he shall find mercy; so, he that scandalizeth his brother, or the church of Christ, ought to be willing, by a private or public confession, and sorrow for his sin, to declare his repentance to those that are offended, who are thereupon to be reconciled to him, and in love to receive him.

CHAPTER XVI
Of Good Works

I. Good works are only such as God hath commanded in his holy Word, and not such as, without the warrant thereof, are devised by men, out of blind zeal, or upon any pretense of good intention.

II. These good works, done in obedience to God's commandments, are the fruits and evidences of a true and lively faith: and by them believers manifest their thankfulness, strengthen their assurance, edify their brethren, adorn the profession of the gospel, stop the mouths of the adversaries, and glorify God, whose workmanship they are, created in Christ Jesus thereunto, that, having their fruit unto holiness, they may have the end, eternal life.

III. Their ability to do good works is not at all of themselves, but wholly from the Spirit of Christ. And that they may be enabled thereunto, beside the graces they have already received, there is required an actual influence of the same Holy Spirit, to work in them to will, and to do, of his good pleasure: yet are they not hereupon to grow negligent, as if they were not bound to perform any duty unless upon a special motion of the Spirit; but they ought to be diligent in stirring up the grace of God that is in them.

IV. They who, in their obedience, attain to the greatest height which is possible in this life, are so far from being able to supererogate, and to do more than God requires, as that they fall short of much which in duty they are bound to do.

V. We cannot by our best works merit pardon of sin, or eternal life at the hand of God, by reason of the great disproportion that is between them and the glory to come; and the infinite distance that is between us and God, whom, by them, we can neither profit, nor satisfy for the debt of our former sins, but when we have done all we can, we have done but our duty, and are unprofitable servants: and because, as they are good, they proceed from his Spirit; and as they are wrought by us, they are defiled, and mixed with so much weakness and imperfection, that they cannot endure the severity of God's judgment.

VI. Notwithstanding, the persons of believers being accepted through Christ, their good works also are accepted in him; not as though they were in this life wholly unblamable and unreprovable in God's sight; but that he, looking upon them in his Son, is pleased to accept and reward that which is sincere, although accompanied with many weaknesses and imperfections.

VII. Works done by unregenerate men, although for the matter of them they may be things which God commands; and of good use both to themselves and others: yet, because they proceed not from an heart purified by faith; nor are done in a right manner, according to the Word; nor to a right end, the glory of God, they are therefore sinful, and cannot please God, or make a man meet to receive grace from God: and yet, their neglect of them is more sinful and displeasing unto God.

CHAPTER XVII
Of the Perseverance of the Saints

I. They, whom God hath accepted in his Beloved, effectually called, and sanctified by his Spirit, can neither totally nor finally fall away from the state of grace, but shall certainly persevere therein to the end, and be eternally saved.

II. This perseverance of the saints depends not upon their own free will, but upon the immutability of the decree of election, flowing from the free and unchangeable love of God the Father; upon the efficacy of the merit and intercession of Jesus Christ, the abiding of the Spirit, and of the seed of God within them, and the nature of the covenant of grace: from all which ariseth also the certainty and infallibility thereof.

III. Nevertheless, they may, through the temptations of Satan and of the world, the prevalency of corruption remaining in them, and the neglect of the means of their preservation, fall into grievous sins; and, for a time continue therein: whereby they incur God's displeasure, and grieve his Holy Spirit, come to be deprived of some measure of their graces and comforts, have their hearts hardened, and their consciences wounded; hurt and scandalize others, and bring temporal judgments upon themselves.

CHAPTER XVIII
Of the Assurance of Grace and Salvation

I. Although hypocrites and other unregenerate men may vainly deceive themselves with false hopes and carnal presumptions of being in the favor of God, and estate of salvation (which hope of theirs shall perish): yet such as truly believe in the Lord Jesus, and love him in sincerity, endeavoring to walk in all good conscience before him, may, in this life, be certainly assured that they are in the state of grace, and may rejoice in the hope of the glory of God, which hope shall never make them ashamed.

II. This certainty is not a bare conjectural and probable persuasion grounded upon a fallible hope; but an infallible assurance of faith founded upon the divine truth of the promises of salvation, the inward evidence of those graces unto which these promises are made, the testimony of the Spirit of adoption witnessing with our spirits that we are the children of God, which Spirit is the earnest of our inheritance, whereby we are sealed to the day of redemption.

III. This infallible assurance doth not so belong to the essence of faith, but that a true believer may wait long, and conflict with many difficulties before he be partaker of it: yet, being enabled by the Spirit to know the things which are freely given him of God, he may, without extraordinary revelation, in the right use of ordinary means, attain thereunto. And therefore it is the duty of everyone to give all diligence to make his calling and election sure, that thereby his heart may be enlarged in peace and joy in the Holy Ghost, in love and thankfulness to God, and in strength and cheerfulness in the duties of obedience, the proper fruits of this assurance; so far is it from inclining men to looseness.

IV. True believers may have the assurance of their salvation divers ways shaken, diminished, and intermitted; as, by negligence in preserving of it, by falling into some special sin which woundeth the conscience and grieveth the Spirit; by some sudden or vehement temptation, by God's withdrawing the light of his countenance, and suffering even such as fear him to walk in darkness and to have no light: yet are they never utterly destitute of that seed of God, and life of faith, that love of Christ and the brethren, that sincerity of heart, and conscience of duty, out of which, by the operation of the Spirit, this assurance may, in due time, be revived; and by the which, in the meantime, they are supported from utter despair.

CHAPTER XIX
Of the Law of God

I. God gave to Adam a law, as a covenant of works, by which he bound him and all his posterity to personal, entire, exact, and perpetual obedience, promised life upon the fulfilling, and threatened death upon the breach of it, and endued him with power and ability to keep it.

II. This law, after his fall, continued to be a perfect rule of righteousness; and, as such, was delivered by God upon Mount Sinai, in ten commandments, and written in two tables: the first four commandments containing our duty towards God; and the other six, our duty to man.

III. Beside this law, commonly called moral, God was pleased to give to the people of Israel, as a church under age, ceremonial laws, containing several typical ordinances, partly of worship, prefiguring Christ, his graces, actions, sufferings, and benefits; and partly, holding forth divers instructions of moral duties. All which ceremonial laws are now abrogated, under the new testament.

IV. To them also, as a body politic, he gave sundry judicial laws, which expired together with the State of that people; not obliging any other now, further than the general equity thereof may require.

V. The moral law doth forever bind all, as well justified persons as others, to the obedience thereof; and that, not only in regard of the matter contained in it, but also in respect of the authority of God the Creator, who gave it. Neither doth Christ, in the gospel, any way dissolve, but much strengthen this obligation.

VI. Although true believers be not under the law, as a covenant of works, to be thereby justified, or condemned; yet is it of great use to them, as well as to others; in that, as a rule of life informing them of the will of God, and their duty, it directs and binds them to walk accordingly; discovering also the sinful pollutions of their nature, hearts, and lives; so as, examining themselves thereby, they may come to further conviction of, humiliation for, and hatred against sin, together with a clearer sight of the need they have of Christ, and the perfection of his obedience. It is likewise of use to the regenerate, to restrain their corruptions, in that it forbids sin: and the threatenings of it serve to show what even their sins deserve; and what afflictions, in this life, they may expect for them, although freed from the curse thereof threatened in the law. The promises of it, in like manner, show them God's approbation of obedience, and what blessings they may expect upon the performance thereof: although not as due to them by the law as a covenant of works. So as, a man's doing good, and refraining from evil, because the law encourageth to the one, and deterreth from the other, is no evidence of his being under the law; and, not under grace.

VII. Neither are the forementioned uses of the law contrary to the grace of the gospel, but do sweetly comply with it; the Spirit of Christ subduing and enabling the will of man to do that freely, and cheerfully, which the will of God, revealed in the law, requireth to be done.

CHAPTER XX
Of Christian Liberty, and Liberty of Conscience

I. The liberty which Christ hath purchased for believers under the gospel consists in their freedom from the guilt of sin, the condemning wrath of God, the curse of the moral law; and, in their being delivered from this present evil world, bondage to Satan, and dominion of sin; from the evil of afflictions, the sting of death, the victory of the grave, and everlasting damnation; as also, in their free access to God, and their yielding obedience unto him, not out of slavish fear, but a childlike love and willing mind. All which were common also to believers under the law. But, under the new testament, the liberty of Christians is further enlarged, in their freedom from the yoke of the ceremonial law, to which the Jewish church was subjected; and in greater boldness of access to the throne of grace, and in fuller communications of the free Spirit of God, than believers under the law did ordinarily partake of.

II. God alone is Lord of the conscience, and hath left it free from the doctrines and commandments of men, which are, in anything, contrary to his Word; or beside it, if matters of faith, or worship. So that, to believe such doctrines, or to obey such commands, out of conscience, is to betray true liberty of conscience: and the requiring of an implicit faith, and an absolute and blind obedience, is to destroy liberty of conscience, and reason also.

III. They who, upon pretense of Christian liberty, do practice any sin, or cherish any lust, do thereby destroy the end of Christian liberty, which is, that being delivered out of the hands of our enemies, we might serve the Lord without fear, in holiness and righteousness before him, all the days of our life.

IV. And because the powers which God hath ordained, and the liberty which Christ hath purchased, are not intended by God to destroy, but mutually to uphold and preserve one another, they who, upon pretense of Christian liberty, shall oppose any lawful power, or the lawful exercise of it, whether it be civil or ecclesiastical, resist the ordinance of God. And, for their publishing of such opinions, or maintaining of such practices, as are contrary to the light of nature, or to the known principles of Christianity (whether concerning faith, worship, or conversation), or to the power of godliness; or, such erroneous opinions or practices, as either in their own nature, or in the manner of publishing or maintaining them, are destructive to the external peace and order which Christ hath established in the church, they may lawfully be called to account, and proceeded against, by the censures of the church.

CHAPTER XXI
Of Religious Worship, and the Sabbath Day

I. The light of nature showeth that there is a God, who hath lordship and sovereignty over all, is good, and doth good unto all, and is therefore to be feared, loved, praised, called upon, trusted in, and served, with all the heart, and with all the soul, and with all the might. But the acceptable way of worshiping the true God is instituted by himself, and so limited by his own revealed will, that he may not be worshiped according to the imaginations and devices of men, or the suggestions of Satan, under any visible representation, or any other way not prescribed in the Holy Scripture.

II. Religious worship is to be given to God, the Father, Son, and Holy Ghost; and to him alone; not to angels, saints, or any other creature: and, since the fall, not without a Mediator; nor in the mediation of any other but of Christ alone.

III. Prayer, with thanksgiving, being one special part of religious worship, is by God required of all men: and, that it may be accepted, it is to be made in the name of the Son, by the help of his Spirit, according to his will, with understanding, reverence, humility, fervency, faith, love, and perseverance; and, if vocal, in a known tongue.

IV. Prayer is to be made for things lawful; and for all sorts of men living, or that shall live hereafter: but not for the dead, nor for those of whom it may be known that they have sinned the sin unto death.

V. The reading of the Scriptures with godly fear, the sound preaching and conscionable hearing of the Word, in obedience unto God, with understanding, faith, and reverence, singing of psalms with grace in the heart; as also, the due administration and worthy receiving of the sacraments instituted by Christ, are all parts of the ordinary religious worship of God: beside religious oaths, vows, solemn fastings, and thanksgivings upon special occasions, which are, in their several times and seasons, to be used in an holy and religious manner.

VI. Neither prayer, nor any other part of religious worship, is now, under the gospel, either tied unto, or made more acceptable by any place in which it is performed, or towards which it is directed: but God is to be worshiped everywhere, in spirit and truth; as, in private families daily, and in secret, each one by himself; so, more solemnly in the public assemblies, which are not carelessly or willfully to be neglected, or forsaken, when God, by his Word or providence, calleth thereunto.

VII. As it is the law of nature, that, in general, a due proportion of time be set apart for the worship of God; so, in his Word, by a positive, moral, and perpetual commandment binding all men in all ages, he hath particularly appointed one day in seven, for a Sabbath, to be kept holy unto him: which, from the beginning of the world to the resurrection of Christ, was the last day of the week; and, from the resurrection of Christ, was changed into the first day of the week, which, in Scripture, is called the Lord's day, and is to be continued to the end of the world, as the Christian Sabbath.

VIII. This Sabbath is then kept holy unto the Lord, when men, after a due preparing of their hearts, and ordering of their common affairs beforehand, do not only observe an holy rest, all the day, from their own works, words, and thoughts about their worldly employments and recreations, but also are taken up, the whole time, in the public and private exercises of his worship, and in the duties of necessity and mercy.

CHAPTER XXII
Of Lawful Oaths and Vows

I. A lawful oath is a part of religious worship, wherein, upon just occasion, the person swearing solemnly calleth God to witness what he asserteth, or promiseth, and to judge him according to the truth or falsehood of what he sweareth.

II. The name of God only is that by which men ought to swear, and therein it is to be used with all holy fear and reverence. Therefore, to swear vainly, or rashly, by that glorious and dreadful Name; or, to swear at all by any other thing, is sinful, and to be abhorred. Yet, as in matters of weight and moment, an oath is warranted by the Word of God, under the new testament as well as under the old; so a lawful oath, being imposed by lawful authority, in such matters, ought to be taken.

III. Whosoever taketh an oath ought duly to consider the weightiness of so solemn an act, and therein to avouch nothing but what he is fully persuaded is the truth: neither may any man bind himself by oath to anything but what is good and just, and what he believeth so to be, and what he is able and resolved to perform.

IV. An oath is to be taken in the plain and common sense of the words, without equivocation, or mental reservation. It cannot oblige to sin; but in anything not sinful, being taken, it binds to performance, although to a man's own hurt. Nor is it to be violated, although made to heretics, or infidels.

V. A vow is of the like nature with a promissory oath, and ought to be made with the like religious care, and to be performed with the like faithfulness.

VI. It is not to be made to any creature, but to God alone: and, that it may be accepted, it is to be made voluntarily, out of faith, and conscience of duty, in way of thankfulness for mercy received, or for the obtaining of what we want, whereby we more strictly bind ourselves to necessary duties; or, to other things, so far and so long as they may fitly conduce thereunto.

VII. No man may vow to do anything forbidden in the Word of God, or what would hinder any duty therein commanded, or which is not in his own power, and for the performance whereof he hath no promise of ability from God. In which respects, popish monastical vows of perpetual single life, professed poverty, and regular obedience, are so far from being degrees of higher perfection, that they are superstitious and sinful snares, in which no Christian may entangle himself.

CHAPTER XXIII
Of the Civil Magistrate

I. God, the supreme Lord and King of all the world, hath ordained civil magistrates, to be, under him, over the people, for his own glory, and the public good: and, to this end, hath armed them with the power of the sword, for the defense and encouragement of them that are good, and for the punishment of evildoers.

II. It is lawful for Christians to accept and execute the office of a magistrate, when called thereunto: in the managing whereof, as they ought especially to maintain piety, justice, and peace, according to the wholesome laws of each commonwealth; so, for that end, they may lawfully, now under the new testament, wage war, upon just and necessary occasion.

III. Civil magistrates may not assume to themselves the administration of the Word and sacraments; or the power of the keys of the kingdom of heaven; or, in the least, interfere in matters of faith. Yet, as nursing fathers, it is the duty of civil magistrates to protect the church of our common Lord, without giving the preference to any denomination of Christians above the rest, in such a manner that all ecclesiastical persons whatever shall enjoy the full, free, and unquestioned liberty of discharging every part of their sacred functions, without violence or danger. And, as Jesus Christ hath appointed a regular government and discipline in his church, no law of any commonwealth should interfere with, let, or hinder, the due exercise thereof, among the voluntary members of *any* denomination of Christians, according to their own profession and belief. It is the duty of civil magistrates to protect the person and good name of all their people, in such an effectual manner as that no person be suffered, either upon pretense of religion or of infidelity, to offer any indignity, violence, abuse, or injury to any other person whatsoever: and to take order, that all religious and ecclesiastical assemblies be held without molestation or disturbance.

IV. It is the duty of people to pray for magistrates, to honor their persons, to pay them tribute or other dues, to obey their lawful commands, and to be subject to their authority, for conscience' sake. Infidelity, or difference in religion, doth not make void the magistrates' just and legal authority, nor free the people from their due obedience to them: from which ecclesiastical persons are not exempted, much less hath the pope any power and jurisdiction over them in their dominions, or over any of their people; and, least of all, to deprive them of their dominions, or lives, if he shall judge them to be heretics, or upon any other pretense whatsoever.

CHAPTER XXIV
Of Marriage and Divorce

I. Marriage is to be between one man and one woman: neither is it lawful for any man to have more than one wife, nor for any woman to have more than one husband, at the same time.

II. Marriage was ordained for the mutual help of husband and wife, for the increase of mankind with legitimate issue, and of the church with an holy seed; and for preventing of uncleanness.

III. It is lawful for all sorts of people to marry, who are able with judgment to give their consent. Yet it is the duty of Christians to marry only in the Lord. And therefore such as profess the true reformed religion should not marry with infidels, papists, or other idolaters: neither should such as are godly be unequally yoked, by marrying with such as are notoriously wicked in their life, or maintain damnable heresies.

IV. Marriage ought not to be within the degrees of consanguinity or affinity forbidden by the Word. Nor can such incestuous marriages ever be made lawful by any law of man or consent of parties, so as those persons may live together as man and wife.

V. Adultery or fornication committed after a contract, being detected before marriage, giveth just occasion to the innocent party to dissolve that contract. In the case of adultery after marriage, it is lawful for the innocent party to sue out a divorce: and, after the divorce, to marry another, as if the offending party were dead.

VI. Although the corruption of man be such as is apt to study arguments unduly to put asunder those whom God hath joined together in marriage: yet, nothing but adultery, or such willful desertion as can no way be remedied by the church, or civil magistrate, is cause sufficient of dissolving the bond of marriage: wherein, a public and orderly course of proceeding is to be observed; and the persons concerned in it not left to their own wills, and discretion, in their own case.

CHAPTER XXV
Of the Church

I. The catholic or universal church, which is invisible, consists of the whole number of the elect, that have been, are, or shall be gathered into one, under Christ the Head thereof; and is the spouse, the body, the fullness of him that filleth all in all.

II. The visible church, which is also catholic or universal under the gospel (not confined to one nation, as before under the law), consists of all those throughout the world that profess the true religion; and of their children: and is the kingdom of the Lord Jesus Christ, the house and family of God, out of which there is no ordinary possibility of salvation.

III. Unto this catholic visible church Christ hath given the ministry, oracles, and ordinances of God, for the gathering and perfecting of the saints, in this life, to the end of the world: and doth, by his own presence and Spirit, according to his promise, make them effectual thereunto.

IV. This catholic church hath been sometimes more, sometimes less visible. And particular churches, which are members thereof, are more or less pure, according as the doctrine of the gospel is taught and embraced, ordinances administered, and public worship performed more or less purely in them.

V. The purest churches under heaven are subject both to mixture and error; and some have so degenerated, as to become no churches of Christ, but synagogues of Satan. Nevertheless, there shall be always a church on earth, to worship God according to his will.

VI. There is no other head of the church but the Lord Jesus Christ. Nor can the pope of Rome, in any sense, be head thereof.

CHAPTER XXVI

Of the Communion of Saints

I. All saints, that are united to Jesus Christ their Head, by his Spirit, and by faith, have fellowship with him in his graces, sufferings, death, resurrection, and glory: and, being united to one another in love, they have communion in each other's gifts and graces, and are obliged to the performance of such duties, public and private, as do conduce to their mutual good, both in the inward and outward man.

II. Saints by profession are bound to maintain an holy fellowship and communion in the worship of God, and in performing such other spiritual services as tend to their mutual edification; as also in relieving each other in outward things, according to their several abilities and necessities. Which communion, as God offereth opportunity, is to be extended unto all those who, in every place, call upon the name of the Lord Jesus.

III. This communion which the saints have with Christ, doth not make them in any wise partakers of the substance of his Godhead; or to be equal with Christ in any respect: either of which to affirm is impious and blasphemous. Nor doth their communion one with another, as saints, take away, or infringe the title or propriety which each man hath in his goods and possessions.

CHAPTER XXVII

Of the Sacraments

I. Sacraments are holy signs and seals of the covenant of grace, immediately instituted by God, to represent Christ, and his benefits; and to confirm our interest in him: as also, to put a visible difference between those that belong unto the church, and the rest of the world; and solemnly to engage them to the service of God in Christ, according to his Word.

II. There is, in every sacrament, a spiritual relation, or sacramental union, between the sign and the thing signified: whence it comes to pass, that the names and effects of the one are attributed to the other.

III. The grace which is exhibited in or by the sacraments rightly used, is not conferred by any power in them; neither doth the efficacy of a sacrament depend upon the piety or intention of him that doth administer it: but upon the work of the Spirit, and the word of institution, which contains, together with a precept authorizing the use thereof, a promise of benefit to worthy receivers.

IV. There be only two sacraments ordained by Christ our Lord in the Gospel; that is to say, baptism, and the Supper of the Lord: neither of which may be dispensed by any, but by a minister of the Word lawfully ordained.

V. The sacraments of the old testament, in regard of the spiritual things thereby signified and exhibited, were, for substance, the same with those of the new.

CHAPTER XXVIII

Of Baptism

I. Baptism is a sacrament of the new testament, ordained by Jesus Christ, not only for the solemn admission of the party baptized into the visible church; but also, to be unto him a sign and seal of the covenant of grace, of his ingrafting into Christ, of regeneration, of remission of sins, and of his giving up unto God, through Jesus Christ, to walk in newness of life. Which sacrament is, by Christ's own appointment, to be continued in his church until the end of the world.

II. The outward element to be used in this sacrament is water, wherewith the party is to be baptized, in the name of the Father, and of the Son, and of the Holy Ghost, by a minister of the gospel, lawfully called thereunto.

III. Dipping of the person into the water is not necessary; but baptism is rightly administered by pouring, or sprinkling water upon the person.

IV. Not only those that do actually profess faith in and obedience unto Christ, but also the infants of one, or both, believing parents, are to be baptized.

V. Although it be a great sin to contemn

or neglect this ordinance, yet grace and salvation are not so inseparably annexed unto it, as that no person can be regenerated, or saved, without it; or, that all that are baptized are undoubtedly regenerated.

VI. The efficacy of baptism is not tied to that moment of time wherein it is administered; yet, notwithstanding, by the right use of this ordinance, the grace promised is not only offered, but really exhibited, and conferred, by the Holy Ghost, to such (whether of age or infants) as that grace belongeth unto, according to the counsel of God's own will, in his appointed time.

VII. The sacrament of baptism is but once to be administered unto any person.

CHAPTER XXIX
Of the Lord's Supper

I. Our Lord Jesus, in the night wherein he was betrayed, instituted the sacrament of his body and blood, called the Lord's Supper, to be observed in his church, unto the end of the world, for the perpetual remembrance of the sacrifice of himself in his death; the sealing all benefits thereof unto true believers, their spiritual nourishment and growth in him, their further engagement in and to all duties which they owe unto him; and, to be a bond and pledge of their communion with him, and with each other, as members of his mystical body.

II. In this sacrament, Christ is not offered up to his Father; nor any real sacrifice made at all, for remission of sins of the quick or dead; but only a commemoration of that one offering up of himself, by himself, upon the cross, once for all: and a spiritual oblation of all possible praise unto God, for the same: so that the popish sacrifice of the mass (as they call it) is most abominably injurious to Christ's one, only sacrifice, the alone propitiation for all the sins of his elect.

III. The Lord Jesus hath, in this ordinance, appointed his ministers to declare his word of institution to the people; to pray, and

bless the elements of bread and wine, and thereby to set them apart from a common to an holy use; and to take and break the bread, to take the cup, and (they communicating also themselves) to give both to the communicants; but to none who are not then present in the congregation.

IV. Private masses, or receiving this sacrament by a priest, or any other, alone; as likewise, the denial of the cup to the people, worshiping the elements, the lifting them up, or carrying them about, for adoration, and the reserving them for any pretended religious use; are all contrary to the nature of this sacrament, and to the institution of Christ.

V. The outward elements in this sacrament, duly set apart to the uses ordained by Christ, have such relation to him crucified, as that, truly, yet sacramentally only, they are sometimes called by the name of the things they represent, to wit, the body and blood of Christ; albeit, in substance and nature, they still remain truly and only bread and wine, as they were before.

VI. That doctrine which maintains a change of the substance of bread and wine, into the substance of Christ's body and blood (commonly called transubstantiation) by consecration of a priest, or by any other way, is repugnant, not to Scripture alone, but even to common sense, and reason; overthroweth the nature of the sacrament, and hath been, and is, the cause of manifold superstitions; yea, of gross idolatries.

VII. Worthy receivers, outwardly partaking of the visible elements, in this sacrament, do then also, inwardly by faith, really and indeed, yet not carnally and corporally but spiritually, receive, and feed upon, Christ crucified, and all benefits of his death: the body and blood of Christ being then, not corporally or carnally, in, with, or under the bread and wine; yet, as really, but spiritually, present to the faith of believers in that ordinance, as the elements themselves are to their outward senses.

VIII. Although ignorant and wicked men receive the outward elements in this sacrament; yet, they receive not the thing signified thereby; but, by their unworthy coming thereunto, are guilty of the body and blood of the Lord, to their own damnation. Wherefore, all ignorant and ungodly persons, as they are unfit to enjoy communion with him, so are they unworthy of the Lord's table; and cannot, without great sin against Christ, while they remain such, partake of these holy mysteries, or be admitted thereunto.

CHAPTER XXX
Of Church Censures

I. The Lord Jesus, as King and Head of his church, hath therein appointed a government, in the hand of church officers, distinct from the civil magistrate.

II. To these officers the keys of the kingdom of heaven are committed; by virtue whereof, they have power, respectively, to retain, and remit sins; to shut that kingdom against the impenitent, both by the Word, and censures; and to open it unto penitent sinners, by the ministry of the gospel; and by absolution from censures, as occasion shall require.

III. Church censures are necessary, for the reclaiming and gaining of offending brethren, for deterring of others from the like offenses, for purging out of that leaven which might infect the whole lump, for vindicating the honor of Christ, and the holy profession of the gospel, and for preventing the wrath of God, which might justly fall upon the church, if they should suffer his covenant, and the seals thereof, to be profaned by notorious and obstinate offenders.

IV. For the better attaining of these ends, the officers of the church are to proceed by admonition; suspension from the sacrament of the Lord's Supper for a season; and by excommunication from the church; according to the nature of the crime, and demerit of the person.

CHAPTER XXXI
Of Synods and Councils

I. For the better government, and further edification of the church, there ought to be such assemblies as are commonly called synods or councils: and it belongeth to the overseers and other rulers of the particular churches, by virtue of their office, and the power which Christ hath given them for edification and not for destruction, to appoint such assemblies; and to convene together in them, as often as they shall judge it expedient for the good of the church.

II. It belongeth to synods and councils, ministerially to determine controversies of faith, and cases of conscience; to set down rules and directions for the better ordering of the public worship of God, and government of his church; to receive complaints in cases of maladministration, and authoritatively to determine the same: which decrees and determinations, if consonant to the Word of God, are to be received with reverence and submission; not only for their agreement with the Word, but also for the power whereby they are made, as being an ordinance of God appointed thereunto in his Word.

III. All synods or councils, since the Apostles' times, whether general or particular, may err; and many have erred. Therefore they are not to be made the rule of faith, or practice; but to be used as a help in both.

IV. Synods and councils are to handle, or conclude nothing, but that which is ecclesiastical: and are not to intermeddle with civil affairs which concern the commonwealth, unless by way of humble petition in cases extraordinary; or, by way of advice, for satisfaction of conscience, if they be thereunto required by the civil magistrate.

CHAPTER XXXII

Of the State of Men after Death, and of the Resurrection of the Dead

I. The bodies of men, after death, return to dust, and see corruption: but their souls, which neither die nor sleep, having an immortal subsistence, immediately return to God who gave them: the souls of the righteous, being then made perfect in holiness, are received into the highest heavens, where they behold the face of God, in light and glory, waiting for the full redemption of their bodies. And the souls of the wicked are cast into hell, where they remain in torments and utter darkness, reserved to the judgment of the great day. Besides these two places, for souls separated from their bodies, the Scripture acknowledgeth none.

II. At the last day, such as are found alive shall not die, but be changed: and all the dead shall be raised up, with the selfsame bodies, and none other (although with different qualities), which shall be united again to their souls forever.

III. The bodies of the unjust shall, by the power of Christ, be raised to dishonor: the bodies of the just, by his Spirit, unto honor; and be made conformable to his own glorious body.

CHAPTER XXXIII

Of the Last Judgment

I. God hath appointed a day, wherein he will judge the world, in righteousness, by Jesus Christ, to whom all power and judgment is given of the Father. In which day, not only the apostate angels shall be judged, but likewise all persons that have lived upon earth shall appear before the tribunal of Christ, to give an account of their thoughts, words, and deeds; and to receive according to what they have done in the body, whether good or evil.

II. The end of God's appointing this day is for the manifestation of the glory of his mercy, in the eternal salvation of the elect; and of his justice, in the damnation of the reprobate, who are wicked and disobedient. For then shall the righteous go into everlasting life, and receive that fullness of joy and refreshing, which shall come from the presence of the Lord; but the wicked who know not God, and obey not the gospel of Jesus Christ, shall be cast into eternal torments, and be punished with everlasting destruction from the presence of the Lord, and from the glory of his power.

III. As Christ would have us to be certainly persuaded that there shall be a day of judgment, both to deter all men from sin;

and for the greater consolation of the godly in their adversity: so will he have that day unknown to men, that they may shake off all carnal security, and be always watchful,

because they know not at what hour the Lord will come; and may be ever prepared to say, Come Lord Jesus, come quickly, Amen.

Finis.

This text of the Westminster Confession of Faith is that adopted by the Orthodox Presbyterian Church in 1936 and by the Presbyterian Church in America in 1973. It is derived from a 1646 manuscript edited by S. W. Carruthers and incorporates revisions adopted by American Presbyterian churches as early as 1789.

THE
SHORTER
CATECHISM

1. **Q. What is the chief end of man?**
   A. Man's chief end is to glorify God, and to enjoy him forever.

2. **Q. What rule hath God given to direct us how we may glorify and enjoy him?**
   A. The Word of God, which is contained in the Scriptures of the Old and New Testaments, is the only rule to direct us how we may glorify and enjoy him.

3. **Q. What do the Scriptures principally teach?**
   A. The Scriptures principally teach, what man is to believe concerning God, and what duty God requires of man.

4. **Q. What is God?**
   A. God is a Spirit, infinite, eternal, and unchangeable, in his being, wisdom, power, holiness, justice, goodness, and truth.

5. **Q. Are there more Gods than one?**
   A. There is but one only, the living and true God.

6. **Q. How many persons are there in the Godhead?**
   A. There are three persons in the Godhead: the Father, the Son, and the Holy Ghost; and these three are one God, the same in substance, equal in power and glory.

7. **Q. What are the decrees of God?**

The Westminster Assembly wrote the Shorter Catechism in 1647 as a concise question-and-answer summary of the biblical doctrines expressed in the Westminster Confession of Faith.
It was written as an instructional tool for use by the family and by the church.

A. The decrees of God are, his eternal purpose, according to the counsel of his will, whereby, for his own glory, he hath foreordained whatsoever comes to pass.

8. Q. **How doth God execute his decrees?**
A. God executeth his decrees in the works of creation and providence.

9. Q. **What is the work of creation?**
A. The work of creation is, God's making all things of nothing, by the word of his power, in the space of six days, and all very good.

10. Q. **How did God create man?**
A. God created man male and female, after his own image, in knowledge, righteousness, and holiness, with dominion over the creatures.

11. Q. **What are God's works of providence?**
A. God's works of providence are, his most holy, wise, and powerful preserving and governing all his creatures, and all their actions.

12. Q. **What special act of providence did God exercise towards man in the estate wherein he was created?**
A. When God had created man, he entered into a covenant of life with him, upon condition of perfect obedience; forbidding him to eat of the tree of the knowledge of good and evil, upon pain of death.

13. Q. **Did our first parents continue in the estate wherein they were created?**
A. Our first parents, being left to the freedom of their own will, fell from the estate wherein they were created, by sinning against God.

14. Q. **What is sin?**
A. Sin is any want of conformity unto, or transgression of, the law of God.

15. Q. **What was the sin whereby our first parents fell from the estate wherein they were created?**
A. The sin whereby our first parents fell from the estate wherein they were created, was their eating the forbidden fruit.

16. Q. **Did all mankind fall in Adam's first transgression?**
A. The covenant being made with Adam, not only for himself, but for his posterity; all mankind, descending from him by ordinary generation, sinned in him, and fell with him, in his first transgression.

17. Q. **Into what estate did the fall bring mankind?**
A. The fall brought mankind into an estate of sin and misery.

18. Q. **Wherein consists the sinfulness of that estate whereinto man fell?**
A. The sinfulness of that estate whereinto man fell, consists in the guilt of Adam's first sin, the want of original righteousness, and the corruption of his whole nature, which is commonly called original sin; together with all actual transgressions which proceed from it.

19. Q. **What is the misery of that estate whereinto man fell?**
A. All mankind by their fall lost communion with God, are under his wrath and curse, and so made liable to all the miseries of this life, to death itself, and to the pains of hell forever.

20. Q. **Did God leave all mankind to perish in the estate of sin and misery?**
A. God, having out of his mere good pleasure, from all eternity, elected some to everlasting life, did enter into a covenant of grace to deliver them out of the estate of sin and misery, and to bring them into an estate of salvation by a Redeemer.

21. Q. **Who is the Redeemer of God's elect?**
A. The only Redeemer of God's elect is

the Lord Jesus Christ, who, being the eternal Son of God, became man, and so was, and continueth to be, God and man in two distinct natures, and one person, forever.

22. Q. How did Christ, being the Son of God, become man?

A. Christ, the Son of God, became man, by taking to himself a true body, and a reasonable soul, being conceived by the power of the Holy Ghost, in the womb of the virgin Mary, and born of her, yet without sin.

23. Q. What offices doth Christ execute as our Redeemer?

A. Christ, as our Redeemer, executeth the offices of a prophet, of a priest, and of a king, both in his estate of humiliation and exaltation.

24. Q. How doth Christ execute the office of a prophet?

A. Christ executeth the office of a prophet, in revealing to us, by his Word and Spirit, the will of God for our salvation.

25. Q. How doth Christ execute the office of a priest?

A. Christ executeth the office of a priest, in his once offering up of himself a sacrifice to satisfy divine justice, and reconcile us to God, and in making continual intercession for us.

26. Q. How doth Christ execute the office of a king?

A. Christ executeth the office of a king, in subduing us to himself, in ruling and defending us, and in restraining and conquering all his and our enemies.

27. Q. Wherein did Christ's humiliation consist?

A. Christ's humiliation consisted in his being born, and that in a low condition, made under the law, undergoing the miseries of this life, the wrath of God, and the cursed death of the cross; in being buried, and continuing under the power of death for a time.

28. Q. Wherein consisteth Christ's exaltation?

A. Christ's exaltation consisteth in his rising again from the dead on the third day, in ascending up into heaven, in sitting at the right hand of God the Father, and in coming to judge the world at the last day.

29. Q. How are we made partakers of the redemption purchased by Christ?

A. We are made partakers of the redemption purchased by Christ, by the effectual application of it to us by his Holy Spirit.

30. Q. How doth the Spirit apply to us the redemption purchased by Christ?

A. The Spirit applieth to us the redemption purchased by Christ, by working faith in us, and thereby uniting us to Christ in our effectual calling.

31. Q. What is effectual calling?

A. Effectual calling is the work of God's Spirit, whereby, convincing us of our sin and misery, enlightening our minds in the knowledge of Christ, and renewing our wills, he doth persuade and enable us to embrace Jesus Christ, freely offered to us in the gospel.

32. Q. What benefits do they that are effectually called partake of in this life?

A. They that are effectually called do in this life partake of justification, adoption, and sanctification, and the several benefits which in this life do either accompany or flow from them.

33. Q. What is justification?

A. Justification is an act of God's free grace, wherein he pardoneth all our sins, and accepteth us as righteous in his sight, only for the righteousness of Christ imputed to us, and received by faith alone.

34. Q. What is adoption?

A. Adoption is an act of God's free grace, whereby we are received into the number, and have a right to all the privileges, of the sons of God.

35. Q. What is sanctification?

A. Sanctification is the work of God's free grace, whereby we are renewed in the whole man after the image of God, and are enabled more and more to die unto sin, and live unto righteousness.

36. Q. What are the benefits which in this life do accompany or flow from justification, adoption, and sanctification?

A. The benefits which in this life do accompany or flow from justification, adoption, and sanctification, are, assurance of God's love, peace of conscience, joy in the Holy Ghost, increase of grace, and perseverance therein to the end.

37. Q. What benefits do believers receive from Christ at death?

A. The souls of believers are at their death made perfect in holiness, and do immediately pass into glory; and their bodies, being still united to Christ, do rest in their graves, till the resurrection.

38. Q. What benefits do believers receive from Christ at the resurrection?

A. At the resurrection, believers, being raised up in glory, shall be openly acknowledged and acquitted in the Day of Judgment, and made perfectly blessed in the full enjoying of God to all eternity.

39. Q. What is the duty which God requireth of man?

A. The duty which God requireth of man, is obedience to his revealed will.

40. Q. What did God at first reveal to man for the rule of his obedience?

A. The rule which God at first revealed to man for his obedience, was the moral law.

41. Q. Wherein is the moral law summarily comprehended?

A. The moral law is summarily comprehended in the Ten Commandments.

42. Q. What is the sum of the Ten Commandments?

A. The sum of the Ten Commandments is, to love the Lord our God with all our heart, with all our soul, with all our strength, and with all our mind; and our neighbor as ourselves.

43. Q. What is the preface to the Ten Commandments?

A. The preface to the Ten Commandments is in these words, *I am the* LORD *thy God, which have brought thee out of the land of Egypt, out of the house of bondage.*

44. Q. What doth the preface to the Ten Commandments teach us?

A. The preface to the Ten Commandments teacheth us, that because God is the Lord, and our God, and Redeemer, therefore we are bound to keep all his commandments.

45. Q. Which is the first commandment?

A. The first commandment is, *Thou shalt have no other gods before me.*

46. Q. What is required in the first commandment?

A. The first commandment requireth us to know and acknowledge God to be the only true God, and our God; and to worship and glorify him accordingly.

47. Q. What is forbidden in the first commandment?

A. The first commandment forbiddeth the denying, or not worshiping and glorifying, the true God as God, and our God; and the giving of that worship and glory to any other, which is due to him alone.

48. Q. What are we specially taught by these words *before me* in the first commandment?

A. These words *before me* in the first commandment teach us, that God, who seeth all things, taketh notice of, and is much displeased with, the sin of having any other God.

49. Q. Which is the second commandment?

A. The second commandment is, *Thou shalt not make unto thee any graven image, or any likeness of anything that is in heaven above, or that is in the earth beneath, or that is in the water under the earth: Thou shalt not bow down thyself to them, nor serve them: for I the LORD thy God am a jealous God, visiting the iniquity of the fathers upon the children unto the third and fourth generation of them that hate me; and showing mercy unto thousands of them that love me, and keep my commandments.*

50. Q. What is required in the second commandment?

A. The second commandment requireth the receiving, observing, and keeping pure and entire, all such religious worship and ordinances as God hath appointed in his Word.

51. Q. What is forbidden in the second commandment?

A. The second commandment forbiddeth the worshiping of God by images, or any other way not appointed in his Word.

52. Q. What are the reasons annexed to the second commandment?

A. The reasons annexed to the second commandment are, God's sovereignty over us, his propriety in us, and the zeal he hath to his own worship.

53. Q. Which is the third commandment?

A. The third commandment is, *Thou shalt not take the name of the LORD thy God in vain: for the LORD will not*

hold him guiltless that taketh his name in vain.

54. Q. What is required in the third commandment?

A. The third commandment requireth the holy and reverent use of God's names, titles, attributes, ordinances, Word, and works.

55. Q. What is forbidden in the third commandment?

A. The third commandment forbiddeth all profaning or abusing of anything whereby God maketh himself known.

56. Q. What is the reason annexed to the third commandment?

A. The reason annexed to the third commandment is, that however the breakers of this commandment may escape punishment from men, yet the Lord our God will not suffer them to escape his righteous judgment.

57. Q. Which is the fourth commandment?

A. The fourth commandment is, *Remember the Sabbath day to keep it holy. Six days shalt thou labor, and do all thy work: but the seventh day is the Sabbath of the LORD thy God: in it thou shalt not do any work, thou, nor thy son, nor thy daughter, thy manservant, nor thy maidservant, nor thy cattle, nor thy stranger that is within thy gates: For in six days the LORD made heaven and earth, the sea and all that in them is, and rested the seventh day: wherefore the LORD blessed the Sabbath day, and hallowed it.*

58. Q. What is required in the fourth commandment?

A. The fourth commandment requireth the keeping holy to God such set times as he hath appointed in his Word; expressly one whole day in seven, to be a holy Sabbath to himself.

59. Q. Which day of the seven hath God

appointed to be the weekly Sabbath?

A. From the beginning of the world to the resurrection of Christ, God appointed the seventh day of the week to be the weekly Sabbath; and the first day of the week ever since, to continue to the end of the world, which is the Christian Sabbath.

60. Q. How is the Sabbath to be sanctified?

A. The Sabbath is to be sanctified by a holy resting all that day, even from such worldly employments and recreations as are lawful on other days; and spending the whole time in the public and private exercises of God's worship, except so much as is to be taken up in the works of necessity and mercy.

61. Q. What is forbidden in the fourth commandment?

A. The fourth commandment forbiddeth the omission, or careless performance, of the duties required, and the profaning the day by idleness, or doing that which is in itself sinful, or by unnecessary thoughts, words, or works, about our worldly employments or recreations.

62. Q. What are the reasons annexed to the fourth commandment?

A. The reasons annexed to the fourth commandment are, God's allowing us six days of the week for our own employments, his challenging a special propriety in the seventh, his own example, and his blessing the Sabbath day.

63. Q. Which is the fifth commandment?

A. The fifth commandment is, *Honor thy father and thy mother: that thy days may be long upon the land which the LORD thy God giveth thee.*

64. Q. What is required in the fifth commandment?

A. The fifth commandment requireth the preserving the honor, and performing the duties, belonging to everyone in their several places and relations, as superiors, inferiors, or equals.

65. Q. What is forbidden in the fifth commandment?

A. The fifth commandment forbiddeth the neglecting of, or doing anything against, the honor and duty which belongeth to everyone in their several places and relations.

66. Q. What is the reason annexed to the fifth commandment?

A. The reason annexed to the fifth commandment is, a promise of long life and prosperity (as far as it shall serve for God's glory and their own good) to all such as keep this commandment.

67. Q. Which is the sixth commandment?

A. The sixth commandment is, *Thou shalt not kill.*

68. Q. What is required in the sixth commandment?

A. The sixth commandment requireth all lawful endeavors to preserve our own life, and the life of others.

69. Q. What is forbidden in the sixth commandment?

A. The sixth commandment forbiddeth the taking away of our own life, or the life of our neighbor, unjustly, or whatsoever tendeth thereunto.

70. Q. Which is the seventh commandment?

A. The seventh commandment is, *Thou shalt not commit adultery.*

71. Q. What is required in the seventh commandment?

A. The seventh commandment requireth the preservation of our own and our neighbor's chastity, in heart, speech, and behavior.

72. Q. What is forbidden in the seventh commandment?

A. The seventh commandment forbiddeth all unchaste thoughts, words, and actions.

73. Q. Which is the eighth commandment?
A. The eighth commandment is, *Thou shalt not steal.*

74. Q. What is required in the eighth commandment?
A. The eighth commandment requireth the lawful procuring and furthering the wealth and outward estate of ourselves and others.

75. Q. What is forbidden in the eighth commandment?
A. The eighth commandment forbiddeth whatsoever doth, or may, unjustly hinder our own, or our neighbor's, wealth or outward estate.

76. Q. Which is the ninth commandment?
A. The ninth commandment is, *Thou shalt not bear false witness against thy neighbor.*

77. Q. What is required in the ninth commandment?
A. The ninth commandment requireth the maintaining and promoting of truth between man and man, and of our own and our neighbor's good name, especially in witness bearing.

78. Q. What is forbidden in the ninth commandment?
A. The ninth commandment forbiddeth whatsoever is prejudicial to truth, or injurious to our own, or our neighbor's, good name.

79. Q. Which is the tenth commandment?
A. The tenth commandment is, *Thou shalt not covet thy neighbor's house, thou shalt not covet thy neighbor's wife, nor his manservant, nor his maidservant, nor his ox, nor his ass, nor anything that is thy neighbor's.*

80. Q. What is required in the tenth commandment?
A. The tenth commandment requireth

full contentment with our own condition, with a right and charitable frame of spirit toward our neighbor, and all that is his.

81. Q. What is forbidden in the tenth commandment?
A. The tenth commandment forbiddeth all discontentment with our own estate, envying or grieving at the good of our neighbor, and all inordinate motions and affections to anything that is his.

82. Q. Is any man able perfectly to keep the commandments of God?
A. No mere man, since the fall, is able in this life perfectly to keep the commandments of God, but doth daily break them in thought, word, and deed.

83. Q. Are all transgressions of the law equally heinous?
A. Some sins in themselves, and by reason of several aggravations, are more heinous in the sight of God than others.

84. Q. What doth every sin deserve?
A. Every sin deserveth God's wrath and curse, both in this life, and that which is to come.

85. Q. What doth God require of us, that we may escape his wrath and curse, due to us for sin?
A. To escape the wrath and curse of God, due to us for sin, God requireth of us faith in Jesus Christ, repentance unto life, with the diligent use of all the outward means whereby Christ communicateth to us the benefits of redemption.

86. Q. What is faith in Jesus Christ?
A. Faith in Jesus Christ is a saving grace, whereby we receive and rest upon him alone for salvation, as he is offered to us in the gospel.

87. Q. What is repentance unto life?
A. Repentance unto life is a saving

grace, whereby a sinner, out of a true sense of his sin, and apprehension of the mercy of God in Christ, doth, with grief and hatred of his sin, turn from it unto God, with full purpose of, and endeavor after, new obedience.

88. Q. What are the outward and ordinary means whereby Christ communicateth to us the benefits of redemption?

A. The outward and ordinary means whereby Christ communicateth to us the benefits of redemption are, his ordinances, especially the Word, sacraments, and prayer; all which are made effectual to the elect for salvation.

89. Q. How is the Word made effectual to salvation?

A. The Spirit of God maketh the reading, but especially the preaching, of the Word, an effectual means of convincing and converting sinners, and of building them up in holiness and comfort, through faith, unto salvation.

90. Q. How is the Word to be read and heard, that it may become effectual to salvation?

A. That the Word may become effectual to salvation, we must attend thereunto with diligence, preparation, and prayer; receive it with faith and love, lay it up in our hearts, and practice it in our lives.

91. Q. How do the sacraments become effectual means of salvation?

A. The sacraments become effectual means of salvation, not from any virtue in them, or in him that doth administer them; but only by the blessing of Christ, and the working of his Spirit in them that by faith receive them.

92. Q. What is a sacrament?

A. A sacrament is a holy ordinance instituted by Christ; wherein, by sensible signs, Christ, and the benefits of the new covenant, are represented, sealed, and applied to believers.

93. Q. Which are the sacraments of the New Testament?

A. The sacraments of the New Testament are, baptism, and the Lord's Supper.

94. Q. What is baptism?

A. Baptism is a sacrament, wherein the washing with water in the name of the Father, and of the Son, and of the Holy Ghost, doth signify and seal our ingrafting into Christ, and partaking of the benefits of the covenant of grace, and our engagement to be the Lord's.

95. Q. To whom is baptism to be administered?

A. Baptism is not to be administered to any that are out of the visible church, till they profess their faith in Christ, and obedience to him; but the infants of such as are members of the visible church are to be baptized.

96. Q. What is the Lord's Supper?

A. The Lord's Supper is a sacrament, wherein, by giving and receiving bread and wine, according to Christ's appointment, his death is showed forth; and the worthy receivers are, not after a corporal and carnal manner, but by faith, made partakers of his body and blood, with all his benefits, to their spiritual nourishment, and growth in grace.

97. Q. What is required for the worthy receiving of the Lord's Supper?

A. It is required of them that would worthily partake of the Lord's Supper, that they examine themselves of their knowledge to discern the Lord's body, of their faith to feed upon him, of their repentance, love, and new obedience; lest, coming unworthily, they eat and drink judgment to themselves.

98. Q. What is prayer?

A. Prayer is an offering up of our desires unto God, for things agreeable to his will, in the name of Christ, with confession of our sins, and thankful acknowledgment of his mercies.

99. Q. What rule hath God given for our direction in prayer?

A. The whole Word of God is of use to direct us in prayer; but the special rule of direction is that form of prayer which Christ taught his disciples, commonly called the Lord's Prayer.

100. Q. What doth the preface of the Lord's Prayer teach us?

A. The preface of the Lord's Prayer, which is, *Our Father which art in heaven,* teacheth us to draw near to God with all holy reverence and confidence, as children to a father, able and ready to help us; and that we should pray with and for others.

101. Q. What do we pray for in the first petition?

A. In the first petition, which is, *Hallowed be thy name,* we pray that God would enable us, and others, to glorify him in all that whereby he maketh himself known; and that he would dispose all things to his own glory.

102. Q. What do we pray for in the second petition?

A. In the second petition, which is, *Thy kingdom come,* we pray that Satan's kingdom may be destroyed; and that the kingdom of grace may be advanced, ourselves and others brought into it, and kept in it; and that the kingdom of glory may be hastened.

103. Q. What do we pray for in the third petition?

A. In the third petition, which is, *Thy will be done in earth, as it is in heaven,* we pray that God, by his grace, would make us able and willing to know, obey, and submit to his will in all things, as the angels do in heaven.

104. Q. What do we pray for in the fourth petition?

A. In the fourth petition, which is, *Give us this day our daily bread,* we pray that of God's free gift we may receive a competent portion of the good things of this life, and enjoy his blessing with them.

105. Q. What do we pray for in the fifth petition?

A. In the fifth petition, which is, *And forgive us our debts, as we forgive our debtors,* we pray that God, for Christ's sake, would freely pardon all our sins; which we are the rather encouraged to ask, because by his grace we are enabled from the heart to forgive others.

106. Q. What do we pray for in the sixth petition?

A. In the sixth petition, which is, *And lead us not into temptation, but deliver us from evil,* we pray that God would either keep us from being tempted to sin, or support and deliver us when we are tempted.

107. Q. What doth the conclusion of the Lord's Prayer teach us?

A. The conclusion of the Lord's Prayer, which is, *For thine is the kingdom, and the power, and the glory, forever. Amen,* teacheth us to take our encouragement in prayer from God only, and in our prayers to praise him, ascribing kingdom, power, and glory to him; and, in testimony of our desire, and assurance to be heard, we say, *Amen.*

The text printed here is the original version, which was adopted by the Orthodox Presbyterian Church in 1936 and by the Presbyterian Church in America in 1973.

INDEXES

COPYRIGHT HOLDERS

Individuals and publishers who have granted permission to print their copyrighted material in *Trinity Hymnal* are listed below and a credit line appears at the end of the appropriate hymns. If you wish to reproduce any of the copyrighted words or music, please contact the copyright holder directly for permission.

Abingdon Press
c/o The Copyright Company
1025 16th Ave. South, #204
Nashville, TN 37212
615/244-5588

Augsburg Fortress Publishers
100 South 5th Street, #700
Minneapolis, MN 55402
612/330-3300

Barnes, Jonathan
15 South Canterbury Road
Canterbury, Kent CT1 3LH
ENGLAND

Blanton, Leonard C.
1320 Second Avenue
Laurel, MS 39440

Fred Bock Music Co.
P. O. Box 333
Tarzana, CA 91356
818/996-6181

Bowdler, Margaret
272 Valley Road
Lillington
Leamington Spa
Warwickshire, ENGLAND

Breitkopf & Härtel
Walkmülstrasse 52
Postfach 1707
D6200 Wiesbaden 1
GERMANY

Brentwood-Benson
741 Cool Springs Boulevard
Franklin, TN 37067
615/261-3300

Broadman Press
127 Ninth Avenue North
Nashville, TN 37234
615/251-2533

Bud-John Songs, Inc.
c/o EMI Christian Music
P. O. Box 5085
Brentwood, TN 37024
615/371-4300

Burnam, Jack W.
2400 West 17th Street
Wilmington, DE 19806
302/658-7326

Celebration Press
c/o Gaither Copyright
   Management
P. O. Box 737
Alexandria, IN 46001
765/724-8281

Chappell and Co., Intl.
c/o Hal Leonard Publishing
960 East Mark Street
Winona, MN 55987
507/454-2920

Christianity Today
465 Gundersen Drive
Carol Stream, IL 60188
312/260-6200

Norman Clayton Publishing
See Word Publishing

Clowney, Edmund P.
1218 Courtyard Drive
Charlottesville, VA 22903
434/296-9634

Concordia Publishing House
3558 South Jefferson Avenue
Saint Louis, MO 63118
314/664-7000

CPP/Belwin, Inc.
P. O. Box 4340
Miami, FL 33014
305/620-1500

CRC Publications
2850 Kalamazoo Avenue, SE
Grand Rapids, MI 49560
616/246-0753

EMI Christian Music
   Publishing
P. O. Box 5085
Brentwood, TN 37024
615/371-4300

Evangelical Covenant Church
5101 North Francisco
Avenue
Chicago, IL 60625-3699
312/784-3000

Hope Publishing Co.
380 South Main Place
Carol Stream, IL 60188
708/665-3200

881

The Hymn Society
Texas Christian University
c/o Hope Publishing Co.

InterVarsity Christian
  Fellowship
P. O. Box 1400
Downers Grove, IL 60515
708/887-2500

Jabusch, Willard F.
5040 Warren, #404
Skokie, IL 60077

James Ward Music
4106 St. Elmo Avenue
Chattanooga, TN 37409
info@jameswardmusic.com

Judson Press
P. O. Box 851
Valley Forge, PA 19482

Lillenas Publishing Company
c/o The Copyright Company
1025 16th Ave. South, #204
Nashville, TN 37212
615/244-5588

Majesty Music
Box 6524
Greenville, SC 29606
803/242-6722

Manna Music, Inc.
35255 Brooten Road
Pacific City, OR 97135
503/965-6112

Miladin, George C.
9141 Brier Road
La Mesa, CA 91942
619/464-3312

OMF International (IHQ) Ltd.
2 Cluny Road
Singapore 1025
REPUBLIC OF SINGAPORE
CD@omf.org.sg

Ortlund, Anne
4500 Campus Drive, Suite 662
Newport Beach, CA 92660

Oxford University Press
Music Department
Great Clarendon Street
Oxford OX2 6DP
ENGLAND
music.permissions.uk
  @oup.com

John W. Peterson Music Co.
6501 East Greenway Parkway
Suite 102, #435
Scottsdale, AZ 85254-2065
480/483-3306

The Presbyterian Church in
  Canada
50 Wynford Drive
Don Mills, Ontario M3C 1J7
CANADA

Theodore Presser Co.
588 North Gulph Road
King of Prussia, PA 19406
215/525-3636

RAM Music Publications
4109 Colony Drive
Hatboro, PA 19040
215/957-0674

E. C. Schirmer Music Co.
138 Ipswich Street
Boston, MA 02215
617/236-1935

G. Schirmer, Inc.
257 Park Avenue, South
20th Floor
New York, NY 10010
212/254-2100

Scripture in Song
c/o Integrity Music
1000 Cody Road
Mobile, AL 36695
251/633-9000

Smith, Gail
2041 Northeast 54th Court
Ft. Lauderdale, FL 33308
305/491-6683

Stainer & Bell, Ltd.
U. S. Agent:
E. C. Schirmer Music Co.

United Church Press
700 Prospect Avenue East
Cleveland OH 44115
216/736-3700

United Reformed Church
86 Tavistock Place
London WC1H 9RT
ENGLAND

Watson, Sydney
Estate administered by:
Musicians Benevolent Fund
16 Ogle Street
London W1P 7L6
ENGLAND
017-636-4481

Word Publishing
c/o Warner-Chappell Music
20 Music Square East
Nashville, TN 37203

World Student Christian
  Federation
5, Route des Morillons
1218 Grand-saconnex
Geneva
SWITZERLAND

AUTHORS, TRANSLATORS AND SOURCES OF HYMNS

COMPOSERS,
ARRANGERS
AND
SOURCES OF TUNES

Stainer, John (1840–1901) 245, 258, 565, 730
Stanford, Charles V. (1852–1924) 292, 451
Stebbins, George C. (1846–1945) 403, 503, 537, 688
Steggall, Charles (1826–1893) 559
Steurlein, Johann (1546–1613) 716
Stevenson, John A. (1761–1833) 491
Stockton, John H. (1813–1877) 675
Stralsund Gesangbuch (1665) 53
Strasbourg Psalter (1545) 14, 613
Strattner, Georg C. (1650–1705) 652
Straub, S. W. (1842–1899) 135
Strover, Christian (b. 1932) 23, 666
Sullivan, Arthur S. (1842–1900) 169, 266, 357,
    399, 439, 461, 517, 540, 545, 572, 626, 668,
    692
Sumner, John B. (1838–1918) 525
Swedish melody 44, 131, 496
Sweney, John R. (1837–1899) 234, 538

Tallis, Thomas (ca. 1505–1585) 401, 732
Tate and Brady's *Supplement to the New Version*
    (1708) 30, 713
Taylor, Cyril V. (b. 1907) 742
Terry, R. R. (1865–1938) 596
Teschner, Melchior (1584–1635) 75, 156, 235
Thomas, Rhys 509, 631
Thompson, John 42
Thompson, Will L. (1847–1909) 479, 653
Thornton, Jim (b. 1947) 564
Tomer, William G. (1833–1896) 386
Tours, Berthold (1838–1897) 236
Towner, Daniel B. (1850–1919) 465, 617, 672
Traditional melody 663
Tredinnick, Noël (b. 1949) 24, 315
Turton, Thomas (1780–1864) 35, 583
Tye, Christopher (ca. 1508–1572) 27

Urhan, Chrétien (1790–1845) 546, 551

Valerius, Adrianus, *Nederlandtsch Gedenckclanck*
    (1626) 97, 363
Van Andel, Henry J. (b. 1882) 556
Vanderhoven, John (1888–1974) 549
Vaughan Williams, Ralph (1872–1958) 79, 119,
    163, 193, 227, 285, 358, 385
Venua, Frederick M. A. (1788–1872) 9, 19, 65
Vincent, Charles J. (1852–1934) 702
Viner, William L. (1790–1867) 416

Vulpius, Melchior (ca. 1560–1615) 270, 667

Wade, John Francis, *Cantus Diversi* (1751)
    208, 318
Wainwright, John (1723–1768) 209
Walch, James (1837–1901) 6, 444
Walter, William H. (1825–1893) 242, 370
Walther, Johann (16th cent.) 279, 554
Walther, Johann, *Gesangbüchlein* (1524) 554
Walton, James G. (1821–1905) 570
Ward, James C. (b. 1950) 287, 500
Warren, George William (1828–1902) 710
Warren, Norman L. (b.1934) 212, 280, 419, 612
    663
Watson, Sydney (b. 1903) 435
Webb, George J. (1803–1887) 571
Webbe, Samuel (1740–1816) 615
Webbe, Samuel, Jr. (1770–1843) 83
Weber, Carl Maria von (1786–1826) 409,
    685, 694
Weeden, Winfield S. (1847–1908) 562
Weimar Gesangbuch (1681) 108
Welsh hymn melody 255, 349, 437, 482, 497
Welsh melody 38, 95, 125, 159, 250, 405, 643
Wesley, Samuel S. (1810–1876) 54, 311,
    347, 727
Whelpton, George (1847–1930) 728
White, J. T., *The Sacred Harp* (1844) 28, 352
Willan, Healey (1880–1968) 716
Willcox, John H. (1827–1875) 17
Williams, Aaron (1731–1776) 353, 700
Williams, Robert (ca. 1781–1821) 273, 290
Williams, Thomas John (1869–1944) 283, 535
Willis, Richard S. (1819–1900) 200
Wilson, David G. (b. 1940) 71, 124, 563
Wilson, Hugh (1766–1824) 254
Wilson, John F. (b. 1929) 288, 611
Witty, Robert 704
Wood, Charles (1866–1926) 228, 284
Wood, Dale (b. 1934) 47
Woodman, Jonathan C. (1813–1894) 627
Woodward, George R. (1848–1934) 36, 278
Wyatt, Janet 81

Young, Carlton (b. 1926) 736

Zeuner, Heinrich C. (1795–1857) 440
Zundel, John (1815–1882) 434, 464, 529

TUNES

METERS

SCRIPTURE
REFERENCES

TOPICS

927

935

TITLES
AND
FIRST LINES

*Indicates first line of hymn where different from title; this hymn is also listed by title.

936